Introduction to Automated Modeling with FEniCS

L. Ridgway Scott

University of Chicago

L. Ridgway Scott

University of Chicago

Chicago, Illinois

USA

Cover photo by Cristina Gottardi on Unsplash

Typeset using LaTeX

ISBN 978-1-949133-00-4

Library of Congress Control Number: 2018905482

Contents

Chapter 1

PDE's and FEniCS

Mathematical models of varying complexity are used to explain and predict phenomena of interest in many fields. These can be as simple as the exponential function to explain the rate of growth of bacteria [274]. Or they can be very complex, such as predicting the landfall of a hurricane, where the implications of the projections involve billions of dollars and can involve possible unnecessary loss of life if they are inaccurate. In between, such models are used ubiquitously in ways that we do not realize to build things whose design process we take for granted.

The mathematical complexity of every model should be chosen conservatively to reflect the level of detail desired [35, 162, 278]. But in cases where detailed information is required, and spatial relationships are important, models using partial differential equations (PDEs) are preferred. These are some of the most complicated models from a mathematical point of view, but they are also the most accurate and predictive.

PDEs are used pervasively in science, engineering, and technology to model phenomena of interest [95, 167, 197, 231, 246]. Analytical techniques for solving PDEs remain useful, but they are severely limited in scope, being able to solve only the simplest model problems. Modern computers and the development of reliable numerical methods made it possible to solve PDEs quite generally. The most widely used technique to convert a PDE into a computable form is the finite element method.

This book is primarily about PDEs as they are used in models. Our emphasis is on the diversity of PDEs that occur in practice, their features and their foibles. Our intent is to enable exploration of new models and to show how easily this can be done. However, this approach is not without caveats. We describe pitfalls in various aspects of the use of PDE models. We show how to be sure that a PDE model is well posed in many cases. In particular, we use this theory to understand appropriate boundary conditions.

Secondarily, the book introduces basic concepts of numerical methods for approximating the solutions of PDEs. This is done so that the language used by software from the FEniCS Project can be properly understood. We limit the discussion of numerical methods as much as possible, except when it is essential to avoid catastrophes.

A tertiary objective is to present some examples of the modeling process. One important type of model is derived by specializing a more general model. An important example of this is the plate model in structural mechanics. We show how the plate model is derived from the general elasticity model and indicate some issues that arise related to it. When relevant, we explain other modeling approaches as well. Ultimately, FEniCS can support

Figure 1.1: Solution of a PDE with complex geometry.

an automated approach to modeling [206, 249, 131, 226, 227, 247].

1.1 The finite element method

The finite element method grew out of what were called matrix methods of structural mechanics [136, 204]. It was ultimately realized that finite element methods could be viewed as variational methods for solving PDEs. Although the use of variational methods to solve PDEs can be traced earlier [138, 101], the development of the finite element method started in earnest in the 1950's [96]. In the late 1960's, the term 'finite element method' became well established. The first edition of Zienkiewicz's book [292] was published in 1967 entitled "The finite element method in structural and continuum mechanics" and the second edition appeared in 1971 under the title "The finite element method in engineering science."

Finite element analysis is used in essentially all industrial design. A hallmark of the finite element is the ability to model complex geometries, as indicated in Figure 1.1. The gold standard software for five decades has been NASTRAN, code developed in Fortran using software development techniques of the 1960's era. Based largely on this type of software alone, the industry has grown to produce multi-billion-dollars of revenue each year. However, the simulation challenges of today and tomorrow, involving new materials with poorly understood fundamental properties, are stressing NASTRAN and its descendants to a breaking point. Moreover, as advanced technology becomes more highly refined and optimized, the need for more complex simulations will continue to grow. We predict that

> *soon the simulation software itself will become the majority of the value in product design. Thus the time is right to rethink technical simulation.*

In 2002, the FEniCS Project started at the University of Chicago, devoted to automating the modeling process. This has profoundly changed the state of the art in simulation technology. The FEniCS Project has many strengths that allow it to address a rapidly changing field of simulation challenges. FEniCS could become the basis for the next generation of simulation technology. The FEniCS Project originated in academic research, but now commercial support for FEniCS tools is available, and for the development of customer-driven applications based on the FEniCS structure.

We next review the history of NASTRAN and FEniCS in some detail.

1.2 NASTRAN

NASTRAN (NASA STRucture ANalysis) is a finite element analysis program that was originally developed (with NASA funding) in the late 1960s to support the aerospace industry. NASTRAN was released to the public in 1971 by NASA's Office of Technology Utilization.

1.2.1 Software architecture

NASTRAN is written primarily in FORTRAN and contains over one million lines of code. NASTRAN was designed using software techniques of the 1960's to consist of several modules. A module is a collection of FORTRAN subroutines designed to perform a specific task, such as processing model geometry, assembling matrices, applying constraints, solving matrix problems, calculating output quantities, conversing with the database, printing the solution, and so on.

1.2.2 Scope

NASTRAN is primarily a solver for finite element analysis. It does not have functionality that provides mesh generation or any type of model building. All input to and output from the program is in the form of text files. It does not have any native graphics or visualization capability.

1.3 FEniCS

The FEniCS Project started in an informal gathering in Hyde Park (Chicago) in 2002. It was loosely based on experiences gained in developing an earlier software system called Analysa, a commercial project funded largely by Ridgway Scott and Babak Bagheri [25], together with the experiences derived by a group based in Sweden led by Claes Johnson.

The FEniCS Project was publicly launched at the University of Chicago in 2003, and it has grown to an international collaboration involving primary developers at sites in the Czech Republic, England, Holland, Luxembourg, Norway, and Sweden, as well as three sites in the US. It has many users world-wide.

It was estimated by `openhub.net` in 2015 that the FEniCS Project represented 34 person-years of effort, with 25,547 software commits to a public repository, made by 87 contributors, and representing 134,932 lines of code. At that time, it was estimated that there were about 50,000 downloads per year through a variety of sites, and Google Analytics estimated that the FEniCS Project web page had about 10,000 monthly visitors.

The FEniCS Project also receives significant numbers of citations in the technical literature. This connotes more than just academic praise. It shows that the technical community feels that FEniCS tools are of significant value. For example, in September 2017 the FEniCS book [205] had accumulated almost 1,000 citations, and the DOLFIN paper [206] had over 360 citations.

FEniCS is a polymorphic acronym (e.g., Finite Elements nurtured in Computer Science, or For Everything new in Computational Science).

1.3.1 Leverage

The FEniCS Project leverages mathematical structure inherent in scientific models to automate the generation of simulation software. What makes FEniCS different from previous generations of software is that it uses compiler technology to generate software where possible, instead of just accumulating and integrating hand-coded software libraries. A major discovery was an optimized way to compute finite element matrices that makes finite element computation essentially as efficient as finite difference computation, while still retaining the geometric generality that is unique to finite element methods [176, 177, 178]. In 2012, a book was released [205] explaining both how FEniCS tools were developed as well as how they are used in a broad range of applications.

1.3.2 FEniCS advantages

FEniCS utilizes many modern software techniques. One of these is Just-in-Time (JIT) compilations, as did Analysa [25]. This allows a user to modify the physical models being used and quickly re-simulate. Similar tools allow for the order or type of finite element to be changed at will. FEniCS thus can go far beyond the standard concept of multi-physics. Instead of just mixing a few different physics models, FEniCS allows a continuum of models to be explored. This is one reason why such a diversity of physical applications are presented in the book [205].

But there are many more examples of advantages. FEniCS is the first system to implement the full Periodic Table of Finite Elements [14]. This means that FEniCS users can utilize elements never before available for a variety of complicated models in finite element analysis. FEniCS also uses tensor representations [176, 177, 178, 179, 248] to make matrix generation more efficient. In addition, FEniCS interfaces to components that are state-of-the-art in different domains such as system solution and mesh generation. For example, FEniCS programs easily take advantage of PETSc (developed at Argonne National Laboratory), Trilinos (developed at Sandia National Laboratory), and other linear and nonlinear system solvers. FEniCS also interfaces with CGAL, one of the leading mesh generation systems.

1.4 Format of a PDE

There are various ways to describe partial differential equations, and we have chosen the one that occurs most frequently in mathematics. In other disciplines, the underlying equations may be expressed in a different way that relates to a phenomenological emphasis. Thus a translation table may be necessary to facilitate conversion to different domains of application. We have chosen the mathematical notation for two reasons. First of all, we need something that is universal for all applications, and a domain specific notation would be natural for only one domain and confusing in another domain. More importantly, we want to expose the underlying mathematical structure behind simulation software. We realize that this forces the reader to use a language that may seem foreign, but the benefit is that it strips away non-essential trappings that can often mask fundamental behavior.

The general form of a PDE involves a function, which we often call u since it is *unknown* at the beginning, defined on a domain $\Omega \subset \mathbb{R}^n$. For an explanation of our set notation, see Section 31.1. The function u represents some quantity defined at all points of Ω, and this quantity can be a vector, in which case we might write it in bold face, viz. $\mathbf{u}$. The function

u depends on some data for the problem, and this data is often called f since it *forces* the solution u to take a particular form. In fact, f is sometimes called a forcing function, and it often represents forces applied to the material whose density is described by u.

Finally, the E in PDE refers to an equation that relates derivatives of u to the data f. In the one-dimensional case, this may be familiar. The *ordinary* differential equation (ODE) $u' = f$ is something considered in calculus, and we know from the Fundamental Theorem of Calculus that the ODE means that u is related to the integral of f. But when partial derivatives are involved in an equation, it is not at all clear why it should be possible to find a function u that satisfies such a relationship, even for particular data f. We consider this question in detail in Section 27.4. But it turns out that a simple theory developed here is sufficient to guarantee that the combinations of partial derivatives arising in most problems of interest are admissible.

What is missing from the terminology used so far is that there are often boundary conditions for PDEs that are the most critical factor. The term **boundary-value problem** is often used to describe a PDE, and this has the right emphasis. Although there is a general theory to assess whether a PDE makes sense locally (Section 27.4), the theoretical foundations related to finding the right boundary conditions are more diffuse. We attempt to develop intuition regarding boundary conditions by a combination of theoretical results and computational experiments.

1.5 Range of behavior

Often PDE models have smooth solutions that pose no significant difficulties for simulation. We depict such a solution in Figure 1.1. But PDE models can sometimes have singularities that are unanticipated. An example is given in Section 6.1.3 related to a change in type of boundary condition on a smooth boundary where otherwise one would not expect singular behavior. We depict such a solution in Figure 1.2. There are singularities in many other contexts, such as boundary layers, which can arise in different contexts. We focus on problems of this type to raise awareness of what to expect.

1.6 Computational methods

The type of singularities that arise in PDE solutions would cause significant impediments to efficient simulation if it were not for a major computational advance of the last few decades, adaptive mesh refinement. That this can be done automatically and reliably is a major achievement of computational mathematics. We explain this in Chapter 16 in simple terms to give a feeling of how the technology works, and we demonstrate its use on critical problems.

In some PDE models, there are significant issues related to finding appropriate discretizations. Fluid-flow problems present a central difficulty, related to incompressibility, that also arise in other contexts. We spend significant time to explain

- what goes wrong,
- the limitations of widely used techniques, and
- successful methods that have somewhat complicated implementations.

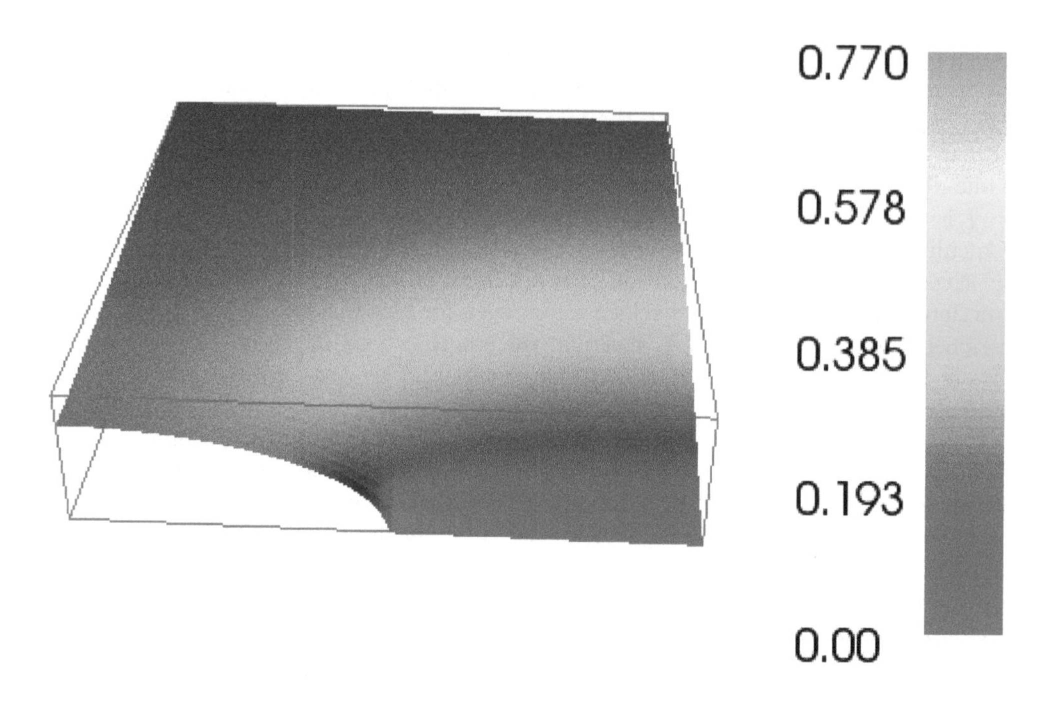

Figure 1.2: Solution of a PDE with a singularity on the boundary.

Fortunately, the expressiveness of the tools developed by the FEniCS Project allow even very complicated algorithms to be programmed easily, as will be demonstrated in many examples.

In many cases, numerical issues are just resolution issues, that is, they can be resolved by taking the mesh finer or the polynomial degree higher. Even the complicated stories about fluid flow (Chapter 13) and locking in structural mechanics (Section 19.7) can be viewed as just resolution issues (using higher-degree elements makes the difficulties disappear). But sometimes you hit the limit of mesh refinement and/or polynomial increase, due to computer storage limitations and/or simulation time constraints. Then the extensive research on more sophisticated numerical techniques appropriate for limited resources can provide enabling technology. However, here we focus on the simplest case which can often be solved just by increasing resolution.

One exception to this rule is the use of singular functions, which we explore in Section 15.2. This idea [20] plays a significant role in many areas, such as interface problems [158], crack problems [54, 287], and more. A full exploration of these areas is just beyond our scope in this book.

1.7 Why automation?

We can quantify the variability of PDEs used in modeling as follows. We use here the variational formulation of PDEs for a variety of reasons. There are three basic ingredients in the variational formulation of PDEs:

- the variational form that defines the PDE,

- the boundary conditions, often reflected in the variational space,
- the form that the data takes.

In Section 31.8, we summarize the number of major variational forms covered in this book. This number is in the dozens, and it represents only the tip of the iceberg. For many of these, there are also minor variations of interest that are covered. We feature four types of boundary conditions, and the number of different types of data presented here is large. Thus using just these three dimensions to describe elementary PDE problems shows that the number of combinations is in the thousands. Real applications of PDEs increase this number by orders of magnitude. Not mentioned so far is the variety of numerical methods that are used. Thus the number of possibilities of numerical methods for solving PDEs is enormous. Clearly then, automation of the generation of PDE software is beneficial.

But automation is not just convenient, it is essential. Each PDE, type of boundary condition, formulation of the data for the problem, and choice of numerical method is a discrete entity. One could employ a lot of people writing a code to implement each one separately. But in applied mathematics, when the number of discrete variables reaches this size, we begin to model it as a continuous variable. Ultimately, we want to think of PDE models as a continuum variable tuned to represent faithfully application reality. To support this view, automation is required to perform model optimization.

1.8 About this book

The first 5 chapters form the introductory unit. The following two chapters present variations of the Poisson equation. Chapter 8 presents the one-dimensional case as a review of the theoretical concepts in the simplest case. That chapter provides an opportunity to solidify understanding of the variational formulation of PDEs. Subsequent chapters study individual PDEs and many can be read in any order.

There are a few dependencies. Chapters 13 and 14 cover the Stokes equations and the former should be read before the latter. Similarly, Chapter 18 depends on Chapter 17. Chapter 19 on solid mechanics depends to a certain extent on information in the chapters on Stokes. Chapters 20 and 21 on the Navier-Stokes equations are a capstone for the book. These equations have nonlinearity (Chapter 9), a combination of diffusion and advection (Chapter 15), and are based on the Stokes equations (Chapters 13 and 14).

The attempt here has been to take the reader to the brink of research topics in many areas. For example, recent progress in non-Newtonian fluids [95, 141] can be exploited based on extensions of Chapters 20 and 21 on the Navier-Stokes equations. An extreme example of this appears in Chapters 23 and 24. In the latter chapter, we describe recent research that demonstrates behavior more complex than previously realized.

Some chapters are primarily about numerical methods. The most important of these is Chapter 16 on mesh adaptivity. Chapter 22 introduces methods to deal with curved domains and can be skipped. Chapter 25 presents a very brief discussion of linear solvers and can be used as an introduction to this important aspect of the simulation process. Similarly, Chapter 26 presents a very brief introduction to eigenvalue problems.

Chapter 27 summarizes various pitfalls in solving PDEs both theoretically and numerically. It provides an epilogue that should not be skipped.

Chapters 28, 29, and 30 are tutorial in nature and should be consulted as needed. Chapter 31 summarizes notation used throughout the book and should also be consulted as needed. Chapter 32 provides solutions of some exercises.

1.9 About code

We have included only rudimentary introductions to the FEniCS software. Tutorials [191] and on-line resources should be consulted for more details. Codes have been included for most chapters to document what was used to produce the figures presented. The details of such implementations will change over time, so they should be used only as a guide. On-line sources should be consulted for up-to-date syntax.

Chapter 2

Variational Formulations

The finite element method is based on the variational formulation of partial differential equations (PDEs). The variational formulation has three advantages:

- it provides a language to define PDEs suitable for compilation into executable code, and
- it provides a basis for a theory of PDEs that allows one to know whether or not a given model is well posed.
- it provides a basis for the approximation theory used to justify the finite element method.

We explain the first of these points via a simple example, Laplace's equation. Subsequently, a large variety of problems will be shown to fit into this framework. The latter two points are covered in subsequent chapters.

2.1 Laplace-Poisson equation

It is possible to define an unknown function u in a domain $\Omega \subset \mathbb{R}^d$, in part, by specifying its **Laplacian** (in terms of data f) in the interior of the domain:

$$-\Delta u = f \text{ in } \Omega, \tag{2.1}$$

where the **Laplacian operator** Δ is defined by (compare Section 31.6.3)

$$\Delta u = \sum_{i=1}^{d} \frac{\partial^2 u}{\partial x_i^2} .$$

There is a fundamental question as to why we are allowed to combine partial derivatives in this way to define a solution, and this will be explored in detail in Section 27.4. But for now, we presume that this is feasible. Indeed, we will see that the variational formulation allows us to prove this.

The equation (2.1) alone is insufficient to specify u, since we can add a harmonic function v to any solution and still have a solution of (2.1). A harmonic function v is any function

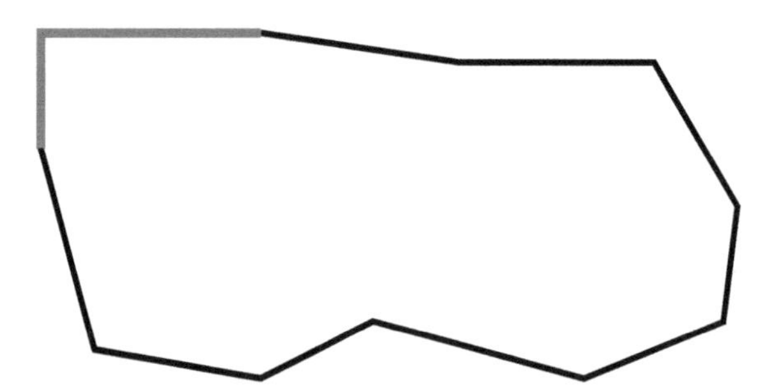

Figure 2.1: Domain Ω with Γ indicated in red.

such that $\Delta v \equiv 0$, and there are very many of them [18]. Here we are utilizing the fact that (2.1) represents a linear equation, so that

$$-\Delta(u+v) = (-\Delta u) - (\Delta v) = f - 0 = f.$$

This uses just the fact that the derivative of a sum is the sum of derivatives. Thus we must impose **boundary conditions** on u to make sense of the problem.

To contrast different possibilities, we consider two types of boundary conditions

$$\begin{aligned} u &= 0 \text{ on } \Gamma \subset \partial\Omega \qquad \text{(Dirichlet), and} \\ \frac{\partial u}{\partial n} &= 0 \text{ on } \partial\Omega\backslash\Gamma \qquad \text{(Neumann),} \end{aligned} \tag{2.2}$$

where $\frac{\partial u}{\partial n}$ denotes the derivative of u in the direction normal to the boundary, $\partial\Omega$. Here, $\partial\Omega$ denotes the boundary of the domain Ω, and $\partial\Omega\backslash\Gamma$ means the set of point in $\partial\Omega$ that are *not* in Γ. This is depicted in Figure 2.1. For more details on notation, see Chapter 31.

We let $\mathbf{n}$ denote the outward unit normal vector to $\partial\Omega$, and we set $\frac{\partial u}{\partial n} = \mathbf{n}\cdot\nabla u$. We will also use the notation

$$u_i = \frac{\partial u}{\partial x_i}, \quad u_{ii} = \frac{\partial^2 u}{\partial x_i^2}, \quad i = 1, \ldots, d.$$

Thus $\Delta u = u_{11} + \cdots + u_{dd}$ and $\nabla u = (u_1, \ldots, u_d)$. To avoid confusion, we will sometimes use the notation $u_{,i} = \frac{\partial u}{\partial x_i}$ to distinguish differentiation (the comma denotes this) from a standard vector subscript. For a summary of such notation, see Chapter 31.

The equation (2.1) is known variously as Poisson's equation or Laplace's equation (especially when $f \equiv 0$). We will use Poisson as the generic name, but the name Laplace is frequently used for the general case ($f \neq 0$), and we will sometimes revert to this common usage as well.

This equation forms the basis of a remarkable number of physical models. It serves as a basic equation for diffusion, elasticity, electrostatics, gravitation, and many more domains. In potential flow [222], the gradient of u is the velocity of incompressible, inviscid, irrotational fluid flow. The boundary $\partial\Omega$ is the surface of an obstacle moving in the flow, and one solves the equation on the exterior of Ω.

2.1.1 Sobolev spaces

We will see that is important to look for solutions of PDEs in well-defined spaces of functions with prescribed regularity. However, there are several possible choices which one might

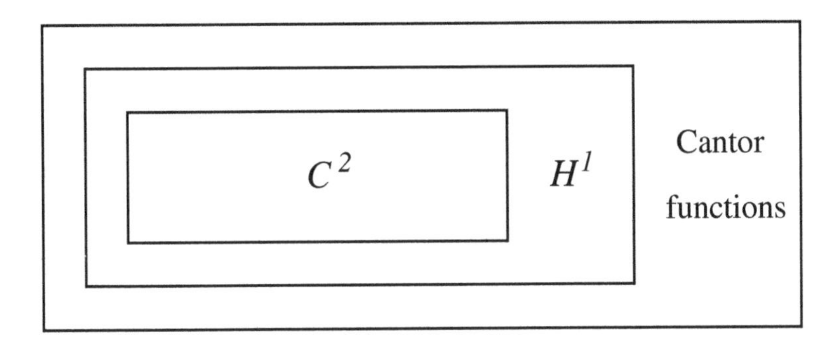

Figure 2.2: Different possible spaces in which to look for a solution. One is too big, so that spurious solutions abound, as described in Section 27.3. One is too small, so that many physically relevant solutions do not exist in that space, as described in Section 6.1. But we will see that the Sobolev spaces are just right.

imagine, as indicated Figure 2.2. Perhaps most surprising is that the obvious choice for Poisson's equation is *not* the space $C^2(\Omega)$ of functions with continuous derivatives of all orders up to two. In this space, all of the differential operators are defined classically.

Instead, we need to relax the standard of regularity to include solutions that are quite natural, as explained in Section 6.1. But just how much do we need to relax regularity constraints? In Section 27.3, we see that well defined functions (Cantor functions) display disconcerting behavior as solutions of PDEs. A space containing such functions is just to big. Thus we conclude that the right place to look for the solution of such an equation is a Sobolev space. The simplest of these is $H^1(\Omega)$, defined by

$$H^1(\Omega) = \left\{ v \in L^2(\Omega) \ : \ \nabla v \in L^2(\Omega)^d \right\}, \tag{2.3}$$

where by $L^2(\Omega)$ we mean functions which are square integrable on Ω, and $L^2(\Omega)^d$ means d copies of $L^2(\Omega)$ (Cartesian product).

2.1.2 Inner-products

There is a natural inner-product, and associated norm, on $L^2(\Omega)$ defined by

$$(v, w)_{L^2(\Omega)} = \int_\Omega v(\mathbf{x})\, w(\mathbf{x})\, d\mathbf{x}, \qquad \|v\|_{L^2(\Omega)} = \sqrt{(v, v)_{L^2(\Omega)}} = \left(\int_\Omega v(\mathbf{x})^2\, d\mathbf{x} \right)^{1/2}. \tag{2.4}$$

Thus we can say that $v \in L^2(\Omega)$ if and only if $\|v\|_{L^2(\Omega)} < \infty$. Similarly, we define

$$(v, w)_{H^1(\Omega)} = \int_\Omega v(\mathbf{x})\, w(\mathbf{x})\, d\mathbf{x} + \int_\Omega \nabla v \cdot \nabla w\, d\mathbf{x}, \qquad \|v\|_{H^1(\Omega)} = \sqrt{(v, v)_{H^1(\Omega)}}\,. \tag{2.5}$$

For a vector-valued function $\mathbf{w}$, e.g., $\mathbf{w} = \nabla v$, we define

$$\|\mathbf{w}\|_{L^2(\Omega)} = \| |\mathbf{w}| \|_{L^2(\Omega)} = \left(\int_\Omega |\mathbf{w}(\mathbf{x})|^2\, d\mathbf{x} \right)^{1/2},$$

where $|\xi|$ denotes the Euclidean norm of the vector $\xi \in \mathbb{R}^d$.

2.2 Variational formulation of Poisson's equation

Now consider the equation (2.1) augmented with boundary conditions (2.2). To begin with, we assume that Γ has nonzero measure (that is, length or area, or even volume, depending on dimension). Later, we will return to the case when Γ is empty, the pure Neumann[1] case. A typical domain Ω is shown in Figure 2.1, with Γ shown in red.

To formulate the variational equivalent of (2.1) with boundary conditions (2.2), we define a variational space that incorporates the essential, i.e., Dirichlet, part of the boundary conditions in (2.2):

$$V := \left\{ v \in H^1(\Omega) \,:\, v|_\Gamma = 0 \right\}. \tag{2.6}$$

The proper interpretation of the restriction (or trace) $v|_\Gamma$ of v to Γ will be explained in Section 30.1. See Table 2.1 for an explanation of the various names used to describe different boundary conditions.

The appropriate formalism for the variational problem is determined by multiplying Poisson's equation by a suitably smooth function, integrating over Ω and then integrating by parts:

$$\begin{aligned} (f,v)_{L^2(\Omega)} &= \int_\Omega (-\Delta u) v \, d\mathbf{x} = \int_\Omega \nabla u \cdot \nabla v \, d\mathbf{x} - \oint_{\partial\Omega} v \frac{\partial u}{\partial n} \, ds \\ &= \int_\Omega \nabla u \cdot \nabla v \, d\mathbf{x} = a(u,v), \end{aligned} \tag{2.7}$$

where we defined the bilinear form

$$a(u,v) = \int_\Omega \nabla u \cdot \nabla v \, d\mathbf{x}. \tag{2.8}$$

The integration-by-parts formula (2.7) derives from the divergence theorem

$$\int_\Omega \nabla \cdot \mathbf{w}(\mathbf{x}) \, d\mathbf{x} = \oint_{\partial\Omega} \mathbf{w}(s) \cdot \mathbf{n}(s) \, ds \tag{2.9}$$

which holds for any sufficiently smooth vector function $\mathbf{w} = (w_1, \ldots, w_d)$. Recall that the divergence operator is defined by

$$\nabla \cdot \mathbf{w} = \sum_{i=1}^{d} \frac{\partial w_i}{\partial x_i} = \sum_{i=1}^{d} w_{i,i},$$

where we use the notation $w_{i,j}$ to denote $\frac{\partial w_i}{\partial x_j}$.

We apply the divergence theorem (2.9) to $\mathbf{w} = v\nabla u$, together with the observations that $\frac{\partial u}{\partial n} = (\nabla u) \cdot \mathbf{n}$ and $\Delta u = \nabla \cdot (\nabla u)$ (Exercise 2.2). Here, $\mathbf{n}$ is the outward-directed normal to $\partial\Omega$. More precisely, we observe that

$$\nabla \cdot (v \nabla u) = \sum_{i=1}^{d} \big((v \nabla u)_i \big)_{,i} = \sum_{i=1}^{d} (v\, u_{,i})_{,i} = \sum_{i=1}^{d} \big(v_{,i} u_{,i} + v\, u_{,ii} \big) = \nabla v \cdot \nabla u + v \Delta u.$$

[1] Carl Gottfried Neumann (1832—1925) was the son of Franz Ernst Neumann (1798–1895) who was a teacher of Kirchhoff. Carl (a.k.a. Karl) is also known for the Neumann series for matrices, and he was the thesis advisor of William Edward Story who at Clark University was the thesis advisor of Solomon Lefschetz.

generic name	example	honorific name
essential	$u = 0$	Dirichlet
natural	$\frac{\partial u}{\partial n} = 0$	Neumann

Table 2.1: Nomenclature for different types of boundary conditions for the variational formulation (2.11) of Poisson's equation.

Thus the divergence theorem applied to $\mathbf{w} = v\nabla u$ gives

$$\oint_{\partial\Omega} v\nabla u(s)\cdot\mathbf{n}(s)\,ds = \int_\Omega \big(\nabla\cdot(v\nabla u)\big)(\mathbf{x})\,d\mathbf{x} = \int_\Omega (\nabla v\cdot\nabla u + v\Delta u)(\mathbf{x})\,d\mathbf{x},$$

which means that

$$\int_\Omega -v(\mathbf{x})\Delta u(\mathbf{x})\,d\mathbf{x} = \int_\Omega \nabla v(\mathbf{x})\cdot\nabla u(\mathbf{x})\,d\mathbf{x} - \oint_{\partial\Omega} v\,\frac{\partial u}{\partial n}\,ds. \tag{2.10}$$

This verifies (2.7).

The boundary term in (2.7) vanishes for $v \in V$ because either v or $\frac{\partial u}{\partial n}$ is zero on any part of the boundary. Thus, u can be characterized via the **variational formulation**:

$$\boxed{\text{Find } u \in V \text{ satisfying } a(u,v) = (f,v)_{L^2(\Omega)} \quad \forall v \in V.} \tag{2.11}$$

The function v in the variational equation is called a **test function** since it is used to test the validity of the solution. Similarly, function u, and especially its analog in the finite element approximation, is often called the **trial function**, since it is being tried out as a possible solution. Correspondingly, we refer to V as the trial space and the test space. In general, the test and trial spaces could be different, but typically here we will have them equal.

The companion result that a solution of the variational problem in (2.11) solves Poisson's equation can also be proved [57], under suitable regularity conditions on u so that the relevant expressions in (2.1) and (2.2) are well defined. We sketch how it is done in Section 3.5 and give more detail in the one-dimensional case in Section 8.2.3.

2.3 Method of manufactured solutions

We now demonstrate the power of the variational formulation as a language for PDEs. In Program 2.1, we present a complete code that solves Laplace's equation and maps in a clear way to the ingredients of the variational formulation. But first we need a way to tell that the code is really working correctly.

We can test our technology by considering a problem with a known solution. One way to do this is to use the method of **manufactured solutions** [211]. Consider

$$\begin{aligned} -\Delta u &= 2\pi^2 \sin(\pi x)\sin(\pi y) \text{ in } \Omega = [0,1]\times[0,1] \\ u &= 0 \text{ on } \partial\Omega, \end{aligned} \tag{2.12}$$

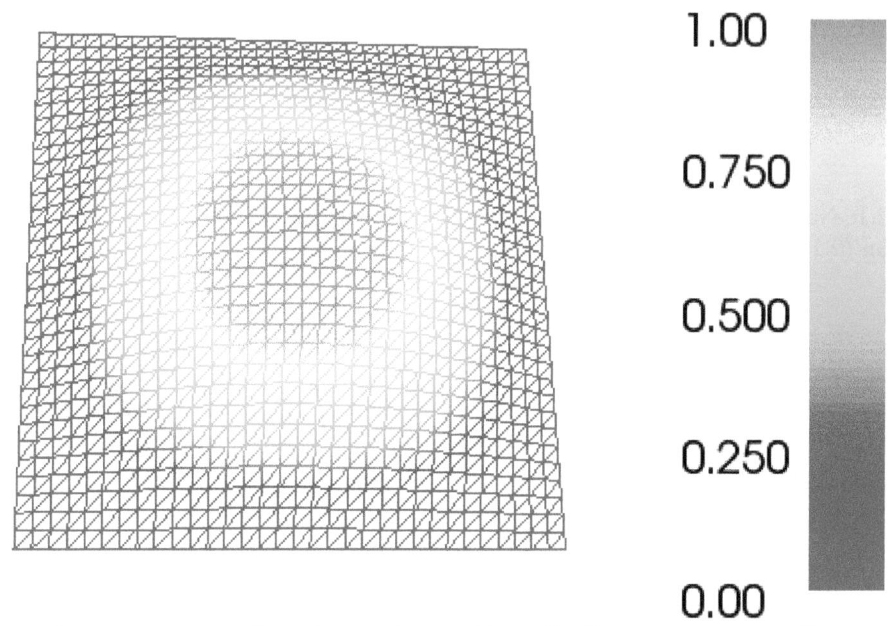

Figure 2.3: Solution of the boundary value problem (2.12), implemented in Program 2.1.

technique	specification	example where used
keyword	"on_boundary"	Program 2.1
reserved function	DomainBoundary()	Program 4.1
defined function	boundary	Program 2.2, Program 6.1

Table 2.2: Different ways to specify the boundary of a domain.

whose solution is $u(x,y) = \sin(\pi x)\sin(\pi y)$. Of course, we started with the solution $u(x,y) = \sin(\pi x)\sin(\pi y)$ and then computed its Laplacian to get $f = 2\pi^2 \sin(\pi x)\sin(\pi y)$. The solution of this problem is depicted in Figure 2.3. The implementation of this problem is given in Program 2.1.

The code is a faithful representation of the variational formulation. The domain is represented by `mesh` which encapsulates both the definition of the domain and a subdivision of it. The form `a` in line 15 is just missing an integral sign and the domain of integration. The latter is implicit due to the link with the variational space `V` which encodes this information. The symbol `dx` stands for Lebesgue measure over the domain represented by `mesh`. It is necessary to specify this as other integrals, such as boundary integrals, will appear shortly.

In line 9 in Program 2.1, the third variable in `DirichletBC` specifies where Dirichlet boundary conditions are to be specified. Table 2.2 specifies two other ways of achieving the same thing. In Program 2.2, a logical function `boundary` is defined that is `True` if a point is outside the domain, and `False` otherwise. A small parameter `DOLFIN_EPS` (machine precision) is used to avoid floating point numbers being very close to zero. Thus for any points very close to the boundary of the square, the function `boundary` will evaluate to `True`. We leave as Exercise 2.1 to implement Program 2.1 and check to see if it gets the right answer.

```
1  from dolfin import *
2
3  # Create mesh and define function space
4  mesh = UnitSquareMesh(32, 32)
5  V = FunctionSpace(mesh, "Lagrange", 1)
6
7  # Define boundary condition
8  u0 = Constant(0.0)
9  bc = DirichletBC(V, u0, "on_boundary")
10
11 # Define variational problem
12 u = TrialFunction(V)
13 v = TestFunction(V)
14 you = Expression("(sin(3.141592*x[0]))*(sin(3.141592*x[1]))",degree=1)
15 a = inner(grad(u), grad(v))*dx
16 L = (2*3.141592*3.141592)*you*v*dx
17
18 # Compute solution
19 u = Function(V)
20 solve(a == L, u, bc)
21 plot(u, interactive=True)
```

Program 2.1: Code to implement the problem (2.12). The code in line 4 defines the domain (a square) and the boundary conditions are specified in lines 8 and 9. The code in lines 12 to 16 defines the ingredients of the variational formulation. The solution of this problem is depicted in Figure 2.3.

2.4 Formulation of the pure Neumann problem

In Section 2.2, we introduced the variational formulation for Poisson's equation with a combination of boundary conditions, but they all contained some essential (i.e., Dirichlet) component. The situation for the case of pure Neumann (or natural) boundary conditions

$$\frac{\partial u}{\partial n} = 0 \text{ on } \partial\Omega \tag{2.13}$$

(i.e., when $\Gamma = \emptyset$) is a bit different. This will be explained in more detail in the one-dimensional case (cf. Exercise 8.1). In particular, solutions are unique only up to an additive constant (Exercise 2.8), and they can exist only if the right-hand side f in (2.1) satisfies

$$\int_\Omega f(\mathbf{x})\,d\mathbf{x} = \int_\Omega -\Delta u(\mathbf{x})\,d\mathbf{x} = \int_\Omega \nabla u(\mathbf{x})\cdot\nabla 1\,d\mathbf{x} - \oint_{\partial\Omega} \frac{\partial u}{\partial n}\,ds = 0, \tag{2.14}$$

using the integration-by-parts formula (2.7) with v being the constant function, $v \equiv 1$. A variational space appropriate for the present case is

$$V = \Big\{ v \in H^1(\Omega) \;:\; \int_\Omega v(\mathbf{x})\,d\mathbf{x} = 0 \Big\}. \tag{2.15}$$

This space specifies the additive constant to obtain uniqueness.

```
def boundary(x):
    return x[0] < DOLFIN_EPS or           \
           x[0] > 1.0 - DOLFIN_EPS or     \
           x[1] < DOLFIN_EPS or           \
           x[1] > 1.0 - DOLFIN_EPS
```

Program 2.2: Code to define the boundary of a square explicitly.

For any integrable function g, we define its *mean*, $\bar{g}$, as follows:

$$\bar{g} := \frac{1}{\text{measure}(\Omega)} \int_\Omega g(\mathbf{x})\, d\mathbf{x}, \tag{2.16}$$

where measure(Ω) is the length, area or volume (depending on the dimension) of Ω. For any $v \in H^1(\Omega)$, note that $v - \bar{v} \in V$. Then $u - \bar{u}$ satisfies the variational formulation (2.11) with V defined as in (2.15).

Conversely, if $u \in H^2(\Omega)$ solves the variational equation (2.11) with V defined as in (2.15), then u solves Poisson's equation (2.1) with a right-hand-side given by

$$\tilde{f}(\mathbf{x}) := f(\mathbf{x}) - \bar{f} \quad \forall \mathbf{x} \in \Omega \tag{2.17}$$

with boundary conditions (2.13), as discussed in Section 3.7.

2.5 Linear functionals as data

The expression $(f, v)_{L^2(\Omega)}$ on the right-hand side of (2.11) is an example of a **linear functional**. The right-hand side of (2.11) can be written succinctly as

$$F(v) = (f, v)_{L^2(\Omega)} \qquad \forall v \in V. \tag{2.18}$$

The expression F is called a linear functional because (a) it is linear and (b) it has scalar values. By linear, we mean that $F(u+av) = F(u)+aF(v)$ for any scalar a and any $u, v \in V$.

The critical condition on a linear functional (a.k.a., **linear form**) for success in a variational formulation is that it be *bounded* or *continuous*. A **bounded linear functional** (equivalently a **continuous linear functional**) F on a normed space V must satisfy

$$|F(v)| \leq C_F \|v\|_V \quad \forall v \in V. \tag{2.19}$$

A natural norm $\|\cdot\|_V$ for the space V defined in (2.6) or (2.15) is

$$\|v\|_a = \sqrt{a(v, v)}.$$

The smallest possible constant C_F for which this holds is called the **dual norm** of F and is defined by

$$\|F\|_{V'} := \sup_{0 \neq v \in V} \frac{|F(v)|}{\|v\|_V}. \tag{2.20}$$

We will see many bounded linear forms as right-hand sides in variational formulations. But there are many which are not bounded, such as

$$F(v) := v'(x_0) \tag{2.21}$$

for some $x_0 \in [0,1]$. This form is linear, but consider what it should do for the function $v \in H^1([0,1])$ given by

$$v(x) := |x - x_0|^{2/3} \tag{2.22}$$

(see Exercise 8.2).

2.5.1 Inhomogeneous Neumann problem

An important illustration of the need for general linear functionals as data for PDE problems is given by the inhomogeneous Neumann problem, where we pose $\frac{\partial u}{\partial n} = g$ on $\Omega \backslash \Gamma$. As before, we assume that we have homogeneous boundary conditions posed on $\Gamma \subset \partial\Omega$, and we define

$$V = \left\{ v \in H^1(\Omega) \ : \ v = 0 \text{ on } \Gamma \right\}.$$

If we combine (2.10) and (2.11), we see that the formulation of the inhomogeneous Neumann problem has the variational expression

$$u \in V \text{ satisfying } a(u,v) = (f,v)_{L^2(\Omega)} + \oint_{\Omega\backslash\Gamma} g(s)v(s)\,ds \quad \forall v \in V. \tag{2.23}$$

Thus we find another example of the general variational problem

$$u \in V \text{ satisfying } a(u,v) = F(v) \quad \forall v \in V, \tag{2.24}$$

where the linear functional F is given by

$$F(v) = (f,v)_{L^2(\Omega)} + \oint_{\Omega\backslash\Gamma} g(s)v(s)\,ds \quad \forall v \in V. \tag{2.25}$$

It requires some Sobolev technology to prove it, but F is continuous on $H^1(\Omega)$. For more information, see Section 30.1.

2.5.2 Inhomogeneous Neumann example

As an example, consider the following problem on the unit square $\Omega = [0,1]^2$ with homogeneous Dirichlet data posed on

$$\Gamma = \{(x,y) \in \partial\Omega \ : \ x = 0 \text{ or } y = 0 \text{ or } y = 1\}.$$

Thus $\partial\Omega\backslash\Gamma = \{(x,y) \in \partial\Omega \ : \ x = 1\}$. Define $g(y) = y(1-y)$ and $f(x,y) = 2x$. As always, define $V = \left\{ v \in H^1(\Omega) \ : \ v = 0 \text{ on } \Gamma \right\}$. The variational formulation of

$$\begin{aligned} -\Delta u &= f \text{ in } \Omega \\ u &= 0 \text{ on } \Gamma \\ \frac{\partial u}{\partial n} &= g \text{ on } \partial\Omega\backslash\Gamma \end{aligned} \tag{2.26}$$

(whose exact solution is $u(x,y) = xy(1-y)$) is to find $u \in V$ such that

$$a(u,v) = (f,v)_{L^2(\Omega)} + \oint_{\Omega\backslash\Gamma} g(s)v(s)\,ds \quad \forall v \in V, \tag{2.27}$$

where as before $a(u,v) = \int_\Omega \nabla u(\mathbf{x}) \cdot \nabla v(\mathbf{x})\,d\mathbf{x}$. The solution is depicted in Figure 2.4, and the code to generate the figure is given in Program 2.3.

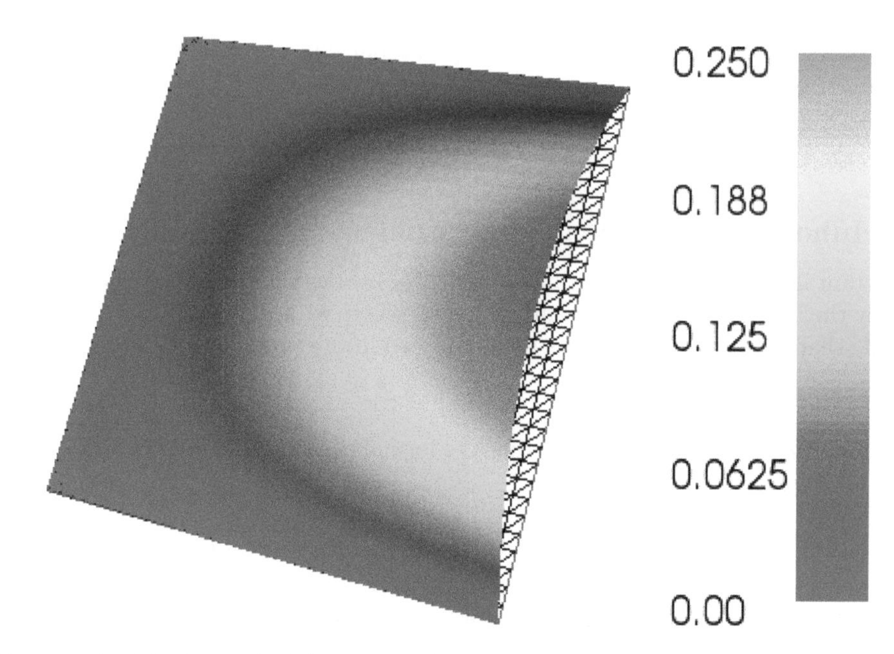

Figure 2.4: Solution of (2.26) computed using piecewise linears on a 32×32 mesh.

2.6 Exercises

Exercise 2.1 *Run Program 2.1 and check visually that it is getting the expected answer.*

Exercise 2.2 *Verify the vector identity* $\Delta u = \nabla\cdot(\nabla u)$.

Exercise 2.3 *Modify Program 2.1 by using a different way to specify the boundary as described in Table 2.2. Make sure it gives a reasonable answer.*

Exercise 2.4 *Use the method of manufactured solutions to generate a polynomial solution on the square. Define* $q(t) = t(1-t)$ *and let* $u(x,y) = q(x)q(y)$. *Note that* u *satisfies homogeneous Dirichlet boundary conditions* $u = 0$ *on* $\partial\Omega$. *Find* f *such that* $-\Delta u = f$. *Modify Program 2.1 using this* f *and* u. *Verify that it gets the right answer (explain).*

Exercise 2.5 *Use the method of manufactured solutions to generate a solution to the pure Neumann problem with boundary conditions (2.13) on the square. Start with* $u(x,y) = (\cos\pi x)(\cos\pi y)$ *and compute the corresponding* f *such that* $-\Delta u = f$. *Modify Program 2.1 using this* f *and* u. *(Hint:* `dolfin` *does not allow the definition of the space (2.15), so proceed naïvely and use the full space. See Section 25.1.2 for more details.)*

Exercise 2.6 *Implement the code for the inhomogeneous Neumann boundary conditions* $\frac{\partial u}{\partial n} = g$ *described in Section 2.5.2, whose exact solution is* $u(x,y) = xy(1-y)$. *Use the expression*

```
ue = Expression("x[0]*x[1]*(1-x[1])")
```

together with the code

```
uze=interpolate(ue,V)
```

```
 1 # Create mesh and define function space
 2 mesh = UnitSquareMesh(32, 32)
 3 V = FunctionSpace(mesh, "Lagrange", 1)
 4
 5 #Dirichlet boundary (x=0 or y=0 or y=1)
 6 def boundary(x):
 7   return x[0] < DOLFIN_EPS or x[1] < DOLFIN_EPS or x[1] > 1 - DOLFIN_EPS
 8
 9 # Define boundary condition
10 u0 = Constant(0.0)
11 bc = DirichletBC(V, u0, boundary)
12
13 # Define variational problem
14 u = TrialFunction(V)
15 v = TestFunction(V)
16 f = Expression("2.0*x[0]",degree=pdeg)
17 g = Expression("x[1]*(1-x[1])",degree=pdeg)
18 a = inner(grad(u), grad(v))*dx
19 L = f*v*dx + g*v*ds
20
21 # Compute solution
22 u = Function(V)
23 solve(a == L, u, bc)
```

Program 2.3: Code to solve the PDE (2.26).

to create a piecewise linear interpolant of u. Compare the computed solution `u` *from Program 2.3 with* `uze` *(a) by plotting* `u - uze` *and (b) by computing a norm of* `u - uze`.

Exercise 2.7 *Prove that $u(x,y) = xy(1-y)$ solves (2.26). Be sure to check the boundary conditions.*

Exercise 2.8 *Suppose that u is a solution of the pure Neumann problem*

$$-\Delta u = f \text{ in } \Omega, \qquad \frac{\partial u}{\partial n} = 0 \text{ on } \partial\Omega.$$

Show that $u + c$ is also a solution for any constant c.

Chapter 3

Variational Theory of PDEs

We now outline the PDE theory based on the variational formulation. This provides confidence in our models and a guide to choosing correct ones. Further, it demystifies the variational approach and allows us to connect it to more common representations of PDEs. In particular, we need to see why the variational representation of natural boundary conditions succeeds in imposing the required normal derivatives.

Often the most critical condition for the well-posedness of a problem is the coercivity of the variational form, so we begin with that.

3.1 Bilinear forms

We say that an expression $a(\cdot,\cdot)$ is a **bilinear form** if it is linear in each argument separately. We can think of this abstractly in the following way. Fix $w \in V$ and define a form $F(v) = a(v, w)$ for all $v \in V$. For $a(\cdot,\cdot)$ to be bilinear, we require that F be linear. Similarly, if we define $G(v) = a(w, v)$ for all $v \in V$, we also require that G be linear. That is, we require $a(\cdot,\cdot)$ to be linear in each of its arguments separately, hence the name **bi**linear.

More concretely, to verify that a form is bilinear, we have to verify a number of conditions. Linearity in the first argument of $a(\cdot,\cdot)$ means that

$$a(u + cv, w) = a(u, w) + ca(v, w) \tag{3.1}$$

for all $u, v, w \in V$ and any constant c. Linearity in the second argument of $a(\cdot,\cdot)$ means that

$$a(u, cv + w) = ca(u, v) + a(u, w) \tag{3.2}$$

for all $u, v, w \in V$ and any constant c. If both conditions (3.1) and (3.1) hold, then $a(\cdot,\cdot)$ is bilinear. The variational form $a(\cdot,\cdot)$ introduced in (2.8) is bilinear because the integral is linear: the integral of the sum of two functions is the sum of the integral of the functions.

3.2 Coercivity

The variational form $a(\cdot,\cdot)$ introduced in (2.8) is **coercive** on the corresponding spaces V defined in (2.6) and (2.15) (see [57]): there is a constant c_0 depending only on Ω (and Γ in the case of (2.6)) such that

$$\|v\|_{H^1(\Omega)}^2 \le c_0 a(v,v) \quad \forall v \in V. \tag{3.3}$$

We prove this in Section 8.4 in the one-dimensional case. We demonstrate coercivity for the space (2.15) in Section 30.3.2 and for the space (2.6) in Section 30.5. Note that

$$(u,v)_{H^1(\Omega)} = a(u,v) + (u,v)_{L^2(\Omega)}, \tag{3.4}$$

so that (3.3) follows if we can show that

$$\|v\|_{L^2(\Omega)}^2 \le (c_0 - 1) a(v,v) \quad \forall v \in V. \tag{3.5}$$

From (3.3), it follows that the problem (2.11) is well-posed, as we will subsequently show. In particular, we easily see that the solution to the problem must be unique, for if f is identically zero then so is the solution:

$$\|u\|_{H^1(\Omega)}^2 \le c_0 a(u,u) = (f,u)_{L^2(\Omega)} = 0.$$

In the finite-dimensional case, this uniqueness also implies existence, and a similar result holds in the setting of infinite dimensional Hilbert spaces such as V, as we will see. In particular, the coercivity condition immediately implies a stability result, namely

$$\|u\|_{H^1(\Omega)} \le \frac{c_0 a(u,u)}{\|u\|_{H^1(\Omega)}} = c_0 \frac{(f,u)_{L^2(\Omega)}}{\|u\|_{H^1(\Omega)}} \le c_0 \|f\|_{V'}, \tag{3.6}$$

where $\|f\|_{V'}$ is defined in (2.20).

When coercivity holds, the **Lax-Milgram Theorem** 3.1 guarantees that the variational problem (2.11) has a unique solution. There is an additional **continuity condition** that usually is straight-forward, namely that the form $a(\cdot,\cdot)$ is bounded on V, that is,

$$|a(u,v)| \le c_1 \|u\|_{H^1(\Omega)} \|v\|_{H^1(\Omega)} \quad \text{for all } u,v \in V. \tag{3.7}$$

In most cases, this condition is evident, but not in all as we describe in Section 7.2.1. What is often easy to see is that

$$a(v,v) \le C \|v\|_{H^1(\Omega)}^2 \quad \forall v \in V.$$

For the form in (2.8), this follows from (3.4) with $C = 1$. The connection between this condition and (3.7) is given by the Cauchy-Schwarz inequality (3.15), as we explain shortly.

To state a general theorem, consider the variational formulation to find

$$u \in V \ \text{ satisfying } \ a(u,v) = F(v) \quad \forall v \in V. \tag{3.8}$$

Theorem 3.1 (Lax-Milgram) *Suppose that the variational form $a(\cdot,\cdot)$ is coercive (3.3) and continuous (3.7) (bounded) on $H^1(\Omega)$. Then the variational problem (3.8) has a unique solution u for every continuous (bounded) linear functional F defined on $H^1(\Omega)$. Moreover,*

$$\|u\|_{H^1(\Omega)} \le c_1 c_0 \sup_{v \in H^1(\Omega)} \frac{|F(v)|}{\|v\|_{H^1(\Omega)}} = c_1 c_0 \|F\|_{H^1(\Omega)'}, \tag{3.9}$$

where c_0 is the constant in (3.3) and c_1 is the constant in (3.7).

The Lax-Milgram theorem implies the well-posedness of the partial differential equations related to the variational formulation. The same type of bound as in (3.6) holds for discrete approximations as well under a very simple condition, indicated in (4.5). In this case, the bound corresponds to the **stability** of the numerical scheme.

3.3 Cauchy-Schwarz inequality

There is one small detail that we have let slip pass. The space V is defined using the requirement that $a(v,v) < \infty$, but what we need to know is that $a(u,v)$ is well defined for all $u, v \in V$. The latter is a consequence of the former, as follows.

Let $t \in \mathbb{R}$ be arbitrary, and expand $a(u - t\,v, u - t\,v)$ to get

$$a(u-t\,v,u-t\,v) = a(u-t\,v,u)-t\,a(u-t\,v,v) = a(u,u)-t\,a(v,u)-t\,a(u,v)+t^2a(v,v). \quad (3.10)$$

The bilinear form $a(\cdot,\cdot)$ is symmetric: $a(v,w) = a(w,v)$, so (3.10) implies

$$a(u - t\,v, u - t\,v) = a(u,u) - 2t\,a(v,u) + t^2a(v,v) = a(u,u) - 2t\,a(u,v) + t^2a(v,v). \quad (3.11)$$

In particular, since $a(u - t\,v, u - t\,v) \geq 0$,

$$2t\,a(u,v) \leq a(u,u) + t^2a(v,v). \quad (3.12)$$

For example, suppose that $a(v,v) = 0$. Choose the sign of t to be the sign of $a(u,v)$ and we conclude that

$$2|t|\,|a(u,v)| \leq a(u,u). \quad (3.13)$$

Since this holds for all $t \in \mathbb{R}$, we can let $|t| \to \infty$ to conclude that $a(u,v) = 0$. If $a(v,v) \neq 0$, define $t = \operatorname{sign}(a(u,v))\|u\|_a/\|v\|_a$. If by chance $a(u,u) = 0$, then we reverse the previous argument to conclude that again $a(u,v) = 0$. If it is not zero, and thus $t \neq 0$, we can divide by $|t|$ in (3.12) to get

$$2|a(u,v)| \leq \frac{1}{|t|}a(u,u) + |t|\,a(v,v) = 2\|u\|_a\|v\|_a. \quad (3.14)$$

Thus we have proved the Cauchy-Schwarz inequality, which we summarize as follows.

Lemma 3.1 *Suppose that $a(\cdot,\cdot)$ is a symmetric, bilinear form such that $a(v,v) \geq 0$ for all $v \in V$. Then*

$$|a(u,v)| \leq \|u\|_a\|v\|_a \quad (3.15)$$

for all $u, v \in V$, where $\|v\|_a = \sqrt{a(v,v)}$ for any $v \in V$.

The Cauchy-Schwarz inequality is generally true for any non-negative, symmetric bilinear form. It is often stated as a property of an **inner-product**. Our bilinear form $a(\cdot,\cdot)$ is almost an inner-product except that it lacks one condition, nondegeneracy. In our case $a(v,v) = 0$ if v is constant, and for an inner-product, this is not allowed. One example of an inner-product is the bilinear form

$$(u,v)_{L^2(\Omega)} = \int_\Omega u(x)\,v(x)\,dx. \quad (3.16)$$

Here we see that $(v,v)_{L^2(\Omega)} = 0$ implies that $v \equiv 0$. But the Cauchy-Schwarz inequality does not require this additional property to be valid.

3.4 Well-posedness of the Laplace-Poisson problem

We can now use our theory to show that the Laplace-Poisson boundary value problem introduced in Section 2.1 is well posed. It is remarkable that we can do that so easily with only the tools introduced in this chapter. But this is one of the major theoretical achievements of the variational formulation. Of course, we have argued only conceptually why the variational form $a(u,v)$ defined in (2.8) is coercive when the Dirichlet part Γ of the boundary $\partial\Omega$ is non-trivial:

$$(v,v)_{H^1(\Omega)} \le c_\Gamma\, a(v,v) \quad \forall v \in V. \tag{3.17}$$

The full theoretical proof of this involves properties of the Sobolev spaces [57], but the crux of the matter is to observe that nonzero constants cannot appear in the variational space V defined in (2.6). The continuity of $a(u,v)$ follows from

$$(u,v)_{H^1(\Omega)} = a(u,v) + (u,v)_{L^2(\Omega)},$$

with the constant c_1 in (3.7) equal to 1. Thus the Lax-Milgram Theorem 3.1 applies to yield the following theorem.

Theorem 3.2 *The variational formulation (2.11) of the Laplace-Poisson boundary value problem in Section 2.1 has a unique solution $u \in H^1(\Omega)$, satisfying $u = 0$ on $\Gamma \subset \partial\Omega$, for every continuous (bounded) linear functional F defined on $H^1(\Omega)$. Moreover,*

$$\|u\|_{H^1(\Omega)} \le c_\Gamma \sup_{v\in H^1(\Omega)} \frac{|F(v)|}{\|v\|_{H^1(\Omega)}} = c_\Gamma \|F\|_{H^1(\Omega)'}, \tag{3.18}$$

where c_Γ is the constant in (3.17).

3.5 Connection to classical notions

We now discuss the meaning of a variational solution of a PDE in more classical, pointwise terms. Let $C^2(\Omega)$ denote the space of all functions whose derivatives of order up to 2 are continuous.

Suppose that $u \in C^2(\Omega)$ and V is defined by (2.6). Recall the integration-by-parts formula (2.8), which we write as

$$\int_\Omega (-\Delta u) v \, d\mathbf{x} = a(u,v) + \oint_{\partial\Omega} v \frac{\partial u}{\partial n}\, ds. \tag{3.19}$$

If $a(u,v) = (f,v)_{L^2(\Omega)}$ for all $v \in V$, then

$$\int_\Omega \big((-\Delta u)(\mathbf{x}) - f(\mathbf{x})\big) v(\mathbf{x})\, d\mathbf{x} = \oint_{\partial\Omega} v(s) \frac{\partial u}{\partial n}(s)\, ds. \tag{3.20}$$

We can choose $v \in V$ to be zero on the boundary, and in this case

$$\int_\Omega \big((-\Delta u)(\mathbf{x}) - f(\mathbf{x})\big) v(\mathbf{x})\, d\mathbf{x} = 0. \tag{3.21}$$

In particular, suppose that

$$(-\Delta u)(\mathbf{x}_0) - f(\mathbf{x}_0) \ne 0$$

for some $\mathbf{x}_0 \in \Omega$ satisfying

$$d := \text{distance}(\mathbf{x}_0, \partial\Omega) > 0.$$

Suppose now that both f and Δu are continuous. Then there is an $\epsilon > 0$ such that $\epsilon < d$ and $|(-\Delta u)(\mathbf{x}) - f(\mathbf{x})| > 0$ for all $|\mathbf{x} - \mathbf{x}_0| < \epsilon$. Choose

$$v(\mathbf{x}) = \begin{cases} 1 - \epsilon^{-1}|\mathbf{x} - \mathbf{x}_0| & |\mathbf{x} - \mathbf{x}_0| < \epsilon \\ 0 & |\mathbf{x} - \mathbf{x}_0| \geq \epsilon \end{cases}. \tag{3.22}$$

Note that $v \geq 0$ and $v > 0$ for $|\mathbf{x} - \mathbf{x}_0| < \epsilon$, and that $v \in H_0^1(\Omega)$ (Exercise 3.4). But this would mean that

$$\int_\Omega \big((-\Delta u)(\mathbf{x}) - f(\mathbf{x})\big) v(\mathbf{x})\, d\mathbf{x} \neq 0,$$

yielding a contradiction. This means that wherever both f and Δu are continuous, we must have $f = -\Delta u$, so that the variational solution is also a classical solution.

3.6 Meaning of natural boundary conditions

We now explain why we can use a boundary integral as in (2.27) to represent boundary conditions involving the normal derivative. We consider the variational problem (2.24) with right-hand-side F given by (2.25). Under the conditions of Section 3.5, we conclude that $-\Delta u = f$ in Ω provided they are both continuous on Ω. Thus the integration-by-parts formula, in the form (3.19), implies

$$\int_\Omega f(\mathbf{x})v(\mathbf{x})\, d\mathbf{x} = a(u,v) + \oint_{\partial\Omega} v(s)\, \frac{\partial u}{\partial n}(s)\, ds \tag{3.23}$$

for all $v \in V$. Comparing (3.19) and (2.24), we conclude that

$$\oint_{\partial\Omega} g(s)v(s)\, ds = \oint_{\partial\Omega} v(s)\, \frac{\partial u}{\partial n}(s)\, ds = \oint_{\partial\Omega\backslash\Gamma} v(s)\, \frac{\partial u}{\partial n}(s)\, ds \tag{3.24}$$

for all $v \in V$, where V is defined by (2.6). Suppose that $s_0 \in \partial\Omega\backslash\Gamma$ with distance$(s_0, \Gamma) > 0$, and suppose that $g(s_0) - \frac{\partial u}{\partial n}(s_0) \neq 0$. If both g and $\frac{\partial u}{\partial n}$ are continuous near s_0, there is an $\epsilon > 0$ such that $|g(s) - \frac{\partial u}{\partial n}(s)| > 0$ for all $s \in \partial\Omega$ satisfying $|s - s_0| < \epsilon$. Choose v as in (3.22). Then we reach a contradiction with (3.24), since we must have

$$\oint_{\partial\Omega\backslash\Gamma} v(s)\Big(g(x) - \frac{\partial u}{\partial n}(s)\Big)\, ds \neq 0.$$

Thus we conclude that $\frac{\partial u}{\partial n}(s) = g(s)$ wherever they are both continuous.

3.7 Pure Neumann problem

Corresponding results for the pure Neumann problem require only slight modifications of the arguments in Sections 3.5 and 3.6. Suppose that $u \in V$ satisfies

$$a(u,v) = \int_\Omega f(\mathbf{x})v(\mathbf{x})\, d\mathbf{x} + \oint_{\partial\Omega} v(s)\, g(s)\, ds \quad \forall v \in V, \tag{3.25}$$

where V is defined by (2.15) and we assume the required compatibility condition

$$\int_\Omega f(\mathbf{x})\,d\mathbf{x} + \oint_{\partial\Omega} g(s)\,ds = 0.$$

Then

$$a(u, v+C) = \int_\Omega f(\mathbf{x})(v(\mathbf{x})+C)\,d\mathbf{x} + \oint_{\partial\Omega} (v(s)+C)\,g(s)\,ds \quad \forall v \in V,\ C \in \mathbb{R} \tag{3.26}$$

because $a(u, C) = 0$ for any $C \in \mathbb{R}$. Thus we conclude that

$$a(u, v) = \int_\Omega f(\mathbf{x})v(\mathbf{x})\,d\mathbf{x} + \oint_{\partial\Omega} v(s)\,g(s)\,ds \quad \forall v \in H^1(\Omega), \tag{3.27}$$

since for any $v \in H^1(\Omega)$, $v - \overline{v} \in V$ (recall the definition of the mean $\overline{v}$ in (2.16)). Thus we can pick v as in (3.22) to conclude that $-\Delta u = f$ wherever they are continuous and to conclude that $\frac{\partial u}{\partial n} = g$ wherever they are both continuous.

3.8 Exercises

Exercise 3.1 *Inhomogeneous Dirichlet boundary conditions $u = g$ on $\partial\Omega$ can be posed in two equivalent ways. Let us assume that $g \in H^1(\Omega)$ for simplicity. We can think of finding $u \in V + g$ such that*

$$a(u, v) = (f, v)_{L^2} \quad \forall v \in V.$$

Here $V = H^1_0(\Omega) = \{v \in H^1(\Omega) \,:\, v = 0 \text{ on } \partial\Omega\}$, and $V + g = \{v \in H^1(\Omega) \,:\, v - g \in V\}$. The other way that we can define u is by writing $u = u_0 + g$ with $u_0 \in V$ determined by

$$a(u_0, v) = (f, v)_{L^2} - a(g, v) \quad \forall v \in V.$$

Note that the linear functional $F(v) = (f, v)_{L^2} - a(g, v)$ is well defined and bounded for $v \in H^1(\Omega)$. But in either case, we need to justify the variational formulation. In the latter approach, u_0 is well defined since this is a standard variational formulation, but what we need to see is that it gives an unambiguous answer. For suppose that $u^i = u^i_0 + g^i$ for g^1 and g^2 that are the same on the boundary, that is, $g^1 - g^2 \in V$. Define

$$a(u^i_0, v) = (f, v)_{L^2} - a(g^i, v) \quad \forall v \in V.$$

Show that $u^1 = u^2$, that is, the solution depends only on the values of g on the boundary. (Hint: show that $u^1 - u^2 \in V$ and derive a variational expression for $u^1 - u^2$.)

Exercise 3.2 *Prove that norms can often be evaluated by duality, motivating the definition (2.20). For example, consider the Euclidean norm $|x| = \sqrt{x^t x}$ for $x \in \mathbb{R}^d$. Prove that*

$$|x| = \sup_{0 \neq y \in \mathbb{R}^d} \frac{y^t x}{|y|}.$$

(Hint: use the Cauchy-Schwarz inequality in Section 3.3 to prove that

$$|x| \geq \frac{y^t x}{|y|} \quad \forall 0 \neq y \in \mathbb{R}^d,$$

and then pick $y = x$ to show that equality must hold.)

Exercise 3.3 *Suppose that it is known that*

$$(v, v)_{L^2(\Omega)} \leq \gamma\, a(v, v) \quad \forall v \in V,$$

where $a(u, v)$ *is defined in (2.8) and* V *is defined in (2.6). Prove that (3.17) holds with* $c_\Gamma = \gamma + 1$. *Show that it would suffice to take* $\gamma = 1/\lambda$ *where* λ *is defined by*

$$\lambda = \min_{v \in V} \frac{a(v, v)}{(v, v)_{L^2(\Omega)}}.$$

How could you compute λ*?*

Exercise 3.4 *Explain why the function* v *defined in (3.22) is in* $H_0^1(\Omega)$. *More precisely, first explain why* v *vanishes on* $\partial\Omega$ *and then show that it is in* $H^1(\Omega)$.

Chapter 4

Variational Approximation

We now address the third feature of the variational formulation, the basis for convergence of the finite element method using approximation theory. We have seen by examples that approximation by piecewise linear functions can be effective. We will justify that here but also present a broader class of approximation spaces, and we will see more in subsequent chapters. Here we provide a glimpse of what makes such spaces of functions useful for computation. We focus on Poisson's equation, but much of what is derived is applicable more broadly.

The first step is to construct the approximation spaces. This allows us to discern requirements on meshes required for optimal approximation of problems with Dirichlet boundary conditions.

4.1 Variational approximation of Poisson's equation

Let $\mathcal{T}_h$ denote a subdivision of Ω; typically this will be what is called a triangulation, made of triangles in two dimensions or tetrahedra in three dimensions. A triangulation of the domain in Figure 2.1 is shown in Figure 4.1(a). The main requirement for a triangulation is that no vertex of a triangle can be in the middle of an edge. However, more general subdivisions can be used that violate this property [28, 254, 267].

The main concept of the finite element method was to use each element of the subdivision as a separate domain in which to reason about the balance of forces or other concepts in the model. Mathematically, this corresponds to choosing a set of functions on each element

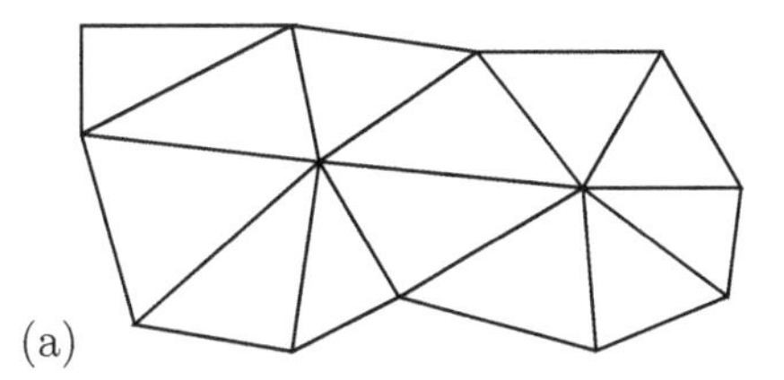

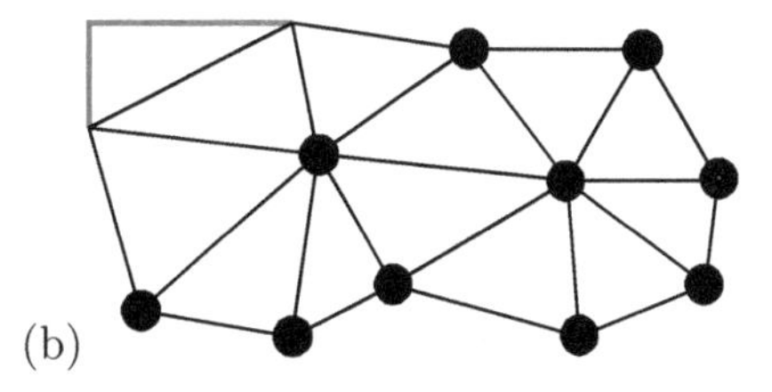

Figure 4.1: (a) Triangulation of the domain Ω. (b) Nodal positions for V_h are indicated by the black dots; note that vertices in Γ are not included, to respect the essential (Dirichlet) boundary condition.

to represent the variables used in the model. Often, the same set of functions is used on each element, although this is not necessary [254, 267, 100]. In this way, one constructs a finite dimensional space V_h which can be used in what is known as the **Galerkin method** to approximate the variational formulation (3.8), as follows:

$$\text{find } u_h \in V_h \text{ satisfying } a(u_h, v) = (f, v) \quad \forall v \in V_h. \tag{4.1}$$

Here we can think of h as designating the subdivision, or perhaps as a parameter that denotes the size of the elements of the subdivision.

The coercivity condition implies stability for the discrete approximation, namely

$$\|u_h\|_{H^1(\Omega)} \leq \frac{Ca(u_h, u_h)}{\|u_h\|_{H^1(\Omega)}} = C\frac{(f, u_h)}{\|u_h\|_{H^1(\Omega)}} \leq C\|f\|_{V'}, \tag{4.2}$$

where we will explain the meaning of $\|f\|_{V'}$ in Section 8.2.1. In particular, if $f \equiv 0$, then $u_h \equiv 0$. Provided V_h is finite dimensional, this implies that (4.1) always has a unique solution. We can see this more clearly by choosing a basis $\{\phi_i \in V_h \; : \; i = 1, \ldots, N_h\}$. Write $u_h = \sum_i U_i\phi_i$. Using the linearity of the form $a(\cdot, \cdot)$ in each of its variables, we obtain the linear system $AU = F$ where

$$A_{ij} = a(\phi_i, \phi_j) \; \forall i, j = 1, \ldots, N_h, \qquad F_i = \int_\Omega f(\mathbf{x}) \, \phi_i(\mathbf{x}) \, d\mathbf{x} \; \forall i = 1, \ldots, N_h. \tag{4.3}$$

That is, since A is symmetric ($A_{ji} = a(\phi_j, \phi_i) = a(\phi_i, \phi_j) = A_{ij}$), we have

$$\begin{aligned} F_j &= \int_\Omega f(\mathbf{x}) \, \phi_j(\mathbf{x}) \, d\mathbf{x} = a(u_h, \phi_j) = a\big(\sum_i U_i\phi_i, \phi_j\big) \\ &= \sum_i U_i a(\phi_i, \phi_j) = \sum_i U_i A_{ij} = \sum_i A_{ji} U_i = (AU)_j \end{aligned} \tag{4.4}$$

for all $j = 1, \ldots, N_h$. We know from linear algebra that the solution to a linear system $AU = F$ exists uniquely if and only if the only solution for $F = \mathbf{0}$ is $U = \mathbf{0}$. The latter is guaranteed by the coercivity condition (3.6).

4.1.1 Piecewise linears

Given a triangulation, the simplest space V_h that we can construct is the set of continuous piecewise linear functions. This means that on each triangle (or tetrahedron), such functions are linear, and moreover we contrive to make them continuous. A linear function is determined by its values at the vertices of a simplex. This is easy to see in one or two dimensions; the graph of the function is a line or plane going through the specified values at the vertices. If we demand that the values of $v \in V_h$ at vertices agree in all of the triangles meeting there, then it is not hard to see that the resulting function is continuous. In two dimensions, the values along edges are specified completely by the values at the vertices. Furthermore, we can define a basis for V_h in terms of functions that satisfy $\phi_i(\mathbf{x}_j) = \delta_{ij}$ (Kronecker δ). Such a function is depicted in Figure 4.2.

The vertices of a triangulation provide the **nodes** of the space V_h; these are shown as black dots in Figure 4.1. Note that we have indicated only the vertices where the nodal values are non-zero, respecting the boundary condition that $v = 0$ on Γ for $v \in V_h \subset V$.

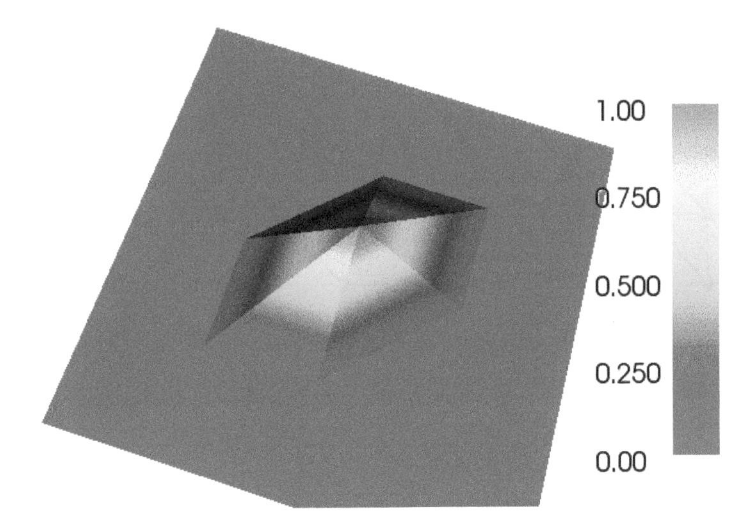

Figure 4.2: Typical basis function for continuous piecewise linear functions.

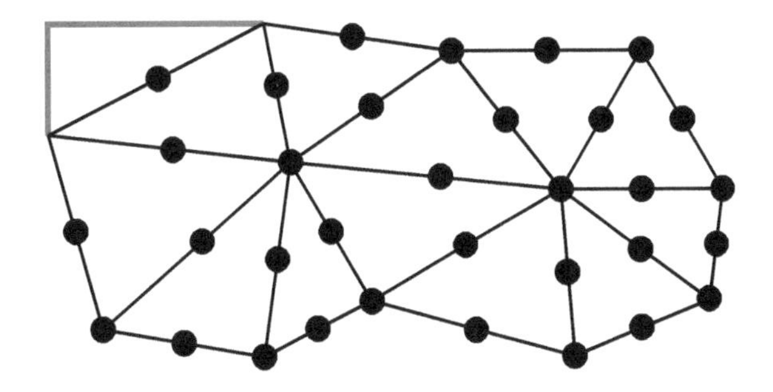

Figure 4.3: Nodes for quadratics: vertices and edge midpoints.

In order to approximate the variational problem (3.8) with variational space (2.6), we need to insure that

$$V_h \subset V, \tag{4.5}$$

in order to apply Céa's Theorem [57, 2.8.1], which says the following.

Theorem 4.1 (Céa) *Suppose that $V_h \subset V$, that the variational form $a(\cdot,\cdot)$ is coercive (3.3) and continuous (3.7) (bounded) on $H^1(\Omega)$, and that F is well defined and bounded on $H^1(\Omega)$. Then*

$$\|u - u_h\|_{H^1(\Omega)} \leq c_1 c_0 \inf_{v \in V_h} \|u - v\|_{H^1(\Omega)}, \tag{4.6}$$

where c_0 is the constant in (3.3) and c_1 is the constant in (3.7).

4.1.2 Piecewise quadratic approximation

To obtain a more accurate solution in a cost effective way, it is often useful to use higher-order polynomials in each element in a subdivision. In Figure 4.3 we see the nodes for

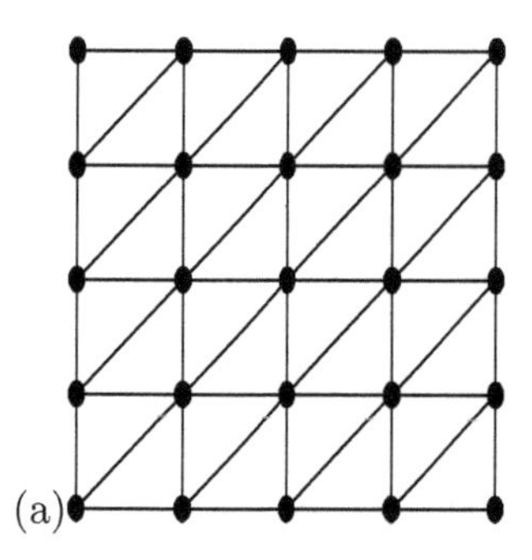

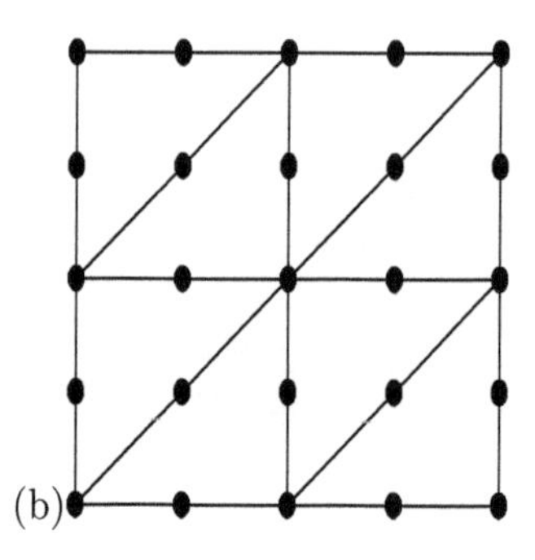

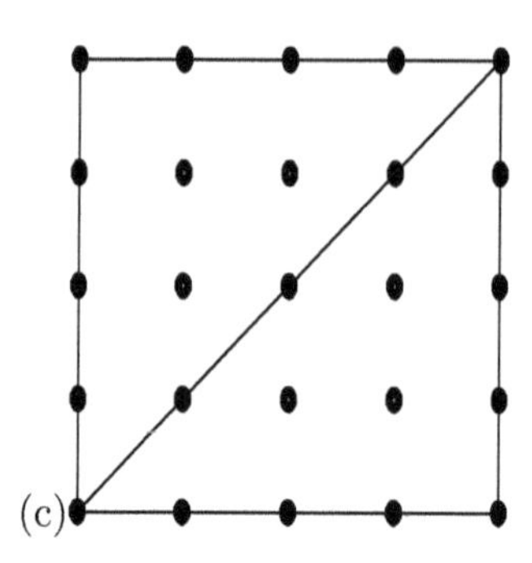

Figure 4.4: Varying mesh number M and polynomial degree k with the same number of nodes: (a) $M = 4$, $k = 1$ (linears), (b) $M = 2$, $k = 2$ (quadratics), (c) $M = 1$, $k = 4$ (quartics).

piecewise quadratic functions for the triangulation in Figure 4.1(a), respecting the essential boundary condition posed on Γ shown in red in Figure 2.1.

Again, we can define a basis for the space V_h of continuous piecewise quadratics in terms of functions that satisfy $\phi_i(\mathbf{x}_j) = \delta_{ij}$ (Kronecker δ), where the $\mathbf{x}_j$'s are the nodes in Figure 4.3. But now it is not so clear how we can be sure that this is a valid representation. What we need to know is that this nodal representation is **unisolvent** on each triangle, meaning that on each triangle you can solve uniquely for a quadratic given the values at the specified nodes, the vertices and edge midpoints.

The way this is done is by degree reduction. On each edge, we have three distinct points that determine uniquely a quadratic, simply by invoking the fundamental theorem of algebra. In particular, we thus know that if all of the nodal values on one edge vanish, then the corresponding quadratic $q(x, y)$ must vanish on that edge. For simplicity, and without loss of generality, let us suppose that edge lies on the x-axis. Then $q(x, y) = y\ell(x, y)$ where ℓ is a linear polynomial in x and y. This can be verified by expanding q in powers of x and y (there are 6 terms) and invoking the fact that $q(x, y)$ vanishes on the edge lying on the x-axis. Now we use the fact that q also vanishes on the other two edges of the triangle, neither of which can lie on the x-axis, so that means that ℓ must also vanish on these edges. But this clearly implies that $\ell \equiv 0$, and thus $q \equiv 0$. By a simple result in linear algebra, we know that uniqueness of the representation implies existence of a representation, because we have made sure that we have exactly 6 nodal variables matching exactly the dimension (6) of the space of quadratic polynomials in two dimensions. Complete details are found in [57, Chapter 3].

4.1.3 Arbitrary degree polynomials

There is no limit on the degree of polynomials that can be used. The general family of elements is called the **Lagrange elements**. There is even some regularity to the pattern of nodes, as shown in Figure 4.4.

We can see the effect of varying the polynomial degree with a simple problem, using the method of manufactured solutions [211] (Section 2.3) using the problem (2.12), whose solution is $u(x, y) = \sin(\pi x)\sin(\pi y)$, which was first implemented in Program 2.1. A more sophisticated version is presented in Program 4.1. The main differences between Program 2.1 and Program 4.1 are found on lines 3–7 in Program 4.1. Line 3 imports the library `sys`

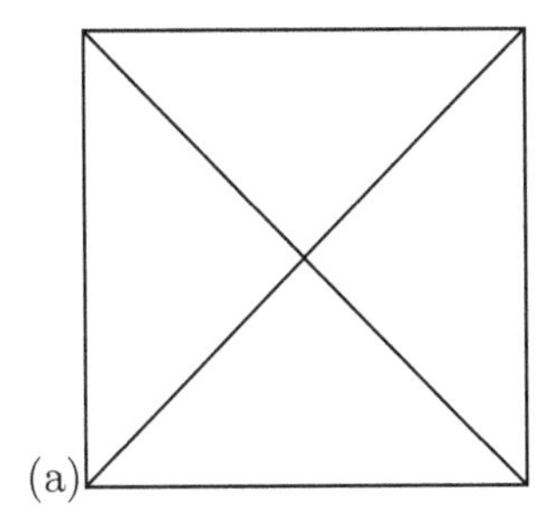

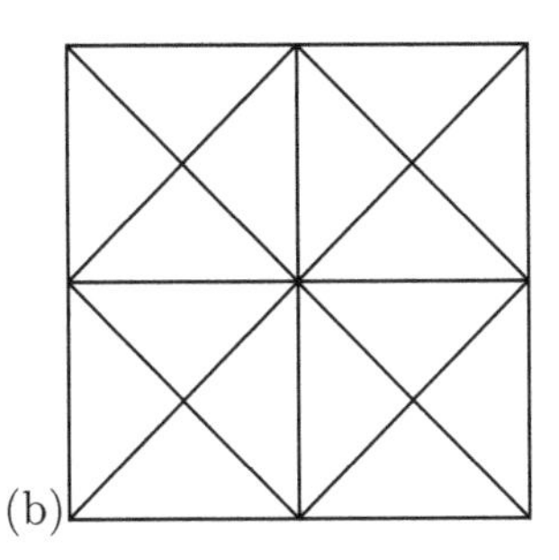

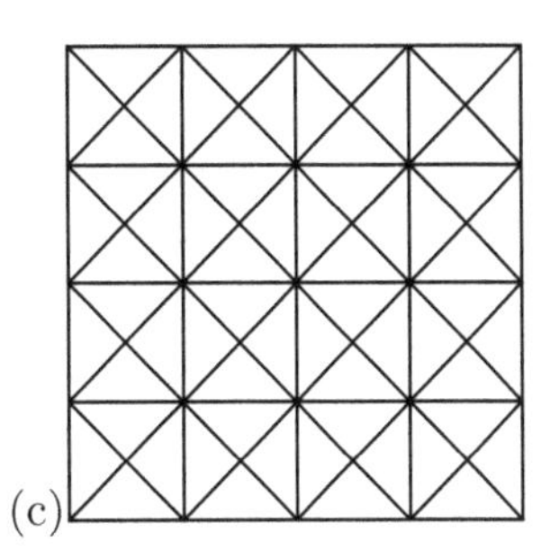

Figure 4.5: Crossed meshes with (a) mesh number 1, (b) mesh number 2, (c) mesh number 4.

to define the variables `sys.argv` and also imports an appropriate timer from the indicated library. Line 4 also imports an appropriate timer from the indicated library. The code in lines 6 and 7 are used to input data about the mesh size and polynomial degree from the command line. The importation of the library `math` in line 3 allows us to use $\pi =$ `math.pi` (lines 25 and 27) with full accuracy. In line 19, a construct is used to pass a parameter into the expression `f`. It is not allowed to include a variable, even a constant, inside the quotation marks in an `Expression` unless its value is defined in the `Expression` statement itself. The print command is standard Python, but it includes a `dolfin` command `errornorm` that we explain now.

One way to quantify the quality of a numerical solution is to compute the errors

$$\|u_h - u\|_{L^2(\Omega)} = \|u_h - (2\pi^2)^{-1} f\|_{L^2(\Omega)} \tag{4.7}$$

for different meshes (of the type shown in Figure 4.4) and polynomial degrees. Such errors, together with execution times for computing the numerical solution, are given in Table 4.1. The implementation of the error norm is given via the function `errornorm` in line 35 in Program 4.1. Recall that `f` is the exact solution and `u` is the finite element approximation. But `f` is an abstract expression, whereas `u` is in the finite element variational space (line 30). The function `errornorm` expects inputs of exactly this type as the first two entries. The third entry specifies which norm to compute. The final, optional entry deals with the issue of accuracy. Since the first entry is an exact expression, it can be evaluated to arbitrary accuracy, and the final entry specifies using a quadrature rule with accuracy three higher than would naturally be required just for computing the finite element (polynomial) degree accurately.

What we see in Table 4.1 is that the error can be reduced substantially by using higher-order polynomials. Increasing the mesh number for linear Lagrange elements does reduce the error, but the execution time grows commensurately with the error reduction. Using linears on a mesh of size 256 gives half the error of quadratics on a mesh of size 16, but the latter computation requires one-tenth of the time. For the same amount of time as this computation with quadratics, using quartics on a mesh of size 8 gives an error almost two orders of magnitude smaller.

Each mesh with double the number of mesh points was derived from the one with the smaller number of points by subdividing each triangle into four similar triangles. The cases with mesh number equal to 1, 2, and 4 are shown in Figure 4.5 in the case that crossed meshes are used.

To get the highest accuracy, the best strategy is to use higher polynomial order, up

degree	mesh number	L^2 error	rate	time (s)
1	32	2.11e-03	NA	0.09
1	64	5.29e-04	2.00	0.13
1	128	1.32e-04	2.00	0.31
1	256	3.31e-05	2.00	1.07
2	8	5.65e-04	NA	0.08
2	16	6.93e-05	3.03	0.08
2	32	8.62e-06	3.01	0.11
2	64	1.08e-06	3.00	0.23
4	8	7.78e-07	NA	0.08
4	16	2.44e-08	4.99	0.11
4	32	7.64e-10	5.00	0.23
4	64	2.39e-11	5.00	0.74
4	128	4.95e-12	2.27	3.0
8	2	7.29e-08	NA	0.08
8	4	1.42e-10	9.00	0.09
8	8	3.98e-12	5.16	0.13
8	16	1.67e-11	-2.07	0.33
8	32	6.78e-11	-2.02	1.11
16	1	1.61e-09	NA	0.09
16	2	1.42e-09	0.18	0.12
16	4	5.13e-09	-1.85	0.25
16	8	2.14e-08	-2.06	0.80

Table 4.1: Computational experiments with solving the problem (2.12). Degree refers to the polynomial degree, mesh number indicates the number of edges along each boundary side as indicated in Figure 4.5, L^2 error is the error measured in the $L^2([0,1]^2)$ norm, cf. (4.7), rate is defined in (4.18), and time is in seconds. Meshes used are of the type shown in Figure 4.4. Results generated using Program 4.1.

to a point. The most accurate computation occurs with polynomial degree 8 with a mesh number of 8. But the error quits decreasing at a certain point due to the amplification of round-off error due to increasing condition number of the numerical system. We will discuss the effects of finite precision arithmetic is more detail in Section 11.4.

The times presented here should be viewed as approximate. There is significant variation due to system load from run to run. These computations were done on a MacBook Pro with 2.3 GHz Intel Core i7 and 16 GB 1600 MHz DDR3 memory. However, we do see order of magnitude variation depending on the mesh size and polynomial degree.

4.2 Quantifying smoothness

We need to have a way to quantify the smoothness of solutions in order to predict accuracy of approximation. It is natural to do so in the framework of Sobolev spaces, and so we introduce the general Sobolev space $H^m(\Omega)$:

$$H^m(\Omega) = \left\{ v \in L^2(\Omega) \;:\; \nabla^k v \in L^2(\Omega)^{d^k}, \quad \forall k \le m \right\}, \tag{4.8}$$

for m any positive integer. Here, $\nabla^k v$ denotes the tensor of all partial derivatives of v of order k. For $k=1$, this is just the gradient we have seen before. For $k=2$, $\nabla^2 v$ is a matrix, often called the Hessian of v (and it is also the Jacobian of the vector-valued function ∇v). We can define an associated norm by

$$\|v\|_{H^m(\Omega)} = \left(\sum_{k=0}^{m} \int_\Omega \left|\nabla^k v(\mathbf{x})\right|^2 d\mathbf{x} \right)^{1/2}, \tag{4.9}$$

where $\left|T\right|$ denotes the Euclidean norm of the tensor T written as a vector. For example,

$$\left|\nabla^2 v(\mathbf{x})\right|^2 = \sum_{i,j=1}^{d} \left(\frac{\partial^2 v(\mathbf{x})}{\partial x_i \partial x_j} \right)^2 .$$

It is easy to see that our two definitions of H^1 are the same, and that we can think of L^2 as the same as H^0.

4.3 Initial error estimates

It is easy to understand the basic error behavior for the finite element method. In the case of both piecewise linear and piecewise quadratics, we described the nodal basis functions ϕ_i which satisfy $\phi_i(x_j) = \delta_{ij}$ (Kronecker δ), where x_j denotes a typical node. For linears, the nodes are the vertices, and for quadratics the edge midpoints are added. For higher degree Lagrange elements, more edge nodes are involved, as well as interior nodes. For example, with cubics, the centroid of each triangle is a node.

Using such a nodal representation, we can define what is known as a **global interpolant** $\mathcal{I}_h$ defined on continuous functions, by

$$\mathcal{I}_h u = \sum_i u(\mathbf{x}_i)\phi_i. \tag{4.10}$$

Thus $\mathcal{I}_h$ maps continuous functions into the space V_h used in finite element computations.

Let $\mathcal{I}_h$ denote a global interpolant for a family of finite elements based on the components of $\mathcal{T}^h$. Let us suppose that $\mathcal{I}_h u$ is continuous, i.e., that the family of elements involved are C^0, as is true for the Lagrange family of elements. Further, suppose that the corresponding shape functions have an approximation order, m, that is

$$\|u - \mathcal{I}_h u\|_{H^1(\Omega)} \leq C h^{m-1} |u|_{H^m(\Omega)}. \tag{4.11}$$

In order to have good approximation, we need to have

$$\mathcal{I}_h \left(V \cap C^k(\Omega) \right) \subset V_h, \tag{4.12}$$

where k is the highest order of differentiation in the definition of $\mathcal{I}_h$, that is, $k=0$ for Lagrange elements. However, we allow for the possibility that $k>0$ since this holds for other element families.

If conditions (4.5) and (4.6) hold, then the unique solution, $u_h \in V_h$, to the variational problem

$$a(u_h, v) = (f, v) \quad \forall v \in V_h$$

```
1  from dolfin import *
2  import sys,math
3  from timeit import default_timer as timer
4  startime=timer()
5  meshsize=int(sys.argv[1])
6  pdeg=int(sys.argv[2])
7  # Create mesh and define function space
8  mesh = UnitSquareMesh(meshsize, meshsize)
9  V = FunctionSpace(mesh, "Lagrange", pdeg)
10 # Define boundary condition
11 u0 = Constant(0.0)
12 bc = DirichletBC(V, u0, DomainBoundary())
13 # Define variational problem
14 u = TrialFunction(V)
15 v = TestFunction(V)
16 f = Expression("(sin(mypi*x[0]))*(sin(mypi*x[1]))",mypi=math.pi,degree=pdeg)
17 a = inner(grad(u), grad(v))*dx
18 L = (2*math.pi*math.pi)*f*v*dx
19 # Compute solution
20 u = Function(V)
21 solve(a == L, u, bc)
22 aftersolveT=timer()
23 totime=aftersolveT-startime
24 print " ",pdeg," ",meshsize, \
25       " %.2e"%errornorm(f,u,norm_type='l2', degree_rise=3)," %.3f"%totime
```

Program 4.1: Code to implement the problem (2.12) allowing variable mesh size and polynomial degree input from the command line.

satisfies

$$\|u-u_h\|_{H^1(\Omega)} \leq C \inf_{v\in V_h} \|u-v\|_{H^1(\Omega)}. \tag{4.13}$$

If conditions (4.11) and (4.12) hold, then

$$\|u-u_h\|_{H^1(\Omega)} \leq Ch^{m-1}|u|_{H^m(\Omega)}. \tag{4.14}$$

4.4 Estimates in other norms

The behavior of the error in other norms is often of interest. We will consider two cases.

4.4.1 L^2 estimates

Frequently, it is the case that the $L^2(\Omega)$ norm is better by one power of h:

$$\|u-u_h\|_{L^2(\Omega)} \leq Ch^m|u|_{H^m(\Omega)}. \tag{4.15}$$

This follows by a duality relationship. Denote the error $e_h = u - u_h$. We solve Poisson's problem with e_h as the data:

$$a(\phi, v) = (e_h, v)_{L^2(\Omega)} \quad \forall v \in V.$$

Then we have an expression for $\|e_h\|_{L^2(\Omega)}$:

$$\|e_h\|^2_{L^2(\Omega)} = (e_h, e_h)_{L^2(\Omega)} = a(\phi, e_h).$$

Subtracting the variational formulations for u and u_h, we find $a(e_h, v) = 0$ for all $v \in V_h$, so

$$\|e_h\|^2_{L^2(\Omega)} = a(\phi - v, e_h)$$

for all $v \in V_h$. Choosing v appropriately, we find

$$\|e_h\|^2_{L^2(\Omega)} \leq Ch\|\phi\|_{H^2(\Omega)}\|e_h\|_{H^1(\Omega)}. \tag{4.16}$$

For smooth problems,

$$\|\phi\|_{H^2(\Omega)} \leq C\|e_h\|_{L^2(\Omega)}, \tag{4.17}$$

so we conclude that

$$\|e_h\|^2_{L^2(\Omega)} \leq Ch\|e_h\|_{L^2(\Omega)}\|e_h\|_{H^1(\Omega)}.$$

Dividing by $\|e_h\|_{L^2(\Omega)}$, we find

$$\|e_h\|_{L^2(\Omega)} \leq Ch\|e_h\|_{H^1(\Omega)}.$$

This proves (4.15) provided (4.17) holds. As we will see, this is not always the case.

4.4.2 L^∞ estimates

Since the Galerkin method is a type of least-squares method, we might not expect errors to behave well uniformly. For example, it would not be surprising that errors near the boundary would be slightly worse but in a small region. Thus it is quite significant that this is not generally the case. Rather, it is possible to prove that $\|u - u_h\|_{W^1_\infty(\Omega)}$ and $\|u - u_h\|_{H^1(\Omega)}$ are of the same order of accuracy in h [242]. Similarly, $\|u - u_h\|_{L^2(\Omega)}$ and $\|u - u_h\|_{L^\infty(\Omega)}$ are of the same order of accuracy in h, with one small exception. More precisely, with piecewise linear approximation, $\|u - u_h\|_{L^\infty(\Omega)}$ can be worse by a factor of $|\log h|$ than $\|u - u_h\|_{L^2(\Omega)}$ [57]. Uniform bounds for the finite element method are much more complex to prove than the duality argument used to prove L^2 estimates in Section 4.4.1, but they have been extended to many complicated systems such as the Navier-Stokes equations [142].

4.5 A reality check

The error estimates (4.14) and (4.15) provide a check on the performance of a code. For example, if we consider two meshes, of size h and $h/2$, then we expect that

$$\|u - u_h\|_{H^1(\Omega)}/\|u - u_{h/2}\|_{H^1(\Omega)} \approx h^{m-1}/(h/2)^{m-1} = 2^{m-1}.$$

Thus we would have

$$m - 1 = \log_2\left(\|u - u_h\|_{H^1(\Omega)}/\|u - u_{h/2}\|_{H^1(\Omega)}\right).$$

Similarly, if (4.15) holds, we have

$$\|u - u_h\|_{L^2(\Omega)}/\|u - u_{h/2}\|_{L^2(\Omega)} \approx h^m/(h/2)^m = 2^m.$$

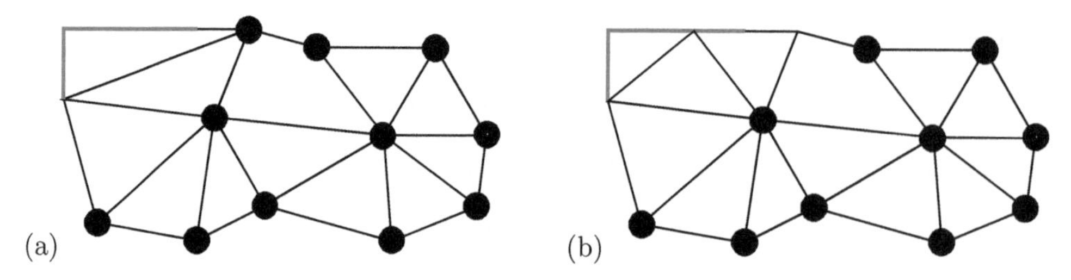

Figure 4.6: Two different meshes that lead to incompatibility. (a) Functions in V_h do not vanish on the edge on the top left of the domain and thus $V_h \not\subset V$. (b) Functions in V_h vanish on two edges on the top left of the domain and thus $I_h v \notin V^h$.

Thus we define the quantity "rate" in Table 4.1 via

$$\text{rate} = \log_2 \left(\|u - u_h\|_{L^2(\Omega)} / \|u - u_{h/2}\|_{L^2(\Omega)} \right). \tag{4.18}$$

Recall that we expect $m \approx k+1$ where k is the degree of piecewise polynomials used for the simulation. Of course, this is only a "not to exceed" rate, so your experience may differ, as we see for the larger values of k in Table 4.1. In fact, the observed rate can be negative, due to round-off error amplification via the condition number of the system.

4.6 Mesh constraints

The requirements (4.5) and (4.12) place a constraint on the subdivision in the case that Γ is neither empty nor all of the boundary. These requirements provide the **consistency** of the numerical approximation. In such a case, it is necessary to choose the mesh so that it aligns properly with the points where the boundary conditions change from Dirichlet to Neumann. For example, in two dimensions, if one uses Lagrange elements and insures that the points where the boundary conditions change are vertices in the triangulation, then defining

$$V_h := \mathcal{I}_h \left(V \cap C^0(\Omega) \right)$$

is equivalent to defining V_h to be the space of piecewise polynomials that vanish on edges contained in Γ.

Since we have chosen the mesh so that the edges contained in Γ form a subdivision of the latter, it follows that (4.5) holds. On the other hand, if the set of edges where functions in V_h vanish is too big, as indicated in Figure 4.6(a), (4.12) fails to hold. If the set of edges where functions in V_h vanish is too small, as indicated in Figure 4.6(b), we fail to obtain (4.5).

In the case of pure Dirichlet data, i.e., $\Gamma = \partial\Omega$, then V_h is just the set of piecewise polynomials that vanish on the entire boundary. In the case of pure Neumann data, i.e., $\Gamma = \emptyset$, V_h is the entire set of piecewise polynomials with no constraints at the boundary.

Even if we match the finite element space correctly with the set Γ where Dirichlet boundary conditions are imposed, there is an intrinsic singularity associated with changing boundary condition type along a straight boundary. This effect is explored in detail in Section 6.1.3.

4.7 Exercises

Exercise 4.1 *Repeat the experiments recorded in Table 4.1 but with the manufactured solution in Exercise 2.4. Explain why the error is so small for high-degree polynomial approximation even for a coarse mesh.*

Exercise 4.2 *Modify Program 2.3 to use higher-order elements to solve the inhomogeneous Neumann problem in Section 2.5.2. Mimic the experiments recorded in Table 4.1. Explain why the error is so small for high-degree polynomial approximation even for a coarse mesh.*

Exercise 4.3 *Repeat the experiments recorded in Table 4.1 solving (2.12) but computing the $H^1(\Omega)$ norm of the error as well as the $L^2(\Omega)$ error. Explain what you find. Do you find the expected improvement in accuracy as described in Section 4.4.1? (Hint: augment Program 4.1 using* `norm(u,norm_type='H1')`*.)*

Chapter 5

More Boundary Conditions

We have now explored three dimensions of the variational theory,

- as a language for PDEs (Chapter 2),
- as the basis for PDE theory (Chapter 3),
- as the foundation for convergence analysis via approximation theory (Chapter 4).

As part of this, we have seen some variations of the basic theme:

- changing the space V in the pure Neumann problem, and
- changing the linear form F in the inhomogeneous Neumann problem.

Here we explore further variations of the basic theme based on boundary conditions. One of these will lead to a change in the variational form $a(\cdot,\cdot)$.

5.1 Inhomogeneous Dirichlet conditions

When boundary conditions are equal to zero, we often call them homogeneous, whereas we refer to nonzero boundary conditions as inhomogeneous. Inhomogeneous Dirichlet boundary conditions are easily treated. For example, suppose that we wish to solve Poisson's equation (2.1) ($-\Delta u = f$) with boundary conditions

$$u = g_D \text{ on } \Gamma \subset \partial\Omega \qquad \text{and} \qquad \frac{\partial u}{\partial n} = g_N \text{ on } \partial\Omega\backslash\Gamma, \tag{5.1}$$

where g_D and g_N are given. We have already explained how to incorporate nonzero (inhomogeneous) Neumann data g_N in the variational formulation in Section 2.5.1. Now we extend this to nonzero (inhomogeneous) Dirichlet data g_D.

For simplicity, let us assume that g_D is defined on all of Ω, with $g_D \in H^1(\Omega)$ and that $g_N \in L^2(\partial\Omega\backslash\Gamma)$. Define V to be the space (2.6), that is,

$$V := \left\{ v \in H^1(\Omega) \,:\, v|_\Gamma = 0 \right\}.$$

Then the variational formulation of Poisson's equation (2.1), together with the boundary conditions (5.1), is as follows: find u such that $u - g_D \in V$ and such that

$$a(u,v) = (f,v)_{L^2(\Omega)} + \oint_{\partial\Omega\backslash\Gamma} g_N v\, ds \quad \forall v \in V. \tag{5.2}$$

This is well posed since the linear form

$$F(v) := (f,v)_{L^2(\Omega)} + \oint_{\partial\Omega\backslash\Gamma} g_N v\, ds$$

is well defined (and continuous) for all $v \in V$. The equivalence of these formulations follows from (2.10): for any $v \in V$,

$$\int_\Omega (-\Delta u) v\, d\mathbf{x} = \int_\Omega \nabla u \cdot \nabla v\, d\mathbf{x} - \oint_{\partial\Omega} v \frac{\partial u}{\partial n}\, ds = a(u,v) - \oint_{\partial\Omega\backslash\Gamma} v \frac{\partial u}{\partial n}\, ds. \tag{5.3}$$

Thus, if u solves (2.1) with boundary conditions (5.1), then (5.2) follows as a consequence. Conversely, if u solves (5.2) then choosing v to vanish near $\partial\Omega$ shows that (2.1) holds, and thus

$$\oint_{\partial\Omega\backslash\Gamma} g_N v\, ds - \oint_{\partial\Omega\backslash\Gamma} v \frac{\partial u}{\partial n}\, ds = 0 \quad \forall v \in V.$$

Choosing v to be arbitrary proves that (5.1) follows. Such arguments are explained more fully in Section 3.5 and [57], and they are given in detail in Section 8.2.3 in the one-dimensional case.

The finite element approximation of (5.2) involves, typically, the use of an interpolant, $\mathcal{I}_h g_D$, of the Dirichlet data. We pick a subspace V_h of V just as before, and we seek u_h such that $u_h - \mathcal{I}_h g_D \in V_h$ and such that

$$a(u_h,v) = (f,v)_{L^2(\Omega)} + \oint_{\partial\Omega\backslash\Gamma} g_N v\, ds \quad \forall v \in V_h. \tag{5.4}$$

We can cast this in a more standard form as: find $\hat{u}_h = u_h - \mathcal{I}_h g_D \in V_h$ such that

$$a(\hat{u}_h,v) = (f,v)_{L^2(\Omega)} + \oint_{\partial\Omega\backslash\Gamma} g_N v\, ds - a(\mathcal{I}_h g_D, v) \quad \forall v \in V_h. \tag{5.5}$$

Then we can set $u_h = \hat{u}_h + \mathcal{I}_h g_D$.

5.2 Affine variational formulation

The simplicity and generality of the treatment of inhomogeneous Dirichlet boundary values allow an extension of the standard variational formulation. Thus we can write (5.2) as:

Find $u \in V + g_D$ such that

$$a(u,v) = (f,v)_{L^2(\Omega)} + \oint_{\partial\Omega\backslash\Gamma} g_N v\, ds \quad \forall v \in V. \tag{5.6}$$

Here the affine space $V + g_D$ is defined by

$$V + g_D = \{v + g_D \,:\, v \in V\}. \tag{5.7}$$

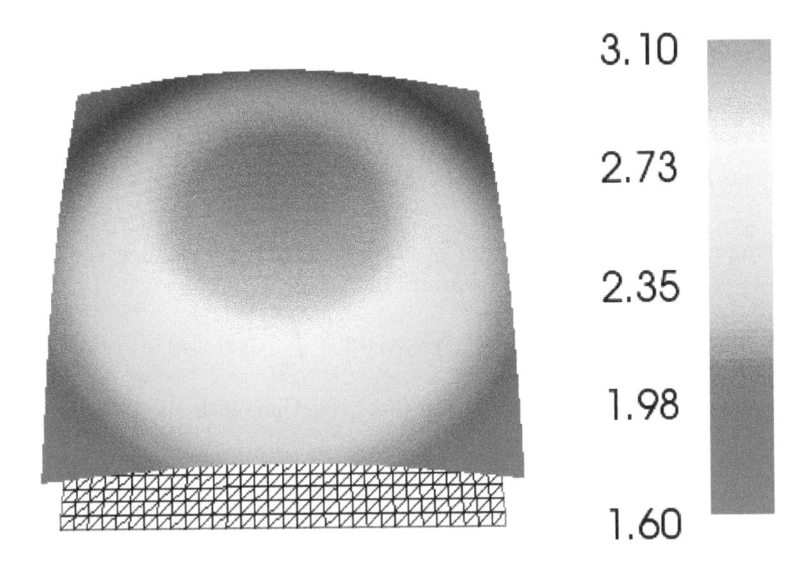

Figure 5.1: Solution to the Robin boundary condition problem obtained using Program 5.1.

The discrete approximation (5.5) can be written similarly:

Find $u_h \in V_h + \mathcal{I}_h g_D$ such that

$$a(u_h, v) = (f, v)_{L^2(\Omega)} + \oint_{\partial\Omega\backslash\Gamma} g_N v \, ds \quad \forall v \in V_h. \tag{5.8}$$

The original variational formulation has three ingredients: the space V, the bilinear form $a(\cdot,\cdot)$, and the right-hand side data linear form $F(\cdot)$. The affine variational formulation has four ingredients: the space V, the bilinear form $a(\cdot,\cdot)$, the right-hand side data linear form $F(\cdot)$, **and** the Dirichlet data function g_D (or some approximation to it, such as $\mathcal{I}_h g_D$). This simplifies greatly the formulation of many PDE problems. Fortunately, the `dolfin` built-in function `solve` automates all of this, so that the Dirichlet data function g_D needs to be specified just in the call to `solve`.

5.3 Robin boundary conditions

It is frequently the case that more complex boundary conditions arise in physical models. The so-called Robin boundary conditions take the form

$$\alpha u + \frac{\partial u}{\partial n} = 0 \text{ on } \partial\Omega\backslash\Gamma, \tag{5.9}$$

where α is a positive measurable function. (If α vanishes on some part of the boundary, then the boundary condition reduces to the standard Neumann condition there.) This will be coupled as before with a Dirichlet condition on Γ.

A variational formulation for this problem can be derived as follows. Let V be the space defined in (2.6) with the added proviso that $V = H^1(\Omega)$ in the case that $\Gamma = \emptyset$. From

(2.10), we get

$$
\begin{aligned}
(f, v)_{L^2(\Omega)} &= \int_\Omega (-\Delta u(\mathbf{x}))v(\mathbf{x})\, d\mathbf{x} = \int_\Omega \nabla u(\mathbf{x}) \cdot \nabla v(\mathbf{x})\, d\mathbf{x} - \oint_{\partial\Omega} v(s) \frac{\partial u}{\partial n}(s)\, ds \\
&= \int_\Omega \nabla u(\mathbf{x}) \cdot \nabla v(\mathbf{x})\, d\mathbf{x} + \oint_{\partial\Omega} \alpha(s)\, v(s)\, u(s)\, ds,
\end{aligned}
\tag{5.10}
$$

after substituting the boundary condition $\frac{\partial u}{\partial n} = -\alpha u$ on $\partial\Omega\backslash\Gamma$ and using the condition (2.6) that $v = 0$ on Γ. Thus we define a new variational form

$$
a_{\text{Robin}}(u, v) := \int_\Omega \nabla u(\mathbf{x}) \cdot \nabla v(\mathbf{x})\, d\mathbf{x} + \oint_{\partial\Omega} \alpha(s)\, v(s)\, u(s)\, ds. \tag{5.11}
$$

The variational formulation for the equation (2.1) together with the Robin boundary condition (5.9) takes the usual form

$$
u \in V \quad \text{satisfies} \quad a_{\text{Robin}}(u, v) = (f, v)_{L^2(\Omega)} \quad \forall v \in V. \tag{5.12}
$$

The companion result that a solution to the variational problem in (5.12) solves both (2.1) and (5.9) can also be proved under suitable smoothness conditions.

Note that $a_{\text{Robin}}(\cdot, \cdot)$ is coercive on $H^1(\Omega)$, that is there is a constant $C < \infty$ such that

$$
\|v\|^2_{H^1(\Omega)} \le C a_{\text{Robin}}(v, v) \quad \forall v \in H^1(\Omega), \tag{5.13}
$$

provided that $\alpha > 0$. Thus the stability estimate (3.6) holds as well in this case.

A code implementing Robin boundary conditions (5.9) for the problem

$$
-\Delta u = \sin(\pi x) \sin(\pi y) \text{ in } \Omega
$$

is given in Program 5.1.

5.4 Exercises

Exercise 5.1 *Use Program 5.1 to explore the effect of the parameter α in Robin boundary conditions. Show that as $\alpha \to \infty$ that the solution tends to the solution of the Dirichlet problem. More precisely, compute the norm of the difference of the Robin solution from the known exact solution for the Dirichlet problem for large values of α. What happens when $\alpha \to 0$? Explain.*

Exercise 5.2 *Consider a regular mesh on $\Omega = [0, 1] \times [0, 1]$ which consists of 45° right triangles. Compute the "difference stencil" at the boundary points corresponding to using piecewise linear functions on this mesh in the variational approximation for the Robin boundary condition.*

Exercise 5.3 *Using an existing* `dolfin` *code for the standard boundary-value problem for Laplace's equation, derive a code for Robin boundary conditions by implementing the form $a_{\text{Robin}}(\cdot, \cdot)$ using the standard form $a(\cdot, \cdot)$.*

Exercise 5.4 *Consider the modification of the boundary value problem (2.12) given by*

$$
-\Delta u = 2\pi^2 \sin(\pi x) \sin(\pi y) \textit{ in } \Omega = [0, 1] \times [0, 1], \quad u = 1 \textit{ on } \partial\Omega.
$$

Modify Program 2.1 to solve this problem. Explain what you expect to see and compare it to what you observe. (Hint: just change the line `u0 = Constant(...)`*.)*

```
1  from dolfin import *
2
3  # Create mesh and define function space
4  mesh = UnitSquareMesh(32, 32)
5  V = FunctionSpace(mesh, "Lagrange", 1)
6
7  # Define variational problem
8  u = TrialFunction(V)
9  v = TestFunction(V)
10 f = Expression("(sin(3.141592*x[0]))*(sin(3.141592*x[1]))",degree=1)
11 alfa = 1.0
12 a = inner(grad(u), grad(v))*dx + alfa*u*v*ds
13 L = (2*3.141592*3.141592)*f*v*dx
14
15 # Compute solution
16 u = Function(V)
17 solve(a == L, u)
18
19 # Plot solution
20 plot(u, interactive=True)
```

Program 5.1: Code to implement Robin boundary conditions. Note that the `solve` function in line 17 does not have a boundary condition function included in it.

Exercise 5.5 *Consider the modification of the boundary value problem (2.12) given in Exercise 5.4. Describe the implementation given in Section 5.1 for this problem. Take the expression* $g_D(\mathbf{x}) = 1$. *What does the right-hand-most term* $a(\mathcal{I}_h g_D, v)$ *in (5.5) contribute in this case? Explain what is going on.*

Chapter 6

Singularities and the Laplace Equation

Singularities can arise in solutions for a variety of reasons. Here we consider two. The first is based on an intrinsic singularity associated with certain types of boundary conditions, especially at points where the boundary is not smooth or the type of the boundary condition changes abruptly. The second arises from singularities in the data of the problem.

6.1 Geometry matters

The geometry of the domain boundary has a significant impact on the regularity of the solution. We begin by considering the problem

$$\begin{aligned} -\Delta u &= 0 \text{ in } \Omega \\ u &= g \text{ on } \partial\Omega, \end{aligned} \tag{6.1}$$

where Ω is a polygonal domain in $\mathbb{R}^2$. We will see that the principal singularity of the solution can be identified, associated with what are often called re-entrant vertices.

6.1.1 L-shaped domain

The **L-shaped** domain Ω is depicted in Figure 6.1(a):

$$\Omega = [-1,1]^2 \cap \left\{(x,y) = (r\cos\theta, r\sin\theta) \,:\, 0 \le r,\ 0 < \theta < \tfrac{3}{2}\pi\right\}, \tag{6.2}$$

defined using polar coordinates $(x,y) = r(\cos\theta, \sin\theta)$. Again using polar coordinates, define

$$g(r(\cos\theta, \sin\theta)) = r^{2/3}\sin(\tfrac{2}{3}\theta). \tag{6.3}$$

We can think of $\partial\Omega$ consisting of two parts: the convex part $\Gamma_c = A \cup B \cup C \cup D$ where

$$\begin{aligned} A &= \{(1,y) \,:\, 0 \le y \le 1\}, & B &= \{(x,1) \,:\, -1 \le x \le 1\}, \\ C &= \{(-1,y) \,:\, -1 \le y \le 1\}, & D &= \{(x,-1) \,:\, 0 \le x \le 1\}, \end{aligned} \tag{6.4}$$

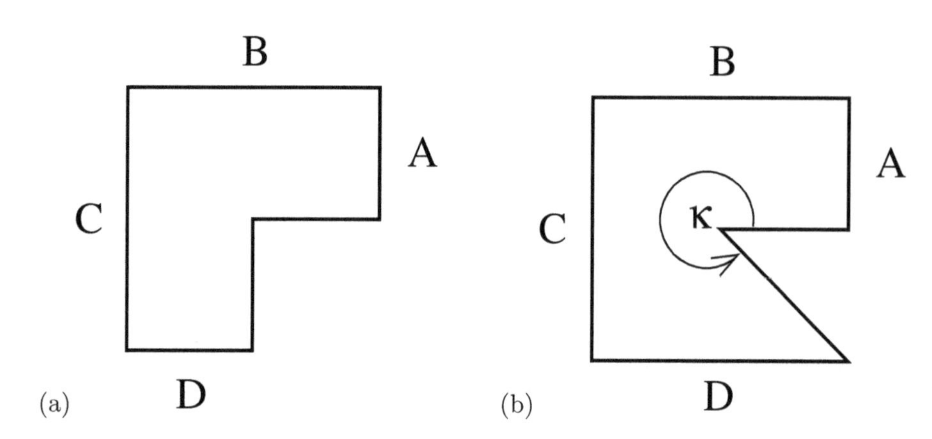

Figure 6.1: (a) L-shaped domain, (b) re-entrant corner of angle κ.

(see Figure 6.1) and the re-entrant part

$$\Gamma_{re} = \{(0,y) \;:\; -1 \le y \le 0\} \cup \{(x,0) \;:\; 0 \le x \le 1\}. \tag{6.5}$$

Then our data $g = 0$ on Γ_{re}. Moreover, it is not hard to see that g is **harmonic**, meaning $\Delta g = 0$, at least inside the open set Ω. This follows immediately from complex analysis, since g is the imaginary part of the complex analytic function $e^{(2/3)z}$. Deriving such a result is not easy using calculus, as we can indicate. First of all, using polar coordinates $(x,y) = r(\cos\theta, \sin\theta)$, we find the identities

$$\nabla r = \frac{(x,y)}{r} \qquad \text{and} \qquad \nabla\theta = \frac{(-y,x)}{r^2}.$$

This means that

$$\begin{aligned}
\nabla g(x,y) &= \tfrac{2}{3}\Big((\nabla r) r^{-1/3}\sin(\tfrac{2}{3}\theta) + (\nabla\theta) r^{2/3}\cos(\tfrac{2}{3}\theta)\Big)\\
&= \tfrac{2}{3} r^{-4/3}\big((x,y)\sin(\tfrac{2}{3}\theta) + (-y,x)\cos(\tfrac{2}{3}\theta)\big)\\
&= \tfrac{2}{3} r^{-4/3}\big(x\sin(\tfrac{2}{3}\theta) - y\cos(\tfrac{2}{3}\theta), y\sin(\tfrac{2}{3}\theta) + x\cos(\tfrac{2}{3}\theta)\big)\\
&= \tfrac{2}{3} r^{-1/3}\big((\cos\theta)\sin(\tfrac{2}{3}\theta) - (\sin\theta)\cos(\tfrac{2}{3}\theta), (\sin\theta)\sin(\tfrac{2}{3}\theta) + (\cos\theta)\cos(\tfrac{2}{3}\theta)\big)\\
&= \tfrac{2}{3} r^{-1/3}\big(-\sin(\tfrac{1}{3}\theta), \cos(\tfrac{1}{3}\theta)\big),
\end{aligned} \tag{6.6}$$

where we used the trigonometric identities that flow from the expressions ($\iota = \sqrt{-1}$)

$$\begin{aligned}
\cos(\tfrac{1}{3}\theta) - \iota\sin(\tfrac{1}{3}\theta) &= \cos(-\tfrac{1}{3}\theta) + \iota\sin(-\tfrac{1}{3}\theta) = e^{-\iota(1/3)\theta} = e^{-\iota\theta} e^{\iota(2/3)\theta}\\
&= \big(\cos(-\theta) + \iota\sin(-\theta)\big)\big(\cos(\tfrac{2}{3}\theta) + \iota\sin(\tfrac{2}{3}\theta)\big)\\
&= \big(\cos\theta - \iota\sin\theta\big)\big(\cos(\tfrac{2}{3}\theta) + \iota\sin(\tfrac{2}{3}\theta)\big)\\
&= \big(\cos\theta\cos(\tfrac{2}{3}\theta) + \sin\theta\sin(\tfrac{2}{3}\theta)\big) + \iota\big(-\sin\theta\cos(\tfrac{2}{3}\theta) + \cos\theta\sin(\tfrac{2}{3}\theta)\big).
\end{aligned} \tag{6.7}$$

The immediate result of the calculation (6.6) is that, for $0 < \theta < \frac{3}{2}\pi$, $|\nabla g(x,y)|$ blows up like $|(x,y)|^{-1/3}$, since

$$|\nabla g(x,y)| = |\nabla g(r\cos\theta, r\sin\theta)| = \tfrac{2}{3} r^{-1/3} = \tfrac{2}{3}|(x,y)|^{-1/3}.$$

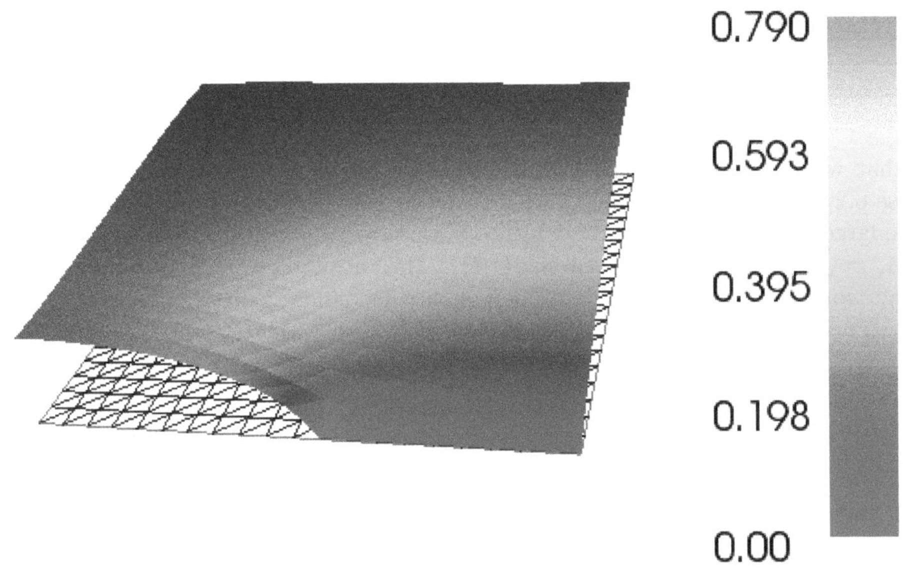

Figure 6.2: Illustration of the singularity that can occur when boundary condition types are changed, cf. (6.10), as well as a cut-away of the solution to the slit problem (6.9). Computed with piecewise linears on the indicated mesh.

Therefore $|\nabla g(x,y)|$ is square integrable, but it is obviously not bounded. Thus we see the benefit of working with Sobolev spaces, since this allows g to be considered a reasonable function even though it has an infinite gradient.

We can in principle use the vector calculus identity $\nabla\cdot(\phi\boldsymbol{\psi}) = \nabla\phi\cdot\boldsymbol{\psi} + \phi\nabla\cdot\boldsymbol{\psi}$ to compute $\Delta g = \nabla\cdot(\nabla g)$ to verify that $\Delta g = 0$, but the algebra is daunting. Instead, we can simply compute the solution via the standard variational problem (5.4) and see if we find $u = g$ throughout Ω. We leave this as Exercise 6.1. We also leave as Exercise 6.4 to verify that $\Delta g = 0$ by more classical analytical techniques.

6.1.2 General non-convex domains

The singularity for the L-shaped domain occurs for any domain with **non-convex vertex** as depicted in Figure 6.1(b), where the angle of the **re-entrant vertex** is κ. The L-shaped domain corresponds to $\kappa = \frac{3}{2}\pi$.

Definition 6.1 *Consider a boundary value problem*

$$\text{find } u \in V \quad \text{such that} \quad a(u,v) = F(v) \quad \text{for all } v \in V$$

for which $u \in H^1(\Omega)$ but $u \notin H^2(\Omega)$ in general. We say that $g \in H^1(\Omega)$ is the **principal singularity** *if there is a constant c_F such that $u - c_F g \in H^2(\Omega)$ for all F.*

In general, there may be several principal singularities for a given problem if there are multiple re-entrant corners. The coefficient c_F is related to the **stress intensity factor** in certain contexts [54]. Note that there may be certain data F such that $c_F = 0$.

The principal singularity for Poisson's problem on a domain with a single re-entrant vertex with angle κ is of the form

$$g_\kappa(r(\cos\theta,\sin\theta)) = r^{\pi/\kappa}\sin((\pi/\kappa)\theta). \tag{6.8}$$

Note that when $\kappa < \pi$ (a convex vertex), the gradient of g_κ is bounded. We leave as Exercise 6.2 to explore this general case for various values of κ.

The largest that κ can be is 2π which corresponds to a **slit domain**. In this case, we have $g_{2\pi} = \sqrt{r}\sin(\frac{1}{2}\theta)$, which is still in $H^1(\Omega)$. The slit domain is often a model for **crack propagation**. An illustration of a problem on a slit domain is given by

$$\begin{aligned} -\Delta u &= 1 \text{ in } [0,1]\times[-1,1] \\ u = 0 \text{ on } \Gamma,\ &\frac{\partial u}{\partial n} = 0 \text{ on } \partial\Omega\backslash\Gamma, \end{aligned} \tag{6.9}$$

where $\Gamma = \{(x,0)\ :\ x\in[\frac{1}{2},1]\}$. The solution of (6.9) is depicted in Figure 6.2, where only the top half of the domain (that is, $[0,1]\times[0,1]$) is shown. The solution in the bottom half of the domain can be obtained by symmetric reflection across the x-axis.

The range of κ values for a realistic polygonal domain excludes a region around $\kappa = 0$ and $\kappa = \pi$. In particular, we see that $\kappa = \pi$ does not yield a singularity; the boundary is a straight line in this case, and $g_\pi(x,y) = r\sin\theta = y$, which is not singular. When $\kappa = 0$, there is no interior in the domain near this point. Thus for any polygonal domain with a finite number of vertices with angles κ_j, there is some $\epsilon > 0$ such that $\kappa_j \in [\epsilon,\pi-\epsilon]\cup[\pi+\epsilon,2\pi]$ for all j.

In three dimensions, the set of possible singularities is much greater [99]. Edge singularities correspond to the vertex singularities in two dimensions, but in addition, vertex singularities appear [283]. The effect of smoothing singular boundaries is considered in [120].

6.1.3 Changing boundary condition type

The slit domain problem also allows us to assess the singularity that potentially occurs when boundary conditions change type along a straight line. Suppose that we have a domain $\Omega = \{(x,y)\in\mathbb{R}^2\ :\ x\in[-1,1],\ y\in[0,1]\}$ and we impose homogeneous Dirichlet conditions on $\Gamma = \{(x,0)\in\mathbb{R}^2\ :\ x\in[0,1]\}$ and Neumann conditions on $\Gamma^* = \partial\Omega\backslash\Gamma$. We can reflect the domain Ω around the line $y = 0$, and we get the domain $[-1,1]^2$ with a slit given by Γ. Therefore we see that $g_{2\pi} = \sqrt{r}\sin(\frac{1}{2}\theta)$ is harmonic in Ω, satisfies Dirichlet conditions on Γ and Neumann conditions on Γ^*.

We can expect such a singularity any time we switch from Dirichlet to Neumann boundary conditions along a straight boundary segment, even with homogeneous boundary conditions. We illustrate this with the following problem:

$$\begin{aligned} -\Delta u &= 1 \text{ in } [0,1]^2 \\ u = 0 \text{ on } \Gamma,\ &\frac{\partial u}{\partial n} = 0 \text{ on } \partial\Omega\backslash\Gamma, \end{aligned} \tag{6.10}$$

where $\Gamma = \{(x,0)\ :\ x\in[\frac{1}{2},1]\}$, whose solution is depicted in Figure 6.2. The code for solving this problem is given in Program 6.1 We leave as Exercise 6.3 to explore this problem in more detail. In Section 16.4.2 we consider adaptive meshes for solving this problem, as depicted in Figure 16.1.

```
from dolfin import *
import sys,math

meshsize=int(sys.argv[1])
pdeg=int(sys.argv[2])

# Create mesh and define function space
mesh = UnitSquareMesh(meshsize, meshsize)
V = FunctionSpace(mesh, "Lagrange", pdeg)

# Define Dirichlet boundary ( 0.5 < x < 1 and y = 0 )
def gamma(x):
  return x[0] > 0.5-DOLFIN_EPS and x[1] < DOLFIN_EPS

# Define boundary condition
u0 = Expression("0.0",degree=pdeg)
bc = DirichletBC(V, u0, gamma)

# Define variational problem
u = TrialFunction(V)
v = TestFunction(V)
f = Expression("1.0",degree=pdeg)
a = (inner(grad(u), grad(v)))*dx
L = f*v*dx

# Compute solution
u = Function(V)
solve(a == L, u, bc)

# Plot solution
plot(u, interactive=True)
```

Program 6.1: Code to implement the problem (6.10). In lines 12 and 13, we see code that defines the subset Γ of $\partial\Omega$ on which Dirichlet conditions are set.

6.2 An ill-posed problem?

It is tempting to idealize localized behavior in a physical system as occurring at a single point. For example, one might wonder what the shape of a drum head would be if one pushes down on it with a sharp pin. The Laplace equation models to a reasonable extent the deformation of the drum head (for small deformations), so one might consider

$$\begin{aligned} -\Delta u =& 0 \text{ in } \Omega \\ u(\mathbf{x}_0) =& u_0 \end{aligned} \tag{6.11}$$

where u_0 denotes the prescribed position of a knife edge. However, this problem is not well-posed. The difficulty is that one cannot constrain a function in $H^1(\Omega)$ at a single point. This is illustrated by the function

$$v(\mathbf{x}) = \log|\log|\mathbf{x}|| \tag{6.12}$$

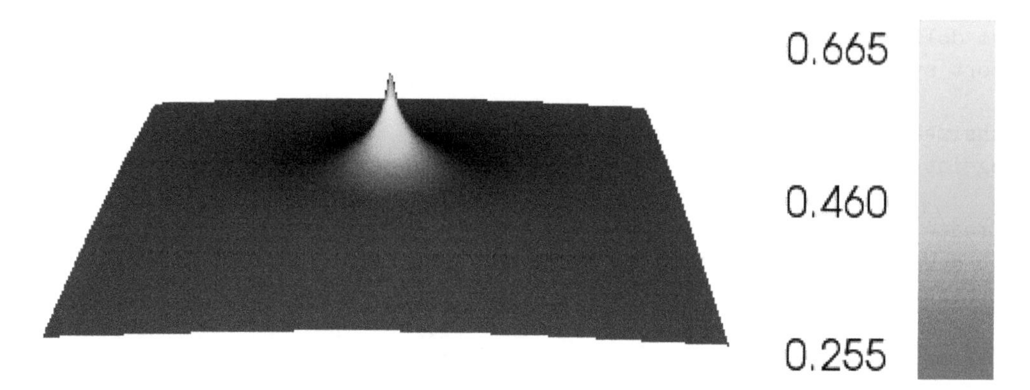

Figure 6.3: Solution of (6.16) computed with Program 6.2. Computed with a mesh size of 512 with piecewise linears and $A = 10,000$.

degree	mesh number	amplitude	error	check-sum
1	128	10,000	5.27e-03	-2.34e-02
1	256	10,000	2.50e-03	-4.57e-09
1	512	10,000	1.47e-03	-2.22e-16
1	1024	10,000	1.08e-03	5.11e-15
4	256	10,000	9.73e-04	-1.02e-10
1	512	100,000	9.67e-04	-1.06e-03
1	1024	100,000	5.24e-04	-1.98e-14

Table 6.1: Data for the solution of (6.16). The amplitude is A, error is $\|u_h^A - g\|_{L^2(\Omega)}$, check-sum is the value $1 - \int_\Omega \left(\delta_{\mathbf{x}_0}^A\right)_h d\mathbf{x}$ where $\left(\delta_{\mathbf{x}_0}^A\right)_h$ denotes the interpolant of $\delta_{\mathbf{x}_0}^A$ in V_h.

which satisfies $v \in H^1(B)$ where $B = \left\{\mathbf{x} \in \mathbb{R}^2 \,:\, |\mathbf{x}| < \frac{1}{2}\right\}$ [57, Example 1.4.3]. This function does not have a well-defined point value at the origin. By shifting this function around, we realize that functions in H^1 may not have point values on a dense set of points. Thus setting a point value for a function in H^1 does not make sense.

It is possible to change to a Dirichlet problem

$$\begin{aligned} -\Delta u =& 0 \text{ in } \Omega \\ u =& u_0 \text{ on } \Gamma \end{aligned} \tag{6.13}$$

where Γ is a small curve representing the point of contact of the pencil with the drum head, and u_0 is some function defined on Γ. As long as Γ has positive length, this problem is well-posed. However, its behavior will degenerate as the length of Γ is decreased.

Another approach to modeling such phenomena is using the Dirac δ-function [57]:

$$\begin{aligned} -\Delta u =& \delta_{\mathbf{x}_0} \text{ in } \Omega \\ u =& 0 \text{ on } \partial\Omega, \end{aligned} \tag{6.14}$$

where $\delta_{\mathbf{x}_0}$ is the linear functional $\delta_{\mathbf{x}_0}(v) = v(\mathbf{x}_0)$. Again, there is an issue since this linear functional is not bounded on V, as the function v defined in (6.12) illustrates. On the other hand, the solution to (6.14) is known as the Green's function for the Laplacian on Ω (with

Dirichlet conditions). It is possible to make sense of (6.14) using more sophisticated Sobolev spaces [57]. However, rather than taking that approach, we take one that effectively resolves the issue in conventional spaces. What we do is replace $\delta_{\mathbf{x}_0}$ by a smooth function $\delta^A_{\mathbf{x}_0}$ with the property that

$$\int_\Omega \delta^A_{\mathbf{x}_0}(\mathbf{x})\, v(\mathbf{x})\, d\mathbf{x} \to v(\mathbf{x}_0) \text{ as } A \to \infty \tag{6.15}$$

for sufficiently smooth v. We then consider the problem

$$\begin{aligned} \Delta u^A &= \delta^A_{\mathbf{x}_0} \text{ in } \Omega \\ u^A &= g \text{ on } \partial\Omega. \end{aligned} \tag{6.16}$$

Note that we can pick g to be the fundamental solution, and thus we have $u^A \to g$ as $A \to \infty$. For example, we can choose $\delta^A_{\mathbf{x}_0}$ to be Gaussian function of amplitude A and integral 1. In particular, in two dimensions,

$$\delta^A_{\mathbf{x}_0} = A\, e^{-\pi A|\mathbf{x}-\mathbf{x}_0|^2}. \tag{6.17}$$

We check our requirement that the integral is 1 via the change of variables $\mathbf{y} = \sqrt{\pi A}\,\mathbf{x}$:

$$\int_{\mathbb{R}^2} \pi A\, e^{-\pi A|\mathbf{x}-\mathbf{x}_0|^2}\, d\mathbf{x} = \int_{\mathbb{R}^2} e^{-|\mathbf{y}-\mathbf{y}_0|^2}\, d\mathbf{y} = 2\pi \int_0^\infty e^{-r^2} r\, dr = \pi \int_0^\infty e^{-s}\, ds = \pi.$$

In our experiments, $\mathbf{x}_0$ was chosen to be near the middle of the square $\Omega = [0,1]^2$, that is, $\mathbf{x}_0 = (0.50001, 0.50002)$ to avoid having the singularity at a grid point. The fundamental solution for the Laplace equation in two dimensions is

$$g(\mathbf{x}) = -\frac{1}{2\pi} \log|\mathbf{x} - \mathbf{x}_0|,$$

and so we took as boundary conditions $g(\mathbf{x}) = -\frac{1}{2\pi}\log|\mathbf{x}-\mathbf{x}_0|$ for $\mathbf{x} \in \partial\Omega$.

Computational data for such computations with various meshes, polynomial degrees, and amplitudes A are shown in Table 6.1. We see that the approximation of the Green's function is only first order accurate, reflecting its limited regularity. Increasing the order of polynomials used is only of modest benefit. Increasing the amplitude of the approximate δ-function is useful up to a point, but making it larger is only of value if the mesh can be suitably refined. Code to generate the data in Table 6.1 is given in Program 6.2.

Now we turn to a more obvious, but also more common, type of solution singularity due to a mismatch in boundary conditions, depicted in Figure 6.4.

6.3 Mismatch in boundary conditions

A mismatch between boundary conditions can lead to a singularity. Consider the boundary value problem

$$\begin{aligned} -\Delta u &= 0 \text{ in } \Omega \\ u &= 0 \text{ on } \Gamma \\ \frac{\partial u}{\partial n} &= g \text{ on } \Omega\backslash\Gamma, \end{aligned} \tag{6.18}$$

```
1  from dolfin import *
2  import sys,math
3
4  meshsize=int(sys.argv[1])
5  pdeg=int(sys.argv[2])
6  amps=float(sys.argv[3])
7  ba=amps*math.pi
8  dfac=1/(4*math.pi)
9
10 # Create mesh and define function space
11 mesh = UnitSquareMesh(meshsize, meshsize)
12 V = FunctionSpace(mesh, "Lagrange", pdeg)
13
14 # Define boundary condition
15 u0 = Expression("-d*log(pow(x[0]-0.50001,2)+pow(x[1]-0.50002,2))",\
16                  d=dfac,degree=pdeg)
17 onec = Expression("1.0",degree=pdeg)
18 bc = DirichletBC(V, u0, DomainBoundary())
19 a = (inner(grad(u), grad(v)))*dx
20 f = Expression("aa*exp(-(pow(x[0]-0.50001,2) + pow(x[1]-0.50002,2))*b)",\
21                  aa=amps,b=ba,degree=pdeg)
22 L = f*v*dx
23
24 # Compute solution
25 u = Function(V)
26 solve(a == L, u, bc)
27 uone=project(onec,V)
28 fo=interpolate(f,V)
29 efo= 1-assemble(onec*fo*dx)
30 print " ",pdeg," ",meshsize," %.2e"%amps, \
31       " %.2e"%errornorm(u0,u,norm_type='l2', degree_rise=0)," %.2e"%efo
```

Program 6.2: Code to implement the singularity problem (6.16). Solution shown in Figure 6.3.

where $\Omega = [0,1]^2$, $g(y) = 1$ and

$$\Gamma = \{(x,y) \in \partial\Omega \, : \, x = 0 \text{ or } y = 0 \text{ or } y = 1\}.$$

Thus $\Omega\backslash\Gamma = \{(x,y) \in \partial\Omega \, : \, x = 1\}$. Define $\Gamma_0 = \{(x,y) \in \partial\Omega \, : \, y = 0 \text{ or } y = 1\} \subset \Gamma$. Since $u \equiv 0$ on Γ, it follows that $\frac{\partial u}{\partial x} = 0$ on Γ_0, But $\frac{\partial u}{\partial x} = 1$ on $\Omega\backslash\Gamma$, so there is a discontinuity in $\frac{\partial u}{\partial x}$ at $(1,0)$ and $(1,1)$. In particular, it can be shown that second derivatives of u blow up like r^{-1} where r is the distance to $(1,0)$ or $(1,1)$. Thus $u \notin H^2(\Omega)$.

To visualize this phenomenon, we have plotted $\frac{\partial u}{\partial x}$ in Figure 6.4. As expected, $\frac{\partial u}{\partial x} = 0$ on Γ, and $\frac{\partial u}{\partial x} = 1$ on $\Omega\backslash\Gamma$ away from the singular points $(1,0)$ or $(1,1)$. At these points, the approximation can exhibit unpredictable behavior for some meshes. The code used to compute $\frac{\partial u}{\partial x}$ is given in Program 6.3.

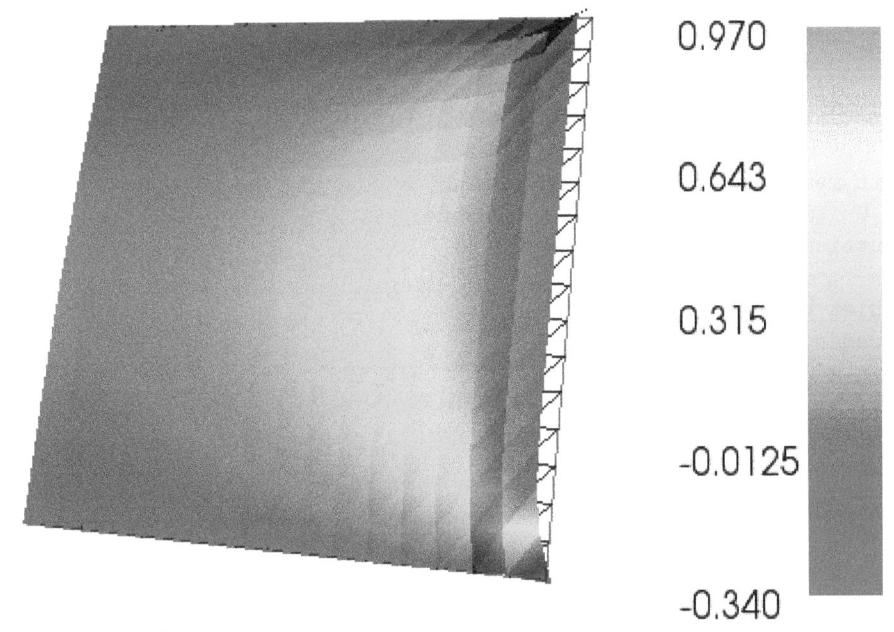

Figure 6.4: Plot of $\frac{\partial u}{\partial x}$ where u is the solution of (6.18) approximated with piecewise linears on a 16×16 mesh. We see that $\frac{\partial u}{\partial x} = 0$ on Γ_0 (top and bottom sides of $\Omega = [0,1]^2$) and $\frac{\partial u}{\partial x} = 1$ on $\partial\Omega\backslash\Gamma$ (right side of $\Omega = [0,1]^2$).

6.4 Exercises

Exercise 6.1 *Compute the solution to the problem (6.1) on the L-shaped domain defined in (6.2) with data g specified by (6.3). As solution metric, compute the norm of $u - g$. How does this depend on mesh size and polynomial order? (Hint: to construct the domain, see Chapter 28.)*

Exercise 6.2 *Pick a value of κ in the range $\pi < \kappa < 2\pi$. Compute the solution to the problem (6.1) on the domain depicted in Figure 6.1(b) with data g_κ specified by (6.8). As solution metric, compute the norm of $u_\kappa - g_\kappa$. How does this depend on κ, mesh size and polynomial order? (Hint: to construct the domain, see Chapter 28.)*

Exercise 6.3 *Let $\Omega = [0,1]^2$ and $\Gamma = \big\{(x,0) \in \mathbb{R}^2 \,:\, x \in [\frac{1}{2},1]\big\}$. Solve $-\Delta u = 1$ in Ω with homogeneous Dirichlet conditions on Γ and homogeneous Neumann conditions on $\partial\Omega\backslash\Gamma$ (see Figure 6.2). Identify a constant c such that $u = cg_{2\pi} + w$ where w is smoother than u.*

Exercise 6.4 *The method of manufactured solutions can benefit from many techniques of classical (analytical) applied mathematics. For example, the Laplace operator in polar coordinates is well known:*

$$\Delta f = f_{,rr} + r^{-1} f_{,r} + r^{-2} f_{,\theta\theta}.$$

Use this formula to verify that $\Delta g = 0$ for g specified by (6.3). If this goes well, also verify $\Delta g_\kappa = 0$ for g_κ specified by (6.8).

```
from dolfin import *
import sys,math

meshsize=int(sys.argv[1])

# Create mesh and define function space
mesh = UnitSquareMesh(meshsize, meshsize)
V = FunctionSpace(mesh, "Lagrange", 1)

#Dirichlet boundary (x=0 or y=0 or y=1)
def boundary(x):
  return x[0] < DOLFIN_EPS or x[1] < DOLFIN_EPS or x[1] > 1 - DOLFIN_EPS

# Define boundary condition
u0 = Expression("0.0",degree=1)
bc = DirichletBC(V, u0, boundary)

# Define variational problem
u = TrialFunction(V)
v = TestFunction(V)
f = Expression("0.0",degree=1)
g = Expression("1.0",degree=1)
a = inner(grad(u), grad(v))*dx
L = f*v*dx + g*v*ds

# Compute solution
u = Function(V)
solve(a == L, u, bc)
v=grad(u)[0]
plot(v, interactive=True)
```

Program 6.3: Code to implement the singularity problem (6.18). Solution shown in Figure 6.4.

Exercise 6.5 *Consider the boundary value problem*

$$\begin{aligned} -\Delta u &= 1 \text{ in } \Omega \\ u &= 0 \text{ on } \partial\Omega \end{aligned} \tag{6.19}$$

where $\Omega = \{(x,y) \in \mathbb{R}^2 : x^2 + y^2 < 1\}$ *is the unit disk. Show that the exact solution is* $u(x,y) = \frac{1}{4}(1 - x^2 + y^2)$*. (Hint: compare Exercise 6.4.)*

Exercise 6.6 *Consider the boundary value problem as in (6.18) but with different data:*

$$\begin{aligned} -\Delta u &= f \text{ in } \Omega \\ u &= 0 \text{ on } \Gamma \\ \frac{\partial u}{\partial n} &= g \text{ on } \Omega \backslash \Gamma, \end{aligned} \tag{6.20}$$

where $\Omega = [0,1]^2$, $f = 2x$, $g(y) = y(1-y)$ *and*

$$\Gamma = \{(x,y) \in \partial\Omega \ : \ x = 0 \ or \ y = 0 \ or \ y = 1\}.$$

Verify that the exact solution is $u(x,y) = xy(1-y)$. *Modify Program 6.3 to solve (6.20) numerically. Compute* $\|u - u_h\|_{L^2(\Omega)}$ *for various values of* h *and for polynomial degrees* $k = 1, 2, 3$, *and report what you find. Explain why there is no mismatch in boundary conditions, contrary to the situation with the boundary value problem in (6.18).*

Exercise 6.7 *Let* $\Omega = [0,1]^2$. *Solve* $-\Delta u = 1$ *in* Ω *with homogeneous Dirichlet conditions on* $\partial\Omega$ *with various meshes and polynomial degrees. What symmetries does the solution exhibit? Is it smooth at the corners? Is there a compatibility condition (see Section 10.3 and [166]) at the corners that is violated? If so, what derivatives are not continuous, and where? Can you find an exact solution for this problem in the literature? (Hint:* $u = 0$ *on* $\partial\Omega$ *so* $u_{xx} = 0$ *on the top and bottom of* Ω *and* $u_{yy} = 0$ *on the left and right sides of* Ω.*)*

Exercise 6.8 *Consider Poisson's problem on a domain* Ω *with a single re-entrant corner with angle* κ *in the range* $\pi < \kappa < 2\pi$. *Show that the constant* c_F *in Definition 6.1 is unique and depends linearly on* F.

Chapter 7

Laplacian Plus Potential

We now augment the equation (2.1) with a potential Z, which is simply a function defined on Ω with real values. The PDE takes the form

$$-\Delta u + Zu = f \text{ in } \Omega \tag{7.1}$$

together with the boundary conditions (2.2). To formulate the variational equivalent of (2.1) with boundary conditions (2.2), we again use the variational space

$$V := \left\{ v \in H^1(\Omega) \; : \; v|_\Gamma = 0 \right\}. \tag{7.2}$$

Let Z denote a real valued function on Ω. The appropriate bilinear form for the variational problem is then

$$a_Z(u,v) = \int_\Omega \nabla u(\mathbf{x}) \cdot \nabla v(\mathbf{x}) + Z(\mathbf{x})u(\mathbf{x})v(\mathbf{x})\, d\mathbf{x}. \tag{7.3}$$

In the case of homogeneous boundary conditions, we seek a solution $u \in V$ to

$$a_Z(u,v) = \int_\Omega f(\mathbf{x})v(\mathbf{x})\, d\mathbf{x} \quad \forall\, v \in V. \tag{7.4}$$

7.1 Bounded V

The simplest case is when Z is a constant, in which case (7.1) is often called the **Helmholtz equation**. This problem becomes interesting if Z is large, or equivalently, there is a small coefficient in front of Δ in (7.1). We propose Exercise 7.1 to explore this problem.

To understand coercivity in such problems, we first consider the eigenvalue problem

$$-\Delta u = \lambda u \text{ in } \Omega \tag{7.5}$$

together with the boundary conditions (2.2). Let us denote the solution of (7.5) by u_λ.

Let λ_0 be the lowest eigenvalue, and $u_{\lambda_0} \in V$ the corresponding eigenvector, for the eigenproblem problem (7.5), which we can write in variational form as

$$a_0(u_\lambda, v) = \lambda \int_\Omega u_\lambda(\mathbf{x})v(\mathbf{x})\, d\mathbf{x} \quad \forall\, v \in V, \tag{7.6}$$

where $a_0(\cdot,\cdot)$ denotes the case $Z \equiv 0$, which is thus the same as the bilinear form $a(\cdot,\cdot)$ in (2.8). Coercivity (3.3) of the bilinear form $a_0(\cdot,\cdot)$ shows that $\lambda_0 > 0$. Moreover, if $Z(\mathbf{x}) > -\lambda_0$ for all $\mathbf{x} \in \Omega$, then the problem (7.4) is well-posed since it is still coercive.

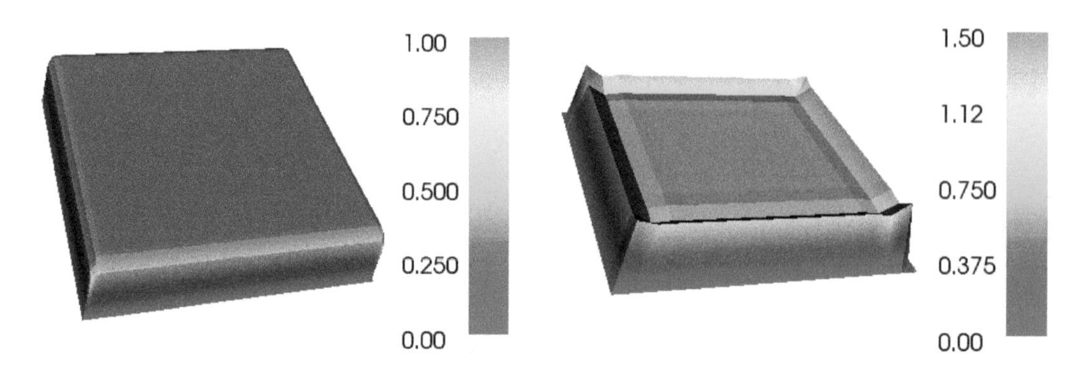

Figure 7.1: Boundary layer problem with $\epsilon = 0.0001$ approximated with piecewise linears: (left) 64×64 mesh and (right) 16×16 mesh.

degree	mesh number	L^2 difference	ϵ
1	256	1.43e-01	1.00e-04
1	512	1.42e-01	1.00e-04
1	256	8.64e-02	1.00e-05
1	512	8.14e-02	1.00e-05
1	1024	8.00e-02	1.00e-05
1	1024	4.72e-02	1.00e-06

Table 7.1: Boundary layer problem with various values of ϵ. Degree refers to the polynomial degree, mesh number indicates the number of edges along each boundary side as indicated in Figure 4.5, L^2 difference is $\|u - f\|_{L^2([0,1]^2)}$.

7.1.1 Boundary layers

Let $\epsilon > 0$. Consider the problem

$$-\epsilon \Delta u_\epsilon + u_\epsilon = f \text{ in } \Omega,$$

together with boundary conditions $u = 0$ on $\partial\Omega$, where f is held fixed independent of ϵ. This is known as a **singular perturbation** problem.

Under certain conditions, we expect $u_\epsilon \to f$ as $\epsilon \to 0$, since this is what we get if the term $\epsilon \Delta u_\epsilon$ goes to zero as $\epsilon \to 0$. But this can only be correct if $f = 0$ on $\partial\Omega$. We leave as Exercise 7.1 to investigate what happens when $f = 0$ on $\partial\Omega$ does hold.

But in many cases, the data f does not satisfy the constraint $f = 0$ on $\partial\Omega$, and in that case something has to be compromised. In the typical situation, $u_\epsilon \to f$ as $\epsilon \to 0$ everywhere except in a small **boundary layer** near $\partial\Omega$. To gain intuition, we consider an example.

7.1.2 Boundary layer example

Let $\epsilon > 0$. Consider the problem

$$-\epsilon \Delta u_\epsilon + u_\epsilon = f \text{ in } \Omega = [0,1]^2,$$

together with boundary conditions $u = 0$ on $\partial\Omega$, where $f \equiv 1$ is held fixed independent of ϵ. In this case, f does not satisfy the boundary conditions. The solution is depicted in Figure 7.1. On the left side of Figure 7.1, the mesh is fine enough to resolve the boundary layer, but on the right side of Figure 7.1, we see a numerical artifact (an over-shoot).

In Table 7.1, we see evidence that $u_\epsilon \to f$ in $L^2(\Omega)$.

7.2 Unbounded Z

For certain unbounded potentials, it is still possible to show that (7.4) is well-posed. For example, if Z is either the Coulombic or gravitational potential $Z(\mathbf{x}) = -|\mathbf{x}|^{-1}$, then the eigenvalue problem

$$a_Z(u_\lambda, v) = \lambda \int_\Omega u_\lambda(\mathbf{x}) v(\mathbf{x})\, d\mathbf{x} \quad \forall\, v \in V, \tag{7.7}$$

is well-posed, even in the case $\Omega = \mathbb{R}^3$. In this case, eigensolutions correspond to the wave functions of the hydrogen atom [230]. We propose Exercise 7.4 to explore this problem.

7.2.1 van der Waals interaction

The van der Waals interaction energy between two hydrogen atoms, separated by a distance R, is asymptotically of the form $-C_6 R^{-6}$ where the constant C_6 can be computed [72] by solving a two-dimensional PDE, as follows. Let $\Omega = [0,\infty] \times [0,\infty]$ and consider the PDE

$$-\frac{1}{2}\Delta u(r_1, r_2) + (\kappa(r_1) + \kappa(r_2))\, u(r_1, r_2) = -\frac{1}{\pi}(r_1 r_2)^2 e^{-r_1 - r_2} \text{ in } \Omega, \tag{7.8}$$

where the function κ is defined by

$$\kappa(r) = r^{-2} - r^{-1} + \tfrac{1}{2}. \tag{7.9}$$

The minimum of κ occurs at $r = 2$, and we have $\kappa(r) \geq \frac{1}{4}$. The problem (7.8) is well-posed in $H_0^1(\Omega)$, i.e., given Dirichlet conditions on the boundary of the quarter-plane Ω. The variational form for (7.8) is

$$a_\kappa(u, v) = \int_\Omega \tfrac{1}{2}\nabla u(r_1, r_2) \cdot \nabla v(r_1, r_2) + \big(\kappa(r_1) + \kappa(r_2)\big) u(r_1, r_2)\, v(r_1, r_2)\, dr_1 dr_2, \tag{7.10}$$

defined for all $u, v \in H_0^1(\Omega)$, and it is coercive on $H_0^1(\Omega)$, since $\kappa(r_1) + \kappa(r_2) \geq \frac{1}{2}$. In particular,

$$a(v, v) \geq \frac{1}{2} \int_\Omega |\nabla v(r_1, r_2)|^2 + v(r_1, r_2)^2\, dr_1 dr_2, \tag{7.11}$$

for all $v \in H_0^1(\Omega)$. The form $a(\cdot, \cdot)$ is continuous on $H_0^1(\Omega)$ because of the Hardy inequality

$$\int_0^\infty \big(u(r)/r\big)^2\, dr \leq 4 \int_0^\infty \big(u'(r)\big)^2\, dr \tag{7.12}$$

for $u \in H_0^1(0,\infty)$. Note that it would not be continuous on all of $H^1(0,\infty)$; without the Dirichlet boundary condition, the form would be infinite for some functions in $H^1(0,\infty)$.

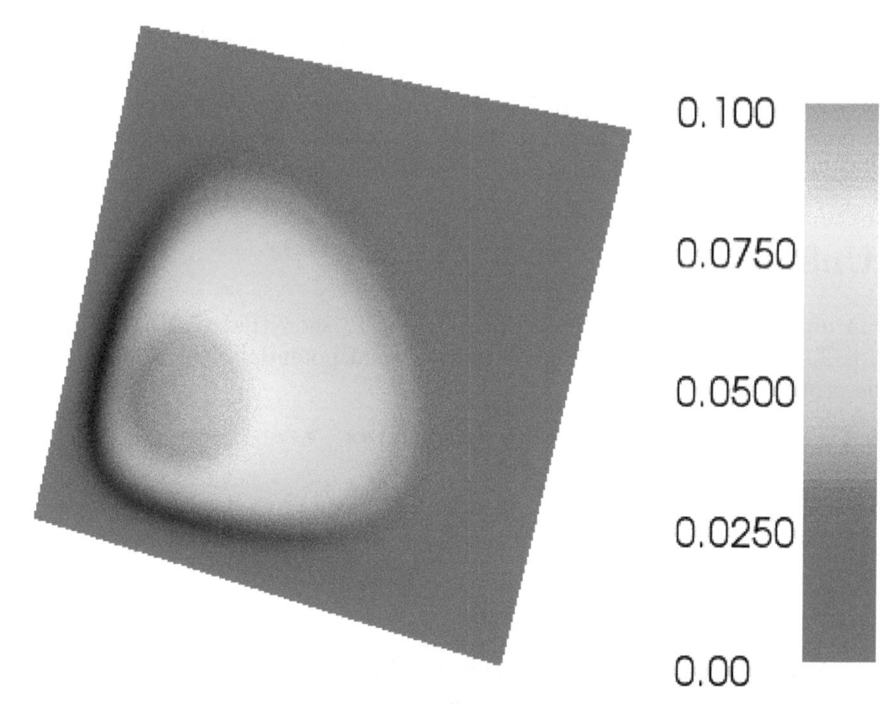

Figure 7.2: Asymptotic wavefunction perturbation computed with quartics on a mesh of size 100, with $L = 7$, computed using the code in Program 7.1.

To be able to render this problem computationally feasible, we replace Ω by a square Ω_L of side L in length; $\Omega_L = [0, L] \times [0, L]$. Define $U(r_1, r_2) = u(Lr_1, Lr_2)$. Then $\Delta U(r_1, r_2) = L^2 \Delta u(Lr_1, Lr_2)$. Thus

$$\begin{aligned} -\frac{1}{2} L^{-2} \Delta U(r_1, r_2) &= -\frac{1}{2} \Delta u(Lr_1, Lr_2) = -\left(\kappa(Lr_1) + \kappa(Lr_2)\right) u(Lr_1, Lr_2) \\ &\quad - \frac{L^4}{\pi} (r_1 r_2)^2 e^{-Lr_1 - Lr_2} \\ &= -\left(\hat{\kappa}_L(r_1) + \hat{\kappa}_L(r_2)\right) U(r_1, r_2) - \frac{L^4}{\pi} (r_1 r_2)^2 e^{-Lr_1 - Lr_2}, \end{aligned} \tag{7.13}$$

where $\hat{\kappa}_L(r) = L^{-2} r^{-2} - L^{-1} r^{-1} + \frac{1}{2}$. Therefore U satisfies

$$-\tfrac{1}{2} L^{-2} \Delta U(r_1, r_2) + \left(\hat{\kappa}_L(r_1) + \hat{\kappa}_L(r_2)\right) U(r_1, r_2) = -\frac{L^4}{\pi} (r_1 r_2)^2 e^{-Lr_1 - Lr_2}, \tag{7.14}$$

which we can pose with homogeneous Dirichlet boundary conditions ($u = 0$) on $\Omega_1 = [0, 1] \times [0, 1]$. Multiplying by $2L^2$, we obtain the equation

$$-\Delta U(r_1, r_2) + \left(\kappa_L(r_1) + \kappa_L(r_2)\right) U(r_1, r_2) = -\frac{2L^6}{\pi} (r_1 r_2)^2 e^{-Lr_1 - Lr_2} = f(r_1, r_2), \tag{7.15}$$

where $\kappa_L(r) = 2r^{-2} - 2Lr^{-1} + L^2$ and

$$f(r_1, r_2) = -\frac{2L^6}{\pi} (r_1 r_2)^2 e^{-Lr_1 - Lr_2}. \tag{7.16}$$

Thus we introduce the variational form

$$a_L(u,v) = \int_{[0,1]^2} \nabla u(r_1,r_2)\cdot\nabla v(r_1,r_2) + \big(\kappa_L(r_1)+\kappa_L(r_2)\big)u(r_1,r_2)\,v(r_1,r_2)\,dr_1dr_2 \tag{7.17}$$

Again, we have a variational problem in standard form: find $u_L \in V = H_0^1([0,1]^2)$ such that

$$a_L(u_L,v) = \int_{[0,1]^2} f(r_1,r_2)\,v(r_1,r_2)\,dr_1dr_2 \tag{7.18}$$

for all $v \in V$. The solution is shown in Figure 7.2 with $L = 7$ computed on a mesh of size 100 with quartic Lagrange piecewise polynomials. The code for solving this problem is given in Program 7.1.

The main quantity of interest [72, equation (3.25)] is

$$\begin{aligned} C_6 &= -\frac{32\pi}{3}\int_0^\infty\int_0^\infty r_1^2r_2^2e^{-(r_1+r_2)}u(r_1,r_2)\,dr_1dr_2 \\ &\approx -\frac{32\pi}{3}\int_0^L\int_0^L r_1^2r_2^2e^{-(r_1+r_2)}u(r_1,r_2)\,dr_1dr_2 \\ &\approx -\frac{32\pi}{3}\int_0^L\int_0^L r_1^2r_2^2e^{-(r_1+r_2)}U(r_1/L,r_2/L)\,dr_1dr_2 \\ &= -\frac{32\pi}{3}\int_0^1\int_0^1 L^4R_1^2R_2^2e^{-(LR_1+LR_2)}U(R_1,R_2)\,L^2\,dR_1dR_2 \\ &= -\frac{16\pi^2}{3}\frac{2L^6}{\pi}\int_0^1\int_0^1 R_1^2R_2^2e^{-(LR_1+LR_2)}U(R_1,R_2)\,dR_1dR_2 \\ &= \frac{16\pi^2}{3}\int_0^1\int_0^1 f(R_1,R_2)\,U(R_1,R_2)\,dR_1dR_2, \end{aligned} \tag{7.19}$$

where we made the substitution $r_i = LR_i$, $i = 1,2$, and f is defined in (7.16).

To avoid singularities in the coefficients, we modified the potential to be

$$\kappa_L^\epsilon(r) = 2(\epsilon+r)^{-2} - 2L(\epsilon+r)^{-1} + L^2. \tag{7.20}$$

Computational results are shown in Table 7.2. The results were insensitive to ϵ for $\epsilon \le 10^{-9}$.

7.2.2 Another formulation

The singularity $(r_i)^{-2}$ is difficult to deal with. But we can integrate by parts to soften its effect, as follows:

$$\begin{aligned} \int_\Omega (r_i)^{-2}u(r_1,r_2)\,v(r_1,r_2)\,dr_1dr_2 &= -\int_\Omega \Big(\frac{\partial}{\partial r_i}(r_i)^{-1}\Big)u(r_1,r_2)\,v(r_1,r_2)\,dr_1dr_2 \\ &= \int_\Omega (r_i)^{-1}\frac{\partial}{\partial r_i}\big(u(r_1,r_2)\,v(r_1,r_2)\big)\,dr_1dr_2, \end{aligned} \tag{7.21}$$

degree	quadrature	mesh number	C_6 error	ϵ	L	time
4	6	100	4.57e-07	1.00e-09	15.0	1.47
4	8	80	4.57e-07	1.00e-09	15.0	0.917
4	10	100	4.57e-07	1.00e-09	15.0	1.595
4	10	200	4.56e-07	1.00e-09	15.0	7.469
4	8	250	4.56e-07	1.00e-09	15.0	12.5
2	4	400	3.97e-07	1.00e-09	15.0	1.912
2	4	600	4.45e-07	1.00e-09	15.0	4.738
2	3	600	4.41e-07	1.00e-09	15.0	4.747
2	2	250	-1.22e-07	1.00e-09	15.0	0.786
2	3	250	-6.78e-08	1.00e-09	15.0	0.789
2	3	255	-2.74e-08	1.00e-09	15.0	0.786
2	3	260	9.14e-09	1.00e-09	15.0	0.792
2	3	265	4.23e-08	1.00e-09	15.0	0.837
2	4	250	5.41e-08	1.00e-09	15.0	0.788
2	4	240	-1.87e-08	1.00e-09	15.0	0.739

Table 7.2: Using finite element computation of $C_6 = 6.4990267054$ [72]. The potential was modified as in (7.20). Computations were done with 4 cores via MPI and a PETSc Krylov solver. Error values were the same for $\epsilon = 10^{-9}$ and $\epsilon = 10^{-12}$.

where for simplicity we define $\Omega = [0,1]^2$ here and for the remainder of this subsection. We have assumed that $u, v \in V = H_0^1(\Omega)$ in (7.21). Thus

$$\begin{aligned}
&\int_\Omega ((r_1)^{-2} + (r_2)^{-2}) u(r_1,r_2)\, v(r_1,r_2)\, dr_1 dr_2 \\
&\quad = \int_\Omega \big((r_1)^{-1}, (r_2)^{-1}\big) \cdot \nabla\big(u(r_1,r_2)\, v(r_1,r_2)\big)\, dr_1 dr_2 \qquad (7.22) \\
&\quad = \int_\Omega \big((r_1)^{-1}, (r_2)^{-1}\big) \cdot \Big(\big(\nabla u(r_1,r_2)\big)\, v(r_1,r_2) + \big(\nabla v(r_1,r_2)\big)\, u(r_1,r_2)\Big)\, dr_1 dr_2
\end{aligned}$$

Thus we introduce a new variational form (cf. (7.17))

$$\begin{aligned}
\hat{a}_L^\epsilon(u,v) = &\int_\Omega \nabla u(r_1,r_2) \cdot \nabla v(r_1,r_2) + \big(\hat{\kappa}_L^\epsilon(r_1) + \hat{\kappa}_L^\epsilon(r_2)\big) u(r_1,r_2)\, v(r_1,r_2)\, dr_1 dr_2 \\
+ 2 &\int_\Omega \widehat{\beta}(r_1,r_2) \cdot \big(\big(\nabla u(r_1,r_2)\big)\, v(r_1,r_2) + u(r_1,r_2)\big(\nabla v(r_1,r_2)\big)\big)\, dr_1 dr_2
\end{aligned} \qquad (7.23)$$

where

$$\widehat{\beta}(r_1,r_2) = \big((r_1+\epsilon)^{-1}, (r_2+\epsilon)^{-1}\big), \qquad \hat{\kappa}_L^\epsilon(r) = -2L(r+\epsilon)^{-1} + 2L^2. \qquad (7.24)$$

7.3 Laguerre Galerkin approximation

We propose to approximate (7.8) using a Galerkin approach based on the variational formulation

$$a_\kappa(u,v) = -\int_\Omega r_1^2 r_2^2 \psi_0(r_1,r_2) v(r_1,r_2)\, dr_1 dr_2 \qquad (7.25)$$

for all $v \in H_0^1(\Omega)$. Instead of using finite elements, we propose a different space of functions called Laguerre functions.

Let $\sigma_{n,\alpha}(r) = e^{-\alpha r} r^n$, $n = 1, 2, \ldots$. These form a basis for Laguerre functions [207, 262]. We propose to use tensor products of these functions for $\alpha = 1$ to approximate the solution of (7.8). To do so, we develop some preliminaries. First of all, we have

$$\int_0^\infty \sigma_{n,1}(r)\, dr = \int_0^\infty e^{-r} r^n\, dr = n! \tag{7.26}$$

because

$$\int_0^\infty e^{-r} r^n\, dr = n \int_0^\infty e^{-r} r^{n-1}\, dr, \tag{7.27}$$

as may be verified by integration by parts ($n \geq 1$), and $\int_0^\infty e^{-r}\, dr = 1$. Similarly, the change of variables $y = \alpha r$ shows that

$$\int_0^\infty \sigma_{n,\alpha}(r)\, dr = n!/\alpha^{n+1}. \tag{7.28}$$

Note that $\sigma_n \sigma_m = \sigma_{m+n,2}$.

To shorten notation, let $\sigma_n = \sigma_{n,1}$. Note that $\sigma_n' = -\sigma_n + n\sigma_{n-1}$, and the maximum of σ_n occurs at n. In general, for $n \geq 2$,

$$\begin{aligned} \sigma_n''(r) &= \sigma_n(r) - 2n\sigma_{n-1}(r) + n(n-1)\sigma_{n-2}(r) \\ \frac{\sigma_n'(r)}{r} &= -\tfrac{1}{2}\sigma_{n-1}(r) + n\sigma_{n-2}(r) \\ \frac{\sigma_n(r)}{r^i} &= \sigma_{n-i}(r). \end{aligned} \tag{7.29}$$

Thus

$$\begin{aligned} \int_0^\infty \sigma_n' \sigma_m'\, dr &= \int_0^\infty (-\sigma_n + n\sigma_{n-1})(-\sigma_m + m\sigma_{m-1})\, dr \\ &= \int_0^\infty \sigma_{m+n,2} - (m+n)\sigma_{m+n-1,2} + mn\sigma_{m+n-2,2}\, dr \\ &= (m+n)!/2^{m+n+1} - (m+n)!/2^{m+n} + mn((m+n-2)!)/2^{m+n-1} \\ &= -(m+n)!/2^{m+n+1} + mn((m+n-2)!)/2^{m+n-1} \\ &= -(m+n-2)!\left((m+n)(m+n-1) - 4mn\right)/2^{m+n+1} \\ &= (m+n-2)!\left((m+n) - (m-n)^2\right)/2^{m+n+1}. \end{aligned} \tag{7.30}$$

Define a variational form

$$\hat{a}(u,v) = \int_0^\infty \tfrac{1}{2} u'v' + \kappa(r) uv\, dr, \tag{7.31}$$

where κ is given in (7.9). To compute the corresponding matrix, we need to have

$$\int_0^\infty \sigma_n \sigma_m r^{-i}\, dr = \int_0^\infty \sigma_{m+n-i,2}\, dr = (m+n-i)!/2^{m+n-i+1}. \tag{7.32}$$

Thus

$$
\begin{aligned}
\hat{a}(\sigma_n, \sigma_m) &= (m+n-2)!\left((m+n)-(m-n)^2\right)/2^{m+n+2} \\
&\quad + (m+n-2)!/2^{m+n-1} - (m+n-1)!/2^{m+n} - \lambda_0(m+n)!/2^{m+n+2} \\
&= (m+n-2)!\big((m+n)-(m-n)^2 \\
&\quad + 8 - 4(m+n-1) - \lambda_0(m+n)(m+n-1)\big)/2^{m+n+2}.
\end{aligned} \tag{7.33}
$$

It will also be useful to identify the corresponding "mass" matrix

$$
\mu(\sigma_n, \sigma_m) = \int_0^\infty \sigma_n \sigma_m \, dr = (m+n)!/2^{m+n+1}. \tag{7.34}
$$

It is worth noting that $\sigma = \sigma_2 + \frac{1}{2}\sigma_3 = (r^2 + \frac{1}{2}r^3)e^{-r}$ is an exact solution to $\hat{a}(\sigma, v) = (\sigma_2, v)$ for all v.

7.3.1 Tensor product approximation

Now we consider approximation by tensor products

$$
v(r_1, r_2) = \sum_{i=1}^{k}\sum_{j=1}^{k} c_{ij}\sigma_i(r_1)\sigma_j(r_2). \tag{7.35}
$$

Using the variational form (7.10), we seek solutions u of the form (7.35) to

$$
a_\kappa(u, v) = (f, v) \tag{7.36}
$$

for all v of the form (7.35), where

$$
(f, v) = \int_0^\infty \int_0^\infty f(r_1, r_2) v(r_1, r_2) \, dr_1 dr_2. \tag{7.37}
$$

In particular, we will be interested in the case

$$
f(r_1, r_2) = -\sigma_2(r_1)\sigma_2(r_2), \tag{7.38}
$$

so the computation of the integrals on the right-hand side in (7.36) are simplified.

Now we consider a typical matrix element corresponding to (7.36):

$$
\begin{aligned}
A_{(i,j),(m,n)} &= a(\sigma_i(r_1)\sigma_j(r_2), \sigma_m(r_1)\sigma_n(r_2)) \\
&= \tfrac{1}{2}\int_0^\infty \int_0^\infty \sigma_i'(r_1)\sigma_m'(r_1)\sigma_j(r_2)\sigma_n(r_2) \\
&\quad + \sigma_i(r_1)\sigma_m(r_1)\sigma_j'(r_2)\sigma_n'(r_2) + (\kappa(r_1) + \kappa(r_2))\,\sigma_i(r_1)\sigma_j(r_2)\sigma_m(r_1)\sigma_n(r_2)\, dr_1 dr_2 \\
&= \int_0^\infty \left(\int_0^\infty \tfrac{1}{2}\sigma_i'(r_1)\sigma_m'(r_1) + \kappa(r_1)\sigma_i(r_1)\sigma_m(r_1)\, dr_1\right) \sigma_j(r_2)\sigma_n(r_2)\, dr_2 \\
&\quad + \int_0^\infty \left(\int_0^\infty \tfrac{1}{2}\sigma_j'(r_2)\sigma_n'(r_2) + \kappa(r_2)\sigma_j(r_2)\sigma_n(r_2)\, dr_2\right) \sigma_i(r_1)\sigma_m(r_1)\, dr_1 \\
&= \hat{a}(\sigma_i, \sigma_m)\mu(\sigma_j, \sigma_n) + \hat{a}(\sigma_j, \sigma_n)\mu(\sigma_i, \sigma_m),
\end{aligned} \tag{7.39}
$$

k	C_6 values	k	C_6 values	k	C_6 values
		6	6.499025	11	6.49902670534
2	6.17	7	6.4990266	12	6.49902670539
3	6.486	8	6.49902669	13	6.499026705401
4	6.4985	9	6.499026703	14	6.499026705404
5	6.49900	10	6.4990267051	15	6.499026705403

Table 7.3: Convergence of C_6 values as a function of the degree k of polynomials used in the Laguerre function approximation.

where μ is the mass matrix defined in (7.34). When f takes the form (7.38), the right-hand side in the corresponding linear equation is

$$-\mu(\sigma_2,\sigma_m)\mu(\sigma_2,\sigma_n) = -(m+2)!(n+2)!/2^{m+n+6}, \tag{7.40}$$

where μ is defined and evaluated in (7.34). The quantity of most interest is

$$(u,u) = \int_0^\infty \int_0^\infty u(r_1,r_2)^2\, dr_1 dr_2 = c\cdot Mc, \tag{7.41}$$

for u of the form (7.35) and M is the matrix

$$M_{(i,j),(m,n)} = \mu(\sigma_i,\sigma_m)\mu(\sigma_j,\sigma_n). \tag{7.42}$$

Using this approach, we compute C_6 as indicated in Table 7.3.

7.3.2 Computational details

Instead of using orthogonal representations of the Laguerre functions, we worked directly with the basis functions σ_n. This simplifies the computation of matrix entries at the expense of obtaining matrices with extreme scales. To compensate for this, we used diagonal scaling for the linear system. More precisely, recall the matrix A defined in (7.39). The system $Au = f$ was modified to $DADy = Df$ where $u = Dy$. The diagonal matrix D was chosen to be, in `octave` notation, `D=inv(diag(sqrt(diag(A))))`. With this scaling, round-off errors only appeared beyond the twelfth digits using sixteen digit computation in `octave`, at least for $k \le 15$.

7.4 Exercises

Exercise 7.1 *Let $\epsilon > 0$. Consider the problem*

$$-\epsilon\Delta u_\epsilon + u_\epsilon = f \text{ in } \Omega = [0,1]^2,$$

together with homogeneous Dirichlet conditions on all of $\partial\Omega$, where $f(x,y) = (\sin\pi x)(\sin\pi y)$, which does satisfy the boundary conditions (2.2), See what happens for small ϵ. Does $u_\epsilon \to f$? In what norm(s)? Is there a boundary layer? If the homogeneous boundary conditions hold on only a part Γ of the boundary, is there a boundary layer away from Γ?

degree	mesh number	L^2 difference	time
1	256	6.86e-02	1.11
1	512	5.34e-02	5.1
1	1024	4.72e-02	29
2	512	4.54e-02	23
4	256	4.48e-02	18
8	128	4.47e-02	25
8	8	7.74e-02	23

Table 7.4: Boundary layer problem with $\epsilon = 10^{-6}$. Degree refers to the polynomial degree, mesh number indicates the number of edges along each boundary side as indicated in Figure 4.5, L^2 difference is $\|u - f\|_{L^2([0,1]^2)}$, and time is in seconds.

Exercise 7.2 *Let $\epsilon > 0$. Consider the problem*

$$-\epsilon \Delta u_\epsilon + u_\epsilon = f \text{ in } \Omega = [0,1]^2,$$

together with boundary condition $u = 0$ on Γ, where

$$\Gamma = \{(x,y) \in \Omega = [0,1]^2 \,:\, x = 0\}.$$

Take $f = 1$ (it does not satisfy the boundary conditions). Does $u_\epsilon \to f$ except in a small boundary layer? In what norm(s)? Is there a boundary layer away from Γ or just near it?

Exercise 7.3 *Let $\epsilon > 0$. Implement the problem*

$$-\epsilon \Delta u_\epsilon + u_\epsilon = f \text{ in } \Omega = [0,1]^2,$$

together with homogeneous Dirichlet conditions on all of $\partial\Omega$, where $f(x,y) = 1$, which does not satisfy the boundary conditions (2.2). See what happens for small ϵ. Does $u_\epsilon \to f$? In what norm(s)? Is there a boundary layer? Compare the data in Table 7.4 and experiment with other values of ϵ. Note that the best results require a large number of nodes to resolve the boundary layer, but among the different choices (linear, quadratics, and so forth), the results are about the same and take about the same time to compute. In particular, using a high-order polynomial does not provide particular benefit in this case.

Exercise 7.4 *Consider the problem*

$$-\tfrac{1}{2}\Delta u(\mathbf{x}) - \frac{1}{|\mathbf{x}|}u(\mathbf{x}) = -\tfrac{1}{2}e^{-|\mathbf{x}|} \text{ for } x \in \mathbb{R}^3$$

and the condition at infinity that $u(\mathbf{x}) \to 0$ as $\mathbf{x} \to \infty$. First truncate the infinite domain to a box $[-L,L]^3$, and impose homogeneous Dirichlet conditions on the boundary of the box. Make a variational formulation for this problem and solve for $u = u_L$ for various values of L. Compare with the exact solution $u(\mathbf{x}) = ce^{-|\mathbf{x}|}$. Evaluate c by plotting $u_L(\mathbf{x})e^{+|\mathbf{x}|}$.

```
1  from dolfin import *
2  import sys,math
3  from timeit import default_timer as timer
4  parameters["form_compiler"]["quadrature_degree"] = 12
5  startime=timer()
6  meshsize=int(sys.argv[1])
7  pdeg=int(sys.argv[2])
8  ell=float(sys.argv[3])
9  myeps=float(sys.argv[4])
10 # Create mesh and define function space
11 mesh = UnitSquareMesh(meshsize, meshsize)
12 V = FunctionSpace(mesh, "Lagrange", pdeg)
13 # Define boundary condition
14 u0 = Constant(0.0)
15 bc = DirichletBC(V, u0, DomainBoundary())
16 # Define variational problem
17 u = TrialFunction(V)
18 v = TestFunction(V)
19 f = Expression("-(2.0*pow(el,6)/mypi)*pow(x[0]*x[1],2)* \
20                exp(-el*x[0]-el*x[1])",el=ell,mypi=math.pi,degree=pdeg)
21 kay = Expression("(2.0/(me+pow(x[0],2)))-2.0*(el/(me+x[0])) \
22                 +(2.0/(me+pow(x[1],2)))-2.0*(el/(me+x[1])) \
23                 +2.0*el*el",me=myeps,el=ell,degree=pdeg)
24 a = (inner(grad(u), grad(v))+kay*u*v)*dx
25 RHS = f*v*dx
26 # Compute solution
27 u = Function(V)
28 solve(a == RHS, u, bc)
29 aftersolveT=timer()
30 mfu= (16.0*pow(math.pi,2)/3.0)*assemble(u*f*dx)
31 mer=mfu-6.49902670540
32 totime=aftersolveT-startime
33 print " ",pdeg," ",meshsize," %.2e"%mer," %.2e"%myeps, \
34       " %.1f"%ell," %.3f"%totime
```

Program 7.1: Code to implement the problem (7.18).

Chapter 8

Variational Formulations in One Dimension

Here we develop all of the concepts of the variational formulation for differential equations. By considering the one-dimensional case, we are able to explain in detail many of the concepts.

8.1 Exact solution

Consider the two-point boundary-value problem

$$\begin{aligned} -\frac{d^2u}{dx^2} &= f \text{ in } (0,1) \\ u(0) = g_0, \quad & u'(1) = g_1. \end{aligned} \tag{8.1}$$

The solution can be determined from f via two integrations. First of all, we can write

$$\frac{du}{dx}(t) = \int_t^1 f(s)\,ds + g_1 \tag{8.2}$$

using the boundary condition at $x = 1$. Integrating again shows that

$$u(x) = \int_0^x \int_t^1 f(s)\,ds\,dt + g_1 x + g_0 \tag{8.3}$$

using the boundary condition at $x = 0$. This shows that (8.1) is well-posed.

It will not be this easy to demonstrate the well-posedness of all the differential equations studied here. However, every investigation should (in principle) begin with this step.

The variational approach to differential equations is a powerful technique for studying their well-posedness and behavior as well as a critical step in generating a broad class of discretization schemes. It is often called the "weak" formulation as it allows the differential equation to be posed in a set of functions that allows a broader range of solutions. This generalization is not just a mathematical curiosity; rather it often allows the problems of most physical relevance to be addressed.

8.2 Weak formulation of boundary value problems

Suppose that u is the solution of (8.1) with $g_0 = 0$. Let v be any (sufficiently regular) function such that $v(0) = 0$. Then integration by parts yields

$$(f, v)_{L^2([0,1])} = \int_0^1 f(x)v(x)dx = \int_0^1 -u''(x)v(x)dx = \int_0^1 u'(x)v'(x)dx - g_1 v(1). \quad (8.4)$$

Define

$$a(u, v) := \int_0^1 u'(x)v'(x)dx \quad (8.5)$$

and

$$V = \left\{v \in L^2([0,1]) \ : \ a(v,v) < \infty \text{ and } v(0) = 0\right\}. \quad (8.6)$$

Then we can say that the solution u to (8.1) is characterized by

$$u \in V \quad \text{such that} \quad a(u,v) = (f,v)_{L^2([0,1])} + g_1 v(1) \qquad \forall v \in V, \quad (8.7)$$

which is the variational formulation or **weak formulation** of (8.1).

The relationship (8.7) is called "variational" because the function v is allowed to vary arbitrarily. It has a natural interpretation in the setting of Hilbert spaces [57]. The Dirichlet boundary condition $u(0) = 0$ is called an **essential boundary condition** because it appears in the variational space. The Neumann boundary condition $u'(1) = 0$ is called an **natural boundary condition** because it does not appear in the variational space but rather is implied in the formulation.

Inhomogeneous Dirichlet boundary conditions are handled as follows in the variational formulation. Let u_0 be some function satisfying the inhomogeneous Dirichlet boundary conditions (but not necessarily the Neumann boundary conditions). Then

$$u - u_0 \in V \quad \text{such that} \quad a(u,v) = (f,v)_{L^2([0,1])} + g_1 v(1) \qquad \forall v \in V. \quad (8.8)$$

Equivalently, this can be written as $u = w + u_0$ where

$$w \in V \quad \text{such that} \quad a(w,v) = (f,v)_{L^2([0,1])} + g_1 v(1) - a(u_0, v) \qquad \forall v \in V. \quad (8.9)$$

Note that the general problem (8.8) can be written

$$w \in V \quad \text{such that} \quad a(w,v) = F(v) \qquad \forall v \in V \quad (8.10)$$

where F denotes a **linear functional** on the space V, i.e., a linear function defined for any $v \in V$ having a single real number as its value.

8.2.1 Linear functionals

The right-hand side of (8.9) can be written succinctly as

$$F(v) = (f,v)_{L^2([0,1])} + g_1 v(1) - a(u_0, v) \qquad \forall v \in V. \quad (8.11)$$

The expression F is called a linear functional because (a) it is linear and (b) it has scalar values. By linear, we mean that $F(u+av) = F(u) + aF(v)$ for any scalar a and any $u, v \in V$.

The critical condition on a linear functional for success in a variational formulation is that it be *bounded* or *continuous*. A **bounded linear functional** (equivalently a **continuous linear functional**) F on a normed space V must satisfy

$$|F(v)| \le C_F \|v\|_V \quad \forall v \in V. \tag{8.12}$$

A natural norm $\|\cdot\|_V$ for the space V defined in (8.6) is

$$\|v\|_a = \sqrt{a(v,v)}.$$

The smallest possible constant C_F for which this holds is called the **dual norm** of F and is defined by

$$\|F\|_{V'} := \sup_{0 \ne v \in V} \frac{|F(v)|}{\|v\|_V}. \tag{8.13}$$

The main point is that all the linear forms considered so far *are* bounded (see Exercise 8.3), in particular the Dirac δ-function, defined by $\delta(v) = v(1)$, as we show in Section 8.2.2. But it is also easy to think of others which are not, such as

$$F(v) := v'(x_0) \tag{8.14}$$

for some $x_0 \in [0,1]$. This form is linear, but consider what it should do for the function $v \in V$ given by

$$v(x) := |x - x_0|^{2/3} \tag{8.15}$$

(see Exercise 8.2).

The general variational formulation (8.10) can be shown to be completely equivalent to the original differential equation (see [57, Theorem 0.1.4]). Moreover, it actually provides a framework that allows less regular data (arbitrary continuous linear functionals for F) as required by important physical applications. The expression $a(\cdot,\cdot)$ is called a bilinear form (or sometimes a **bilinear functional**) on the space V, since it is a bilinear function defined on the Cartesian product $V \times V$ having a single real number as its value. If we fix one of the variables of a bilinear form, it yields a linear form in the remaining variable.

8.2.2 Sobolev's inequality

Consider the linear form $F(v) = v(x_0)$ for some $x_0 \in [0,1]$. We want to prove that this is bounded on V. We write a function as the integral of its derivative and begin to estimate:

$$v(t) = \int_0^t v'(x)\,dx = \int_0^1 v'(x)w'(x)\,dx = a(v,w), \tag{8.16}$$

where the function $w \in V$ is defined by

$$w(x) = \begin{cases} x & 0 \le x \le t \\ t & x \ge t \end{cases} \tag{8.17}$$

One benefit of our loosened notion of derivative is that such functions are indeed in V, even though the derivative of w is discontinuous. By the Cauchy-Schwarz inequality (3.15)

$$|v(t)| = |a(v,w)| \le \|v\|_a \|w\|_a = \sqrt{t}\|v\|_a \le \|v\|_a \tag{8.18}$$

for all $t \in [0,1]$. Inequality (8.18) is called Sobolev's inequality, and V is an example of a Sobolev space. What Sobolev's inequality inequality tells us is that, even though the functions in V are not smooth in the classical sense (derivatives can even be infinite at isolated points), they nevertheless have some type of classical regularity, namely continuity in this case.

Note that the first step in (8.16) uses the fact that for $v \in V$, $v(0) = 0$. This subtle point is nevertheless essential, since (8.18) is clearly false if this boundary condition is not available. In particular, if v is a constant function, then the right-hand-side of (8.18) is zero for this v whereas the left-hand-side is not (unless $v \equiv 0$). Sobolev's inequality holds in a more general setting, not requiring boundary conditions, but only when the bilinear form is augmented in some way that renders an inner-product.

8.2.3 Natural boundary conditions

We saw that the 'natural' boundary condition, e.g., $u'(1) = 0$ in (8.1) when $g_1 = 0$, disappears in the variational formulation (8.7). But if these are in some sense equivalent formulations (they are), then the natural boundary condition must be encoded in the variational formulation is some way. We can see this by reversing the process used to go from (8.1) to (8.7). So suppose that u satisfies (8.7), and also assume that it is smooth enough for us to integrate by parts:

$$\begin{aligned}(f,v)_{L^2([0,1])} &= \int_0^1 u'(x)v'(x)\,dx = \int_0^1 -u''(x)v(x)\,dx + \left(u'v\right)\Big|_0^1 \\ &= \int_0^1 -u''(x)v(x)\,dx + u'(1)v(1).\end{aligned} \tag{8.19}$$

Choosing first $v \in V$ that vanishes at $x = 1$, we conclude that

$$\int_0^1 \left(f + u''(x)\right)v(x)\,dx = 0$$

for all such v. From this, one can show that we necessarily have $-u'' = f$. Inserting this fact in (8.19), we conclude that $u'(1) = 0$ simply by taking a single v such that $v(1) \neq 0$, e.g., $v(x) = x$. Thus the natural boundary condition emerges from the variational formulation "naturally." And as an intermediate step, we see that u satisfies the first equation in (8.1), proving the equivalence of (8.1) and (8.7).

8.2.4 Review of the Robin boundary condition

Consider the two-point boundary-value problem

$$\begin{aligned} -\frac{d^2u}{dx^2} &= f \text{ in } (0,1) \\ -u'(0) + \alpha u(0) = 0, &\quad u'(1) = g, \end{aligned} \tag{8.20}$$

where $\alpha > 0$. We recognize the boundary condition at 0 to be the analog of the Robin boundary condition studied in Section 5.3; the outward normal derivative of u at 0 is $-u'(0)$. For simplicity we assume that f is a constant. Integrating, we find (compare (8.2))

$$\frac{du}{dx}(t) = \int_t^1 f\,ds + g = f(1-t) + g, \tag{8.21}$$

using the boundary condition at $x = 1$. In particular, $u'(0) = f + g$. Thus the Robin boundary condition at 0 implies that

$$u(0) = \frac{f+g}{\alpha}.$$

Integrating (8.21) shows that

$$u(x) = \frac{f+g}{\alpha} + f(x - \tfrac{1}{2}x^2) + gx. \tag{8.22}$$

Thus we see that the solution goes to ∞ as $\alpha \to 0$, and we conclude that coercivity again has again given us good guidance regarding the model behavior.

8.3 Galerkin approximation

Let $V_h \subset V$ be any (finite dimensional) subspace. Let us consider (8.7) with V replaced by V_h, namely

$$u_h \in V_h \quad \text{such that} \quad a(u_h, v) = (f, v)_{L^2([0,1])} \qquad \forall v \in V_h. \tag{8.23}$$

Then (8.23) represents a square, finite system of equations for u_h which can easily be seen to be invertible [57]. Note how easily a discrete scheme for approximating (8.1) can be defined.

A matrix equation is derived by writing (8.23) in terms of a basis $\{\phi_i : 1 \le i \le n\}$ of V_h. Write u_h in terms of this basis, i.e.,

$$u_h = \sum_{j=1}^{n} U_j \phi_j$$

where the coefficients U_j are to be determined. Define

$$A_{ij} = a(\phi_j, \phi_i), \qquad F_i = (f, \phi_i) \quad \text{for} \quad i, j = 1, ..., n. \tag{8.24}$$

Set $\mathbf{U} = (U_j), \mathbf{A} = (A_{ij})$ and $\mathbf{F} = (F_i)$. Then (8.23) is equivalent to solving the (square) matrix equation

$$\mathbf{AU} = \mathbf{F}. \tag{8.25}$$

If we write $v = \sum V_j \phi_j$ then

$$a(u_h, v) = \mathbf{V}^t \mathbf{AU} \tag{8.26}$$

Therefore the symmetry and positivity of the form $a(\cdot, \cdot)$ is equivalent to the symmetry and positive-definiteness of $\mathbf{A}$. The invertibility of the system can be proved simply by checking that there are no nonzero $v \in V_h$ such that $0 = a(v, v)$. In the current case, this would imply that v is constant. Since $v \in V_h \subset V$ implies $v(0) = 0$, we must have $v \equiv 0$. Therefore, the solution u_h to (8.23) exists and is unique.

The matrix $\mathbf{A}$ is often referred to as the **stiffness matrix**, a name coming from corresponding matrices in the context of structural problems. Another important matrix is the **mass matrix**, namely

$$M_{ij} = (\phi_j, \phi_i)_{L^2([0,1])} \quad \text{for} \quad i, j = 1, ..., n. \tag{8.27}$$

If $f \in V$ with $f = \sum \tilde{F}_j \phi_j$ then (8.23) is equivalent to solving the matrix equation

$$\mathbf{AU} = \mathbf{M\tilde{F}}. \tag{8.28}$$

8.3.1 Piecewise polynomials – finite elements

Let $0 = x_0 < x_1 < ... < x_n = 1$ be a partition of $[0, 1]$, and let V_h be the linear space of functions v such that

- v is continuous everywhere
- $v|_{[x_{i-1},x_i]}$ is a linear polynomial, $i = 1, ..., n$, and
- $v(0) = 0$.

The function space just defined can be described as the set of **continuous piecewise linear** functions with respect to the mesh (x_i).

For each $i = 1, .., n$ define ϕ_i by the requirement that $\phi_i(x_j) = \delta_{ij}$ the Kronecker delta. Then $\{\phi_i : 1 \le i \le n\}$ is called a **nodal basis** for V_h, and $\{v(x_i)\}$ are the **nodal values** of a function v. (The points $\{x_i\}$ are called the **nodes**.)

A function space consisting of **continuous piecewise quadratic** functions, with respect to the mesh (x_i), can be defined similarly. Let V_h be the linear space of functions v such that

- v is continuous everywhere
- $v|_{[x_{i-1},x_i]}$ is a quadratic polynomial, $i = 1, ..., n$, and
- $v(0) = 0$.

However, now there are additional nodes in the middle of each *element* $[x_{i-1}, x_i]$, i.e., at $(x_i + x_{i-1})/2$. Now the nodal numbering gets a bit complicated. Let $y_{2i} = x_i$ and let $y_{2i-1} = (x_i - x_{i-1})/2$ for $i = 1, \ldots, n$. Then the nodal basis is defined by $\phi_i(y_j) = \delta_{ij}$ for $i, j = 1, \ldots, 2n$

The Galerkin method using piecewise polynomials spaces described in terms of nodal values is called the finite-element method.

8.3.2 Relationship to difference methods

The stiffness matrix $\mathbf{A}$ as defined in (8.25), using the basis $\{\phi_i\}$ described in Section 8.3.1, can be interpreted as a difference operator. Let $h_i = x_i - x_{i-1}$. Then the matrix entries $A_{ij} = a(\phi_i, \phi_j)$ can be easily calculated to be

$$A_{ii} = h_i^{-1} + h_{i+1}^{-1}, A_{i,i+1} = A_{i+1,i} = -h_{i+1}^{-1} \qquad (i = 1, ..., n-1) \tag{8.29}$$

and $A_{nn} = h_n^{-1}$ with the rest of the entries of $\mathbf{A}$ being zero. Similarly, the entries of $\mathbf{F}$ can be approximated if f is sufficiently smooth:

$$(f, \phi_i) = \frac{1}{2}(h_i + h_{i+1})(f(x_i) + \mathcal{O}(h)) \tag{8.30}$$

where $h = \max h_i$. Thus, the $i - th$ equation of $\mathbf{AU} = \mathbf{F}$ (for $1 \le i \le n-1$) can be written as

$$\frac{-2}{h_i + h_{i+1}} \left[\frac{U_{i+1} - U_i}{h_{i+1}} - \frac{U_i - U_{i-1}}{h_i} \right] = \frac{2(f, \phi_i)}{h_i + h_{i+1}} = f(x_i) + \mathcal{O}(h). \tag{8.31}$$

The difference operator on the left side of this equation can also be seen to be an $\mathcal{O}(h)$ accurate approximation to the differential operator $-d^2/dx^2$. For a uniform mesh, the equations reduce to the familiar difference equations

$$-\frac{U_{i+1}-2U_i+U_{i-1}}{h^2}=f(x_i)+\mathcal{O}(h^2) \tag{8.32}$$

as we will see later in (11.2). Thus the finite difference and finite element discretization techniques can be seen to produce the same set of equations in many cases.

Even thought the difference method (8.31) is formally only first order accurate, one can show using the variational framework [57] that the resulting error is second order accurate:

$$e_h:=\max_{1\le i\le 2n}|u(y_n)-u_n|\le C_f h^2 \tag{8.33}$$

This shows that it may be useful to view a difference method as a variational method (if possible) for the purposes of analysis.

Note the slight difference between (11.5) and the last equation in (8.29). Because the variational form $a(\cdot,\cdot)$ is symmetric, the Galerkin method will always yield a symmetric matrix as is the case in (8.29). The last equation in (8.29) and (11.5) differ only by a simple factor of two, but this leads to a non-symmetric matrix. In applying boundary conditions with finite difference methods, care must be exercised to retain the symmetry of the original differential equation.

The system of equations obtained for the nodal variables (u_n) in the case of the Galerkin method using continuous piecewise quadratics does not look like a conventional finite difference method. The equations associated with the internal nodes are different from the ones associated with the subdivision points. On the other hand, they yield a more accurate method, satisfying

$$e_h:=\max_{1\le i\le 2n}|u(y_n)-u_n|\le C_f h^3. \tag{8.34}$$

8.4 Coercivity of the bilinear form

The variational form $a(\cdot,\cdot)$ introduced in (8.5) is *coercive* on the corresponding spaces V (see [57]): there is a constant γ depending only on Ω and Γ such that

$$\|v\|_{H^1(\Omega)}^2\le\gamma a(v,v)\quad\forall v\in V. \tag{8.35}$$

The proof of this is elementary. All we need to show is that

$$\|v\|_{L^2(\Omega)}^2\le Ca(v,v)\quad\forall v\in V, \tag{8.36}$$

from which (8.35) follows with constant $\gamma=C+1$. To prove (8.36), we apply Sobolev's inequality (8.18). Thus

$$\int_0^1 v(t)^2\,dt\le a(v,v)\int_0^1 t\,dt\le\tfrac{1}{2}a(v,v) \tag{8.37}$$

which completes the proof of (8.36), with $C=1/2$.

As noted previously, our proof of Sobolev's inequality (8.18) uses the fact that for $v\in V$, $v(0)=0$, and (8.35) is false if this boundary condition is not satisfied. (Choose v to be a nonzero constant function and the right-hand-side of (8.35) is zero but the left-hand-side is not.)

From (8.35), it follows that the problem (8.10) is well-posed. In particular, we easily see that the solution to the problem must be unique, for if F is identically zero then so is the solution. In the finite-dimensional case, this uniqueness also implies existence, and a similar result holds in the setting of infinite dimensional Hilbert spaces such as V. Moreover, the coercivity condition immediately implies a stability result, namely

$$\|u\|_{H^1(\Omega)} \leq \frac{\gamma a(u,u)}{\|u\|_{H^1(\Omega)}} = \gamma \frac{F(u)}{\|u\|_{H^1(\Omega)}} \leq \gamma \|F\|_{H^{-1}(\Omega)}. \tag{8.38}$$

Here we are using the notation $\|F\|_{H^{-1}(\Omega)}$ for the dual norm of F in the dual space of $H^1(\Omega)$, i.e., $H^{-1}(\Omega) := \left(H_0^1(\Omega)\right)'$ [57]. The same result holds for a discrete approximation as well.

As a byproduct, (3.6) proves continuity of the solution as a function of the data since the problem is linear. In particular, if F_i, $i = 1, 2$, are two bounded linear forms, and u_i denotes the corresponding solutions to (8.10), then

$$\|u_1 - u_2\|_{H^1(\Omega)} \leq \gamma \|F_1 - F_2\|_{H^{-1}(\Omega)}. \tag{8.39}$$

8.5 More variational formulations

Consider the two-point boundary-value problem

$$\begin{aligned} -\frac{d^2u}{dx^2} + \alpha(x)\frac{du}{dx} + \beta(x)u = f \text{ in } (0,1) \\ u(0) = g_0, \quad u'(1) = g_1. \end{aligned} \tag{8.40}$$

Then integration by parts can again be used to derive the variational formulation

$$a(u,v) = (f,v)_{L^2([0,1])} \quad \forall v \in V \tag{8.41}$$

where

$$a(u,v) := \int_0^1 u'(x)v'(x) + \alpha(x)u'(x)v(x) + \beta(x)u(x)v(x)\,dx. \tag{8.42}$$

This variational problem introduces the need to integrate the expressions involving α and β. Typically this is done by numerical quadrature.

The question of coercivity of the form (8.42) can be addressed in at least simple cases. If $\beta \equiv 0$ and α is constant, then

$$a(v,v) = \int_0^1 v'(x)^2 + \tfrac{1}{2}\alpha(v^2)'(x)\,dx = \int_0^1 v'(x)^2\,dx + \tfrac{1}{2}\alpha v(1)^2 \quad \forall v \in V. \tag{8.43}$$

If $\alpha > 0$, then this is coercive. Regarding conditions needed on β to retain coercivity, see Exercise 8.5.

8.6 Other Galerkin methods

We have seen in Section 7.3 that it is sometimes useful to use a variational method with spaces of functions other than the typical piecewise polynomials related to the finite element method. We discuss briefly here some other choices of spaces. The first is actually based on piecewise polynomials but with a different philosophy on how to use them.

8.6.1 Spectral elements – P method

The definition of continuous piecewise polynomials of arbitrary degree P can be accomplished as described in Section 4.1.3. In the one-dimensional case, there are $P - 1$ nodal points in the interior of each interval in the subdivision, but otherwise the definition is the same. The use of high-order piecewise polynomials in Galerkin approximations goes by various names. Since the degree P can be used as the approximation parameter (that is, convergence is achieved by letting P increase but with the mesh held fixed), it is often called the 'P' method. It also goes by the name "spectral element" method because there are similarities with so-called spectral methods, yet there is the possibility of subdividing the domain using "elements."

8.6.2 Trigonometric polynomials – spectral methods

Choosing spaces of trigonometric polynomials (sines and cosines) in the Galerkin approximation method leads to the class of discretizations which are popularly known as Spectral Methods [73]. Like the Laguerre methods (Section 7.3), the basis functions extend across the entire domain; they are not localized as with finite elements. For the Laguerre methods, the domain is $[0, \infty]^d$. The domain for spectral methods is restricted typically to $[0, 1]^d$ or something that can be mapped to this in a simple way. For sufficiently smooth, periodic functions, spectral methods converge exponentially fast in terms of the number of basis functions. Such convergence is also observed for the Laguerre basis when approximating functions that decay exponentially, as observed in Section 7.2.1. Such exponential convergence is often referred to as **spectral accuracy**.

8.6.3 Finite volume methods

Finite volume methods are derived variationally [126] and can in some cases be related to finite element methods [76, 10].

8.7 Exercises

Exercise 8.1 *Consider the differential equation*

$$-\frac{d^2u}{dx^2} = f \text{ in } (0, 1) \tag{8.44}$$

with Neumann boundary conditions at both boundary points, that is, $u'(0) = 0$ *and* $u'(1) = 0$. *What function satisfies the differential equation with zero Neumann data? Show that solutions are unique only up to an additive constant, and they can exist only if the right-hand side* f *satisfies*

$$\int_0^1 f(x)\, dx = 0. \tag{8.45}$$

Exercise 8.2 *Consider the function* v *defined in (8.15). Show that it is in* V *(see Definition 8.6). Can one make sense of the linear form defined in (8.14) for this function?*

Exercise 8.3 *Give a separate, formal definition of each of the three different types of linear functionals given in the right-hand-side of (8.9). Can you say why the first and the last are bounded? For the middle one, consult (8.18).*

Exercise 8.4 *Derive the variational formulation for the boundary value problem for the differential equation*

$$-u'' - u = f$$

with boundary conditions $u(0) = g_0$ *and* $u'(1) = g_1$.

Exercise 8.5 *Consider the variational formulation in Exercise 8.4 for the boundary value problem for the differential equation*

$$-u'' - u = f$$

with boundary conditions $u(0) = 0$ *and* $u'(1) = 0$. *Prove that this is coercive (hint: use (8.36)).*

Exercise 8.6 *Consider the differential equation*

$$-u'' = f \text{ in } (0,1) \tag{8.46}$$

with Neumann boundary conditions at both boundary points, that is, $u'(0) = 0$ *and* $u'(1) = 0$ *(see Exercise 8.1). Using the concept of coercivity, explain why this is not well-posed without some constraints on* f *and* u.

Exercise 8.7 *Show that the inhomogeneous Dirichlet boundary-value problem (8.9), with* V *as in (8.6) and with* $f \equiv 0$ *and* $g_1 = 0$ *can be written in the form (8.10) with* $u_0 := g_0(1-x)$ *and*

$$F(v) = -g_0 a(1-x, v) = g_0 \int_0^1 v'\, dx = g_0 v(1) \quad \forall v \in V. \tag{8.47}$$

Investigate the choice $u_0 \equiv b_0$ *(a constant function) and show that this leads to* $F \equiv 0$. *Why do these different variational formulations give equivalent results?*

Exercise 8.8 *Consider the variational form* $a(\cdot,\cdot)$ *in (8.5) and define*

$$\tilde{a}(u,v) := a(u,v) + \gamma u(1) v(1). \tag{8.48}$$

Consider the variational problem (8.7) with $g_1 = 0$ *and* V *as defined in (8.6). Show that this corresponds to having a boundary condition at 1 of Robin/Cauchy type:* $u'(1) + \gamma u(1) = 0$.

Exercise 8.9 *Suppose* α *and* β *are smooth functions. Consider the variational form*

$$a(u,v) := \int_0^1 u'v' + \alpha u v' + (\beta - \alpha') u v\, dx \tag{8.49}$$

and the variational problem (8.7) with $g_1 = 0$ *and* V *as defined in (8.6). Determine the corresponding differential equation and boundary conditions that the solution* u *must satisfy if it is known to be smooth.*

Exercise 8.10 *Suppose* α *and* β *are smooth functions. Consider the variational form*

$$a(u,v) := \int_0^1 u'v' + \alpha u' v + \beta u v\, dx \tag{8.50}$$

and the variational problem (8.7) with $g_1 = 0$ *and* V *as defined in (8.6). Determine the corresponding differential equation and boundary conditions that the solution* u *must satisfy if it is known to be smooth.*

Exercise 8.11 *Examine the equations generated by the finite element method using piecewise linear functions for the problem discussed in Section 8.3.2. What are the equations that arise due to the boundary conditions? How does this compare with the finite difference approach?*

Chapter 9

Nonlinear Problems

So far, we have considered only linear systems. But one hallmark of numerical methods for solving PDEs is that many nonlinear PDEs present no serious difficulties. We begin with a categorization of different types of nonlinearities. These are in increasing order of difficulty.

Our first example is a nonlinear ordinary differential equation to simplify the discussion. We then consider a nonlinear modification of the Poisson equation. In both cases, we explore the issues required to solve the nonlinear PDEs, as well as some of their unusual properties that allow us to check the validity of the numerical solutions.

9.1 Hierarchy of nonlinear problems

We can characterize different levels of difficulty for nonlinear problems. The lowest level have no nonlinearity: they are linear. The next level are **semilinear** equations: the nonlinearities do not appear in the leading-order parts of the equation. We use the multi-index notation in Section 31.4.3, and the tensor notation in Section 31.4.4, for derivatives. That is, the equation is of the form

$$\sum_{|\boldsymbol{\alpha}|=k} c_{\boldsymbol{\alpha}}(\mathbf{x}) D^{\boldsymbol{\alpha}} u + c_0(\mathbf{x}, \nabla^{k-1} u, \ldots, \nabla u, u) = 0.$$

We consider one example of this in Section 9.2. Here, k is the highest order of derivative in the partial differential equation. For the Laplacian, $k = 2$. In Section 12.4, we will see equations of order 3, and in Section 19.4 we will see an equation of order 4.

Next, **quasilinear** equations have nonlinear coefficients in the highest-order terms, but they cannot depend on the highest-order derivatives:

$$\sum_{|\boldsymbol{\alpha}|=k} c_{\boldsymbol{\alpha}}(\mathbf{x}, \nabla^{k-1} u, \ldots, \nabla u, u) D^{\boldsymbol{\alpha}} u + c_0(\mathbf{x}, \nabla^{k-1} u, \ldots, \nabla u, u) = 0.$$

An example of this is given in Section 9.3.

Finally, **fully nonlinear** equations can be of the form

$$\sum_{|\boldsymbol{\alpha}|=k} c_{\boldsymbol{\alpha}}(\mathbf{x}, \nabla^{k} u, \ldots, \nabla u, u) D^{\boldsymbol{\alpha}} u + c_0(\mathbf{x}, \nabla^{k-1} u, \ldots, \nabla u, u) = 0.$$

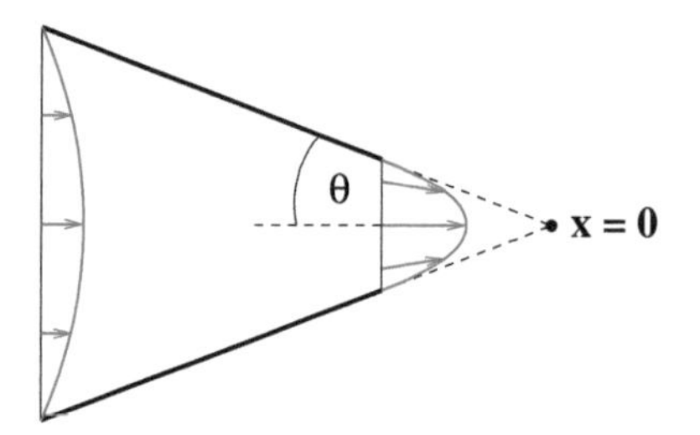

Figure 9.1: Interpretation of solutions of Jeffrey-Hamel equation. Converging flow is indicated by the arrows. For diverging flow, the arrows are reversed in direction.

An example of such an equation is the Monge-Ampère equation [55]. These are beyond our scope in this book.

The nomenclature for nonlinearities has pros and cons. The term "fully nonlinear" is a very accurate description, and they are fully difficult to solve. However, the other two names are confusing. The next term (moving down in terms of difficulty) is quasilinear. However, the meaning of quasi is sometimes described as superficial or nominal. But such nonlinearities are far from superficial. Rather, the correct term might be quasifully nonlinear. Maybe it was at one time and got shortened to just quasilinear. The term semilinear means "half linear" which seems to give it more credit than is due. This would mean that it is also half-fully nonlinear, since fully nonlinear problems give the maximal point on the scale, but they are not so hard. For example, a semilinear problem with leading term given by the Laplacian operator can often be analyzed via a simple perturbation of the Lax-Milgram theory. Using "quasi" for such problems would be more appropriate. The level of difficulty should correspond to the title, so semilinear problems should be semi-tough[1] to solve.

9.2 A semilinear problem

Nonlinear differential equations can be solved often with little more difficulty than linear ones. We illustrate this with the following problem in one dimension:

$$\begin{gathered} -\frac{d^2u}{d\xi^2}(\xi) + 4\,u(\xi) + 6\,u(\xi)^2 = f(\xi) \quad \text{for } \xi \in [0,\theta], \\ u(0) = 0, \quad u'(\theta) = 0. \end{gathered} \tag{9.1}$$

With $f = C$ (C = constant), this describes the profile of the radial component of fluid flow in a converging channel (a.k.a. Jeffrey-Hamel flow), where the angle between the two walls of the channel is 2θ. Symmetry has been used to reduce the size of the problem domain, at the expense of a mixture of Dirichlet and Neumann data. The Neumann condition for $\xi = \theta$ is a consequence of the symmetry. The point $\xi = 0$ corresponds to the lower wall in Figure 9.1. In (9.1), differentiation is with respect to the polar angle ξ.

Given a solution u of (9.1), one can show that

$$\mathbf{u}(x,y) := \nu\,\frac{u(\operatorname{atan}(y/x))}{x^2+y^2}\,\mathbf{x}, \quad \mathbf{x} = (x,y) \in \Omega \tag{9.2}$$

[1]Semi-Tough was a 1977 blockbuster movie starring Burt Reynolds, Kris Kristofferson, and Jill Clayburgh. If it had been called Quasi-Tough, it might have had a smaller audience.

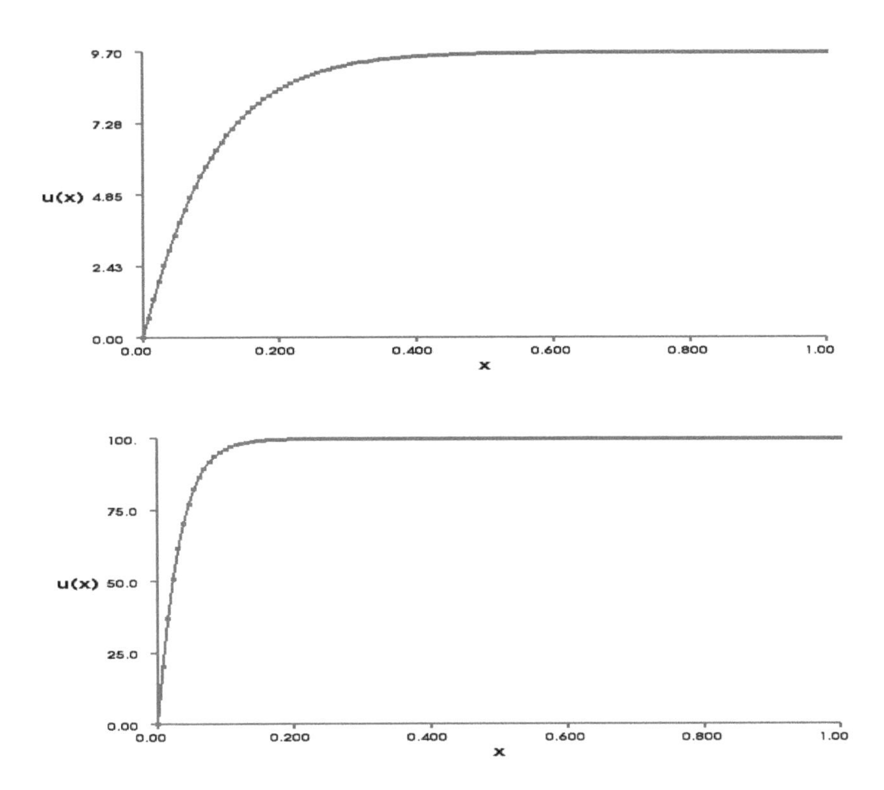

Figure 9.2: Solutions of the Jeffrey-Hamel equation with (top) $C = 600$ and (bottom) $C = 60000$.

solves the steady Navier-Stokes equations (20.1) with kinematic viscosity ν over a wedge domain Ω (cf. [190]). This is indicated schematically in Figure 9.1.

9.2.1 Reality checks

With nonlinear problems, it can be more difficult to derive synthetic solutions as we have done using the method of manufactured solution in Section 2.3. On the other hand, there can be some natural aspects of nonlinear problems that allow some asymptotic estimates that are useful.

In the Jeffrey-Hamel problem (9.1), if the solution u becomes large, then the quadratic term u^2 will be even larger. Dropping the smaller terms in (9.1), we get the equations $6u^2 \approx C$, so that $u \approx \sqrt{C/6}$. We see from Figure 9.2 that indeed when C is large, the solution becomes nearly constant with $u \approx \sqrt{C/6}$ and with a boundary layer near the Dirichlet boundary $\xi = 0$.

On the other hand, when u is very small, u^2 is much smaller than u, so we can consider dropping the quadratic term u^2 in (9.1). Let v be the solution of

$$\begin{aligned} -\frac{d^2v}{d\xi^2} + 4v &= 1 \text{ in } (0,\theta) \\ v(0) = 0, \quad v'(\theta) &= 0. \end{aligned} \tag{9.3}$$

Then for small C we expect that

$$u \approx Cv. \tag{9.4}$$

We see in Figure 11.2 that this is the case.

In this case, we can go one step further since it is possible to solve (9.3) exactly:

$$v(\xi) = 1 - \cos(2\xi) - \tan(2\theta)\sin(2\xi). \tag{9.5}$$

Therefore we can compute $\|u - Cv\|_{L^2(\Omega)}$ to see if it goes to zero as $C \to 0$.

Thus there are useful tests that can be done for nonlinear problems that can determine whether or not the code is producing reasonable answers.

9.2.2 Nonlinear variational problems

We will introduce subsequently a problem whose variational formulation takes the form

$$a(u,v) + n(u,v) = (f,v)_{L^2([0,1])} \quad \forall v \in V \tag{9.6}$$

where

$$a(u,v) = \int_0^\theta u'(x)v'(x) + 4u(x)v(x)\,dx$$

and the nonlinearity has been separated for convenience in the form

$$n(u,v) = 6\int_0^\theta u(x)^2 v(x)\,dx = 6\,(u^2,v)_{L^2([0,1])}. \tag{9.7}$$

Note that this is nonlinear in the trial function u and linear in the test function v.

A Galerkin method for a space with a basis $\{\phi_i : i = 1,\ldots,n\}$ can be written as a system of nonlinear equations

$$F_i(u) := a(u,\phi_i) + n(u,\phi_i) - (f,\phi_i)_{L^2([0,1])} = 0. \tag{9.8}$$

Writing $u = \sum_j U_j\phi_j$, Newton's method for this system of equations for (U_j) can be derived. However, it can also be cast in variational form as follows.

Instead of using a basis function, let us define a function F with coordinates parameterized by an arbitrary $v \in V$:

$$F_v(u) := a(u,v) + n(u,v) - (f,v)_{L^2([0,1])} \tag{9.9}$$

If $v = \phi_i$ then of course we have the previous function. Newton's method requires us to compute the derivative of F with respect to its "coordinates" which in this case correspond to elements of V. The derivative of F_v at u in the direction of $w \in V$ is, as always, a limit of a difference quotient,

$$\frac{F_v(u+\epsilon w) - F_v(u)}{\epsilon}, \tag{9.10}$$

as $\epsilon \to 0$. Expanding, we find that

$$\begin{aligned} F_v(u+\epsilon w) - F_v(u) &= \epsilon a(w,v) + 6\left((u+\epsilon w)^2 - u^2, v\right)_{L^2([0,1])} \\ &= \epsilon a(w,v) + 6\left(2\epsilon uw + \epsilon^2 w^2, v\right)_{L^2([0,1])}. \end{aligned} \tag{9.11}$$

Therefore the Jacobian $J_F(u)$ can be written as

$$J_F(u)_{v,w} = \lim_{\epsilon\to 0} \frac{F_v(u+\epsilon w) - F_v(u)}{\epsilon} = a(w,v) + 12\,(uw,v)_{L^2([0,1])} \tag{9.12}$$

for any $w \in V$. It is then easy to see (see Exercise 9.1) that Newton's method can be characterized by

$$\begin{aligned} u \leftarrow u - w \quad &\text{where } w \text{ solves} \\ a(w,v) + 12\,(uw,v)_{L^2([0,1])} = a(u,v) + n(u,v) - (f,v)_{L^2([0,1])} \quad &(= F_v(u)) \quad \forall v \in V. \end{aligned} \tag{9.13}$$

However, automated systems like `dolfin` are able to deal directly with nonlinear systems such as (9.9). See the `dolfin` code in Program 9.1; the `solve` command in line 27 looks at line 24 to see the definition of the functional `F` and realizes that it is related to a nonlinear problem (that is, the form is not quadratic, it is cubic). Then it decides to apply Newton's method to solve the system. So there is no need to derive the system (9.13) by hand, although the result would be similar.

This automation of nonlinear solvers is a key feature of modern computational systems like `dolfin`. Not only does it make programming easier, it also eliminates potential errors due to hand-derived algorithms. We will return to the general question of nonlinear solvers in Section 9.4 where we will see that nonlinear problems often do present additional challenges that must be addressed in a way adapted to the particular problem.

9.3 A quasi-linear problem

The **p-Laplacian** is a widely studied [196, 203, 276] equation that illustrates many interesting features of nonlinear PDEs. It is defined for $p > 1$ and takes the form

$$-\nabla\cdot\left(|\nabla u|^{p-2}\nabla u\right) = f \text{ in } \Omega, \tag{9.14}$$

with a mix of Dirichlet and Neumann boundary conditions possible on $\partial\Omega$. When $p = 2$, we obtain the standard Poisson equation. For $p < 2$, the coefficient $|\nabla u|^{p-2}$ goes to infinity if $\nabla u \to \mathbf{0}$, and $|\nabla u|^{p-2} \to 0$ if $\nabla u \to \infty$. We saw in Chapter 6 that the latter can happen for nonconvex polygonal domains.

The p-Laplacian is of interest in image processing for $p < 2$ [184]. The p-Laplacian is a model of piles of granular materials (like sand) for large p [17, 122].

9.3.1 p-Laplacian variational form

The p-Laplacian equation (9.14) appears in what is known as **divergence form**. That is, it is of the form $\nabla\cdot(\mathring{A}\nabla u) = f$ for some $\mathring{A}$. Equations in divergence form are often better behaved [68, 69, 168], in part because integration by parts yields a natural variational form. The variational form for the p-Laplacian is

$$a_p(u,v) = \int_\Omega |\nabla u(\mathbf{x})|^{p-2}\nabla u(\mathbf{x})\cdot\nabla v(\mathbf{x})\,d\mathbf{x}. \tag{9.15}$$

Thus we seek u such that

$$a_p(u,v) = F(v) \tag{9.16}$$

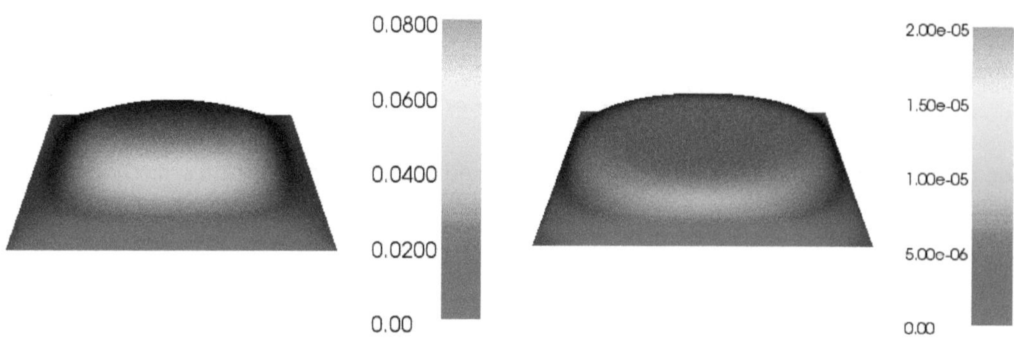

Figure 9.3: Solution of the p-Laplacian on a unit square with $u = 0$ on $\partial\Omega$, computed using piecewise linears on a 128×128 mesh. (left) $p = 2$ and (right) $p = 1.15$. The code to generate this is given in Program 9.2.

for all v in a suitable space V [68, 69, 168], Note that coercivity is problematic:

$$a_p(v, v) = \int_\Omega |\nabla v(\mathbf{x})|^p \, d\mathbf{x}.$$

Thus we need to work with spaces of functions whose gradients are p-th power integrable [69]. Fortunately, this is not a restriction for finite element spaces.

The strong form (9.14) of the p-Laplacian equation is harder to interpret than the variational (or weak) form (9.16). The latter requires more sophisticated spaces [68, 69, 168], for a rigorous interpretation, but from a computational point of view it looks familiar.

Applications of the p-Laplacian are abundant [34], and there are even applications where p is allowed to be a function of $\mathbf{x}$ and vary over the domain Ω [52].

9.3.2 p-Laplacian asymptotics

It is useful to have some idea of what will happen in some limits, as we did in Section 9.2.1. Let us consider a particular problem: $\Omega = [0,1]^2$, $F(v) = \int_\Omega v(\mathbf{x}) \, d\mathbf{x}$ ($f \equiv 1$). In addition, we choose homogeneous Dirichlet boundary conditions ($u = 0$) on $\partial\Omega$. By symmetry, $\nabla u = 0$ at the middle of the square, so if $p < 2$, the expression $|\nabla u|^{p-2}$ is infinite there. To avoid computational difficulties, we redefine

$$a_p(u, v) = \int_\Omega \left(\epsilon^2 + |\nabla u(\mathbf{x})|^2\right)^{(p-2)/2} \nabla u(\mathbf{x}) \cdot \nabla v(\mathbf{x}) \, d\mathbf{x}, \tag{9.17}$$

where ϵ is a small parameter we use to mollify the computations. Note that not only would the coefficient of $\nabla u(\mathbf{x}) \cdot \nabla v(\mathbf{x})$ be infinite if we did not, the fractional power is also not differentiable there, so Newton's method could misbehave. So now the coefficient is just very large, and this will tend to depress u. The reasoning is as follows.

The equation looks a bit like $-\epsilon^{p-2}\Delta u = f$ where ∇u is small, so $-\Delta u = \epsilon^{2-p} f$. Since ϵ^{2-p} is small, we guess that u would tend to be small, proportional to ϵ^{2-p}. Making u smaller tends to flatten u because $u = 0$ on $\partial\Omega$. If we flatten u, then the region where ∇u is small increases. We see that this analysis is born out in Figure 9.3 and Table 9.1.

We leave as Exercises 9.8 and 9.9 to explore what happens as $p \to \infty$.

ϵ	p	L2norm	ϵ	p	L2norm
1.00e-05	2.00	4.13e-02	1.00e-06	1.40	4.07e-03
1.00e-05	1.90	3.46e-02	1.00e-06	1.30	1.17e-03
1.00e-05	1.80	2.78e-02	1.00e-06	1.20	1.02e-04
1.00e-06	1.80	2.78e-02	1.00e-07	1.20	1.02e-04
1.00e-06	1.70	2.10e-02	1.00e-06	1.15	9.41e-06
1.00e-06	1.60	1.45e-02	1.00e-07	1.15	9.36e-06
1.00e-06	1.50	8.70e-03	1.00e-07	1.10	1.03e-07

Table 9.1: $L^2(\Omega)$ norm of solution of the p-Laplacian problem in Section 9.3.2 for various exponents p. The fudge factor ϵ appears in the mollified form (9.17). Computed with piecewise linears on a 128×128 mesh.

9.4 Nonlinear solvers

Newton's method has many benefits. It converges rapidly, and it has a functorial definition that allows it to be applied automatically and very generally. However, it is essentially a local method. It performs well when it is started near a solution. But it may behave badly otherwise (Exercise 9.8). Thus other nonlinear solvers are of interest to provide a more global approach to nonlinear PDEs.

One simple approach is called **continuation**. This method is applied to problems that have a natural parameter. For the p-Laplacian, p is the parameter. To solve for large p, we can start with $p = 2$ (a linear problem) and then increase p, using the solution for lower values of p as starting guesses for larger values of p. Fortunately, in `dolfin`, the solver syntax

```
solve(F == 0, u, bc)
```

is interpreted to mean that if `u` is defined before the `solve` call, then it will be used as the initial guess. Thus we can embed `solve` in a loop to generate a sequence of solutions. For the p-Laplacian problem (Exercise 9.9), these solutions actually converge as p increases, so the Newton method gets faster and faster. Other problems tend to get harder as the parameter is increased, but continuation is still a very useful algorithm.

9.5 Numerical nonuniqueness

Nonlinear equations can have multiple solutions. One sees this early in life in the one-variable, quadratic equation $ax^2 + bx + c = 0$, whose roots satisfy

$$x = \frac{-b \pm \sqrt{b^2 - 4ac}}{2a}.$$

PDEs are no different. We will see this explicitly in Section 21.3 for the Navier-Stokes equations. Here we focus on a slightly different issue where two solutions are so close at one point as to be difficult to distinguish numerically.

Consider the two-point boundary value problem

$$\begin{gathered} -\epsilon \frac{d^2u}{dx^2}(x) + u(x)\frac{du}{dx}(x) = 0 \quad \text{on } [-1,1], \\ \frac{du}{dx}(-1) = \beta_-, \quad \frac{du}{dx}(1) = \beta_+, \end{gathered} \tag{9.18}$$

where $\beta_\pm \in \mathbb{R}$ and $\epsilon > 0$ are fixed parameters. Since these are pure Neumann boundary conditions, we add the constraint that

$$\int_{-1}^{1} u(x)\,dx = 0.$$

We now describe two solutions and explain why this boundary value problem is well posed.

9.5.1 Two solutions

The variety of solutions can be understood by integrating the first equation in (9.18) to get

$$-\epsilon u' + \tfrac{1}{2}u^2 = c \tag{9.19}$$

(see Exercise 9.10). This equation has solutions parameterized by c (see Exercise 9.11). For $c \geq 0$, there are constant solutions $w_\pm = \pm\sqrt{2c}$ and nonconstant solutions involving the hyperbolic tangent function. Thus the boundary conditions determine c and pick out the appropriate solutions.

Now we describe two solutions of (9.18). First of all, the constant function $w(x) \equiv 0$ solves (9.18) with $\beta_\pm = 0$. Now we display a non-constant solution. Consider the function

$$v(x) = \gamma \tanh(-\gamma x/2\epsilon). \tag{9.20}$$

We have (see Exercise 9.12)

$$\frac{dv}{dx}(x) = -\frac{\gamma^2}{2\epsilon}\big(1 - \tanh^2(-\gamma x/\epsilon)\big) = -\frac{\gamma^2}{2\epsilon} + \frac{1}{2\epsilon}v(x)^2. \tag{9.21}$$

Thus

$$-\epsilon\frac{dv}{dx}(x) + \frac{1}{2}v(x)^2 = \frac{\gamma^2}{2} \tag{9.22}$$

for all x. In view of (9.19), v solves the first equation in (9.18). Now examine the Neumann boundary conditions at $x = \pm 1$. Let $M = \gamma/2\epsilon$. Using (9.21), v satisfies the Neumann condition with

$$\beta_\pm = \frac{dv}{dx}(\pm 1) = -\gamma M\big(1 - \tanh^2(\mp M)\big) = -\gamma M\big(1 - (\tanh M)\big)\big(1 + (\tanh M)\big),$$

since $\tanh(-M) = -\tanh(M)$. But (see Exercise 9.12)

$$0 \leq 1 - \tanh M = 1 - \frac{e^M - e^{-M}}{e^M + e^{-M}} = \frac{2e^{-M}}{e^M + e^{-M}} = \frac{2e^{-2M}}{1 + e^{-2M}} \leq 2e^{-2M}.$$

Therefore

$$|\beta_\pm| = \left|\frac{dv}{dx}(\pm 1)\right| \leq 4\gamma M e^{-2M}.$$

Thus $v'(\pm 1)$ is numerically indistinguishable from 0 for M large (ϵ small). For $\gamma = 1$ and $\epsilon = 0.01$, we have $M = 50$ and

$$|\beta_\pm| \leq 4\gamma M e^{-2M} = 200\, e^{-100} < 10^{-41}.$$

Thus the Neumann conditions at ± 1 are numerically the same for v and w.

What we see here is dramatically different from the linear case. For the nonlinear problem (9.18), the ratio

$$\frac{\max\{|v(x)\ :\ x \in [-1,1]\}}{\max\{|\beta_-|,|\beta_+|\}} \geq \frac{\gamma}{4\gamma M e^{-2M}} = \frac{e^{2M}}{4M}$$

is astronomical in size for large $M = \gamma/2\epsilon$, whereas for a linear problem such a ratio would be independent of the size of the data.

9.5.2 Variational form and coercivity

The techniques in Section 5.3 can be used to indicate why the boundary value problem (9.18) is well posed. Multiply the first equation in (9.18) by v, integrate over $\Omega = [-1,1]$, and integrate by parts to get

$$\int_{-1}^{1} u''v\,dx + \int_{-1}^{1} u'v'\,dx = \int_{-1}^{1} (u'v)'\,dx = (u'v)(1) - (u'v)(-1).$$

Thus the natural variational form for the problem (9.18) is

$$n(u,v) = \epsilon \int_{-1}^{1} u'v'\,dx + \int_{-1}^{1} uu'v\,dx + \epsilon\beta_+ v(1) - \epsilon\beta_- v(-1).$$

Define $V = \left\{v \in H^1(\Omega)\ :\ \int_{-1}^{1} v(x)\,dx = 0\right\}$. The variational formulation for (9.18) is then:

find $u \in V$ such that $n(u,v) = \epsilon\beta v(1) - \epsilon\beta_- v(-1)$ for all $v \in V$.

Note that

$$3\int_{-1}^{1} v^2 v'\,dx = \int_{-1}^{1} (v^3)'\,dx = v^3(1) - v^3(-1).$$

Thus

$$n(v,v) = \epsilon \int_{-1}^{1} (v')^2\,dx + \frac{1}{3}v(1)^3 - \frac{1}{3}v(-1)^3.$$

From Poincaré's inequality, $v(\pm 1)^2 \leq Ca(v,v)$ for all $v \in V$. Thus

$$|v(\pm 1)|^3 \leq \epsilon a(v,v)$$

provided that $|v(\pm 1)| \leq \epsilon/C$. Therefore

$$\epsilon a(v,v) \leq n(v,v) + \frac{2}{3}|v(\pm 1)|^3 \leq n(v,v) + \frac{2}{3}\epsilon a(v,v),$$

so that

$$\tfrac{1}{3}\epsilon a(v,v) \leq n(v,v)$$

provided that $|v(\pm 1)| \leq \epsilon/C$. Thus we conclude that the coercivity estimate $n(v,v) \geq c\|v\|^2_{L^2(\Omega)}$ holds at least for v sufficiently small, that is when $|v(1)| \leq \epsilon/C$.

9.6 Exercises

Exercise 9.1 *Show that Newton's method for the system (9.8) (or equivalently (9.9)) can be characterized by the variational formulation (9.13).*

Exercise 9.2 *Another method for solving nonlinear equations $f(u) = 0$ is the fixed-point iteration*

$$u \leftarrow u \pm \epsilon f(u) \tag{9.23}$$

for some parameter ϵ. Give an implementation of the Jeffrey-Hamel problem and compare it with Newton's method.

Exercise 9.3 *Verify that (9.5) provides a solution of (9.3).*

Exercise 9.4 *Prove that (9.3) is well posed in H^1, and in particular, that it has a unique solution, so that (9.5) is the unique solution of (9.3). (Hint: use the variational formulation.)*

Exercise 9.5 *Modify the code Program 9.1 to compute $\|u_h - Cv\|_{L^2(\Omega)}$, where v is given by (9.5). Compute this for $C = 10^{-k}$ for $k = 1, 2, \ldots, 6$ and explain whether you think this is going to zero as C decreases. Pick a mesh size and polynomial degree so that you get consistent results, independent of mesh size and polynomial degree.*

Exercise 9.6 *Implement the code Program 9.1 and see how the number of Newton iterations increases as C increases. In particular, compute the solution for $C = 10^k$ for $k = 1, 2, \ldots, 6$. How would you describe the number of Newton iterations as a function of C?*

Exercise 9.7 *Implement the code Program 9.2 and see how the answers change for higher-degree elements. Make a table like Table 9.1 for quadratics, cubics and quartics. Choose ϵ so that the results are stable (independent of ϵ).*

Exercise 9.8 *Implement the code Program 9.2 and explore what happens for larger values of p. How far can you go? What do you need to pick for ϵ?*

Exercise 9.9 *Modify the code Program 9.2 to implement the continuation method in Section 9.4 for the p-Laplacian problem on the unit square introduced in Section 9.3.2. How large can you let p be? How is the solution affected by ϵ? (Hint: iterate over integer values of p starting with $p = 2$.)*

Exercise 9.10 *Show that any solution of (9.18) must satisfy*

$$-\epsilon u' + \tfrac{1}{2}u^2 = c$$

for some constant c.

Exercise 9.11 *Show that*

$$-\epsilon u' + \tfrac{1}{2}u^2 = c$$

has exactly two families of solutions: (1) the constant solution $u \equiv \sqrt{2c}$ for $c > 0$ and (2) $u(x) = a\tanh(bx)$ for $c < 0$. Specify what a and b are. (Hint: use the fact that $v(x) = \tanh(x)$ satisfies $v'(x) = 1 - (\tanh x)^2$ for all x.)

Exercise 9.12 *Recall that the hyperbolic tangent function is defined by*

$$\tanh x = \frac{e^x - e^{-x}}{e^x + e^{-x}}.$$

Show that

$$\tanh'(x) = 1 - (\tanh x)^2.$$

Exercise 9.13 *Consider the two-point boundary value problem*

$$\begin{aligned} -\epsilon \frac{d^2u}{dx^2}(x) + u(x)\frac{du}{dx}(x) = 0 \quad \text{on } [-1,1], \\ u(-1) = \gamma \tanh(\gamma/2\epsilon), \quad \frac{du}{dx}(1) = \epsilon\beta, \end{aligned} \tag{9.24}$$

where $\beta \in \mathbb{R}$, $\gamma > 0$ and $\epsilon > 0$ are fixed parameters. Show that there are two solutions for exponentially close values of β. Discuss the coercivity properties of the variational formulation.

```
1  from dolfin import *
2  import sys,math
3
4  meshsize=int(sys.argv[1])
5  pdeg=int(sys.argv[2])
6  see=float(sys.argv[3])
7
8  # Create mesh and define function space
9  mesh = UnitIntervalMesh(meshsize)
10 V = FunctionSpace(mesh, "Lagrange", pdeg)
11
12 # Define Dirichlet boundary (x = 0 or x = 1)
13 def boundary(x):
14     return x[0] < DOLFIN_EPS
15
16 # Define boundary condition
17 u0 = Expression("0.0",degree=pdeg)
18 bc = DirichletBC(V, u0, boundary)
19
20 # Define variational problem
21 u = Function(V)
22 v = TestFunction(V)
23 f = Expression("C",C=see,degree=pdeg)
24 F = inner(grad(u), grad(v))*dx + 4.0*u*v*dx + 6.0*u*u*v*dx - f*v*dx
25
26 # Compute solution
27 solve(F == 0, u, bc)
28
29 # Save solution in VTK format
30 file = File("poisson.pvd")
31 file << u
32
33 # Plot solution
34 plot(u, interactive=True)
35
```

Program 9.1: Code to implement the boundary value problem (9.1).

```
from dolfin import *
import sys,math

meshsize=int(sys.argv[1])
pdeg=int(sys.argv[2])
pee=float(sys.argv[3])
ep=float(sys.argv[4])
eps=ep*ep
pmt=(pee-2.0)/2.0

# Create mesh and define function space
mesh = UnitSquareMesh(meshsize, meshsize)
V = FunctionSpace(mesh, "Lagrange", pdeg)

# Define boundary condition
u0 = Expression("0.0",degree=pdeg)

bc = DirichletBC(V, u0, "on_boundary")
# Define variational problem
#u = TrialFunction(V)
u = Function(V)
v = TestFunction(V)
f = Expression("1.0",degree=pdeg)
F = pow(eps+(inner(grad(u), grad(u))),pmt)*(inner(grad(u), grad(v)))*dx \
    - f*v*dx

# Compute solution
solve(F == 0, u, bc)

maxu=norm(u,norm_type='l2')
print "mesh","pdeg","    pmt","    eps","       p=","    L2norm u="
print meshsize," ",pdeg," "," %.2e"%pmt," %.2e"%ep," %.2f"%pee," %.2e"%maxu

# Plot solution
plot(u.leaf_node(), interactive=True)
```

Program 9.2: Code to implement the p-Laplacian. Solution are depicted in Figure 9.3.

Chapter 10

Heat Equation

Heat can be exchanged between two different bodies by diffusion, convection or radiation. The **heat equation** describes the diffusion of thermal energy in a medium [135]. The simplest form of the heat equation takes the form

$$\begin{aligned} \frac{\partial u}{\partial \tau}(\xi,\tau) - c\Delta u(\xi,\tau) = f(\xi,\tau) \quad \forall \xi \in \widetilde{\Omega},\ \tau > 0 \\ u(\xi,0) = u_0(\xi) \quad \forall \xi \in \widetilde{\Omega}, \end{aligned} \tag{10.1}$$

together with boundary conditions imposed on $\partial\widetilde{\Omega}$ that will be discussed subsequently. Thus we are mixing partial derivatives in a new way, with a distinguished variable τ that we think of as "time" [164] together with the spatial variable ξ. The natural domain for the problem is a cylinder domain $\Omega \times [0,T]$ as indicated in Figure 10.1. Further, we have a coefficient c, the diffusion coefficient, that takes care of the mismatch in units; clearly, c has units of length-squared divided by time.

The heat equation is more generally referred to as the **diffusion equation**, and it governs the diffusion of many materials. Some examples of diffusion coefficients are given in Table 10.1. We see that these coefficients can differ by orders of magnitude.

It is frequently useful to remove the units in a PDE, that is, to **nondimensionalize** the

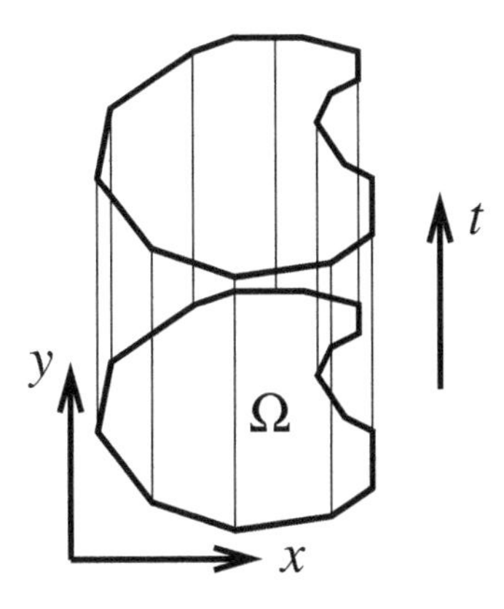

Figure 10.1: Cylinder domain $\Omega \times [0,T]$.

material	diffusion coefficient	medium	conditions
H_2	1.6 cm^2/sec	self	T = 273 K and p = 0.1 MPa
CO_2	.106 cm^2/sec	self	T = 273 K and p = 0.1 MPa
CO_2	1.92×10^{-5} cm^2/sec	water	T=298 K
sucrose	0.52×10^{-5} cm^2/sec	water	T=25 C
hydrogen	1.66×10^{-9} cm^2/sec	iron	T=10 C
hydrogen	1.24×10^{-7} cm^2/sec	iron	T=100 C
aluminum	1.3×10^{-30} cm^2/sec	copper	T=20 C

Table 10.1: Diffusion coefficients for various materials in various media. When the medium is "self" the coefficient is the self-diffusion constant.

equation. For the heat/diffusion equation, this allows us to develop some useful intuition that is independent of the domain of application. We can do this by changing the spatial and time variables:

$$x = a\xi, \quad t = b\tau, \quad a \neq 0, \quad b \neq 0.$$

With this change of variables, the first equation in (10.1) becomes

$$b\frac{\partial u}{\partial t}(x,t) - ca^2\Delta_x u(x,t) = f(x,t) \quad \forall x \in \Omega,\ t > 0, \tag{10.2}$$

where $\Omega = \{x \,:\, a^{-1}x \in \widetilde{\Omega}\}$ and we added the subscript x to Δ to clarify that it is

$$\Delta_x = \partial^2/\partial x_1^2 + \cdots + \partial^2/\partial x_d^2$$

as opposed to the meaning in the first equation in (10.1). Defining $\hat{f}(x,t) = b^{-1}f(x/a, t/b)$, we find

$$\frac{\partial u}{\partial t}(x,t) - \frac{ca^2}{b}\Delta_x u(x,t) = \hat{f}(x,t) \quad \forall x \in \widetilde{\Omega},\ t > 0. \tag{10.3}$$

We then have wide latitude to choose the time and/or space coordinates so that

$$\frac{ca^2}{b} = 1.$$

In such coordinates, the diffusion equation simplifies to

$$\frac{\partial u}{\partial t}(x,t) - \Delta_x u(x,t) = \hat{f}(x,t) \quad \forall x \in \Omega,\ t > 0. \tag{10.4}$$

We now explore this in detail in one space dimension.

10.1 One space dimension

In its simplest, one-dimensional form, the heat/diffusion equation may be written

$$\begin{aligned} \frac{\partial u}{\partial t}(x,t) - \frac{\partial^2 u}{\partial x^2}(x,t) &= f(x,t) \quad \forall x \in [0,1],\ t > 0 \\ u(x,0) &= u_0(x) \quad \forall x \in [0,1], \end{aligned} \tag{10.5}$$

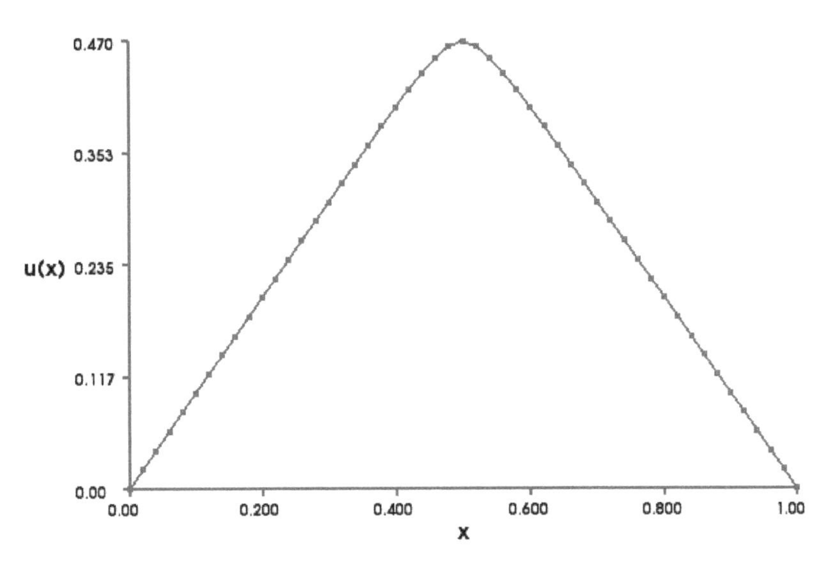

Figure 10.2: Solution of (10.5) with initial data (10.9) at time $t = 0.001$. Computed with piecewise linears with 50 mesh points (uniform mesh).

where $u(x,t)$ denotes the temperature of the medium at any given point x and time t.

A simple example of heat diffusion in one spatial dimension is the transfer of heat across a window. The variable x denotes the distance from one face of the window pane to the other, in the direction perpendicular to the plane of the window. Near the outer edges of the window, three dimensional effects would be evident, but in the middle of the window, equation (10.5) would accurately describe the evolution of the temperature u inside the window.

The function f is included for completeness, but in many cases such a body source of heat would be zero. These equations must be supplemented by boundary conditions similar to the ones considered in Chapter 8. They could be of purely Dirichlet (or essential) type, viz.

$$u(0,t) = g_0(t), \quad u(1,t) = g_1(t) \quad \forall t > 0, \tag{10.6}$$

or of purely Neumann (or natural) type, viz.

$$\frac{\partial u}{\partial x}(0,t) = g_0(t), \quad \frac{\partial u}{\partial x}(1,t) = g_1(t) \quad \forall t > 0, \tag{10.7}$$

or a combination of the two:

$$u(0,t) = g_0(t), \quad \frac{\partial u}{\partial x}(1,t) = g_1(t) \quad \forall t > 0. \tag{10.8}$$

Here g_i, $i = 0, 1$, are given functions of t. It is interesting to note that the pure Neumann condition (10.7) for the heat equation (10.5) does not suffer the same limitations on the data, or nonuniqueness of solutions, that the steady state counterpart does. However, there are compatibility conditions required to obtain smooth solutions.

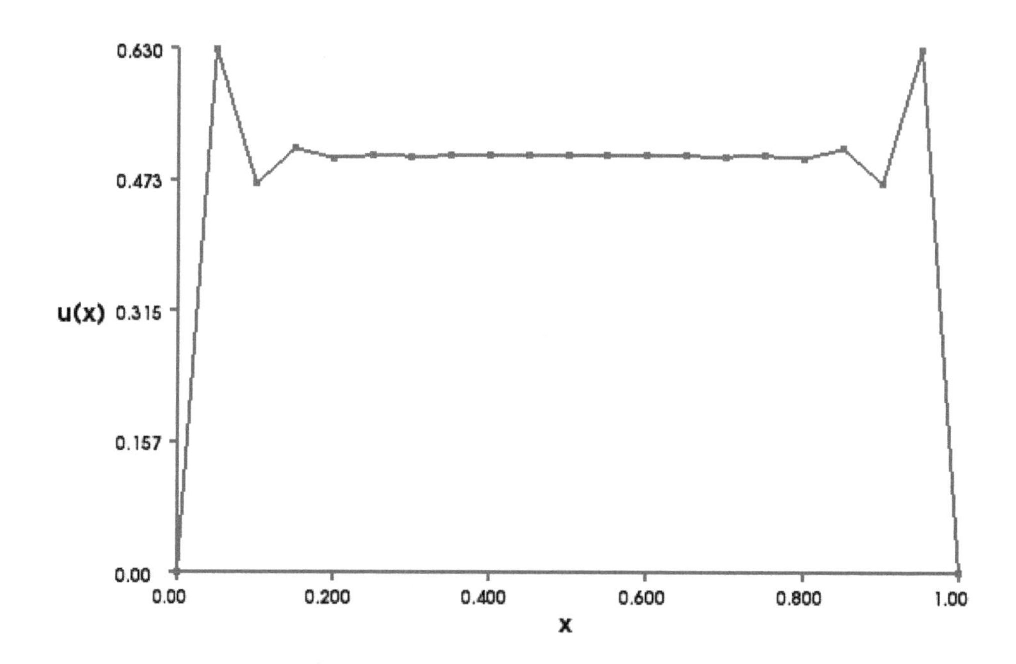

Figure 10.3: Heat equation with incompatible data after one time step with $\Delta t = 10^{-5}$; degree $= 1$, 20 mesh intervals. Initial values $u_0 = 0.5$.

10.2 Basic behavior: smoothing

The main characteristic of the heat equation is that it smoothes any roughness in the initial data. For example, in Figure 10.2 we show the solution at time $t = 0.001$ for the case

$$u_0(x) = \tfrac{1}{2} - |x - \tfrac{1}{2}|. \tag{10.9}$$

We see that the discontinuity of the derivative of u_0 at $x = \frac{1}{2}$ is instantly smoothed. This has a corollary for the backwards heat equation (Section 10.6) that we will explore subsequently. One type of nonsmooth behavior stems from a mismatch between boundary data and initial data. This is governed by compatibility conditions.

The code to generate Figure 10.2 is given in Program 10.1.

10.3 Compatibility conditions

There is a **compatibility condition** for the boundary and initial data for the heat equation in order to have a smooth solution. This can be derived easily from the observation that the values of u on the spatial boundary have been specified twice at $t = 0$. Consider the case (10.8) of combined Dirichlet and Neumann boundary conditions. The first set of compatibility conditions is

$$u_0(0) = u(0,0) = g_0(0) \quad \text{and} \quad u_0'(1) = u_x(1,0) = g_1(0). \tag{10.10}$$

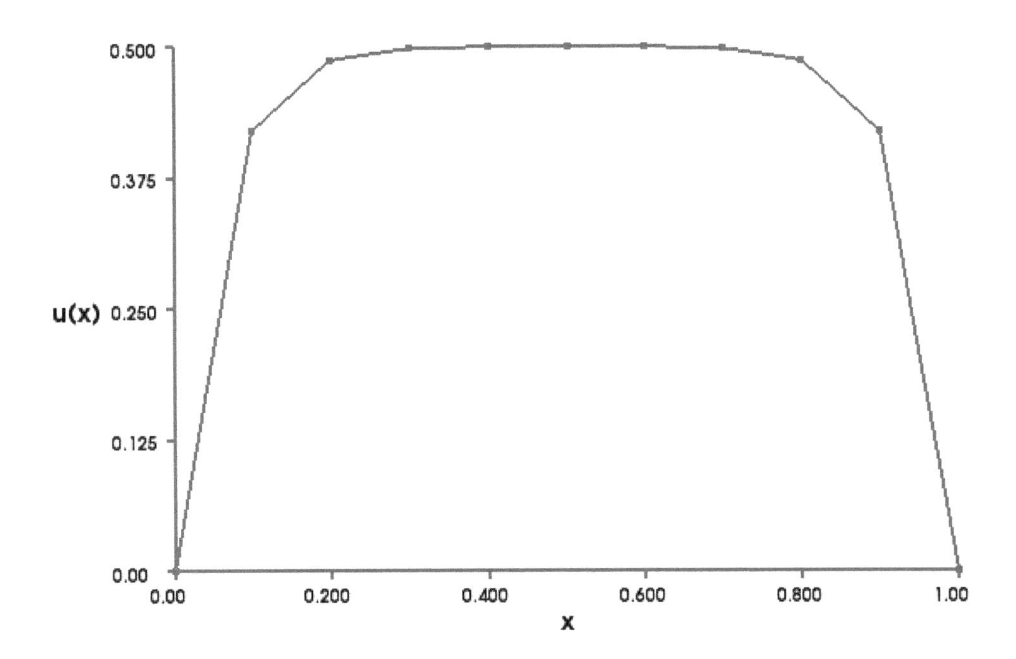

Figure 10.4: Heat equation with incompatible data after one time step with $\Delta t = 10^{-5}$; degree = 2, 10 mesh intervals. Initial values $u_0 = 0.5$.

These are obtained by matching the two ways of specifying the solution at the boundary points $(x,t) = (0,0)$ and $(x,t) = (1,0)$. In the case of pure Dirichlet conditions (10.6) the compatibility conditions become

$$u_0(0) = u(0,0) = g_0(0) \quad \text{and} \quad u_0(1) = u(1,0) = g_1(0). \tag{10.11}$$

In the case of pure Neumann conditions (10.7) the compatibility conditions become

$$u_0'(0) = u_x(0,0) = g_0(0) \quad \text{and} \quad u_0'(1) = u_x(1,0) = g_1(0). \tag{10.12}$$

The conditions involving derivatives (coming from the Neumann boundary conditions) are higher-order compatibility conditions than those for the function values (coming from the Dirichlet boundary conditions). They affect the boundedness of higher-order derivatives.

There are more conditions than this for real smoothness, since u satisfies a differential equation. In fact, for an arbitrary order of smoothness, there are infinitely many such compatibility conditions, the first of these being one of the above, (10.10), (10.11) or (10.12), as appropriate depending on the boundary conditions in force. Again, consider the case (10.8) of combined Dirichlet and Neumann boundary conditions to start with. The second set of conditions arises by using the differential equation $u_{xx} = u_t$ to trade spatial derivatives for temporal ones, then applying this at $t = 0$ and $x = 0$:

$$u_0''(0) = u_{xx}(0,0) = u_t(0,0) = g_0'(0) \quad \text{and} \quad u_0'''(1) = u_{xxx}(1,0) = u_{xt}(1,0) = g_1'(0). \tag{10.13}$$

We leave as exercises (Exercise 10.2 and Exercise 10.3) to give the corresponding second set of compatibility conditions for the pure Dirichlet and Neumann boundary conditions.

If these compatibilities are not satisfied by the data (or by the approximation scheme), wild oscillations (at least in some derivative, if not the solution itself) will result near $t = 0$ and $x = 0, 1$, as shown in Figure 10.3. Using higher resolution can eliminate the oscillations in some cases, as shown in Figure 10.4. In nonlinear problems, this can cause completely wrong results to occur.

The compatibility conditions, e.g. (10.10) and (10.13), do not have to be satisfied for the heat equation (10.5) for it to be well-posed in the usual sense. There is a unique solution in any case, but the physical model may be incorrect as a result if it is supposed to have a smooth solution. Compatibility conditions are a subtle form of constraint on model quality. In many problems they can be described in terms of local differential-algebraic constraints as in (10.10) and (10.13). However, in Section 20.5.2 we will see that such compatibility conditions can lead to global constraints that may be hard to verify or satisfy in practice.

10.4 Variational form of the heat equation

It is possible to derive a variational formulation involving integration over both x and t, but it is more common to use a variational formulation based on x alone. Recalling the notation of Chapter 8, we seek a function $\tilde{u}(t)$ of time with values in V such that $\tilde{u}(0) = u_0$

$$(\tilde{u}'(t), v)_{L^2(\Omega)} + a(\tilde{u}(t), v) = F(v) \quad \forall v \in V,\ t \geq 0, \tag{10.14}$$

where $\Omega = [0, 1]$ and $a(w, v) = \int_0^1 w'(x)v'(x)\,dx$. Since it is a bit awkward to work with a function of one variable (t) which is a function of another (x), we often write (10.14) in terms of $u(x, t) = \tilde{u}(t)(x)$. Using subscript notation for partial derivatives, it becomes

$$(u_t(\cdot, t), v)_{L^2(\Omega)} + a(u(\cdot, t), v) = F(v) \quad \forall v \in V. \tag{10.15}$$

for all t. If we remember the dependence on t, we can write this as

$$(u_t, v)_{L^2(\Omega)} + a(u, v) = F(v) \quad \forall v \in V. \tag{10.16}$$

A stability estimate follows immediately from the variational formulation. For simplicity, suppose that the right-hand-side form $F \equiv 0$ and that the boundary data vanishes as well (i.e., only the initial data is non-zero). Using $v = u$ (at any fixed t, i.e., $v = u(\cdot, t)$) in (10.16), we find

$$\frac{1}{2}\frac{\partial}{\partial t}\|u\|^2_{L^2(\Omega)} = (u_t, u)_{L^2(\Omega)} = -a(u, u) \leq 0 \quad \forall t \geq 0, \tag{10.17}$$

where Ω denotes the spatial interval $[0, 1]$. From this, it follows by integrating in time that

$$\|u(\cdot, t)\|_{L^2(\Omega)} \leq \|u(\cdot, 0)\|_{L^2(\Omega)} = \|u_0\|_{L^2(\Omega)} \quad \forall t \geq 0. \tag{10.18}$$

This result is independent of any compatibility conditions. However, all it says is that the mean-square of the temperature u remains bounded by its initial value. If F is nonzero but bounded on V, i.e.,

$$|F(v)| \leq \|F\|_{H^{-1}(\Omega)}\|v\|_{H^1(\Omega)} \quad \forall v \in V, \tag{10.19}$$

then we retain a bound on $\|u(\cdot,t)\|_{L^2(\Omega)}$:

$$\frac{1}{2}\frac{\partial}{\partial t}\|u\|_{L^2(\Omega)}^2 = (u_t,u)_{L^2(\Omega)} = F(u) - a(u,u) \le \|F\|_{H^{-1}(\Omega)}\|v\|_{H^1(\Omega)} - a(u,u). \tag{10.20}$$

The form $a(\cdot,\cdot)$ always satisfies at least a weak type of coercivity of the form

$$\|v\|_{H^1(\Omega)}^2 \le \gamma_1 a(v,v) + \gamma_2\|v\|_{L^2(\Omega)}^2 \quad \forall v \in V, \tag{10.21}$$

known as **Gårding's inequality**. For example, this holds for the pure Neumann problem (10.7) with $V = H^1(\Omega)$ whereas the stronger form of coercivity (8.35) does not in this case. Applying (10.21) in (10.20) gives

$$\frac{\partial}{\partial t}\|u\|_{L^2(\Omega)}^2 \le 2\|F\|_{H^{-1}(\Omega)}\|u\|_{H^1(\Omega)} - \frac{2}{\gamma_1}\|u\|_{H^1(\Omega)}^2 + \frac{2\gamma_2}{\gamma_1}\|u\|_{L^2(\Omega)}^2. \tag{10.22}$$

Using the arithmetic-geometric mean inequality in the form

$$2rs \le \delta r^2 + \frac{1}{\delta}s^2 \tag{10.23}$$

which holds for any $\delta > 0$ and any real numbers r and s, we find

$$\frac{\partial}{\partial t}\|u\|_{L^2(\Omega)}^2 \le \frac{\gamma_1}{2}\|F\|_{H^{-1}(\Omega)}^2 + \frac{2\gamma_2}{\gamma_1}\|u\|_{L^2(\Omega)}^2. \tag{10.24}$$

Define $\phi(t) = \frac{2\gamma_2}{\gamma_1}\|u(t)\|_{L^2(\Omega)}^2 + \frac{\gamma_1}{2}\|F\|_{H^{-1}(\Omega)}^2$. Then (10.24) can be restated as

$$\frac{\gamma_1}{2\gamma_2}\frac{\partial}{\partial t}\phi \le \phi. \tag{10.25}$$

Gronwall's Lemma [275] implies $\phi(t) \le e^{\frac{2\gamma_2}{\gamma_1}t}\phi(0)$ (see Exercise 10.11). Thus

$$\frac{2\gamma_2}{\gamma_1}\|u(t)\|_{L^2(\Omega)}^2 + \frac{\gamma_1}{2}\|F\|_{H^{-1}(\Omega)}^2 \le e^{\frac{2\gamma_2}{\gamma_1}t}\Big(\frac{2\gamma_2}{\gamma_1}\|u(0)\|_{L^2(\Omega)}^2 + \frac{\gamma_1}{2}\|F\|_{H^{-1}(\Omega)}^2\Big) \quad \forall t \ge 0. \tag{10.26}$$

Therefore

$$\|u(t)\|_{L^2(\Omega)}^2 \le e^{\frac{2\gamma_2}{\gamma_1}t}\|u(0)\|_{L^2(\Omega)}^2 + \Big(e^{\frac{2\gamma_2}{\gamma_1}t} - 1\Big)\frac{\gamma_1^2}{4\gamma_2}\|F\|_{H^{-1}(\Omega)}^2 \quad \forall t \ge 0. \tag{10.27}$$

Another stability result can be derived by using $v = u_t$ (assuming $F \equiv 0$ and the boundary data are zero) in (10.16), to find

$$\|u_t\|_{L^2(\Omega)}^2 = -a(u,u_t) = -\tfrac{1}{2}\frac{\partial}{\partial t}a(u,u). \tag{10.28}$$

This assumes that the test function u_t is in V. If that holds, it must be that $u_0 \in V$, since $u(t) - u(0) = \int_0^t u_t\,dt$. From (10.28), it follows that

$$\frac{\partial}{\partial t}a(u,u) = -2\|u_t\|_{L^2(\Omega)}^2 \le 0 \quad \forall t \ge 0. \tag{10.29}$$

Again integrating in time and using (10.18), we see that

$$\|u(\cdot,t)\|_{H^1(\Omega)} \le \|u(\cdot,0)\|_{H^1(\Omega)} = \|u_0\|_{H^1(\Omega)} \quad \forall t \ge 0. \tag{10.30}$$

This result is again independent of any compatibility conditions (other than $u_0 \in V$), and it says is that the mean-square of the gradient of the temperature u also remains bounded by its initial value. Of course, this presupposes that $u_0 \in V$, and this may not hold. Moreover, if the data F is not zero, this result will not hold. In particular, if the compatibility condition (10.10) does not hold, then $u_0 \notin V$ and $\|u(\cdot,t)\|_{H^1(\Omega)}$ will not remain bounded as $t \to 0$.

10.5 Time discretization

The simplest discretization for the heat equation uses a spatial discretization method for ordinary differential equation in Section 11.1, for that part of the problem and a finite difference method for the temporal part. This technique of decomposing the problem into two parts is an effective technique to generate a numerical scheme, and it allows us to **reuse existing software** already developed for the o.d.e. problem. Many time dependent problems can be treated in the same manner. This technique goes by many names:

- (time) **splitting** since the time and space parts are separated and treated by independent methods

- the **method of lines** since the problem is solved on a sequence of lines (copies of the spatial domain), one for each time step.

10.5.1 Explicit Euler time discretization

The simplest time discretization method for the heat equation uses the forward (or explicit) Euler difference method. It takes the form

$$\begin{aligned} u^{n+1}(x) = u^n(x) + \Delta t \frac{\partial^2 u^n}{\partial x^2}(x,t) \quad \forall x \in [0,1], \\ u^0(x) = u_0(x) \quad \forall x \in [0,1] \\ u^n(0) = g_0(t) \quad \text{and} \quad u^n(1) = g_1(t) \quad \forall n > 0 \end{aligned} \tag{10.31}$$

where $u^n(x)$ denotes an approximation to $u(x, n\Delta t)$. Applying the finite difference or finite element approximation (11.2) to (10.31) yields a simple algorithm. The difficulty with this simple algorithm is that it is *unstable* unless `dt` is sufficiently small. This will be explained in more detail in Section 11.5.

10.5.2 Implicit Euler time discretization

The simplest implicit time discretization method for the heat equation uses the backward (or implicit) Euler difference method. It takes the form

$$\begin{aligned} u^{n+1}(x) = u^n(x) + \Delta t \frac{\partial^2 u^{n+1}}{\partial x^2}(x,t) \quad \forall x \in [0,1], \\ u^0(x) = u_0(x) \quad \forall x \in [0,1] \\ u^n(0) = g_0(t) \quad \text{and} \quad u^n(1) = g_1(t) \quad \forall n > 0 \end{aligned} \tag{10.32}$$

where $u^n(x)$ again denotes an approximation to $u(x, n\Delta t)$. Applying the finite difference or finite element approximation (11.2) to (10.32) yields now a system of equations to be solved at each time step. This algorithm is *stable* for all `dt`, but now we have to solve a system of equations instead of just multiplying by a matrix. Note however that the system to be solved is just the same as in the ODE boundary-value problems studied earlier, so the same family of techniques can be used.

10.5.3 Variational form of the time discretization

The explicit Euler time stepping method can be written in variational form as

$$(u^{n+1}, v)_{L^2(\Omega)} = (u^n, v)_{L^2(\Omega)} + \Delta t \left(F(v) - a(u^n, v)\right) \quad \forall v \in V. \tag{10.33}$$

Solving for u^{n+1} requires inverting the mass matrix (8.27).

The implicit Euler time stepping method can be written in variational form as

$$(u^{n+1}, v)_{L^2(\Omega)} + \Delta t\, a(u^{n+1}, v) = (u^n, v)_{L^2(\Omega)} + \Delta t\, F(v) \quad \forall v \in V. \tag{10.34}$$

Solving for u^{n+1} requires inverting linear combination of the stiffness matrix (8.24) and the mass matrix (8.27). This is now in the familiar form: find $u^{n+1} \in V$ such that

$$a_{\Delta t}(u^{n+1}, v) = F^n_{\Delta t}(v) \quad \forall v \in V,$$

where

$$a_{\Delta t}(v, w) = \int_\Omega vw + \Delta t v' w' \, d\mathbf{x}, \quad F^n_{\Delta t}(v) = (u^n, v)_{L^2(\Omega)} + \Delta t F(v) \quad \forall v, w \in V. \tag{10.35}$$

10.5.4 Mass lumping

It is disconcerting that the explicit Euler time-stepping scheme leads to a system of equations (involving the mass matrix) that has to be inverted at each time step. This can be avoided in many cases by replacing the exact integration in expressions like $(u^n, v)_{L^2(\Omega)}$ by appropriate quadrature. For example, with piecewise linear approximation in one spatial dimension, we could use trapezoidal rule for evaluating the expression in (8.27). In this case, instead of the matrix M, we get the identity matrix, and the algorithm (10.33) gets transformed to

$$\mathbf{U}^{n+1} = \mathbf{U}^n + \Delta t \left(\mathbf{F} - \mathbf{A}\mathbf{U}^n\right), \tag{10.36}$$

where we are using the vector notation preceding (8.25).

Although this explicit formula for advancing in time looks attractive, involving no solution of equations, there is an inherent limitation on the time step that is very restrictive. We explore this in detail in Section 11.5.

10.5.5 Backwards differentiation formulæ

A popular way to achieve increased accuracy in time-dependent problems is to use a **backwards differentiation formula** (BDF)

$$\frac{du}{dt}(t_n) \approx \frac{1}{\Delta t} \sum_{i=0}^{k} a_n u_{n-i}, \tag{10.37}$$

where the coefficients $\{a_i \,:\, i = 0, \dots k\}$ are given in Table 10.2. The BDF for $k = 1$ is the same as implicit Euler. The BDF formulæ satisfy [259]

$$\sum_{i=0}^{k} a_i u_{n-i} = \sum_{j=1}^{k} \frac{(-1)^j}{j} \Delta^j u_n, \tag{10.38}$$

k	a_0	a_1	a_2	a_3	a_4	a_5	a_6	a_7
1	1	-1						
2	3/2	-2	1/2					
3	11/6	-3	3/2	$-1/3$				
4	25/12	-4	6/2	$-4/3$	1/4			
5	137/60	-5	10/2	$-10/3$	5/4	$-1/5$		
6	49/20	-6	15/2	$-20/3$	15/4	$-6/5$	1/6	
7	363/140	-7	21/2	$-35/3$	35/4	$-21/5$	7/6	$-1/7$

Table 10.2: Coefficients of the BDF schemes of degree k.

where Δu_n is the sequence whose n-th entry is $u_n - u_{n-1}$. The higher powers are defined by induction: $\Delta^{j+1}u_n = \Delta(\Delta^j u_n)$. For example, $\Delta^2 u_n = u_n - 2u_{n-1} + u_{n-2}$, and in general Δ^j has coefficients given from Pascal's triangle. We thus see that $a_0 \neq 0$ for all $k \geq 1$; $a_0 = \sum_{i=1}^{k} 1/i$. Similarly, $a_1 = -k$, and for $j \geq 2$, ja_j is an integer conforming to Pascal's triangle.

Given this simple definition of the general case of BDF, it is hard to imagine what could go wrong regarding stability. Unfortunately, the BDF method of order $k = 7$ is unconditionally unstable and hence cannot be used. We leave as exercises to explore the use of the BDF schemes.

10.6 The backwards heat equation

The heat equation is reversible with respect to time, in the sense that if we let time run backwards we get an equation that takes the final values to the initial values. More precisely, let $u(x,t)$ be the solution to (10.5) for $0 \leq t \leq T$. Let $v(x,t) := u(x, T-t)$. Then v solves the backwards heat equation

$$\begin{aligned} \frac{\partial v}{\partial t}(x,t) + \frac{\partial^2 v}{\partial x^2}(x,t) = 0 \quad \forall x \in [0,1],\ t > 0 \\ v(x,0) = v_0(x) = u(x,T) \quad \forall x \in [0,1] \\ v(0,t) = g_0(T-t), \quad v(1,t) = g_1(T-t) \quad \forall t > 0 \end{aligned} \tag{10.39}$$

and $v(x,T)$ will be the same as the initial data u_0 for (10.5).

Although (10.39) has a well-defined solution in many cases (see Exercise 10.1 for an exact solution), it is not well-posed in the usual sense. It has a solution starting only from solutions of the heat equation. Moreover, such solutions may exist only for a short time, and then blow up. Thus great care must be used in attempting to solve the backwards heat equation.

One reason for interest in the backwards heat equation is in information recovery. If a process blurs information via a diffusion process, then running the backwards heat equation can potentially deblur the information. Thus this approach has been considered in image processing [63].

An example of the difficulty in reversing the heat equation is shown in Figure 10.5. What is depicted is an attempt to solve (10.39) with initial data (10.9) at time $t = 0.001$. What we see in Figure 10.5(left) is the result of using a uniform mesh in space with 50 points and

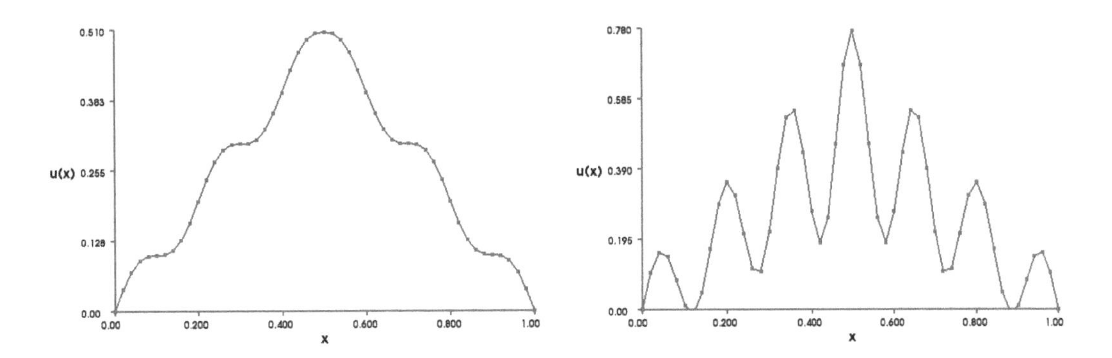

Figure 10.5: Solution of (10.39) with initial data (10.9) at time $t = 0.001$, computed with piecewise linears with 50 mesh points (uniform mesh). (left) One time step with $\Delta t = 0.001$. (right) Two time steps with $\Delta t = 0.0005$.

piecewise linear approximation, using $\Delta t = 0.001$. What we see looks plausible, but when we check this by cutting the time step in half, and doubling the number of time steps, we see in Figure 10.5(right) that we get something radically different, with very many oscillations. If we continue this, by cutting the time step in half and doubling the number of time steps, we find even wilder oscillations.

What is going on? Remember that the heat equation always smoothes the initial data as we move forward in time. Thus when we run time backwards, we must get a solution that is rougher than the initial data. Therefore there could not be a smooth solution for the backwards heat starting with the nonsmooth initial data (10.9). Thus the progression indicated in Figure 10.5 from panel (a) to panel (b) suggests an attempt to generate some very singular object. Recall that the the time in both panels is the same, and (b) represents using better time resolution. We leave as Exercise 10.7 to explore numerical solution of the backwards heat equation further.

One successful way to approximate the solution of the backwards heat equation is to use a regularization. One such approach is to add a term studied by Sobolev [263]. In Exercise 10.8 we suggest an example of this Sobolev-equation approach [124].

10.7 Exercises

Exercise 10.1 *Verify that the Gaussian $u(x,t) := (t+t_o)^{-1/2}e^{-x^2/(t+t_o)}$ is an exact solution of (10.5). Use this to test the accuracy of a numerical code for some $t_o > 0$. What happens if you take $t_o \to 0$?*

Exercise 10.2 *Give the second set of compatibility conditions (10.13) in the case of pure Dirichlet conditions (10.6).*

Exercise 10.3 *Give the second set of compatibility conditions (10.13) in the case of pure Neumann boundary conditions (10.7).*

Exercise 10.4 *Derive the third set of compatibility conditions in the case of pure Dirichlet conditions (10.6), pure Neumann boundary conditions (10.7), and mixed Dirichlet and Neumann boundary conditions (10.8).*

Exercise 10.5 *Show that the inhomogeneous initial and boundary-value problem (10.5)–(10.8) for the heat equation can be written in the form (10.16) with*

$$F(v) = (f, v) + g_1(t)v(1) - g_0(t)a(1 - x, v) \quad \forall v \in V. \tag{10.40}$$

Exercise 10.6 *Examine the numerical solution of (10.31) with incompatible data, e.g., where $u_0(x) = 1 - 2x$ and $g_0(t) = g_1(t) \equiv 0$. How does the error depend on x and t? Does it decrease as t increases? What is the rate of convergence for the solution in the L^2 norm: $\|u(\cdot, t)\|_{L^2(\Omega)}$?*

Exercise 10.7 *Try solving the backwards heat equation (10.39) on $[-L, L]$ with the Gaussian $u_0(x) := t_0^{-1/2} e^{-x^2/t_0}$ as initial data. Use the implicit Euler method for time stepping. What happens? (Hint: see Exercise 10.1 for the exact solution.)*

Exercise 10.8 *Approximate the backwards heat equation (10.39) using a Sobolev equation [263] approximation [124]. That is, let $\beta > 0$ and solve*

$$v_t + v_{xx} - \beta v_{xxt} = 0.$$

Do this on the interval $[-L, L]$ with the Gaussian $u_0(x) := t_0^{-1/2} e^{-x^2/t_0}$ as initial data. Use the implicit Euler method for time stepping. What happens as $\beta \to 0$? (Hint: see Exercise 10.1 for the exact solution of the backwards heat equation.)

Exercise 10.9 *Give a variational formulation of the problem*

$$\begin{aligned} \frac{\partial u}{\partial t}(x,t) - \frac{\partial^2 u}{\partial x^2}(x,t) + \beta \frac{\partial u}{\partial x}(x,t) + \gamma u(x,t) = f \quad \forall x \in [0,1],\ t > 0 \\ u(x,0) = u_0(x) \quad \forall x \in [0,1] \end{aligned} \tag{10.41}$$

with a simple implicit Euler time-stepping. Assume that β and γ are known functions of x.

Exercise 10.10 *Give a variational formulation of the problem*

$$\begin{aligned} \frac{\partial u}{\partial t}(x,t) - \frac{\partial^2 u}{\partial x^2}(x,t) + n(u(x,t)) = f \quad \forall x \in [0,1],\ t > 0 \\ u(x,0) = u_0(x) \quad \forall x \in [0,1] \end{aligned} \tag{10.42}$$

with a simple implicit Euler time-stepping, where n is the nonlinear function $n(u) = u^2$. Describe Newton's method to solve the nonlinear system at each time step.

Exercise 10.11 *Prove Gronwall's lemma, that $\phi' \le c\phi$ implies $\phi(t) \le e^{ct}\phi(0)$. (Hint: let $\psi(t) = e^{-ct}\phi(t)$, then*

$$\psi'(t) = -ce^{-ct}\phi(t) + e^{-ct}\phi'(t) = e^{-ct}\big(-c\phi(t) + \phi'(t)\big) \le 0.$$

Show that $\psi(t) \le \psi(0)$.)

Exercise 10.12 *Consider (10.5) with boundary conditions (10.8) with $g_0 = g_1 \equiv 0$ and with initial conditions $u_0(x) = x(1 - x)$. Show that one of the compatibility conditions (10.10) is violated (which one?). Implement the solution and explain how the lack of this compatibility condition manifests in the solution.*

Exercise 10.13 *Generalize the heat equation (10.5) to two spatial dimensions in which the spatial operator is the Laplace operator. Give a "method of lines" discretization for it. Test the code on the two-dimensional version of the exact solution in Exercise 10.1.*

Exercise 10.14 *Consider the generalized heat equation in two spatial dimensions (Exercise 10.13). Determine the first two compatibility conditions on the initial and boundary data to insure smooth solutions (see (10.10) and (10.10)). Give a demonstration of what happens if these are violated.*

Exercise 10.15 *Define*

$$u(x,t) = t^{-3/2}\big((x^2/t) - \tfrac{1}{2}\big)e^{-x^2/t}.$$

Show that u *solves the equation* $u_t - \frac{1}{4}u_{xx} = 0$. *Use this as a test of a code to solve the heat equation.*

```
1  from dolfin import *
2  import sys, math
3  import time
4
5  dt=float(sys.argv[1])
6  deg=int(sys.argv[2])
7  mno=int(sys.argv[3])
8
9  # Create mesh and define function space
10 mesh = UnitIntervalMesh(mno)
11 V = FunctionSpace(mesh, "Lagrange", deg)
12
13 # Define Dirichlet boundary (x = 0 or x = 1)
14 def boundary(x):
15     return x[0] < DOLFIN_EPS or x[0] > 1.0 - DOLFIN_EPS
16
17 # Define boundary condition
18 g = Expression("0.5-std::abs(x[0]-0.5)",degree=deg)
19 u0 = Expression("0",degree=deg)
20
21 bc = DirichletBC(V, u0, boundary)
22
23 # Define variational problem
24 u = TrialFunction(V)
25 uold = Function(V)
26 v = TestFunction(V)
27 a = dt*inner(grad(u), grad(v))*dx + u*v*dx
28 F = uold*v*dx
29 u = Function(V)
30
31 uold.interpolate(g)
32 u.assign(uold)
33
34 # Compute one time step
35 solve(a == F, u, bc)
36
37 uold.assign(u)
38 plot(u, interactive=True)
```

Program 10.1: Code to implement the problem (10.5).

Chapter 11

Finite Difference Methods

In Section 8.3.2, we saw that finite element methods are closely related to finite difference methods. Moreover, we used a simple difference method to motivate the use of Newton's method for nonlinear problems in Section 11.7. Similarly, we saw in Chapter 10 that in time-dependent problems the time derivative is often approximated by a difference method. Thus we study difference methods in more detail.

Finite difference methods have several advantages. Simplicity is one that we have seen in Section 11.7 and Chapter 10. It allows an analysis at the "bit" level of what a computation is doing, in a simplified context. We will use this here to review explicit methods for the heat equation. The same sort of analysis can be done as well for other time-dependent applications.

11.1 Two-point boundary value problem

The simplest way to approximate a differential equation often is to replace a differential operator with a difference operator. In this way we get the approximation for (8.1)

$$-u(x-h)+2u(x)-u(x+h)\approx h^2 f(x) \tag{11.1}$$

where $h>0$ is the mesh size to be used. Choosing $x=x_n:=nh$ for $n=0,1,\ldots,N$ where $N=1/h$, we get a system of linear equations

$$-u_{n-1}+2u_n-u_{n+1}=h^2 f(x_n) \tag{11.2}$$

where $u_n\approx u(x_n)$, which is the same as the finite element discretization which leads to (8.32).

One of the shortcomings of the finite-difference approach is that the boundary conditions have to be handled in an *ad hoc* way. The boundary condition at $x=0$ translates naturally into $u_0=g_0$. Thus, (11.2) for $n=1$ becomes

$$2u_1-u_2=h^2 f(x_1)+g_0. \tag{11.3}$$

However, the derivative boundary condition at $x=1$ must be approximated by a difference equation. A natural one to use is

$$u_{N+1}-u_{N-1}=2hg_1 \tag{11.4}$$

using a difference over an interval of length $2h$ centered at x_N. The second-difference (11.2) is itself a difference of first-differences over intervals of length h so there is some inconsistency, however both are centered differences (and therefore second-order accurate). See Exercise 8.2 for an example based on a non-centered difference approximation to the derivative boundary condition. Using (11.4), (11.2) for $n = N$ becomes

$$-2u_{N-1} + 2u_N = h^2 f(x_N) + 2hg_1. \tag{11.5}$$

Algebraically, we can express the finite difference method as

$$\mathbf{AU} = \mathbf{F}, \tag{11.6}$$

where $\mathbf{U}$ is the vector with entries u_n and $\mathbf{F}$ is the vector with entries $h^2 f(x_n)$ appropriately modified at $n = 1$ and $n = N$ using the boundary data. The matrix $\mathbf{A}$ has all diagonal entries equal to 2. The first sub- and super-diagonal entries are all equal to -1, except the last sub-diagonal entry, which is -2.

```
dx=pi/(N+1);                % mesh size with N points
%                             define the diagonal matrix entries
i(1:N)=1:N;
j(1:N)=1:N;
v(1:N)= 2/(dx*dx);
%                             define the above-diagonal matrix entries
i(N+(1:(N-1)))=(1:(N-1));
j(N+(1:(N-1)))=1+(1:(N-1));
v(N+(1:(N-1)))= -1/(dx*dx);
%                             define the below-diagonal matrix entries
i((2*N-1)+(1:(N-1)))=1+(1:(N-1));
j((2*N-1)+(1:(N-1)))=(1:(N-1));
v((2*N-1)+(1:(N-1)))= -1/(dx*dx);
%                             convert the entries into a sparse matrix format
A=sparse(i,j,v);
%                             define the right-hand side
F(1:N)=sin(dx*(1:N));
```

Program 11.1: octave code for solving (11.7): $-u''(x) = \sin(x)$ on $[0, \pi]$ with Dirichlet boundary conditions $u(0) = u(\pi) = 0$.

11.2 octave implementation

The creation of the matrix $\mathbf{A}$ in octave can be achieved by various techniques. However, to get reasonable performance for large N, you must restrict to sparse operations, as follows. For simplicity, we us consider the case where the differential equation to be solved is

$$\begin{aligned} -u''(x) &= \sin(x) \text{ for } x \in [0, \pi] \\ u(0) &= u(\pi) = 0. \end{aligned} \tag{11.7}$$

Then $u(x) = \sin(x)$ for $x \in [0, \pi]$. To create the difference operator A for this problem in a sparse format, you must specify only the non-zero entries of the matrix, that is, you give a list of triples: (i, j, A_{ij}). This is followed by an operation that amalgamates these triples into a sparse matrix structure; in `octave`, this operation is called `sparse`. The `octave` code for this is shown in Program 11.1.

In `octave`, the solution to (11.6) can be achieved simply by writing

```
U=A\F ;
```

It is critical that one use vector constructs in `octave` to insure optimal performance. It executes much more rapidly, but the code is not shorter, more readable or less prone to error. See Exercise 11.5 for an example.

11.3 Reality checks

The simplest way to determine whether an approximation to a differential equation is working or not is to attempt to solve a problem with a known solution. For example, we can use the method of manufactured solutions Section 2.3 to help with this. This is only one indication that all is working in one special set of conditions, not a proof of correctness. However, it is a very useful technique.

Comparing a visualization of the approximation with the expected solution is the simplest way to find bugs, but a more demanding approach is often warranted. Using a *norm* to measure the difference between the approximation and the expected solution reduces a complicated comparison to a single number. Moreover, there are extensive error estimates available which describe how various norms of the error should behave as a function of the maximum mesh size h.

For finite difference methods, there are discrete norms that are appropriate to measure errors. For the approximation (u_n) (11.1) of the solution u of equation (11.1) (and ones similar to it) it can be shown [57] that

$$\|(u_n) - u\|_{\ell^\infty} := \max_{1 \le n \le N} |u(x_n) - u_n| \le C_f h^2 \tag{11.8}$$

$$\|(u_n) - u\|_{\ell^2} := \sqrt{h \sum_n (u(x_n) - u_n)^2} \le C_f h^2, \tag{11.9}$$

where C_f is a constant depending only on f. Thus one can do a computational experiment with a known u to see if the relationship (11.8) or (11.9) appears to hold as h is decreased. In particular, if the logarithm of $e_h := \|(u_n) - u\|_{\ell^2}$ is plotted as a function of $\log h$, then the resulting plot should be linear, with a slope of two, as discussed in Section 4.5.

Consider the boundary-value problem (11.7), that is, $-u'' = f$ on $[0, \pi]$ with $f(x) = \sin x$ and $u(0) = u(\pi) = 0$. Then the solution is $u(x) = \sin x$. In Figure 11.1, the resulting mean-squared error (11.9) has been plotted. The line $e_h = 0.1h^2$ has been added for clarity. Thus we see for $h \ge 10^{-4}$, the error diminishes quadratically. However, when the mesh size is much less than 10^{-4}, the amplification of round-off error due to increasing condition number of the linear system causes the accuracy to diminish, and the error even increases as the mesh size is further decreased.

number of grid points	10	100	1000	10000
mesh size	2.86e-01	3.11e-02	3.14e-03	3.14e-04
condition number	4.84e+01	4.13e+03	4.06e+05	4.05e+07

Table 11.1: Condition number of the matrix in Program 11.1 as a function of N. Recall that the mesh size $h = \pi/(N+1)$.

degree	mesh number	L^2 error	time (s)
1	1024	2.07e-06	22.5
2	512	2.11e-09	18.4
4	128	4.95e-12	3.0
8	8	3.98e-12	0.13

Table 11.2: Computational experiments with solving the problem (2.12). Degree refers to the polynomial degree, mesh number indicates the number of edges along each boundary side as indicated in Figure 4.5, L^2 error is the error measured in the $L^2([0,1]^2)$ norm, cf. (4.7). Results with greatest accuracy in Table 4.1 for degrees 4 and 8 have been reproduced. Meshes used are of the type shown in Figure 4.4. Results generated using Program 4.1.

11.4 Pitfall: low accuracy

All discretization methods can suffer from the effects of finite precision arithmetic. The easiest way to see this is that if h^2 is smaller than the smallest "machine ϵ" (defined to be the largest positive number whose addition to 1 in floating point returns 1) relative to the size of f and u, then (11.1) will effectively not distinguish between the real f and $f \equiv 0$.

More subtle effects can also occur due to the increasing condition number of the linear system $\mathbf{A}$ as h tends to zero. We display the condition number for various mesh sizes in Table 11.1, and it appears that the condition number grows proportional to $N^2 \approx h^{-2}$. This effect can be amplified based on the method used to solve the linear system. We see in Figure 11.1 that the error decreases quadratically in the mesh size h up to a certain limit, and then it hits a wall. Accuracy then behaves randomly and even decreases as the mesh size is further decreased. We see that the most accuracy we can achieve is closely related to the condition number multiplied by machine $\epsilon = 2.22 \times 10^{-16}$ in these computations. Thus with $N = 10,000$, we cannot expect accuracy better than about 10^{-9}. Another way that finite-precision arithmetic can affect the accuracy of calculation is in the construction of the matrix $\mathbf{A}$ in more complex applications.

We have already seen the effects of round-off error in Table 4.1. Moreover, that data indicates that higher-order methods do not solve the problem of round-off error in the sense that the maximum accuracy is about the same independent of the degree of approximation. This is because the condition number is linked to the accuracy of the approximation. The condition number of the linear system depends on the largest eigenvalue of the PDE that is resolved. The better the resolution, the larger the condition number. This is a feature of elliptic systems, like Poisson's equation, whereas in time-stepping methods increasing the accuracy always reduces the effects of round-off errors.

On the other hand, higher-order methods do reduce the run time required to achieve maximal accuracy, as indicated in Table 11.2. For this reason, higher-order methods would allow the use of more accurate precision arithmetic at a manageable cost.

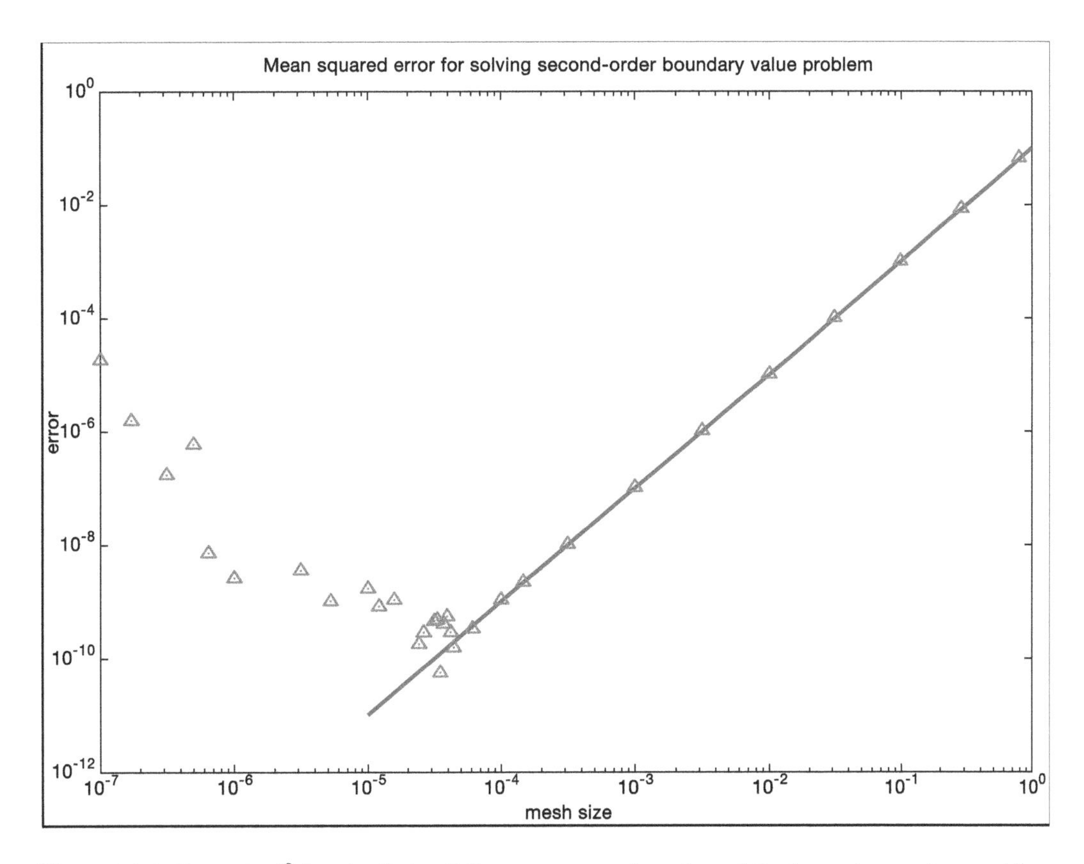

Figure 11.1: Error in ℓ^2 for the finite difference approximation of the boundary value problem for the differential equation $-u'' = \sin(x)$ on the interval $[0, \pi]$, with boundary conditions $u(0) = u(\pi) = 0$, as a function of the mesh size h. The solid line has a slope of 2 as a reference.

11.5 Review of the heat equation

Using the approximations (10.31) and (11.1), we get the following finite difference method for the heat equation:

$$u_j^{n+1} = u_j^n + \frac{\Delta t}{\Delta x^2}\left(u_{j-1}^n - 2u_j^n + u_{j+1}^n\right) = ru_{j-1}^n + (1-2r)u_j^n + ru_{j+1}^n, \tag{11.10}$$

where $r = \Delta t/\Delta x^2$. Here $u(j\Delta x, n\Delta t) \approx u_j^n$. This is very appealing since there are no equations to solve. However, there is a strict stability limitation we now derive.

Suppose that we start with the initial condition $u_j^0 = (-1)^j$. Although this is a rough function, we know that the heat equation should smooth it out. For the moment, let us ignore boundary conditions and assume that (11.10) holds for all j and n. This is equivalent to assuming that $\Omega = \mathbb{R}$. Then we will prove by induction that

$$u_j^n = (1-4r)^n(-1)^j. \tag{11.11}$$

First, by assumption this holds for $n = 0$. Using (11.10) and the induction hypothesis, we have

$$\begin{aligned}
u_j^{n+1} &= ru_{j-1}^n + (1-2r)u_j^n + ru_{j+1}^n \\
&= r(1-4r)^n(-1)^{j-1} + (1-2r)(1-4r)^n(-1)^j + r(1-4r)^n(-1)^{j+1} \\
&= (1-4r)^n(-1)^j(-r + (1-2r) - r) \\
&= (1-4r)^{n+1}(-1)^j,
\end{aligned} \tag{11.12}$$

completing the induction step. Thus (11.11) holds for all n and j.

The ratio $r = \Delta t/\Delta x^2$ is always positive. So $|1-4r| \le 1$ only for $r \le 1/2$. For $r < 1/2$, then u_j^n decreases rapidly to zero, in keeping with what we would expect for the heat equation. If $r > 1/2$, then $|1-4r| > 1$, and the expression (11.11) blows up exponentially. Most insidiously, we have

$$u(x,t) = u(j\Delta x, n\Delta t) \approx u_j^n = (1-4r)^{t/\Delta t}(-1)^j,$$

so the blow up accelerates as $\Delta t \to 0$. Thus the explicit method (11.10) for the heat equation is restricted by the stringent requirement

$$\Delta t \le \frac{\Delta x^2}{2}.$$

Therefore the implicit methods discussed in Section 10.5 are more efficient in many cases, using larger time steps than this Draconian limit.

11.6 Review of the backwards heat equation

The formula (11.11) applies to the backwards heat equation as well. For the backwards heat equation we just reverse the sign in front of the Laplacian operator, so the finite difference formula corresponding to (11.10) is

$$u_j^{n+1} = u_j^n - \frac{\Delta t}{\Delta x^2}\left(u_{j-1}^n - 2u_j^n + u_{j+1}^n\right) = ru_{j-1}^n + (1-2r)u_j^n + ru_{j+1}^n,$$

where $r = -\Delta t/\Delta x^2$. Thus (11.11) again provides a solution, the only difference being that now $r < 0$. But the formula

$$u_j^n = (1-4r)^n(-1)^j = (1-4r)^{t/\Delta t}(-1)^j \quad \text{for } t = n\Delta t$$

explodes exponentially for $r < 0$. Thus the explicit method for the backwards heat equation is not usable.

11.7 Nonlinear finite differences

The solution of (9.1) can be effected using a difference method for the differential operator as in Section 11.1.

$$-u_{n-1} + 2u_n - u_{n+1} + 4h^2 u_n + 6h^2 u_n^2 = h^2 C \tag{11.13}$$

where $u_n \approx u(x_n)$. Since this system of equations is nonlinear, we cannot solve it directly. A standard algorithm to use is Newton's method, which can be written as follows. First, we write the system of equations as $f(u_n) = 0$ where

$$f_n := -u_{n-1} + 2u_n - u_{n+1} + 4h^2 u_n + 6h^2 u_n^2 - h^2 C \tag{11.14}$$

Newton's iteration takes the form

$$u \leftarrow u - J_f(u)^{-1} f(u) \tag{11.15}$$

where $J_f(u)$ denotes the Jacobian of the mapping f evaluated at u. This can be written in `octave` as follows.

Suppose that `A` is defined as in Section 11.2. Then `f` can be written

```
delta=((n+1)/alf)^2;
f = delta*A*uhf - 4*uhf - 6*ujh.*ujh + cvec;
```

where

```
cvec=C*ones(n,1);
```

The Jacobian J of `f` is

```
J = delta*A - 4*eye(n) - 12*diag(ujh,0);
```

Newton's method takes the following form in `octave`.

```
JA = delta*A - 4*eye(n);
ujh =- JA\cvec;
enorm = 1;
while (enorm >> .0000000000001)
    f = JA*ujh - 6*ujh.*ujh + cvec;
    J = JA - 12*diag(ujh,0);
    x = ujh - J\f;
    enorm = norm(ujh-x)/(norm(ujh)+norm(x));
    ujh=x;
end
```

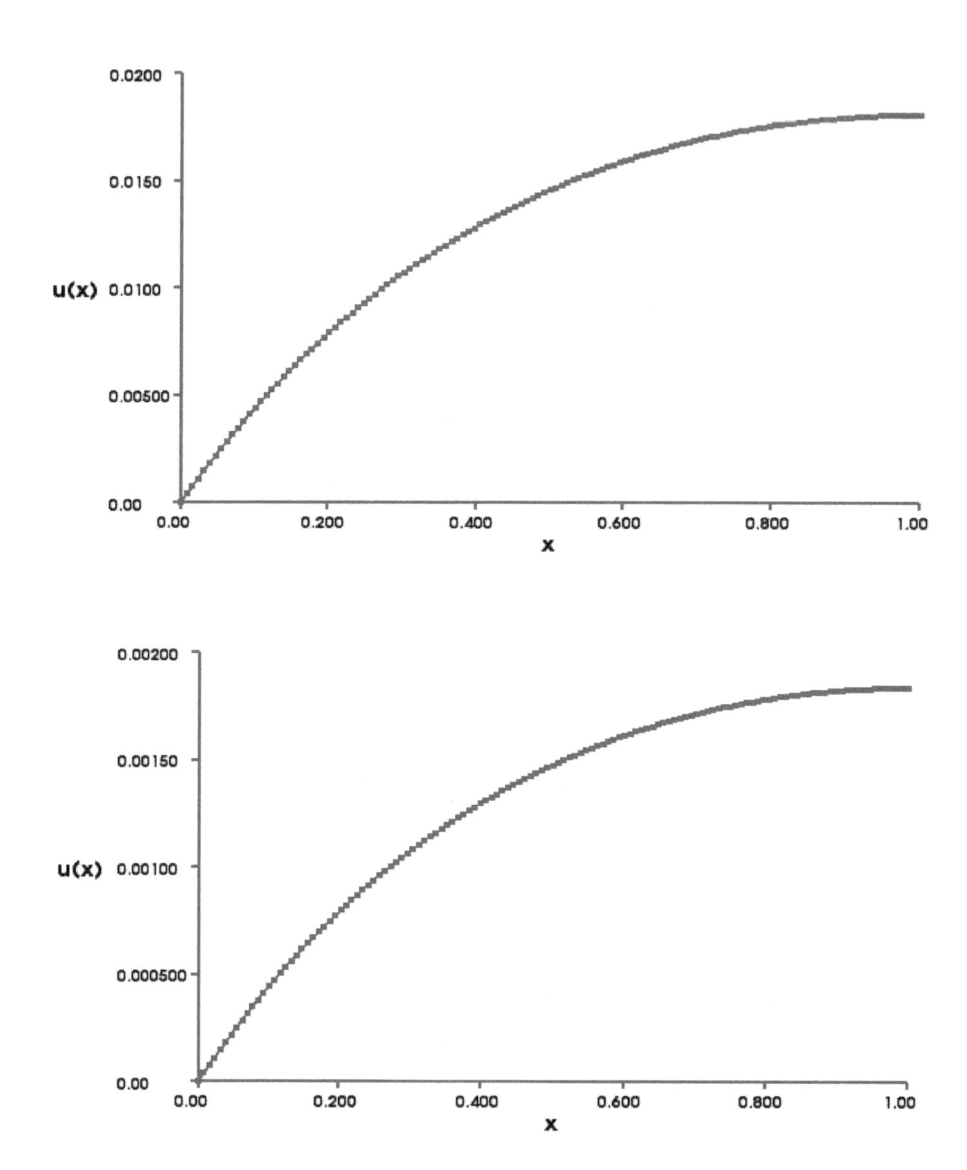

Figure 11.2: Solutions of the Jeffrey-Hamel equation with (top) $C = 0.1$ and (bottom) $C = 0.01$. The solutions have similar shape and scale consistent with the hypothesis (9.4).

11.8 Exercises

Exercise 11.1 *Use Taylor's theorem to derive (11.1).*

Exercise 11.2 *The solution to (8.1) with* $f \equiv 1$ *is* $u(x) = x - \frac{x^2}{2}$*. Use the method in Section 11.1 to approximate this problem. Implement these equations in* `octave` *on this test problem and determine the convergence rate. Where in the interval is the error largest?*

Exercise 11.3 *Replace (11.4) by*

$$u_{N+1} - u_N = 0 \tag{11.16}$$

Give the equation corresponding to (11.5) that results. How is it different? Implement these equations in `octave` *on the test problem in Section 11.3 and determine the convergence rate. Where in the interval is the error largest?*

Exercise 11.4 *Derive the finite difference approximation for the boundary value problem for the differential equation*

$$-u'' - u = f$$

with boundary conditions $u(0) = a$ *and* $u'(1) = b$*. Write an* `octave` *code for this and test it as in Section 11.3 for the exact solution* $u(x) = \sin x$ *with* $f \equiv 0$, $g_0 = 0$ *and* $g_1 = \cos 1$.

Exercise 11.5 *The matrix for the difference method in Section 11.2 can be implemented in* `octave` *as follows.*

```
A=zeros(n);
for i=1:n
    if i>1, A((i-1),i)=-1; end
    if i<n, A((i+1),i)=-1; end
    A(i,i) = 2;
end
```

Compare this with the "vectorized" definition in Section 11.2 and determine the ratio of execution speed for the two methods of computing `A` *for* `n`*=10, 100, 1000 and 10000. Can you identify any trends?*

Exercise 11.6 *Derive the matrix for the difference method in Section 11.2 in the case of Dirichlet boundary conditions at both boundary points, that is,* $u(0) = 0$ *and* $u(1) = 0$*. Implement the matrix in* `octave` *with a "vectorized" definition. Test this on the problem in (11.7).*

Exercise 11.7 *Implement the difference equations (8.31) in* `octave` *for a general mesh* $0 = x_0 < x_1 < x_2 < \cdots < x_N = 1$*. Use this method to approximate the problem in (8.1), with* $f \equiv 1$ *is* $u(x) = x - \frac{x^2}{2}$*. Implement these equations in* `octave` *on this test problem and determine the convergence rate as a function of* $h := \max_i x_i - x_{i-1}$*. Try different methods to generate random meshes. Where in the interval is the error largest?*

Exercise 11.8 *Derive the finite difference approximation corresponding to (8.31) for the boundary value problem for the differential equation*

$$-u'' - u = f$$

with boundary conditions $u(0) = g_0$ *and* $u'(1) = g_1$*. Write an* `octave` *code for this and test it as in Section 11.3 for the exact solution* $u(x) = \sin x$ *with* $f \equiv 0$, $a = 0$ *and* $b = \cos 1$.

Exercise 11.9 *Derive the matrix for the difference method (8.31) in the case of Dirichlet boundary conditions at both boundary points, that is,* $u(0) = 0$ *and* $u(1) = 0$*. Implement the matrix in* `octave` *with a "vectorized" definition.*

Exercise 11.10 *Derive the matrix* A *for the difference method (8.31) in the case of Neumann boundary conditions at both boundary points, that is,* $u'(0) = 0$ *and* $u'(1) = 0$*. Implement the matrix in* `octave` *with a "vectorized" definition. Check to see if the matrix* A *is singular. What function satisfies the differential equation (see Exercise 8.1) with zero Neumann data? What is the associated null vector for the matrix* A*? Under what conditions does the equation* $AX = F$ *have a solution?*

Exercise 11.11 *Derive the matrix* A *for the difference method in Section 11.2 in the case of Neumann boundary conditions at both boundary points, that is,* $u'(0) = 0$ *and* $u'(1) = 0$*. Implement the matrix in* `octave` *with a "vectorized" definition. Check to see if the matrix* A *is singular. What function satisfies the differential equation (see Exercise 8.1) with zero Neumann data? What is the associated null vector for the matrix* A*? Under what conditions does the equation* $AX = F$ *have a solution?*

Chapter 12

Wave Equations

Another class of time-dependent equations goes by the name "wave equations." There are many types of such equations. We focus on just a few to give a flavor of the issues and to contrast them with other equations.

12.1 Classification of PDEs

There are two major classifications of PDEs, one for linear PDEs and one for nonlinearities. This is based on an algebraic trichotomy for second-order differential operators D in two dimensions: elliptic, parabolic, and hyperbolic. This arises from the analogy with conic sections and their algebraic equations, as indicated in Table 12.1.

Examples of elliptic equations are the Laplace/Poisson equations and the variants considered so far. More general forms of elliptic equations are studied in Chapter 17. The heat equation is the prototypical parabolic equation. In the classification in Table 12.1, this leaves hyperbolic equations. Switching variables from y to x, such an equation takes the form

$$u_{tt} - u_{xx} = 0, \tag{12.1}$$

in one space dimension. More generally, what is often called **The wave equation** is

$$u_{tt} - c^2 \Delta u = 0, \tag{12.2}$$

in multiple space dimensions, where c is the wave speed and Δ is the Laplacian (Section 31.6.3).

The speed c may always be taken to be 1 in suitable coordinates. For example, the speed of light in a vacuum is approximately 299792458 meters per second. A meter is about

formula	classification	example	equation	variable substitution
$x^2 + y^2 = 1$	elliptic	Laplace	$u_{,xx} + u_{,yy}$	none
$y = x^2$	parabolic	diffusion/heat	$u_{,t} - u_{,yy}$	$x \to t$
$x^2 - y^2 = 1$	hyperbolic	wave	$u_{,tt} - u_{,yy}$	$x \to t$

Table 12.1: Classification of linear PDEs. The column marked "formula" gives a typical formula for a conic section of whose name gives rise to the PDE classification name.

3.28084 feet. So the speed of light in a vacuum is approximately 9.8357e+08 feet per second. If we define a **big foot** to be 1.0167 feet (about 12.2 inches), then the speed of light in a vacuum is about one big foot per nanosecond. But it is also approximately one giga-big-feet per second. In either of these units, $c = 1$. In one of them, the time unit is small, and in the other the length unit is big, compared to our ordinary perception scales. From now on, we will assume that units are chosen so that $c = 1$.

Grace Hopper[1] famously displayed in her talks a piece of copper wire whose length corresponded to the distance an electrical signal traveled in a nanosecond. Her point was to emphasize the need for careful programming, but it also showed that $c = 1$ makes sense in a computer.

There are other equations of higher order that do not fit the classification in Table 12.1, such as the dispersive **Airy equation** $u_t + u_{xxx} = 0$. On the other hand, using a more sophisticated classification [5], it is possible to view the Stokes equations (Chapter 13) as an elliptic system. So we must consider Table 12.1 as just a starting point for understanding the differences between different PDEs. But it does suggest a new equation to consider which is intimately related to wave motion.

12.2 The wave equation in one space dimension

The one-dimensional wave operator factors, so that (12.1) can be written

$$0 = u_{tt} - u_{xx} = \Big(\frac{\partial}{\partial t} - \frac{\partial}{\partial x}\Big)\Big(\frac{\partial}{\partial t} + \frac{\partial}{\partial x}\Big)u = \Big(\frac{\partial}{\partial t} - \frac{\partial}{\partial x}\Big)(u_t + u_x). \tag{12.3}$$

In particular, $u(x,t) = f(t-x)$ solves (12.3) for any function f of one variable, since $u_t(x,t) = f'(t-x)$ and $u_x(x,t) = -f'(t-x)$, and thus $u_t + u_x = 0$. Thus solutions are constant on the lines $x(t) = t + a$ for any constant a, and they consist of just translating f to the right at constant speed. Similarly, by re-ordering the factorization (12.3), we conclude that another family of solutions consist of translations to the left, without change of shape. Such solutions are easy to visualize, and are markedly different from the behavior for the heat equation, or elliptic equations. In particular, it appears at least formally that smoothness of f does not matter, and that even discontinuous solutions would be allowed.

The behavior of solutions of the wave equation can be formalized in a exact expression known as d'Alembert's formula:

$$u(x,t) = \tfrac{1}{2}f(x-t) + \tfrac{1}{2}f(x+t) + \frac{1}{2}\int_{x-t}^{x+t} g(s)\,ds, \tag{12.4}$$

where $g(x) = u_t(x,0)$ and $f(x) = u(x,0)$. The contributions of d'Alembert are memorialized in the name the wave operator

$$\Box u = u_{tt} - \Delta u,$$

known as the **d'Alembertian operator**.

The formula (12.4) of d'Alembert draws its information from what is known as the **light cone**, depicted in Figure 12.1. Although the corresponding relationship between data and solution is more complex in higher spatial dimensions, the concept of the light cone generalizes naturally.

[1] Grace Brewster Murray Hopper (1906–1992) was an early advocate for automating programming via the use of compilers to translate human-readable descriptions into machine code.

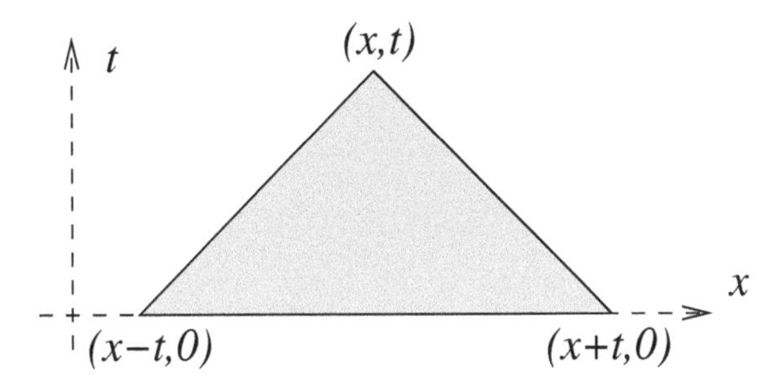

Figure 12.1: The light cone for the wave equation.

Since waves tend to propagate without change of shape, the spatial domain Ω is often infinite. In such cases, we truncate Ω for computational purposes. The fact that information comes only from the light cone allows us to estimate the required size of the computational domain accurately.

12.2.1 One-way propagation

The formula (12.4) of d'Alembert seems to imply that waves always propagate in both directions. But our splitting of the wave operator implied that there are solutions of the form $u_\pm(x,t) = f(x \pm t)$. Suppose that $v(x,t) = f(x+t)$. Then $v_t(x,0) = f'(x)$. So now consider the case where f is given and $g(x) = f'(x)$ for all x. Then (12.4) gives a solution u of the wave equation satisfying

$$\begin{aligned} 2u(x,t) &= f(x-t) + f(x+t) + \int_{x-t}^{x+t} f'(s)\,ds \\ &= f(x-t) + f(x+t) + (f(x+t) - f(x-t)) = 2f(x+t). \end{aligned} \tag{12.5}$$

Thus $u = v$ as expected. Similarly, if we take $g(x) = f'(-x)$, then

$$\begin{aligned} 2u(x,t) &= f(x-t) + f(x+t) + \int_{x-t}^{x+t} f'(-s)\,ds \\ &= f(x-t) + f(x+t) + (f(x-t) - f(x+t)) = 2f(x-t). \end{aligned} \tag{12.6}$$

So we get the expected one-way solutions by choosing an appropriate initial impulse g.

12.2.2 Variational form of wave equation

Using the standard algorithm, following what was done for the heat equation, we obtain the variational expression

$$(u_{tt}, v)_{L^2(\Omega)} + a(u,v) = 0 \quad \forall v \in H^1(\Omega), \tag{12.7}$$

where

$$a(v,w) = \int_\Omega v'(x)w'(x)\,dx. \tag{12.8}$$

12.2.3 Time discretization of wave equation

What is different from the heat equation is that we have a second-order time derivative. We can approximate this, for example, via

$$u_{tt} \approx \frac{u^{n+1} - 2u^n + u^{n-1}}{\tau^2},$$

where $\tau > 0$ is the time step, and u^j denotes an approximation to $u(j\tau)$. We can use this to define the variational formulation

$$(u^{n+1}, v)_{L^2(\Omega)} - 2(u^n, v)_{L^2(\Omega)} + (u^{n-1}, v)_{L^2(\Omega)} + \tau^2 a(u^{n+1}, v) = 0, \tag{12.9}$$

where τ is the time step. Thus we solve

$$(u^{n+1}, v)_{L^2(\Omega)} + \tau^2 a(u^{n+1}, v) = 2(u^n, v)_{L^2(\Omega)} - (u^{n-1}, v)_{L^2(\Omega)} \quad \forall v \in H^1(\Omega). \tag{12.10}$$

We immediately see that we can not solve the wave equation knowing just the initial conditions $u(x, 0)$. In addition, we need to know $u_t(x, 0)$ and we can use this to get a good approximation to u^{-1}. Unfortunately, the time-stepping scheme (12.10) is only first-order accurate in time.

12.2.4 Higher accuracy

Another time-stepping scheme, advocated in [117], is of the form

$$\begin{aligned}(u^{n+1}, v)_{L^2(\Omega)} &- 2(u^n, v)_{L^2(\Omega)} + (u^{n-1}, v)_{L^2(\Omega)} \\ &= -\tau^2 \big(\theta a(u^{n+1}, v) + (1 - 2\theta) a(u^n, v) + \theta a(u^{n-1}, v)\big),\end{aligned} \tag{12.11}$$

where $\theta \in [0, 1]$. Thus we solve

$$\begin{aligned}(u^{n+1}, v)_{L^2(\Omega)} + \theta\tau^2 a(u^{n+1}, v) &= 2(u^n, v)_{L^2(\Omega)} - (u^{n-1}, v)_{L^2(\Omega)} \\ &- \tau^2 \big((1 - 2\theta) a(u^n, v) + \theta a(u^{n-1}, v)\big), \quad \forall v \in H^1(\Omega).\end{aligned} \tag{12.12}$$

We can see the rationale for this approach by doing a Taylor expansion

$$u((n \pm 1)\tau) = u(n\tau) \pm \tau u_t(n\tau) + \tfrac{1}{2}\tau^2 u_{tt}(n\tau) \pm \frac{\tau^3}{6} u_{ttt}(n\tau) + \mathcal{O}\left(\tau^4\right). \tag{12.13}$$

Adding terms and dividing by τ^2, and again making the correspondence $u^j \approx u(j\tau)$, we find

$$\frac{u^{n+1} - 2u^n + u^{n-1}}{\tau^2} = u_{tt}(n\tau) + \mathcal{O}\left(\tau^2\right).$$

Similarly, multiplying (12.13) by θ and adding gives

$$\theta u((n+1)\tau) + (1 - 2\theta) u(n\tau) + \theta u((n-1)\tau) = u(n\tau) + \theta\tau^2 u_{tt}(n\tau) + \mathcal{O}\left(\tau^4\right).$$

Thus for any value of θ we get a second-order approximation:

$$\frac{u^{n+1} - 2u^n + u^{n-1}}{\tau^2} + \theta u^{n+1} + (1 - 2\theta) u^n + \theta u^{n-1} = u_{tt}(n\tau) + u(n\tau) + \mathcal{O}\left(\tau^2\right),$$

and the truncation error is decreasing in θ. If we take $\theta = 0$ we get an explicit scheme with time-step restrictions. In [117], the choice $\theta = 1/4$ was advocated for stability reasons (see Exercise 12.4).

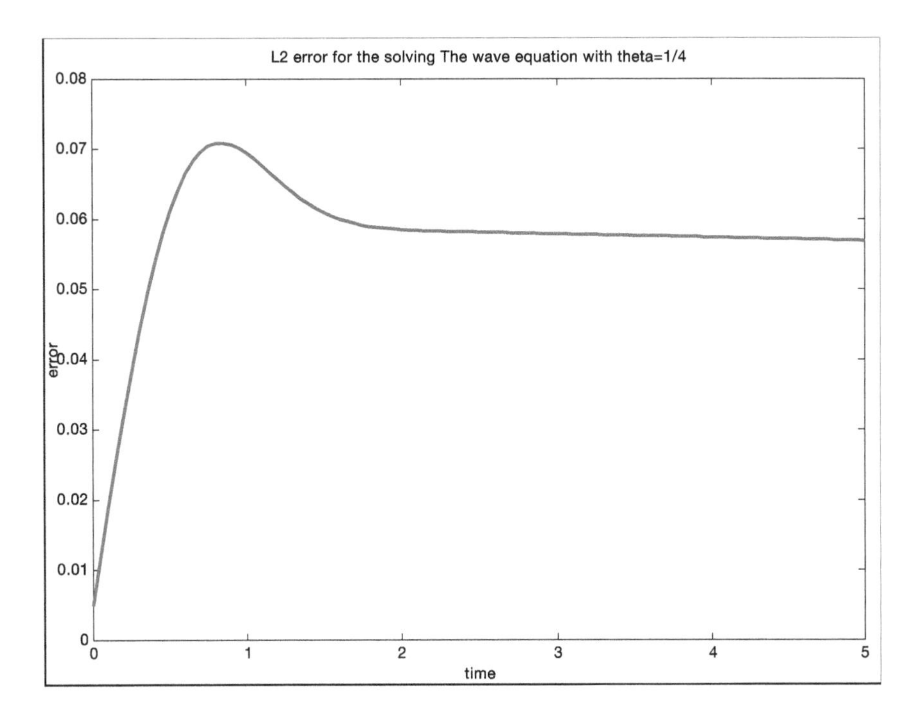

Figure 12.2: Error in $L^2(\Omega)$ as a function of time for the θ scheme with $\theta = 1/4$, $\Delta t = 0.05$, $L = 10$, $T = 5$, and $M = 2000$ mesh points, using piecewise linears.

12.2.5 Computational example

Many wave problems are naturally formulated on an infinite domain, so we have to truncate for computational feasibility. Start the simulation (in one space dimension) with

$$u_0(x) = e^{-x^2}$$

on a domain $\Omega = [-L, L]$. We will take L as large as necessary. Take $u_t(x, 0) = 0$. Then the exact solution follows from d'Alembert's formula:

$$u(x,t) = \tfrac{1}{2}e^{-(t-x)^2} + \tfrac{1}{2}e^{-(t+x)^2}. \tag{12.14}$$

In Program 12.1, a code is given to implement the θ scheme (12.12) with $\theta = 1/4$. The error as a function of time is indicated in Figure 12.2. Note that the error increases rapidly initially but then decreases.

12.2.6 Higher dimensions

The conversion to higher space dimensions is notationally trivial. We have written our bilinear form $a(u, v) = \int_\Omega \nabla u \cdot \nabla v \, d\mathbf{x}$ which makes sense in any number of dimensions. Thus it is just a matter of defining the spatial domain to be multi-dimensional and waiting a bit longer for the answers to appear.

12.3 Helmholtz equation

Consider a special set of solutions U of the wave equation (12.2) given by

$$U(\mathbf{x}, t) = u(\mathbf{x})e^{\iota kt},$$

where $k \in \mathbb{R}$ and $\iota = \sqrt{-1}$. These solutions are known as **standing waves**. Then

$$\Delta U(\mathbf{x}, t) = (\Delta u(\mathbf{x}))e^{\iota kt},$$

and

$$U_{tt}(\mathbf{x}, t) = -k^2 u(\mathbf{x})e^{\iota kt}.$$

Thus the wave equation

$$U_{tt}(\mathbf{x}, t) - \Delta U(\mathbf{x}, t) = f(\mathbf{x})e^{\iota kt}$$

is satisfied if

$$-k^2 u(\mathbf{x}) - \Delta u(\mathbf{x}) = f(\mathbf{x}). \tag{12.15}$$

The equation (12.15) is known as the **Helmholtz equation**. Solving this, say with suitable boundary conditions, can be touchy since the corresponding variational form is not coercive. We look into this issue further in Section 26.4.

If you are bothered by the complex variable ansatz for U, you can replace it with its real counterparts, e.g.,

$$U^1(\mathbf{x}, t) = u(\mathbf{x})\cos(kt), \qquad U^2(\mathbf{x}, t) = u(\mathbf{x})\sin(kt),$$

but the conclusion is the same: U^i solve the wave equation if (12.15) holds (see Exercise 12.8).

12.4 Dispersive waves

Many types of wave behavior can be characterized as **dispersive**. One example is water waves. These are the waves that a child first sees. The main characteristic of these waves is the way that they spread as time evolves, unlike the behavior we saw for The wave equation where waveforms just translate linearly in time as indicated in (12.4).

When the wave length λ is long and the amplitude a is small, compared to the water depth, approximate equations can be derived for surface wave behavior. More precisely, define the Stokes parameter $S = a\lambda^2/d^3$, where d is the (assumed uniform) depth of the water. When $S = \mathcal{O}(1)$, then models for one-way propagation include the KdV equation [286, 45]

$$u_t + u_x + 2uu_x + u_{xxx} = 0,$$

where u is the wave height. The waves are assumed to be propagating in the x-direction, and constant in the y-direction. We see that this equation is a nonlinear perturbation of the one-way wave equation $u_t + u_x = 0$. Another, equivalent [45], model is

$$u_t + u_x + 2uu_x - u_{xxt} = 0. \tag{12.16}$$

The two equations can be related by thinking of them as perturbations of the basic wave equation $u_t + u_x = 0$, which suggests the substitution $u_t \approx -u_x$, and this leads to

$$u_{xxt} \approx -u_{xxx}.$$

Simulations using equation (12.16) have been compared with laboratory experiments [44]. Solutions of (12.16) can be approximated numerically [46] by writing it in the form

$$\Big(I - \frac{\partial^2}{\partial x^2}\Big) u_t = -u_x - 2uu_x = -\big(u + u^2\big)_x, \tag{12.17}$$

where I denotes the identity operator. The left-hand side is a familiar elliptic operator, so we can write a variational equation

$$a(u_t, v) = b(u, v) \quad \text{for all } v \in V, \tag{12.18}$$

where

$$a(v, w) = \int_\Omega v(x)w(x) + v'(x)w'(x)\, dx \tag{12.19}$$

and

$$\begin{aligned} b(v, w) &= -\int_\Omega (u + u^2)'(x), v(x)\, dx = -\int_\Omega (u' + 2uu')(x)v(x)\, dx \\ &= -\int_\Omega (1 + 2u)(x)u'(x)v(x)\, dx. \end{aligned} \tag{12.20}$$

12.4.1 Time-stepping schemes

A variety of time-stepping schemes can be used to discretize (12.18). One family of schemes that work well [46] is the **Runge-Kutta** schemes. These schemes have the useful feature that they can be high order yet not require previous time values of the solution. They are often used as start-up schemes for other schemes that do utilize previous values, as do the θ schemes (12.11). The simplest of these schemes is often called the **modified Euler** scheme:

$$\begin{aligned} a(\hat{u}^{n+1}, v) &= a(u^n, v) - \Delta t\, b(u^n, v)\ \forall v \in V, \\ a(u^{n+1}, v) &= a(u^n, v) + \tfrac{1}{2}\Delta t\big(b(2u^n, v) + b(\hat{u}^{n+1}, v)\big)\ \forall v \in V. \end{aligned} \tag{12.21}$$

The first step in (12.21) is called the **predictor step** and the second step in (12.21) is called the **corrector step**.

12.4.2 An example

In Figure 12.3, we present an example of the use of this scheme with piecewise linear approximation in space. This was computed using Program 12.2. The initial data $u(x, 0) = e^{-x^2}$ evolves into a complex wave form that spreads out as it travels to the right, and even has a part that moves slowly to the left. The wave speed is approximately $1 + 2u$, and in 25 time units the leading wave moves over 60 units to the right. A linear wave (that is, if u were small) would have moved only 25 units to the right.

A common measure of wave length for a complex wave shape is its width at half height. For the function $f(x) = e^{-x^2}$, this is the point x where $e^{-x^2} = 1/2$. Thus $-x^2 = \log(1/2)$, so $x = \sqrt{\log 2} = 0.83\ldots$. Thus the initial wave length is less than 2, whereas the leading wave at $T = 25$ has a width that is about 7 units, over 4 times larger. The dispersion causes the initial narrow wave to spread.

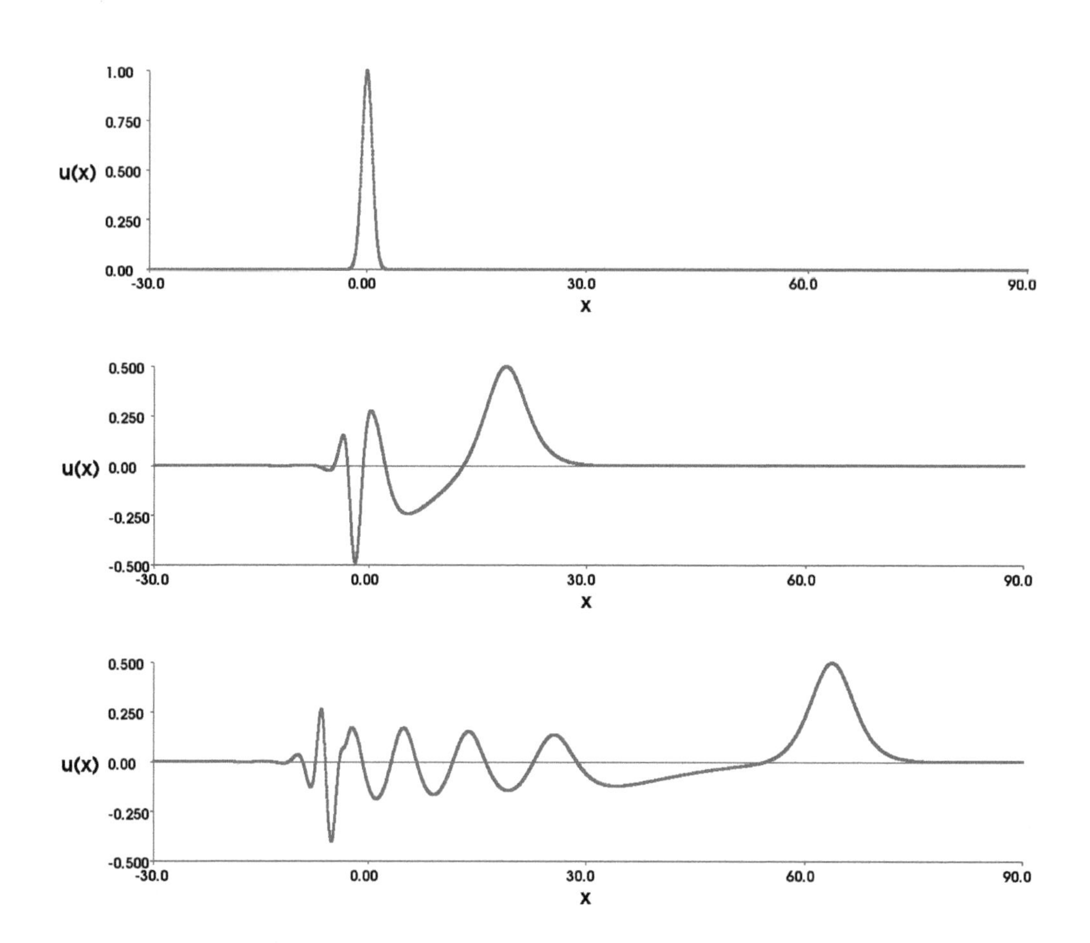

Figure 12.3: BBM solved using the variational form (12.18) via the modified Euler scheme (12.21) with $\Delta t = 0.025$ and $M = 5000$ mesh points, using piecewise linears. Top: initial data $u(x, 0) = e^{-x^2}$. Middle: solution at $T = 8$. Bottom: solution at $T = 25$.

12.4.3 Solitary waves

Despite the fact that there is both dispersion and nonlinearity in (12.17), it is possible to find special wave forms that propagate without change of shape. These are called **solitary waves**. For the equation (12.17), they take the form

$$u(x, t) = \frac{3}{2} A \operatorname{sech}^2\left(\frac{1}{2}\sqrt{\frac{A}{A+1}}(x - (1 + A)t)\right), \tag{12.22}$$

where $A > 0$ can be any positive value. Recall that

$$\operatorname{sech}(z) = \frac{2}{e^z + e^{-z}} = \frac{1}{\cosh(z)}.$$

We leave as Exercise 12.9 to explore these solutions.

12.5 Exercises

Exercise 12.1 *Verify d'Alembert's formula (12.4).*

Exercise 12.2 *Consider the ordinary differential equation*

$$\frac{\partial^2 u}{\partial t^2} + \lambda u = 0$$

and the discrete approximation

$$u^{n+1} - 2u^n + u^{n-1} + \lambda\tau^2\big(\theta u^{n+1} + (1-2\theta)u^n + \theta u^{n-1}\big) = 0. \tag{12.23}$$

Look for solutions of the form $u^n = \xi(\theta,\lambda,\tau)^n$ for ξ a potentially complex number. (Confusing notation: in u^n, n is a superscript index of a sequence, but ξ^n means "raise ξ to the power n.) Start with $\theta = 0$. Are there cases where there are solutions with $|\xi| > 1$ for some value of λ and τ? Experiment numerically with starting values $u_{-1} = 1/2$ and $u_0 = 1$ and report what happens. Explain this in terms of what you found for ξ. (Hint: write $z = \lambda\tau^2$ to simplify notation. Show that solutions only depend on z. You get a quadratic equation for ξ where z is a parameter. Analyze what the quadratic formula tells you. For the case $\theta = 0$, the scheme reduces to $u^{n+1} - (2-z)u^n + u^{n-1} = 0$, so

$$\xi(z) = \frac{2 - z \pm \sqrt{(2-z)^2 - 4}}{2} = 1 - \tfrac{1}{2}z \pm \sqrt{-z + (z/2)^2} = 1 - \tfrac{1}{2}z\Big(1 \pm \sqrt{1 - 4/z}\Big).$$

For $z \le 4$, ξ will be complex but you should get $|\xi(z)| = 1$. What happens if $z >> 4$? Check both signs.)

Exercise 12.3 *Consider the problem in Exercise 12.2 in the case $\theta = \frac{1}{2}$. Show that the discrete approximation in this case becomes*

$$u^{n+1} - 2u^n + u^{n-1} + \lambda\tau^2\big(\tfrac{1}{2}u^{n+1} + \tfrac{1}{2}u^{n-1}\big) = 0.$$

Look for solutions of the form $u^n = \xi^n$ for ξ a potentially complex number. Are there cases where there are solutions with $|\xi| > 1$ for some value of λ and τ? Experiment numerically with starting values $u_{-1} = 1/2$ and $u_0 = 1$ and report what happens. Explain this in terms of what you found for ξ. (Hint: write $z = \frac{1}{2}\lambda\tau^2$ to simplify notation. Show that solutions only depend on z. Solve the quadratic equation for ξ with z as a parameter:

$$(1+z)\xi^2 - 2\xi + (1+z) = 0.$$

Prove that

$$\xi(z) = (1+z)^{-2}\big(1 \pm \iota\sqrt{2z + z^2}\big).$$

Show that $|\xi(z)| = (1+z)^{-2}$ for all $z > 0$.)

Exercise 12.4 *Consider the problem in Exercise 12.2 in the case $\theta = \frac{1}{4}$. Derive the discrete approximation corresponding to (12.23) and verify that it can be written as*

$$(1+z)u^{n+1} - 2(1-z)u^n + (1+z)u^{n-1} = 0,$$

where $z = \frac{1}{4}\lambda\tau^2$. Derive the quadratic equation for solutions of the form $u^n = \xi^n$. Prove that

$$\xi(z) = \frac{1 - z \pm 2\iota\sqrt{z}}{1+z},$$

where $z = \frac{1}{4}\lambda\tau^2$*, and confirm that* $|\xi(z)| = 1$ *for all* $z > 0$*. Show that*

$$\xi(z) = e^{\pm\iota\, t(z)} = \cos t(z) \pm \iota \sin t(z),$$

where $\cos t(z) = (1-z)/(1+z)$ *and* $\sin t(z) = 2\sqrt{z}/(1+z)$*. Show that* $t(0) = 0$ *and* $t(z) \to \pi$ *as* $z \to \infty$*.*

Exercise 12.5 *Modify Program 12.1 to compute the difference between the computed approximation and the exact solution given by d'Alembert's formula (12.4). Compute the error in* $L^2(\Omega)$ *and plot this as a function of time. Stop well before the waves hit the Dirichlet boundary.*

Exercise 12.6 *Modify Program 12.1 to simulate wave propagation in two dimensions. Take the initial condition* $u(\mathbf{x}, 0) = e^{-|\mathbf{x}|^2}$ *and* $u_t = 0$*. Use the box* $\Omega = [-L, L]^2$ *as the computational domain. Describe what happens. How does it depend on the size of* L*?*

Exercise 12.7 *Same as Exercise 12.5, but change to the* θ *scheme with* $\theta = 1/2$*. First write out the scheme (12.12) in variational form notation for the case* $\theta = 1/2$*, then modify the program. Compute the difference between the computed approximation and the exact solution given by d'Alembert's formula (12.4) in* $L^2(\Omega)$ *and plot this as a function of time. Stop well before the waves hit the Dirichlet boundary.*

Exercise 12.8 *Show that* $U^1(\mathbf{x}, t) = u(\mathbf{x})\cos(kt)$ *and* $U^2(\mathbf{x}, t) = u(\mathbf{x})\sin(kt)$ *are solutions of the wave equation if (12.15) holds.*

Exercise 12.9 *Modify Program 12.2 to compute the evolution of the solitary wave (12.22).*

Exercise 12.10 *Modify Program 12.2 to use*

$$u(x, 0) = \epsilon\, e^{-(\delta x)^2}.$$

Take $\epsilon = \delta = 0.1$ *and describe what happens. Does the wave change shape significantly? Try different values for* δ *and* ϵ *to see what happens. When* δ *is small, the dispersive term is small compared to the advection term. When* ϵ *is small, the behavior is linear.*

```
1  import sys, math
2  from dolfin import *
3  dt=0.05
4  enn=400
5  deg=1
6  mno=2000
7  ell=10
8  tau=0.25*dt*dt
9  # Create mesh and define function space
10 mesh = IntervalMesh(mno,-ell,ell)
11 V = FunctionSpace(mesh, "Lagrange", deg)
12 # Define boundary condition
13 g = Expression("exp(-(pow(x[0], 2)))",degree=deg)
14 u0 = Expression("0",degree=deg)
15 bc = DirichletBC(V, u0, "on_boundary")
16 # Define variational problem
17 u = TrialFunction(V)
18 uold = Function(V)
19 uolder = Function(V)
20 v = TestFunction(V)
21 a = tau*inner(grad(u), grad(v))*dx + u*v*dx
22 F = 2.0*uold*v*dx - uolder*v*dx - 2.0*tau*inner(grad(uold), grad(v))*dx \
23     - tau*inner(grad(uolder), grad(v))*dx
24 u = Function(V)
25 T = enn*dt
26 t = 0
27 uold.interpolate(g)
28 uolder.interpolate(g)
29 u.assign(uold)
30 plot(u)
31 time.sleep(3)
32 while t <= T:
33     # Compute solution
34     solve(a == F, u, bc)
35     uolder.assign(uold)
36     uold.assign(u)
37     plot(u)
38     time.sleep(.01)
39     t += dt
40 interactive()
```

Program 12.1: Code to solve the wave equation and create a movie, using the θ scheme (12.12) with $\theta = 1/4$.

```
1  import sys, math
2  from dolfin import *
3  dt=0.025
4  enn=1200
5  deg=1
6  mno=5000
7  ell=90
8  ellmin=-30
9  # Create mesh and define function space
10 mesh = IntervalMesh(mno,ellmin,ell)
11 V = FunctionSpace(mesh, "Lagrange", deg)
12 # Define initial and boundary condition
13 g = Expression("exp(-(pow(x[0], 2)))")
14 u0 = Expression("0")
15 bc = DirichletBC(V, u0, "on_boundary")
16 # Define variational problem
17 u = TrialFunction(V)
18 uold = Function(V)
19 unew = Function(V)
20 v = TestFunction(V)
21 a = inner(grad(u), grad(v))*dx + u*v*dx
22 FP = inner(grad(uold), grad(v))*dx + uold*v*dx \
23     - dt*((1+uold)*uold.dx(0)*v)*dx
24 FC = inner(grad(uold), grad(v))*dx + uold*v*dx \
25     - dt*((1+uold)*uold.dx(0)*v)*dx \
26     - dt*((1+unew)*unew.dx(0)*v)*dx
27 u = Function(V)
28 T = enn*dt
29 t = 0
30 uold.interpolate(g)
31 u.assign(uold)
32 plot(u,window_width=2000,range_min=-0.5,range_max=0.5)
33 time.sleep(3)
34 while t <= T:
35     # Compute solution
36     solve(a == FP, unew, bc)
37     solve(a == FC, u, bc)
38     uold.assign(u)
39     plot(u)
40     time.sleep(.02)
41     t += dt
42 interactive()
```

Program 12.2: Code to solve (12.18) via the modified Euler scheme (12.21) and used to compute Figure 12.3.

Chapter 13

Stokes' Equations

We now study models in which the unknown functions are vector valued. This does not in itself present any major change to the variational formulation framework. However, for incompressible fluids, significant new computational features emerge. This forces attention on the numerical methods used to be sure of having valid simulations.

13.1 Model equations

The model equations for all fluids take the form

$$\mathbf{u}_t + \mathbf{u} \cdot \nabla \mathbf{u} + \nabla p = \nabla \cdot \mathbf{T} + \mathbf{f},$$

where $\mathbf{u}$ is the velocity of the fluid, p is the pressure, $\mathbf{T}$ is called the extra (or deviatoric) stress and $\mathbf{f}$ is externally given data. The models differ based on the way the stress $\mathbf{T}$ depends on the velocity $\mathbf{u}$. Time-independent models take the form

$$\mathbf{u} \cdot \nabla \mathbf{u} + \nabla p = \nabla \cdot \mathbf{T} + \mathbf{f}. \tag{13.1}$$

For incompressible fluids, the equation (13.1) is accompanied by the condition

$$\nabla \cdot \mathbf{u} = 0, \tag{13.2}$$

which we will assume holds in the following discussion. For suitable expressions for $\mathbf{T}$ defined in terms of $\mathbf{u}$, the problem (13.1) and (13.2) can be shown to be well-posed, as we indicate in special cases.

The simplest expression for the stress is linear: $\mathbf{T} = \frac{1}{2}\eta\big(\nabla \mathbf{u} + \nabla \mathbf{u}^t\big)$, where η denotes the viscosity of the fluid. Such fluids are called Newtonian. Scaling by η, (13.1) becomes

$$\frac{1}{\eta}\mathbf{u} \cdot \nabla \mathbf{u} + \nabla \hat{p} - \Delta \mathbf{u} = \hat{\mathbf{f}}, \tag{13.3}$$

where $\hat{p} = (1/\eta)p$ and $\hat{\mathbf{f}} = (1/\eta)\mathbf{f}$. When η is large, the nonlinear term multiplied by η^{-1} is often dropped, resulting in a linear system called the **Stokes equations** when (13.2) is added. When the nonlinear equation is kept, equations (13.3) and (13.2) are called the **Navier-Stokes equations**, which we consider in Chapter 20.

The Stokes equations for the flow of a viscous, incompressible, Newtonian fluid can thus be written

$$\begin{aligned} -\Delta \mathbf{u} + \nabla p &= \mathbf{f} \\ \nabla\cdot \mathbf{u} &= 0 \end{aligned} \tag{13.4}$$

in a domain $\Omega \subset \mathbb{R}^d$, where $\mathbf{u}$ denotes the fluid velocity and p denotes the pressure [190]. Here the dimension d of Ω is either 2 or 3; the two-dimensional case corresponds to fluid flow that is independent of the third dimension.

These equations must be supplemented by appropriate boundary conditions, such as the Dirichlet boundary conditions, $\mathbf{u} = \boldsymbol{\gamma}$ on $\partial\Omega$. The key compatibility condition on the data comes from the divergence theorem:

$$\oint_{\partial\Omega} \boldsymbol{\gamma} \cdot \mathbf{n}\, ds = 0, \tag{13.5}$$

which expresses conservation of mass. From now on, we assume that condition (13.5) holds.

13.1.1 Stokes variational formulation

The variational formulation of (13.4) takes the form: Find $\mathbf{u}$ such that $\mathbf{u}-\boldsymbol{\gamma} \in \mathbf{V}$ and $p \in \Pi$ such that

$$\begin{aligned} a(\mathbf{u},\mathbf{v}) + b(\mathbf{v},p) &= F(\mathbf{v}) \quad \forall \mathbf{v} \in \mathbf{V}, \\ b(\mathbf{u},q) &= 0 \quad \forall q \in \Pi, \end{aligned} \tag{13.6}$$

where, e.g., $a(\cdot,\cdot) = a_{\nabla}(\cdot,\cdot)$ and $b(\cdot,\cdot)$ are given by

$$a_{\nabla}(\mathbf{u},\mathbf{v}) := \int_{\Omega} \nabla\mathbf{u} : \nabla\mathbf{v}\, d\mathbf{x} = \int_{\Omega} \sum_{i,j=1}^{d} u_{i,j} v_{i,j}\, d\mathbf{x}, \tag{13.7}$$

$$b(\mathbf{v},q) := -\int_{\Omega} \sum_{i=1}^{d} v_{i,i} q\, d\mathbf{x}, \tag{13.8}$$

and $F \in \mathbf{V}'$, the dual space of $\mathbf{V}$ defined in Section 2.5. The variational formulation (13.6) is derived (Exercise 13.1) by multiplying (13.4) by $\mathbf{v}$ with a "dot" product, and integrating by parts as usual. Note that the second equations in (13.4) and (13.6) are related by multiplying the former by q and integrating, with no integration by parts.

The spaces $\mathbf{V}$ and Π are as follows. In the case of simple Dirichlet data on the entire boundary, $\mathbf{V}$ consists of the d-fold Cartesian product of the subset $H_0^1(\Omega)$ of $H^1(\Omega)$ of functions vanishing on the boundary. In this case, Π is the subset of $L^2(\Omega)$ consisting of functions having mean zero. The latter constraint corresponds to fixing an ambient pressure. Note that

$$\Pi = \nabla\cdot \mathbf{V}. \tag{13.9}$$

Another variational formulation for (13.4) can be derived which is equivalent in some ways, but not identical to (13.6). Define

$$\boldsymbol{\epsilon}(\mathbf{u})_{ij} = \tfrac{1}{2}\left(u_{i,j} + u_{j,i}\right) \tag{13.10}$$

and

$$a_\epsilon(\mathbf{u},\mathbf{v}) := 2\int_\Omega \sum_{i,j=1}^{d} \epsilon(\mathbf{u})_{ij}\epsilon(\mathbf{v})_{ij}\,d\mathbf{x} = 2\int_\Omega \epsilon(\mathbf{u}) : \epsilon(\mathbf{v})\,d\mathbf{x}. \tag{13.11}$$

Then it can be shown (Exercise 13.2) that

$$a_\epsilon(\mathbf{u},\mathbf{v}) := a_\nabla(\mathbf{u},\mathbf{v}) \tag{13.12}$$

provided only that $\nabla\cdot\mathbf{u} = \mathbf{0}$ in Ω and $\mathbf{v} = \mathbf{0}$ on $\partial\Omega$ or $\nabla\cdot\mathbf{v} = 0$ in Ω and $\mathbf{u} = \mathbf{0}$ on $\partial\Omega$. However, the natural boundary conditions associated with a_ϵ and a_∇ are quite different [154].

Inhomogeneous Dirichlet data can be incorporated in a standard variational problem much like the scalar case (Exercise 3.1 and Section 5.1) but with a twist. The variational formulation (13.6) can be written with $\mathbf{u} = \mathbf{u}_0 + \gamma$ where $\mathbf{u}_0 \in \mathbf{V}$ and $p \in \Pi$ satisfy

$$\begin{aligned} a(\mathbf{u}_0,\mathbf{v}) + b(\mathbf{v},p) &= F(\mathbf{v}) - a(\gamma,\mathbf{v}) \quad \forall\mathbf{v}\in\mathbf{V}, \\ b(\mathbf{u}_0,q) &= -b(\gamma,q) \quad \forall q\in\Pi. \end{aligned} \tag{13.13}$$

The twist is that the second equation becomes inhomogeneous as well, unless by chance γ is divergence free.

Changing notation, if necessary, from $\mathbf{u}_0$ to $\mathbf{u}$, we can thus think of the general Stokes variational problem as being of the following form:

$$\begin{aligned} &\text{Find } \mathbf{u} \text{ such that } \mathbf{u}\in\mathbf{V} \text{ and } p\in\Pi \text{ such that} \\ a(\mathbf{u},\mathbf{v}) + b(\mathbf{v},p) &= F(\mathbf{v}) \quad \forall\mathbf{v}\in\mathbf{V}, \\ b(\mathbf{u},q) &= G(q) \quad \forall q\in\Pi. \end{aligned} \tag{13.14}$$

We now describe the basic theory that justifies the well-posedness of this variational formulation.

13.1.2 Well-posedness of Stokes

We assume, as always, that the bilinear forms satisfy the continuity conditions

$$\begin{aligned} |a(\mathbf{v},\mathbf{w})| &\le C_a\|\mathbf{v}\|_{\mathbf{V}}\|\mathbf{w}\|_{\mathbf{V}} \quad \forall\mathbf{v},\mathbf{w}\in\mathbf{V} \\ |b(\mathbf{v},q)| &\le C_b\|\mathbf{v}\|_{\mathbf{V}}\|q\|_\Pi \quad \forall\mathbf{v}\in\mathbf{V},\ q\in\Pi \end{aligned} \tag{13.15}$$

for finite, positive constants C_a and C_b. This is easily proven for the Stokes problem. However, the Lax-Milgram theory does not suffice to establish the well-posedness of the Stokes equations due in part to the asymmetry of the equations for the variables $\mathbf{u}$ and p. Indeed, the second equation in (13.14) may be thought of as a simple constraint: $\nabla\cdot\mathbf{u} = 0$. Thus it is natural to consider the space $\mathbf{Z}$ defined by

$$\mathbf{Z} = \{\mathbf{v}\in\mathbf{V} \,:\, b(\mathbf{v},q) = 0 \quad \forall q\in\Pi\} = \{\mathbf{v}\in\mathbf{V} \,:\, \nabla\cdot\mathbf{v} = 0\}. \tag{13.16}$$

We may simplify the variational formulation (13.14) to: find $\mathbf{u}\in\mathbf{Z}$ such that

$$a(\mathbf{u},\mathbf{v}) = F(\mathbf{v}) \quad \forall\mathbf{v}\in\mathbf{Z}, \tag{13.17}$$

which is a standard variational formulation. Thus the problem for $\mathbf{u}$ is wellposed if $a(\cdot,\cdot)$ is coercive on $\mathbf{Z}$:

$$\|\mathbf{v}\|_{H^1(\Omega)}^2 \le c_0\, a(\mathbf{v},\mathbf{v}) \quad \forall\mathbf{v}\in\mathbf{Z} \tag{13.18}$$

for some finite, positive constant c_0. We will see that this framework is useful for other, so-called **mixed formulations** as well.

The bound (13.18) can be proved for both of the forms a_∇ and a_ϵ with suitable boundary conditions, for all of $\mathbf{V}$ as well. The proof is familiar in the case of a_∇, since the only functions for which $a_\nabla(\mathbf{v},\mathbf{v})=0$ are constants. The coercivity of a_ϵ is called Korn's inequality [57].

Well-posedness for the pressure follows from the **inf-sup** condition

$$\|q\|_{L^2(\Omega)} \le C \sup_{0\neq\mathbf{v}\in\mathbf{V}} \frac{b(\mathbf{v},q)}{\|\mathbf{v}\|_{H^1(\Omega)}}, \quad \forall q\in\Pi, \tag{13.19}$$

which is proved [13] by solving $\nabla\cdot\mathbf{v}=q$ with $\mathbf{v}\in\mathbf{V}$ and $\|\mathbf{v}\|_{H_0^1}\le C\|q\|_{L^2}$. (For motivation regarding this inequality, see Exercise 3.2.) The term inf-sup encapsulates the fact that we assume that (13.19) holds for all $q\in\Pi$, so that

$$\frac{1}{C} \le \inf_{0\neq q\in\Pi} \sup_{0\neq\mathbf{v}\in H_0^1(\Omega)} \frac{b(\mathbf{v},q)}{\|\mathbf{v}\|_{H^1(\Omega)}\|q\|_{L^2(\Omega)}}.$$

Suppose that $\boldsymbol{\gamma}=\mathbf{0}$ and $F=0$. Then (13.17) implies that $\mathbf{u}=0$, and so from (13.14) we have

$$b(\mathbf{v},p)=0 \quad \forall\mathbf{v}\in\mathbf{V}.$$

It follows from (13.19) that $p=0$. Thus coercivity of $a(\cdot,\cdot)$ and the inf-sup condition (13.19) together guarantee uniqueness of the solution of (13.14). It can similarly be shown that they imply existence and stability [143].

13.2 Mixed method formulation

Here it is useful to abstract the Stokes formulation to a general mixed form. This will be pursued further in Section 18.1. The general formulation of (13.14) is of the form

$$\begin{aligned} a(u,v)+b(v,p) &= F(v) \quad \forall v\in V\\ b(u,q) &= G(q) \quad \forall q\in\Pi, \end{aligned} \tag{13.20}$$

where V and Π are two Hilbert spaces and $F\in V'$ and $G\in\Pi'$ (the "primes" indicate dual spaces, Section 2.5). The general formulation of the discretization of (13.14) is of the form

$$\begin{aligned} a(u_h,v)+b(v,p_h) &= F(v) \quad \forall v\in V_h\\ b(u_h,q) &= G(q) \quad \forall q\in\Pi_h, \end{aligned} \tag{13.21}$$

where the default assumption is that $V_h\subset V$ and $\Pi_h\subset\Pi$. It is called a **mixed method** since the variables v and q are mixed together. For the Stokes problem (13.14), the natural variational formulation is already a mixed method, whereas it is an optional formulation in other settings (see Section 18.1). The main twist in the variational formulation of mixed methods with inhomogeneous boundary conditions is that the term G is not zero [256].

We assume there is a continuous operator $\mathcal{D}: V\to\Pi$ such that

$$b(v,p)=(\mathcal{D}v,p)_\Pi \quad \forall p. \tag{13.22}$$

In the Stokes problem, $\mathcal{D}=\nabla\cdot$.

Let $P_\Pi G$ denote the Riesz representation of G in Π, that is, $P_\Pi G \in \Pi$ satisfies

$$(P_\Pi G, q)_\Pi = G(q) \quad \forall q \in \Pi . \tag{13.23}$$

It is equivalent to pose the variational formulation (13.20) as

$$\begin{aligned} a(u,v) + b(v,p) &= F(v) \quad \forall v \in V \\ b(u,q) &= (g,q)_\Pi \quad \forall q \in \Pi, \end{aligned} \tag{13.24}$$

where $g = P_\Pi G$. This is the form of the mixed-method analyzed in [57]. In the Stokes problem, $g = -\nabla\cdot\gamma$.

In a similar way, we can define the Riesz representation of G in Π_h, $P_{\Pi_h} G \in \Pi_h$, by the variational equation

$$(P_{\Pi_h} G, q)_\Pi = G(q) \quad \forall q \in \Pi_h . \tag{13.25}$$

Then the discrete mixed problem can be written

$$\begin{aligned} a(u_h,v) + b(v,p_h) &= F(v) \quad \forall v \in V_h \\ b(u_h,q) &= (g_h,q) \quad \forall q \in \Pi_h, \end{aligned} \tag{13.26}$$

where $g_h = P_{\Pi_h} G$. Note that the second equation in (13.21) says that

$$P_{\Pi_h} \mathcal{D} u_h = P_{\Pi_h} G = g_h, \tag{13.27}$$

where we also use $P_{\Pi_h} q$ to denote the Π-projection of $q \in \Pi$ onto Π_h ($q = \mathcal{D}u_h$ here).

We assume that the bilinear forms satisfy the continuity conditions (13.15) and the coercivity conditions

$$\alpha \|v\|_V^2 \le a(v,v) \quad \forall v \in Z \cup Z_h, \tag{13.28}$$

$$\beta \|p\|_\Pi \le \sup_{v \in V_h} \frac{b(v,p)}{\|v\|_V} \quad \forall p \in \Pi_h, \tag{13.29}$$

where $\alpha, \beta > 0$. (For motivation regarding the second inequality, see Exercise 3.2.) Here Z and Z_h are defined by

$$Z = \{ v \in V \ : \ b(v,q) = 0 \quad \forall q \in \Pi \} \tag{13.30}$$

and

$$Z_h = \{ v \in V_h \ : \ b(v,q) = 0 \quad \forall q \in \Pi_h \} \tag{13.31}$$

respectively.

The mixed formulation can be posed in the canonical variational form (3.8) by writing

$$\begin{aligned} \mathcal{A}((u,p),(v,q)) :=& a(u,v) + b(v,p) + b(u,q) \\ \mathcal{F}((v,q)) :=& G(q) + F(v) \end{aligned} \tag{13.32}$$

for all $(v,q) \in \mathcal{V} := V \times \Pi$. More precisely, we solve for $(u,p) \in \mathcal{V}$ satisfying

$$\mathcal{A}((u,p),(v,q)) = \mathcal{F}((v,q)) \quad \forall\, (v,q) \in \mathcal{V}. \tag{13.33}$$

The discrete version of (13.33) can be solved by direct methods (e.g., Gaussian elimination). However, this system is not positive definite, and more efficient algorithms can be used in special cases, as we discuss in Section 14.2. You can see that the linear system is not positive definite because it is not coercive:

$$\mathcal{A}((0,q),(0,q)) = 0 \quad \forall q \in \Pi.$$

The system is invertible, so it must have negative eigenvalues, because it is a symmetric matrix.

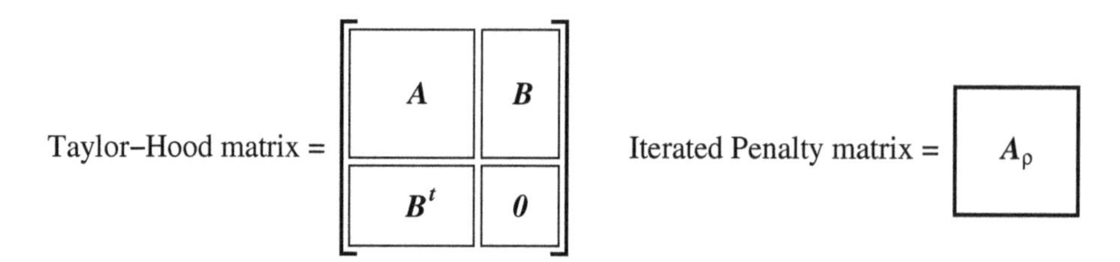

Figure 13.1: Comparison of the matrix sizes for Taylor-Hood and the iterated penalty method. The full matrix for Taylor-Hood includes blocks $\mathbf{B}$ and $\mathbf{B}^t$ corresponding to the variational form $b(v, q)$ for $v \in V_h$ and $q \in \Pi_h$. The iterated penalty method involves a matrix just the size of $\mathbf{A}$, the matrix corresponding to the variational form $a(v, w)$ for $v, w \in V_h$.

13.3 Taylor-Hood method

One of the first widely-used pairs of spaces for the Stokes equations (13.14) was the so-called Taylor-Hood spaces, as follows. Let V_h^k denote C^0 piecewise polynomials of degree k on a triangulation $\mathcal{T}_h$ of a polygonal domain $\Omega \subset \mathbb{R}^d$. Let

$$V_h = \left\{ \mathbf{v} \in \left(V_h^k\right)^d \ : \ \mathbf{v} = 0 \text{ on } \partial\Omega \right\} \tag{13.34}$$

and let

$$\Pi_h = \left\{ q \in V_h^{k-1} \ : \ \int_\Omega q(x)\, d\mathbf{x} = 0 \right\}. \tag{13.35}$$

It has been proved that (13.28) and (13.29) hold for these spaces in both two and three dimensions under very mild restrictions on the mesh [42].

Note that $Z_h \not\subset Z$ for the Taylor-Hood method. One drawback of Taylor-Hood is that the divergence free condition can be substantially violated, leading to a loss of mass conservation [198]. This can be avoided if we force the divergence constraint to be satisfied by a penalty method [66, 75]. Another issue for Taylor-Hood is the need to solve an indefinite linear system. This can be alleviated by an iterated penalty method, as discussed in Section 14.2.

Another difficulty with the Taylor-Hood method is that it is necessary to construct the constrained space Π_h in (13.35). Many systems, including `dolfin`, do not provide a simple way to construct such a subspace of a space like V_h^{k-1} satisfying a constraint (e.g., mean zero). Thus special linear algebra must be performed. Finally, we will see that it is possible to avoid Π_h completely, leading to smaller and better behaved systems (see Figure 13.1) [223]. The study of mixed methods is extensive as indicated in part in the review article [172].

13.4 Constraint counting

Analogous to (13.17), the discrete version of the Stokes equations can be written as: find $\mathbf{u}_h \in Z_h$ such that

$$a(\mathbf{u}_h, \mathbf{v}) = F(\mathbf{v}) \quad \forall \mathbf{v} \in Z_h. \tag{13.36}$$

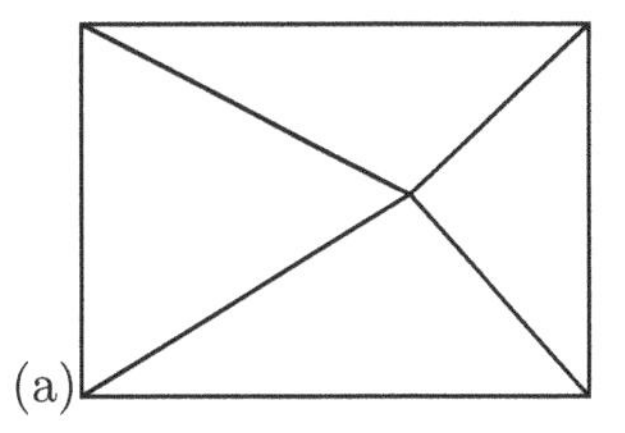

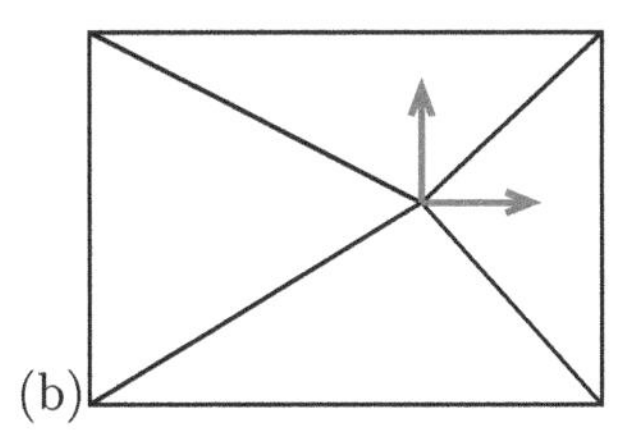

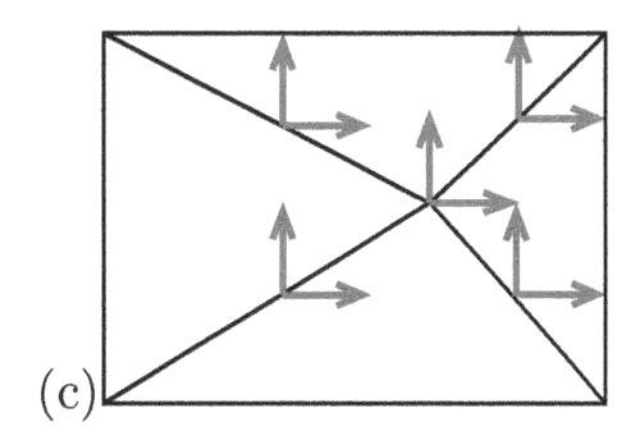

Figure 13.2: (a) A triangulation with only one interior vertex; (b) degrees of freedom for piecewise linear vector functions on this mesh that vanish on the boundary; (c) degrees of freedom for piecewise quadratic vector functions on this mesh that vanish on the boundary.

If we have $Z_h \subset Z$, then Céa's Theorem 4.1 implies the error $\mathbf{u} - \mathbf{u}_h$ is bounded by the best approximation from Z_h:

$$\|\mathbf{u} - \mathbf{u}_h\|_{H^1(\Omega)} \leq \frac{C_a}{\alpha} \|\mathbf{u} - \mathbf{v}\|_{H^1(\Omega)} \quad \forall \mathbf{v} \in Z_h. \tag{13.37}$$

In particular, this shows that the viability of the velocity approximation does not depend on the inf-sup condition (13.29). If V_h is of the form (13.34), the space Z_h contains the curl of C^1 piecewise polynomials of one higher degree ($k+1$), and this space has good approximation properties for sufficiently high degree.

So it might appear that the pressure and its approximation play no significant role, with the only issue being to see that the space Z_h is not over-constrained. But in fact it can be. When we choose the pressure space, we are choosing something to constrain the divergence of the velocity space. This is the main issue with the linkage between the pressure approximation space and the velocity approximation space.

To understand this, take V_h to be vector Lagrange elements of degree k in two dimensions that vanish on $\partial\Omega$, as in (13.34), where Ω is the rectangle depicted in Figure 13.2(a). The divergence of such (vector) elements form a subspace of discontinuous, mean-zero finite elements of degree $k-1$. So we can begin by understanding how these two spaces are related. Let us simply count the number of degrees of freedom for the mesh depicted in Figure 13.2.

There are only two degrees of freedom, as indicated in Figure 13.2(b), for piecewise linear vector functions on this mesh that vanish on the boundary. That is, $\dim V_h = 2$ for $k=1$. If we take Π_h to be piecewise constants on this mesh which have mean zero, then $\dim \Pi_h = 3$ (one for each triangle, minus 1 for the mean-zero constraint.) Thus we see that the inf-sup condition (13.29) cannot hold; V_h is only two-dimensional, so the three-dimensional space Π_h must have a p orthogonal to $\nabla\cdot\mathbf{v}$ for all $\mathbf{v} \in V_h$. Moreover, it is not hard to see that $Z_h = \{\mathbf{0}\}$, the space with only the zero function.

For V_h being piecewise quadratic ($k=2$) vector functions on the mesh in Figure 13.2(a), the dimension of V_h is 10, as shown in Figure 13.2(c); there are 4 edge nodes and 1 vertex node, and 2 degrees of freedom for each. If we take Π_h to be discontinuous piecewise linears on this mesh which have mean zero, then $\dim \Pi_h = 11$ (three for each triangle, minus 1 for the mean-zero constraint.) Thus we see that V_h is still too small to match Π_h, just by dimensional analysis.

One way to resolve this dilemma is to reduce the number of constraints implied by $b(\mathbf{v}, q) = 0$. This could be done by making the pressure space smaller, or (equivalently as it turns out) reducing the accuracy of integration in computing $b(\mathbf{v}, q)$. Such reduced or selective integration has been extensively studied [210]. The Taylor-Hood method makes Π_h smaller by requiring continuity; for $k = 2$, the dimension of Π_h as defined in (13.35) on the mesh in Figure 13.2(a) is 5.

13.4.1 Higher-degree approximation

Another way to eliminate the bad effects of constraints is to go to higher-degree polynomials. We know that the velocity approximation just depends on having good approximation from Z_h, based on (13.37). Moreover, if V_h is as defined in (13.34), then we know that Z_h contains the curl of all C^1 piecewise polynomials of degree $k+1$ (that vanish to second order on the boundary). In two dimensions, the Argyris element [57] is well defined for degree five and higher, so it is natural to examine the case $k \geq 4$ in two dimensions.

For V_h being piecewise quartic ($k = 4$) vector functions on the mesh in Figure 13.2(a), $\dim V_h = 50$ (there are 3 nodes per edge, 3 nodes per triangle and one vertex node). Correspondingly, if Π_h consists of discontinuous piecewise cubics with mean zero, then $\dim \Pi_h = 39$ (10 degrees of freedom per triangle and one mean-zero constraint). Thus we do have $\dim V_h >> \dim \Pi_h$ in this case. However, the counting of constraints has to be more careful. The divergence operator maps V_h to Π_h, with its image being some subspace W_h of Π_h, and its kernel is Z_h. So $\dim V_h = \dim W_h + \dim Z_h$. We hope that $W_h = \Pi_h$, which is true if $\dim W_h = \dim \Pi_h = 39$. Thus we need to show that $\dim Z_h = 11$ in this case. More precisely, since $\dim W_h \leq \dim \Pi_h = 39$,

$$\dim Z_h = \dim V_h - \dim W_h \geq \dim V_h - \dim \Pi_h = 50 - 39 = 11.$$

Thus we need to show that $\dim Z_h \leq 11$.

We can write $Z_h = \operatorname{curl} S_h$ where S_h is the space of C^1 (scalar) piecewise quintic functions on the mesh in Figure 13.2(a) that vanish to second order on the boundary. One can check that, indeed, this space is specified uniquely by 11 parameters [224]. Moreover, under some mesh restrictions, it can be shown [258, 257] that the inf-sup condition (13.29) holds with $\beta > 0$ independent of the mesh size.

When $\Pi_h = \nabla\cdot V_h$, the resulting algorithm is often called the Scott-Vogelius method [66, 75, 199, 200, 257, 258]. In Section 14.2, we consider an algorithm for solving for the velocity and pressure without dealing explicitly with the pressure space Π_h, facilitating the choice $\Pi_h = \nabla\cdot V_h$.

13.4.2 Malkus crossed-quadrilaterals

David Malkus realized that there was something special about triangulations involving crossed-quadrilaterals, that is, quadrilaterals containing four triangles obtained by drawing the two diagonals of the quadrilateral, as shown in Figure 13.3(a). He referred to such elements as **crossed triangles** [209]. The vertices where the diagonals cross are known as **singular vertices** [224, 225]. At such vertices, the characterization of $\nabla\cdot V_h$ changes. In addition to the fact that the average of $p \in \nabla\cdot V_h$ must be zero over the four elements when homogeneous Dirichlet conditions hold on the boundary of the quadrilateral, now there is a local condition constraining p at the singular vertex. Since p is discontinuous, let us denote the four values of p at the singular vertex σ by

$$\pi^1 = p_{ab}(\sigma), \quad \pi^2 = p_{bc}(\sigma), \quad \pi^3 = p_{cd}(\sigma), \quad \pi^4 = p_{da}(\sigma), \tag{13.38}$$

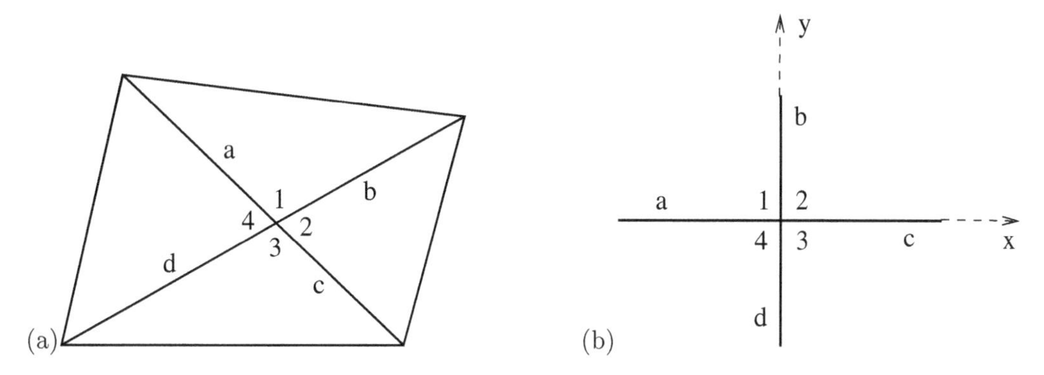

Figure 13.3: (a) A triangulation based on the diagonals of a quadrilateral in which opposite edges are parallel: $a\|c$, $b\|d$. (b) Notation for understanding local constraint at a singular vertex.

where p_{ij} denotes the restriction of p in the triangle with edges i, j at the central vertex σ. Then the singular vertex condition is that

$$\pi^1 - \pi^2 + \pi^3 - \pi^4 = 0. \tag{13.39}$$

To see why (13.39) must hold, it helps to consider a simple example in which the two diagonals are orthogonal, as indicated in Figure 13.3(b). In this case, we can assume, without loss of generality, that the edges lie on the x and y axes, as indicated in Figure 13.3(b). Let the velocity vector be denoted by (u, v). Since u is continuous on the edge a, $u_{,x}$ is also continuous on the edge a. Using notation similar to (13.38), we can say that $u_{ab,x}(\sigma) - u_{ad,x}(\sigma) = 0$. Similarly, $u_{bc,x}(\sigma) - u_{cd,x}(\sigma) = 0$. Subtracting the second expression from the one before gives

$$u_{ab,x}(\sigma) - u_{bc,x}(\sigma) + u_{cd,x}(\sigma) - u_{ad,x}(\sigma) = 0.$$

A similar argument can be applied to $v_{,y}$, and adding the two expressions yields (13.39). We leave an Exercise 13.4 to prove (13.39) in the general case when the diagonals are not perpendicular.

The import of the condition (13.39) is a reduction in the size of the space $\nabla\cdot V_h$. This means that there are only two degrees of freedom in the target discontinuous piecewise constant subspace in the case $k = 1$. Thus the two degrees of freedom indicated in Figure 13.2(b) are just enough to match the corresponding pressure variables, leading to a well-posed numerical method for $k = 1$ on crossed-triangle meshes. Moreover, an explicit basis of Π_h is available. In terms of the π variables, a basis consists of

$$(1, 0, -1, 0) \quad \text{and} \quad (1, 1, -1, -1),$$

in each quadrilateral. Unfortunately, the inf-sup condition (13.29) does not hold uniformly in h: $\beta \to 0$ as $h \to 0$ [238, 239]. However, the velocity approximation is the expected order due to the fact that the space Z_h can be identified as the curl of the Powell space [237]. For more details, see [238, 239]. In particular, these results show that the inf-sup condition is not necessary, only sufficient, for successful velocity approximation.

13.5 Exercises

Exercise 13.1 *Carry out the derivation of the variational formulation (13.6). (Hint: write out the dot-products as a sum and apply the scalar case.)*

Exercise 13.2 *Prove that (13.12) holds provided only that* $\nabla\cdot\mathbf{u}=0$ *in* Ω *and* $\mathbf{v}=\mathbf{0}$ *on* $\partial\Omega$ *or* $\nabla\cdot\mathbf{v}=0$ *in* Ω *and* $\mathbf{u}=\mathbf{0}$ *on* $\partial\Omega$. *(Hint: first verify that*

$$\nabla\mathbf{u}:\nabla\mathbf{v}=2\epsilon(\mathbf{u}):\epsilon(\mathbf{v})-\sum_{i,j=1}^{d}u_{i,j}v_{j,i} \tag{13.40}$$

and then integrate by parts.)

Exercise 13.3 *Define the linear functional* F *in (13.17) that corresponds to the nonhomogeneous Dirichlet problem in the variational formulation (13.14).*

Exercise 13.4 *Prove (13.39) in the general case when the diagonals are not perpendicular.*

Exercise 13.5 *Consider a mesh consisting of crossed quadrilaterals, as shown in Figure 13.4(a). Let* V_h *denote piecewise linears on this mesh that vanish on the boundary. Let* $\Pi_h=\nabla\cdot V_h$. *Prove that* Π_h *consists of piecewise constants satisfying the constraint (13.39) in each quadrilateral together with the global mean-zero constraint. Show that each element of* Π_h *can be represented in each quadrilateral in the form of a sum of three basis functions*

$$P_1=(1,0,-1,0) \quad \text{and} \quad P_2=(1,1,-1,-1) \text{ and } \quad P_3=(1,1,1,1),$$

where the individual values of the four-vector are the values of the basis function in each triangle in a given quadrilateral. Note that the global mean-zero constraint just involves the coefficients of the basis functions P_3 *in each quadrilateral, namely that the sum of the coefficients is zero. Prove the* $\inf-\sup$ *condition for this mesh for the pair* V_h *and* Π_h. *(Hint: In Section 13.4.2, we indicated how to construct* $\mathbf{v}\in V_h$ *such that* $\mathbf{v}$ *is supported in a given triangle and* $\nabla\cdot\mathbf{v}=c_1P_1+c_2P_2$. *Thus we need only construct* $\mathbf{v}$ *to match the pressures that are piecewise constant on each quadrilateral. Consider piecewise linear velocities supported on the mesh indicated in Figure 13.4(b). Construct two different velocity functions whose divergence is as indicated in Figure 13.5. Use these functions to control a discrete form of the gradient of the pressure and modify the argument in [57, Section 12.6].)*

Exercise 13.6 *The term* **spurious modes** *refers to pressure variables that are not properly controlled by the divergence of the velocity test functions. You can have good approximation in the velocity space and yet have spurious pressure modes. Consider the crossed meshes in Figure 13.4(a) and let* V_h *be piecewise linear functions on such a mesh that vanish on the boundary. Let* Π_h *be all piecewise constants that have global mean zero on this mesh. Prove that* Z_h *has good approximation properties. Also show that the spurious modes can be characterized as having the quartet of values given by the checkerboard pattern* $P_4=(+1,-1,+1,-1)$. *(Hint: note that* Z_h *is the same as if we took* $\Pi_h=\nabla\cdot V_h$ *and apply the stability result of Exercise 13.5.)*

Exercise 13.7 *Consider the spaces introduced in Exercise 13.6, that is, let* V_h *be piecewise linear functions on a crossed mesh that vanish on the boundary. Let* Π_h *be all piecewise constants that have global mean zero on this mesh. Compute the solution of a smooth problem with these spaces. What happens?*

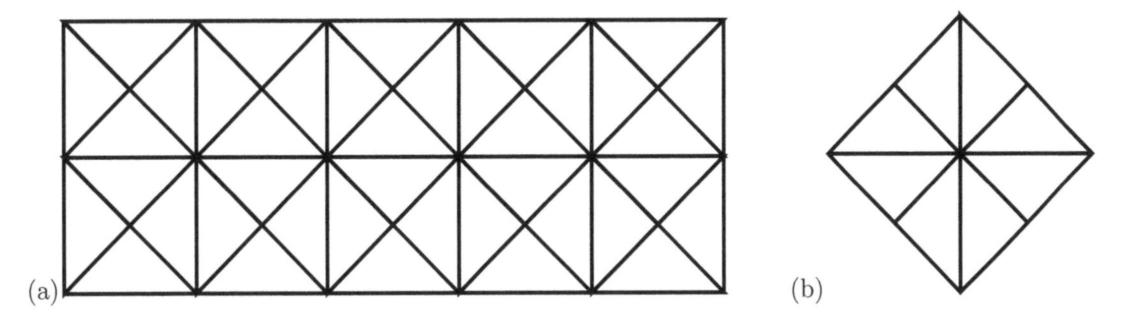

Figure 13.4: (a) A triangulation consisting of crossed quadrilaterals. (b) Support of additional velocity test functions.

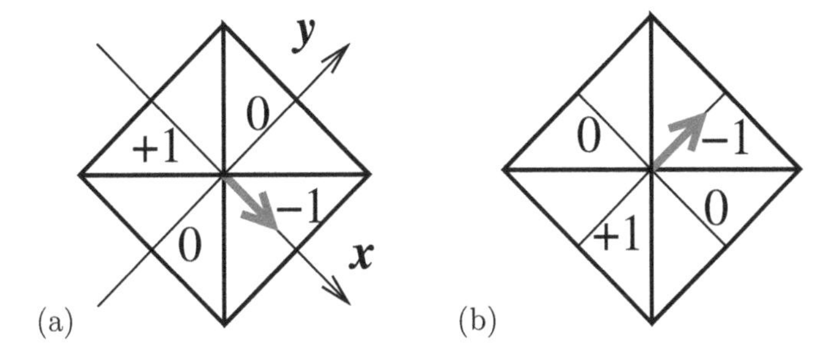

Figure 13.5: Values of divergence of piecewise linear vectors on the mesh indicated in Figure 13.4(a) for two different velocity test functions.

Chapter 14

Exact Divergence Methods

For many fluid problems, the second equation in (13.4) is the most critical [198]. Thus there has been significant interest [128, 172, 157] in numerical methods that can yield velocities with exact divergence zero. The Scott-Vogelius algorithm [257, 258] provided one of the first such methods.

14.1 The Scott-Vogelius algorithm

The Scott-Vogelius algorithm [257, 258] consists of using the velocity spaced defined in (13.34) for the Taylor-Hood method, but instead of using (13.35) for the pressure space, we choose

$$\Pi_h = \nabla\cdot V_h. \tag{14.1}$$

This has been generalized to other choices of V_h [94, 121, 128, 156, 157, 290]. Another approach to exact satisfaction of the divergence constraint is to work in spaces with relaxed regularity [97].

14.1.1 Convergence of Scott-Vogelius

The choice of pressure space (14.1) implies that $Z_h \subset Z$, and so the velocity error is governed by best approximation (13.37). When the inf-sup condition (13.28) holds with β independent of h, then best-approximation from Z_h may be related to best-approximation from V_h:

$$\|\mathbf{u}-\mathbf{u}_h\|_{H^1(\Omega)} \leq \frac{1}{\alpha}\inf_{\mathbf{v}\in Z_h}\|\mathbf{u}-\mathbf{v}\|_{H^1(\Omega)} \leq \frac{C}{\alpha\beta}\inf_{\mathbf{v}\in V_h}\|\mathbf{u}-\mathbf{v}\|_{H^1(\Omega)}. \tag{14.2}$$

When the inf-sup condition holds independently of the mesh, one also obtains the following approximation result for the pressure:

$$\|p-p_h\|_{L^2(\Omega)} \leq \frac{C}{\beta}\Big(\inf_{\mathbf{v}\in V_h}\|\mathbf{u}-\mathbf{v}\|_{H^1(\Omega)} + \inf_{q\in\Pi_h}\|p-q\|_{L^2(\Omega)}\Big). \tag{14.3}$$

Table 14.1 describes mesh restrictions under which the inf-sup bound (13.29) is known to hold with β independent of mesh size, in two and three dimensions, for various values of k. Boundary singular vertices and nearly singular (interior) vertices are defined in [57, page 319]. Note that there is no restriction against having singular interior vertices (crossed

d	k	mesh restrictions	references
2	2	some crossed triangles required	[238, 239]
2	3	some new conditions	[159]
2	≥ 4	no nearly singular vertices	[257, 258, 160]
3	≥ 6	only one family $\mathcal{T}_h$ known	[289]

Table 14.1: Known inf-sup bounds under mesh restrictions for exact divergence-free piecewise polynomials; V_h defined in (13.34) and Π_h given by (14.1). Key: $d =$ dimension of Ω, $k =$ degree of polynomials.

triangles or crossed quadrilaterals) in the mesh in two dimensions. The inf-sup constant can, however, degenerate if such vertices are nonsingular but very close to being singular [57, page 319].

14.1.2 The unified Stokes algorithm

The Scott-Vogelius algorithm produces a very accurate velocity approximation with exact divergence zero, but the corresponding pressure approximation is discontinuous. By contrast, the Taylor-Hood pressure approximation is continuous but the velocity does not preserve mass. The unified Stokes algorithm (USA) combines the best of these two methods and eliminates the bad features. More precisely, the velocity approximation is exactly the same as for the Scott-Vogelius algorithm, but the pressure is obtained by projecting the Scott-Vogelius pressure onto the continuous pressure space (13.35) used in the Taylor-Hood method. Algorithmically, write the Scott-Vogelius pressure $p = \nabla\cdot \mathbf{w}$ for some $\mathbf{w} \in V_h$. Then the unified Stokes pressure $\hat{p}_h$ is defined by

$$(\hat{p}_h, q)_{L^2(\Omega)} = (\nabla\cdot \mathbf{w}, q)_{L^2(\Omega)} \quad \forall q \in \Pi_h.$$

We will show subsequently that $\hat{p}_h$ is easy to compute, by identifying $\mathbf{w}$.

When the inf-sup condition holds independently of the mesh, the unified Stokes pressure $\hat{p}_h$ also satisfies [223]

$$\|p - \hat{p}_h\|_{L^2(\Omega)} \leq \frac{C}{\beta}\Big(\inf_{\mathbf{v}\in V_h} \|\mathbf{u}-\mathbf{v}\|_{H^1(\Omega)} + \inf_{q\in\Pi_h} \|p - q\|_{L^2(\Omega)}\Big). \tag{14.4}$$

14.2 Iterated penalty method

When a system of equations is written as one equation that holds for a constrained set of variables, iterative techniques can be used to solve them that may be efficient. The idea is to represent the constraint via an operator that is applied in an iterative fashion (with some penalty) until the constraint is satisfied to a desired tolerance.

Consider a general mixed method of the form (13.21). To conform to the analysis in [57], suppose now that $\Pi_h = \mathcal{D}V_h$. Let $\rho' \in \mathbb{R}$ and $\rho > 0$. The iterated penalty method defines $u^n \in V_h$ and p^n by

$$\begin{aligned} a(u^n, v) + \rho' (\mathcal{D}u^n, \mathcal{D}v)_\Pi &= F(v) - b(v, p^n) + \rho' G(\mathcal{D}v) \quad \forall v \in V_h \\ p^{n+1} &= p^n + \rho\,(\mathcal{D}u^n - P_{\Pi_h} G), \end{aligned} \tag{14.5}$$

where $P_{\Pi_h} G$ is defined in (13.25) and we start with $p^0 = 0$. One important feature of the iterated penalty method is that the linear system of equations represented by the first equation in (14.5) for u^n is symmetric if $a(\cdot,\cdot)$ is symmetric, and it is positive definite if $a(\cdot,\cdot)$ is coercive and $\rho' > 0$. If we begin with $p^0 = 0$ then, for all $n > 0$,

$$p^n = \rho\mathcal{D}\bigg(\sum_{i=0}^{n-1} u^i\bigg) - n\rho P_{\Pi_h} G = \mathcal{D}w^n - n\rho P_{\Pi_h} G, \tag{14.6}$$

where

$$w^n := \rho \sum_{i=0}^{n-1} u^i. \tag{14.7}$$

Note that

$$b(v, p^n) = (\mathcal{D}v, p^n)_\Pi = (\mathcal{D}v, \mathcal{D}w^n)_\Pi - n\rho(\mathcal{D}v, P_{\Pi_h} G)_\Pi = (\mathcal{D}v, \mathcal{D}w^n)_\Pi - n\rho\, G(\mathcal{D}v), \tag{14.8}$$

since $\mathcal{D}v \in \Pi_h$. Therefore, the iterated penalty method can be written equivalently as

$$\begin{aligned} a(u^n, v) + \rho'\,(\mathcal{D}u^n, \mathcal{D}v)_\Pi &= F(v) - (\mathcal{D}v, \mathcal{D}w^n)_\Pi + n\rho\, G(\mathcal{D}v) + \rho' G(\mathcal{D}v) \quad \forall v \in V_h \\ w^{n+1} &= w^n + \rho u^n, \end{aligned} \tag{14.9}$$

where $w^0 = 0$. In the case $\rho' = \rho$ (14.9) simplifies to

$$\begin{aligned} a(u^n, v) + \rho\,(\mathcal{D}u^n, \mathcal{D}v)_\Pi &= F(v) - (\mathcal{D}v, \mathcal{D}w^n)_\Pi + (n+1)\rho\, G(\mathcal{D}v) \quad \forall v \in V_h \\ w^{n+1} &= w^n + \rho u^n. \end{aligned} \tag{14.10}$$

For a problem with Dirichlet boundary data γ, where $F(v) = -a(\gamma, v)$ and $G(\mathcal{D}v) = -(\mathcal{D}v, \mathcal{D}\gamma)$, the equations (14.9) become

$$\begin{aligned} a(u^n + \gamma, v) + \rho\,(\mathcal{D}(u^n + \gamma), \mathcal{D}v)_\Pi &= -\,(\mathcal{D}v, \mathcal{D}\hat{w}^n)_\Pi \quad \forall v \in V_h \\ \hat{w}^{n+1} &= \hat{w}^n + \rho(u^n + \gamma), \end{aligned} \tag{14.11}$$

where $\hat{w}^n = w^n + n\rho\gamma$. Thus we see that the introduction of inhomogeneous boundary conditions does not have a dramatic impact on the formulation of the iterated penalty method. We can write (14.11) using the affine variational formulation in Section 5.2 as:

Find $\hat{u}^n \in V + \gamma$ such that

$$\begin{aligned} a(\hat{u}^n, v) + \rho\,(\mathcal{D}(\hat{u}^n), \mathcal{D}v)_\Pi &= -\,(\mathcal{D}v, \mathcal{D}\hat{w}^n)_\Pi \quad \forall v \in V_h \\ \hat{w}^{n+1} &= \hat{w}^n + \rho\hat{u}^n. \end{aligned} \tag{14.12}$$

In the case of the Stokes equations, the iterated penalty method with $\rho' = \rho$ is (dropping the hats) as follows:

Find $\mathbf{u}^n \in V + \gamma$ such that

$$\begin{aligned} a(\mathbf{u}^n, \mathbf{v}) + \rho\,(\mathcal{D}\mathbf{u}^n, \mathcal{D}\mathbf{v})_\Pi &= F(\mathbf{v}) - (\mathcal{D}\mathbf{v}, \mathcal{D}\mathbf{w}^n)_\Pi \quad \forall \mathbf{v} \in V_h \\ \mathbf{w}^{n+1} &= \mathbf{w}^n + \rho\,\mathbf{u}^n, \end{aligned} \tag{14.13}$$

starting with $\mathbf{w}^0 = \mathbf{0}$. Note that once the iteration has converged, we can define p_h via (14.6):

$$p_h = \nabla\cdot \mathbf{w}^n,$$

where n is the last iteration number. The unified Stokes pressure $\hat{p}_h \in V_h^{k-1}$ can similarly be defined variationally by

$$(\hat{p}_h, q)_{L^2(\Omega)} = (\nabla\cdot \mathbf{w}^n, q)_{L^2(\Omega)} \quad \forall q \in V_h^{k-1}.$$

14.2.1 Convergence of iterated penalty

In [57, Chapter 13], it is proved that (14.5) converges for any $0 < \rho < 2\rho'$ for ρ' sufficiently large, provided that the forms in (13.20) satisfy (13.15), (13.28) and (13.29), and that $\Pi_h = \mathcal{D}V_h$. From [57, (13.1.10)], we have

$$a(e^n, v) + \rho(\mathcal{D}e^n, \mathcal{D}v)_\Pi = a(e^{n-1}, v) + (\rho - \rho')(\mathcal{D}e^{n-1}, \mathcal{D}v)_\Pi \quad \forall v \in V_h, \tag{14.14}$$

where $e^n = u^n - u_h$. The analysis thus simplifies for the case $\rho = \rho'$, as we now assume. Applying (14.14) with $v = e^n$ and using the Cauchy-Schwarz inequality (3.15) gives

$$a(e^n, e^n) + \rho(\mathcal{D}e^n, \mathcal{D}e^n)_\Pi = a(e^{n-1}, e^n) \le \sqrt{a(e^{n-1}, e^{n-1})}\sqrt{a(e^n, e^n)}.$$

Dividing by $a(e^n, e^n)$, we find

$$\frac{a(e^n, e^n) + \rho(\mathcal{D}e^n, \mathcal{D}e^n)_\Pi}{a(e^n, e^n)} \le \frac{\sqrt{a(e^{n-1}, e^{n-1})}}{\sqrt{a(e^n, e^n)}}. \tag{14.15}$$

Note that $a(u^n, v) = F(v) = a(u_h, v)$ for all $v \in Z_h$. Therefore $e^n \perp_a Z_h$, meaning $a(e^n, v) = 0$ for all $v \in Z_h$. Define

$$Z_h^\perp = \{v \in V_h \ : \ v \perp_a Z_h\} = \{v \in V_h \ : \ a(v, w) = 0 \, \forall w \in Z_h\},$$

and set

$$\lambda = \min_{0 \ne v \in Z_h^\perp} \frac{a(v, v) + \rho(\mathcal{D}v, \mathcal{D}v)_\Pi}{a(v, v)}. \tag{14.16}$$

Combining (14.15) and (14.16), we find

$$\sqrt{a(e^n, e^n)} \le \frac{1}{\lambda}\sqrt{a(e^{n-1}, e^{n-1})}. \tag{14.17}$$

The expression (14.16) is the **Rayleigh quotient** that defines the lowest eigenvalue of the generalized eigenproblem, to find $e \in Z_h^\perp$ and $\lambda > 0$ such that

$$a(e, v) + \rho(\mathcal{D}e, \mathcal{D}v)_\Pi = \lambda\, a(e, v) \quad \forall v \in Z_h^\perp. \tag{14.18}$$

Note that $\lambda = 1 + \rho\kappa$ where

$$\kappa = \min_{0 \ne v \in V_h,\, v \perp_a Z_h} \frac{(\mathcal{D}v, \mathcal{D}v)_\Pi}{a(v, v)}. \tag{14.19}$$

We have $\beta \ge \sqrt{\kappa}$, where β is the constant in the inf-sup condition (13.29), provided we define $\|v\|_V = \sqrt{a(v, v)}$ (see Exercise 14.4). On the other hand, [57, (13.1.16)] implies that

$$\sqrt{\kappa} \ge \beta\Big(\frac{\alpha}{\alpha + C_a}\Big).$$

With the choice of norm $\|v\|_V = \sqrt{a(v, v)}$, then $C_a = \alpha = 1$. Thus β and $\sqrt{\kappa}$ are essentially equivalent parameters measuring the stability of the Stokes approximation. Note that if $e^n = e$, where e is the eigenvector defined in (14.18), then

$$e^{n+1} = \lambda^{-1} e^n = \frac{1}{1 + \rho\kappa} e^n.$$

The following collects results from [57, Chapter 13] and the previous discussion.

Theorem 14.1 *Suppose that the forms in (13.20) satisfy (13.15), (13.28), and (13.29), and that* $\Pi_h = \mathcal{D}V_h$*. Then the algorithm (14.5) converges for any* $0 < \rho < 2\rho'$ *for* ρ' *sufficiently large. For the choice* $\rho = \rho'$*, (14.5) converges geometrically with a rate given by*

$$\frac{1}{1+\kappa\rho},$$

where κ *is defined in (14.19).*

Thus we can always choose ρ large enough to ensure geometric convergence of the iterated penalty algorithm.

14.2.2 Stopping criteria for iterated penalty

The following stopping criterion can be found in [57, Chapter 13].

Theorem 14.2 *Suppose that the forms in (13.20) satisfy (13.15), (13.28) and (13.29), and that* $\Pi_h = \mathcal{D}V_h$*. Then the errors in algorithm (14.5) can be estimated by*

$$\|u^n - u_h\|_V \le \left(\frac{1}{\beta} + \frac{C_a}{\alpha\beta}\right) \|\mathcal{D}u^n - P_{\Pi_h} G\|_\Pi$$

and

$$\|p^n - p_h\|_\Pi \le \left(\frac{C_a}{\beta} + \frac{C_a^2}{\alpha\beta} + \rho' C_b\right) \|\mathcal{D}u^n - P_{\Pi_h} G\|_\Pi.$$

When $G(q) = -b(\gamma, q)$, then $P_{\Pi_h} G = -P_{\Pi_h}\mathcal{D}\gamma$ and since $\mathcal{D}\mathbf{u}^n \in \Pi_h$,

$$\|\mathcal{D}\mathbf{u}^n - P_{\Pi_h} G\|_\Pi = \|P_{\Pi_h}\mathcal{D}\left(\mathbf{u}^n + \gamma\right)\|_\Pi \le \|\mathcal{D}\left(\mathbf{u}^n + \gamma\right)\|_\Pi, \tag{14.20}$$

and the latter norm is easier to compute, avoiding the need to compute $P_{\Pi_h} G$. We formalize this observation in the following result.

Corollary 14.1 *Under the conditions of Theorem 14.2 the errors in algorithm (14.5) for the Stokes equations can be estimated by*

$$\|\mathbf{u}^n - \mathbf{u}_h\|_V \le \left(\frac{1}{\beta} + \frac{C_a}{\alpha\beta}\right) \|\mathcal{D}\left(\mathbf{u}^n + \gamma\right)\|_\Pi$$

and

$$\|p^n - p_h\|_\Pi \le \left(\frac{C_a}{\beta} + \frac{C_a^2}{\alpha\beta} + \rho' C_b\right) \|\mathcal{D}\left(\mathbf{u}^n + \gamma\right)\|_\Pi.$$

A code implementing the iterated penalty method is given in Program 14.1.

14.3 Stokes flow examples

We give here some important examples of Stokes flow. The first of these is elementary and exact, but it is also the basis for many important applications. The others do not have exact solutions, but they provide valuable insight. We begin with flow in a channel.

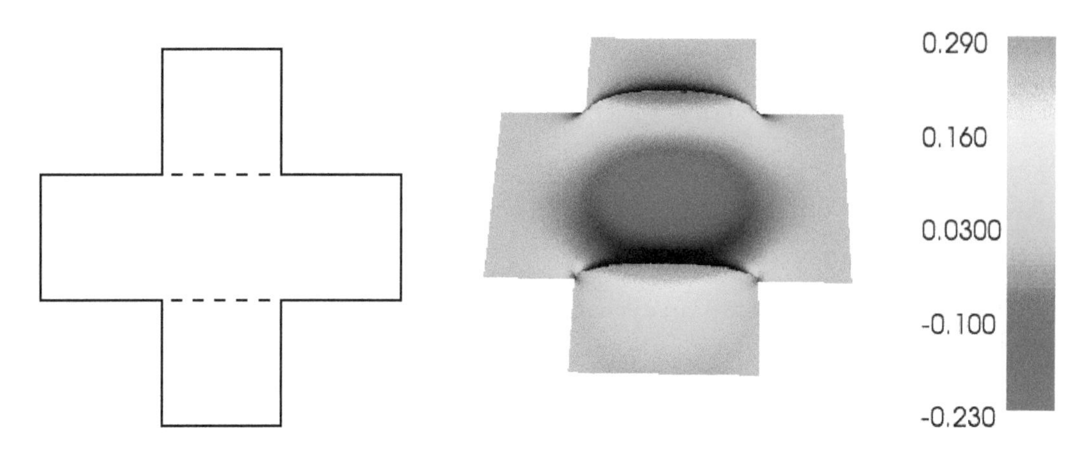

Figure 14.1: (left) The Stokes cross domain Ω for $L = 3$. The dashed lines indicate the set B^x. (right) The half cross: $\mathbf{u}$ is computed using boundary data given by $\mathbf{g}^x$. Plot of $u_x - g_x^x$ (computed with USA using $L = 2$, quartics, and meshsize = 64).

14.3.1 Poiseuille flow

A two-dimensional channel Ω (a long rectangle) is an idealization of a canal. We take the length to be L and the depth to be 1:

$$\Omega = \left\{(x, y) \in \mathbb{R}^2 \,:\, 0 \le x \le L,\ 0 \le y \le 1\right\}.$$

By restricting to two dimensions, we presume that flow is negligible in the third dimension across the width of the canal. Flow in a channel is named for Poiseuille[1] and defined by

$$\mathbf{u}(x, y) = \left(\tfrac{1}{2}y(1 - y), 0\right), \quad \text{for } (x, y) \in \Omega. \tag{14.21}$$

This $\mathbf{u}$ satisfies homogeneous Dirichlet boundary conditions on both the top and bottom of the channel, so we are imagining that we have put a lid on the canal. If we write $\mathbf{u}(x, y) = (u(x, y), v(x, y))$, we see that v is identically zero, and u has a parabolic profile. Moreover, $\Delta u \equiv 1$ and $\nabla\cdot \mathbf{u} = u_x = 0$. Thus define $p(x, y) = x$, and we have

$$-\Delta\mathbf{u}(x, y) + \nabla p(x, y) = 0 \quad \text{for } (x, y) \in \Omega.$$

Three-dimensional flow in a pipe (cylinder) is similar and also is named for Poiseuille. We can think of these flows as being driven by the non-zero pressure gradient.

14.3.2 Stokes cross

Now we consider two channels that cross each other, yielding what is commonly called a cross-slot domain [105]. Let $L \ge 1$. Define domains

$$\Omega^x = \{(x, y) \,:\, |x| < L,\ |y| < 1\} \quad \text{and} \quad \Omega^y = \{(x, y) \,:\, |y| < L,\ |x| < 1\},$$

[1] Jean Louis Marie Poiseuille (1799–1869) is memorialized by the unit *poise* for viscosity, which is equal to one gram per centimeter-second.

and define $\Omega = \Omega^x \cup \Omega^y$. Define vector functions

$$\mathbf{g}^x(x,y) = \begin{cases} (1-y^2, 0) & |x| < L,\ |y| < 1 \\ \mathbf{0} & \text{elsewhere} \end{cases} \quad \text{and} \quad \mathbf{g}^y(x,y) = \begin{cases} (0, 1-x^2) & |y| < L,\ |x| < 1 \\ \mathbf{0} & \text{elsewhere} \end{cases}.$$

By definition, $\mathbf{g}^x$, $\mathbf{g}^y \in H^1(\Omega)$, since the extension by zero is a continuous operation on H^1. Also $\nabla\cdot \mathbf{g}^x = \nabla\cdot \mathbf{g}^y = 0$ in Ω.

Similarly, define scalar functions

$$p^x(x,y) = \begin{cases} -2x & |x| < L,\ |y| < 1 \\ 0 & \text{elsewhere} \end{cases} \quad \text{and} \quad p^y(x,y) = \begin{cases} -2y & |y| < L,\ |x| < 1 \\ 0 & \text{elsewhere} \end{cases}.$$

These are both in $L^2(\Omega)$ and have mean zero. In Ω^x, $-\Delta\mathbf{g}^x = (2,0) = -\nabla p^x$, and in Ω^y, $-\Delta\mathbf{g}^y = (0,2) = -\nabla p^y$. Then $(\mathbf{g}^x, p^x)$ is a strong solution of Stokes in Ω^x, and $(\mathbf{g}^y, p^y)$ is a strong solution of Stokes in Ω^y, with homogeneous Dirichlet boundary conditions on appropriate sides of the two domains.

Extending p^x and p^y by zero outside of Ω^x and Ω^y, respectively, makes them both defined in $L^2(\Omega)$, still with mean zero in the whole domain. Thus $(\mathbf{g}^x, p^x)$ (resp., $(\mathbf{g}^y, p^y)$) is a strong solution of the Stokes equations in $\Omega\backslash B^x$ (resp., $\Omega\backslash B^y$), where

$$B^x = \{(x, \pm 1) \ :\ |x| < 1\} \quad \text{and} \quad B^y = \{(\pm 1, y) \ :\ |y| < 1\}$$

are the sets in Ω where both $\nabla\mathbf{g}^z$ and p^z ($z = x$ or y) have discontinuities.

14.3.3 Stokes box

In the special case $L = 1$, the domains B^x and B^y are empty. Then we get solutions $(\mathbf{g}^x, p^x)$ and $(\mathbf{g}^y, p^y)$ defined on all of $\Omega = [-1,1]^2$. Since the Stokes equations are linear, any linear combination of these solutions is also an exact solution of the Stokes equations.

14.3.4 Nearly a solution

Now return to the general case of the Stokes cross ($L > 1$). Let us determine what variational problem $(\mathbf{g}^z, p^z)$ ($z = x$ or y) solves in Ω.

Take $z = x$ for the moment. Let $\widehat{\Omega}^y = \{(x,y) \in \Omega^y \ :\ |y| > 1\}$. Thus $\Omega = \Omega^x \cup B^x \cup \widehat{\Omega}^y$, and B^x is the boundary between Ω^x and $\widehat{\Omega}^y$. Since both $\mathbf{g}^x$ and p^x vanish in $\widehat{\Omega}^y$,

$$\begin{aligned} \int_\Omega \nabla\mathbf{g}^x : \nabla\mathbf{v}\, d\mathbf{x} - \int_\Omega p^x \nabla\cdot\mathbf{v}\, d\mathbf{x} &= \int_{\Omega^x} (-2y) v_{x,y} + 2x\nabla\cdot\mathbf{v}\, d\mathbf{x} \\ &= \int_{\Omega^x} (-2y) v_{x,y}\, d\mathbf{x} - \int_{\Omega^x} (2,0)\cdot\mathbf{v}\, d\mathbf{x} - \oint_{B^x} (2x\mathbf{v})\cdot\mathbf{n}\, ds, \end{aligned} \tag{14.22}$$

since $\mathbf{v}$ vanishes on $\partial\Omega^x\backslash B^x$. Applying the divergence theorem to $\mathbf{w} = (0, -2y)v_x$, we find

$$\int_{\Omega^x} (-2y) v_{x,y}\, d\mathbf{x} = \int_{\Omega^x} 2 v_x\, d\mathbf{x} - \oint_{B^x} \mathbf{n}\cdot(0, 2y)\, v_x\, ds.$$

Thus

$$\int_\Omega \nabla\mathbf{g}^x : \nabla\mathbf{v}\, d\mathbf{x} - \int_\Omega p^x \nabla\cdot\mathbf{v}\, d\mathbf{x} = -\oint_{B^x} \mathbf{n}\cdot(0,2y)\, v_x\, ds - \oint_{B^x} (2x\mathbf{v})\cdot\mathbf{n}\, ds. \tag{14.23}$$

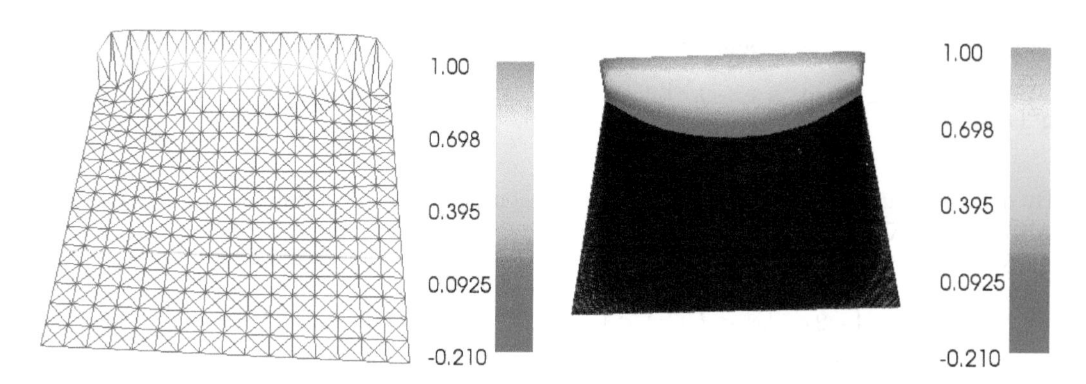

Figure 14.2: Driven cavity problem computed with quartics, horizontal component only. (left) meshsize = 16 and (right) meshsize = 128 showing only where $u \geq 0$.

If we define

$$F(\mathbf{v}) = -\oint_{B^x} \mathbf{n} \cdot (0, 2y)\, v_x + (2x\mathbf{v}) \cdot \mathbf{n}\, ds, \tag{14.24}$$

then we see that we can think of $(\mathbf{g}^x, p^x)$ as solving a Stokes-like problem on Ω with data F given in (14.24). We thus see (on the right side of Figure 14.1) that the difference between $\mathbf{u}$ and $\mathbf{g}^x$ is very localized near B^x.

14.3.5 Driven cavity

Let Ω be the unit square $[0,1]^2$ and let Γ denote the top of the square:

$$\Gamma = \{(x, 1) \,:\, 0 \leq x \leq 1\}.$$

Define Dirichlet boundary conditions

$$\mathbf{u}(x, 1) = (1, 0) \text{ on } \Gamma, \quad \mathbf{u} = \mathbf{0} \text{ on } \partial\Omega\backslash\Gamma. \tag{14.25}$$

The resulting Stokes problem with boundary condition (14.25) is called the **driven cavity** problem.

We imagine the top of the box to be a belt that is continuously moving to the right and causing the fluid to do the same. This is slightly unrealistic, but it is an easy to state problem with an unknown solution that is often used as a test [223]. It is equally difficult to write down a vector function $(g, 0)$ that satisfies (14.25). Using polar coordinates, we can write $g(r, \theta) = \cos\theta$ for r near 0. This has the right boundary conditions near the left-hand side of the lid, but we also see that this function in not in $H^1(\Omega)$. So the driven cavity problem has a singularity that correlates with the difficulty of forcing the belt down onto the top of the box.

The solution of the driven cavity problem is depicted in Figure 14.2, computed with the Scott-Vogelius iterated penalty method using quartics. Plotted is the horizontal component u of the velocity $\mathbf{u} = (u, v)$. The depiction on the left in Figure 14.2 shows the solution for a coarse mesh. Upon closer inspection on the right (computed with a finer mesh) we see that the horizontal velocity becomes negative below a particular curve. This visualization was achieved by including the mesh, which is so dense as to appear black, and is plotted at the level $u = 0$. Thus we see the solution only when it is positive. The curve $u(x, y) = 0$ is a distinctive feature of this problem and can be used to compare solution methods.

14.4 Artificial compressibility

The artificial compressibility method provides another way to enforce the incompressibility condition in the Stokes equations (13.4). It originated in [93] and has been used extensively [189, Section 2.4.2 and Chapter 4]. It has also been extended significantly [108]. The original method [93] is based on the equations

$$\begin{aligned} \mathbf{u}_t - \Delta \mathbf{u} &= -\nabla p + \mathbf{f} \\ \delta p_t &= -\nabla\cdot \mathbf{u}, \end{aligned} \tag{14.26}$$

where $\delta > 0$ is a fixed parameter, the Reynolds number R in [93, equation (3)] has been set to zero, and the artificial density $\rho = \delta p$ was eliminated in favor of an explicit equation for p. The idea is that solving (14.26) instead of the standard Stokes equations (13.4) eliminates the need to work with the incompressibility constraint explicitly. Instead, provided that the solution of (14.26) converges to a steady state, it will converge to a solution of (13.4).

Chorin noted [93] that many different discretizations of (14.26) were possible but picked one that is implicit in the first equation and explicit in the second. One discretization of this type would be

$$\begin{aligned} \mathbf{u}^{n+1} - \tau\Delta \mathbf{u}^{n+1} &= \mathbf{u}^n - \tau\nabla p^n + \tau\mathbf{f} \\ p^{n+1} &= p^n - \frac{\tau}{\delta}\nabla\cdot \mathbf{u}^{n+1}, \end{aligned} \tag{14.27}$$

where τ is the artificial time step and we can start with $p^0 = 0$ and $\mathbf{u}^0 = \mathbf{0}$. We can write $p^n = -\nabla\cdot \mathbf{w}^n$, and (14.27) becomes

$$\begin{aligned} -\Delta \mathbf{u}^{n+1} + \rho'\big(\mathbf{u}^{n+1} - \mathbf{u}^n\big) &= \nabla(\nabla\cdot \mathbf{w}^n) + \mathbf{f} \\ \mathbf{w}^{n+1} &= \mathbf{w}^n + \rho\mathbf{u}^{n+1}, \end{aligned} \tag{14.28}$$

where the parameters $\rho' = \tau^{-1}$ and $\rho = \tau/\delta$ align with the notation of the iterated penalty method (14.9). In the variational formulation of (14.28), $\rho'\big(\mathbf{u}^{n+1} - \mathbf{u}^n, \mathbf{v}\big)_{L^2(\Omega)}$ replaces the term $(\mathcal{D}\mathbf{u}^n, \mathcal{D}\mathbf{v})_{L^2(\Omega)}$ in (14.9). Thus there is an algorithmic similarity between the iterated penalty method and the artificial compressibility method. We leave as Exercise 14.9 to explore a comparison of the iterated penalty method and the artificial compressibility method.

It should be emphasized that the artificial compressibility method does not avoid the difficulties of approximating the divergence constraint. Suppose that (14.28) is applied with a velocity space V_h and that it converges to a steady state, then $p_h = -\nabla\cdot \mathbf{w}_h$ and $\nabla\cdot \mathbf{u}_h = 0$. Thus the artificial compressibility method is simply a way of computing the divergence-free velocity and the pressure in the setting $\Pi_h = \nabla\cdot V_h$. So, if (14.28) is applied with finite element spaces for which having $\Pi_h = \nabla\cdot V_h$ is not a good choice, then the results are not predictable.

14.5 Exercises

Exercise 14.1 *Consider the spaces introduced in Exercise 13.5, that is, let V_h be piecewise linear functions on a crossed mesh that vanish on the boundary, and let $\Pi_h = \nabla\cdot V_h$. Use the iterated penalty method introduced in Section 14.2 to solve the Stokes equations with these spaces.*

Exercise 14.2 *The Darcy-Stokes-Brinkman models [285, 212, 163] involve an operator of the form*

$$-\eta\Delta\mathbf{u} + \gamma\mathbf{u} + \nabla p = f \tag{14.29}$$

together with the usual divergence constraint $\nabla\cdot\mathbf{u} = 0$ *and boundary conditions. Here* γ *can be a matrix function corresponding to the porosity in Darcy flow. When* η *is small, we get Darcy flow. When* γ *is small, we get Stokes flow. In a time stepping scheme for Stokes,* $\gamma = (\Delta t)^{-1}I$, *where* I *is the identity matrix. The name Brinkman is associated with the general model. Experiment with this model using the Scott-Vogelius element, using the iterated penalty method to solve the linear system.*

Exercise 14.3 *Modify the proof of Exercise 3.2 to show that*

$$\|\mathcal{D}w\|_\Pi = \sup_{0\neq v\in Z_h^\perp} \frac{(\mathcal{D}v,\mathcal{D}w)_\Pi}{\|\mathcal{D}v\|_\Pi}$$

for all $w \in Z_h^\perp$.

Exercise 14.4 *Suppose that* $\|v\|_V = \sqrt{a(v,v)}$ *and* $\Pi_h = \nabla\cdot V_h$. *Prove that*

$$\beta = \inf_{0\neq q\in\Pi_h}\sup_{0\neq v\in V_h}\frac{b(v,q)}{\|v\|_V\|q\|_\Pi} = \inf_{0\neq q\in\Pi_h}\sup_{0\neq v\in Z_h^\perp}\frac{b(v,q)}{\|v\|_V\|q\|_\Pi} \geq \sqrt{\kappa},$$

where κ *is defined in (14.19). (Hint: take* $q = \mathcal{D}w$ *where* $w \in Z_h^\perp$ *and show that*

$$\inf_{0\neq w\in Z_h^\perp}\sup_{0\neq v\in Z_h^\perp}\frac{(\mathcal{D}v,\mathcal{D}w)_\Pi}{\|\mathcal{D}w\|_\Pi\|v\|_V} \geq \inf_{0\neq w\in Z_h^\perp}\frac{(\mathcal{D}w,\mathcal{D}w)_\Pi}{\|\mathcal{D}w\|_\Pi\|w\|_V} = \inf_{0\neq w\in Z_h^\perp}\frac{\|\mathcal{D}w\|_\Pi}{\|w\|_V} = \sqrt{\kappa}$$

by taking $v = w$.*)*

Exercise 14.5 *Modify Program 14.1 to compute Poiseuille flow in a two-dimensional channel and compare with the exact solution (14.21) by computing the* $L^2(\Omega)$ *norm of the difference. Take* $L = 3$. *Try this with both regular meshes generated by*

```
UnitSquareMesh(meshsize, meshsize)
```

and with crossed triangles using

```
UnitSquareMesh(meshsize, meshsize, "crossed")
```

Do this for various degrees k *and values of* `meshsize` *and report what you learn.*

Exercise 14.6 *Modify Program 14.1 to compute the Stokes cross solution in Section 14.3.2 and compare with the exact solution described there by computing the* $L^2(\Omega)$ *norm of the difference. Take* $L = 3$. *Try this with both regular meshes generated by*

```
UnitSquareMesh(meshsize, meshsize)
```

and with crossed triangles using

```
UnitSquareMesh(meshsize, meshsize, "crossed")
```

Do this for various degrees k *and values of* `meshsize` *and report what you learn.*

Exercise 14.7 *Modify Program 14.1 to compute the driven cavity problem described in Section 14.3.5. Try this with both regular meshes generated by*

```
UnitSquareMesh(meshsize, meshsize)
```

and with crossed triangles using

```
UnitSquareMesh(meshsize, meshsize, "crossed")
```

Do this for various degrees k and values of `meshsize` *and report what you learn.*

Exercise 14.8 *Solve the driven cavity problem in Section 14.3.5 for the Stokes equations on the unit square $[0,1]^2$. Determine the curve $(x, d(x))$ defined by $u(x, d(x)) = 0$ where u is the horizontal component of the velocity and $d(0) = d(1) = 1$. Is d symmetric around $x = \frac{1}{2}$? If so, find the best quartic approximation $d(x) = 1 - a(x - \frac{1}{2})^2 - b(x - \frac{1}{2})^4$ for coefficients a and b. Plot the error between d and this approximation.*

Exercise 14.9 *Compare the iterated penalty method with the artificial compressibility method (14.27) on various test problems for the Stokes equations. What is the convergence rate for the artificial compressibility method? Also try the method studied in [108].*

```
 1 from dolfin import *
 2 meshsize = 16
 3 mesh = UnitSquareMesh(meshsize, meshsize, "crossed")
 4 k=4
 5 V = VectorFunctionSpace(mesh, "Lagrange", k)
 6 # define boundary condition
 7 gee = Expression(("sin(4*pi*x[0])*cos(4*pi*x[1])", \
 8                   "-cos(4*pi*x[0])*sin(4*pi*x[1])"),degree=k)
 9 bc = DirichletBC(V, gee, "on_boundary")
10 # set the parameters
11 f = Expression(("28*pow(pi, 2)*sin(4*pi*x[0])*cos(4*pi*x[1])", \
12                 "-36*pow(pi, 2)*cos(4*pi*x[0])*sin(4*pi*x[1])"),degree=k)
13 r = 1.0e3
14 # define test and trial functions, and function that is updated
15 u = TrialFunction(V)
16 v = TestFunction(V)
17 w = Function(V)
18 # set the variational problem
19 a = inner(grad(u), grad(v))*dx + r*div(u)*div(v)*dx
20 b = -div(w)*div(v)*dx
21 F = inner(f, v)*dx
22 u = Function(V)
23 pde = LinearVariationalProblem(a, F - b, u, bc)
24 solver = LinearVariationalSolver(pde)
25 # Scott-Vogelius iterated penalty method
26 iters = 0; max_iters = 10; div_u_norm = 1
27 while iters < max_iters and div_u_norm > 1e-10:
28     # solve and update w
29     solver.solve()
30     w.vector().axpy(-r, u.vector())
31     # find the L^2 norm of div(u) to check stopping condition
32     div_u_norm = sqrt(assemble(div(u)*div(u)*dx(mesh)))
33     print "norm(div u)=%.2e"%div_u_norm
34     iters += 1
35 print k,meshsize," %.2e"%errornorm(gee,u,norm_type='l2', degree_rise=3)
```

Program 14.1: Code to implement the iterated penalty method.

Chapter 15

Advection

Many models balance advection and diffusion. In the simplest case, this can be represented as follows. We use notation and concepts from Chapter 2 without reference. The basic advection-diffusion equation in a domain Ω is

$$-\epsilon \Delta u + \boldsymbol{\beta} \cdot \nabla u = f \text{ in } \Omega, \tag{15.1}$$

where $\boldsymbol{\beta}$ is a vector-valued function indicating the advection direction. For simplicity, we again assume that we have boundary conditions

$$\begin{aligned} u &= g \text{ on } \Gamma \subset \partial\Omega \qquad &\text{(Dirichlet)} \\ \frac{\partial u}{\partial n} &= 0 \text{ on } \partial\Omega \backslash \Gamma \qquad &\text{(Neumann)} \end{aligned} \tag{15.2}$$

where $\frac{\partial u}{\partial n}$ denotes the derivative of u in the direction normal to the boundary, $\partial\Omega$. Neumann boundary conditions may or may not be a good model, but they are consistent with a behavior where the solution is not changing much near the Neumann part of the boundary. A major objective of the chapter is to decide where it is good (or bad) to pick Neumann conditions. We will see that it is essential to have Dirichlet boundary conditions on what is called the inflow part of the boundary.

15.1 Posing boundary conditions

In an advection-diffusion model, the quantity u is being advected in the direction of $\boldsymbol{\beta}$. Thus there is a sense of in-flow and out-flow parts of the boundary. Define

$$\Gamma_0 = \{x \in \partial\Omega \,:\, \boldsymbol{\beta}(\mathbf{x}) \cdot \mathbf{n} = 0\}, \qquad \Gamma_\pm = \{x \in \partial\Omega \,:\, \pm\boldsymbol{\beta}(\mathbf{x}) \cdot \mathbf{n} > 0\}, \tag{15.3}$$

where as usual $\mathbf{n}$ denotes the outward-directed normal to $\partial\Omega$. Then Γ_- represents the in-flow part of the boundary, and Γ_+ represents the out-flow part of the boundary. The boundary condition on the out-flow boundary requires some modeling since we often do not know what comes next (after the material exits the domain). We will see what happens if we try to specify something inappropriate there subsequently, but for now let us describe one typical approach.

Since we usually do not know what u will look like near the out-flow part of the domain, it would be best to do something neutral. In general, we would have

$$\frac{\partial u}{\partial n} = g_N \text{ on } \partial\Omega\backslash\Gamma. \tag{15.4}$$

Suppose that we use the variational space V defined in (2.6) and then use (5.2) to define u. If we do not know what g_N should be, we can try $g_N = 0$. This corresponds to the boundary condition

$$\frac{\partial u}{\partial n} = 0 \text{ on } \partial\Omega\backslash\Gamma \tag{15.5}$$

that we have suggested in (15.2). The quality of this model must be assessed carefully, but for now we proceed to see what can be said about the choices for Γ. We will see that $\Gamma_- \subset \Gamma$ is a natural requirement.

15.2 Variational formulation of advection-diffusion

We again use the variational space V defined in (2.6). As before, using the three-step recipe, we define

$$\begin{aligned} a(u,v) &= \int_\Omega \nabla u(\mathbf{x}) \cdot \nabla v(\mathbf{x})\, d\mathbf{x} \\ b(u,v) &= \int_\Omega \big(\boldsymbol{\beta}(\mathbf{x}) \cdot \nabla u(\mathbf{x})\big) v(\mathbf{x})\, d\mathbf{x}. \end{aligned} \tag{15.6}$$

Here we see an alternative formulation: we could have integrated by parts in the advection term. We leave as Exercise 15.8 to explore this possibility.

15.3 Coercivity of the advection term

To see what coercivity means for the advection-diffusion problem, we again invoke the divergence theorem (2.9) to yield

$$\oint_{\partial\Omega} u\, v\, \boldsymbol{\beta} \cdot \mathbf{n}\, ds = \int_\Omega \nabla\cdot (u\, v\, \boldsymbol{\beta})\, d\mathbf{x} = \int_\Omega \big(u\, \boldsymbol{\beta} \cdot \nabla v + v\, \boldsymbol{\beta} \cdot \nabla u + u\, v\, \nabla\cdot \boldsymbol{\beta}\big)\, d\mathbf{x}. \tag{15.7}$$

In particular,

$$b(u,v) + b(v,u) = \oint_{\partial\Omega} u\, v\, \boldsymbol{\beta} \cdot \mathbf{n}\, ds - \int_\Omega u\, v\, \nabla\cdot \boldsymbol{\beta}\, d\mathbf{x}. \tag{15.8}$$

We now consider coercivity of the bilinear form

$$a_\beta(u,v) = \epsilon\, a(u,v) + b(u,v). \tag{15.9}$$

Let us assume that Γ is not empty. Since we already know that $a(\cdot,\cdot)$ is coercive on

$$V = \left\{ v \in H^1(\Omega) \ :\ v = 0 \text{ on } \Gamma \right\},$$

it suffices to determine conditions under which $b(v,v) \geq 0$ for all $v \in V$. From (15.8), we have

$$2b(v,v) = \oint_{\partial\Omega} v^2 \boldsymbol{\beta} \cdot \mathbf{n}\, ds - \int_\Omega v^2\, \nabla\cdot \boldsymbol{\beta}\, d\mathbf{x}. \tag{15.10}$$

An important special case is when $\boldsymbol{\beta}$ is **incompressible**, meaning $\nabla\cdot\boldsymbol{\beta}=0$. In this case, (15.10) simplifies to

$$2b(v,v)=\oint_{\Gamma_-\cup\Gamma_+} v^2\boldsymbol{\beta}\cdot\mathbf{n}\,ds\geq\oint_{\Gamma_-} v^2\boldsymbol{\beta}\cdot\mathbf{n}\,ds, \tag{15.11}$$

since, by definition,

$$\oint_{\Gamma_+} v^2\boldsymbol{\beta}\cdot\mathbf{n}\,ds\geq 0.$$

and of course

$$\oint_{\Gamma_0} v^2\boldsymbol{\beta}\cdot\mathbf{n}\,ds=0.$$

Thus if we suppose that $\Gamma_-\subset\Gamma$, meaning that the part of the boundary where we impose Dirichlet boundary conditions includes all of Γ_-, then $b(v,v)\geq 0$ for all $v\in V$, and thus $a_\beta(\cdot,\cdot)$ is coercive on V. In this case, u can be characterized uniquely via

$$u\in V \text{ satisfies } a_\beta(u,v)=(f,v)_{L^2(\Omega)}\quad\forall v\in V. \tag{15.12}$$

Since it is easy to see that the bilinear form $b(\cdot,\cdot)$ is continuous, the Lax-Milgram Theorem 3.1 implies the following.

Theorem 15.1 *If $\Gamma_-\subset\Gamma$ and $\epsilon>0$, then the variational problem (15.12) is well posed.*

In the case that $\nabla\cdot\boldsymbol{\beta}\neq 0$, but $\nabla\cdot\boldsymbol{\beta}\leq 0$, coercivity of $a_\beta(\cdot,\cdot)$ again follows provided $\Gamma_-\subset\Gamma$. However, for more general $\boldsymbol{\beta}$, no guarantees can be made.

15.4 Examples

We now use an augmented version of the method of manufactured solutions (Section 2.3) in which we examine singular limits as $\epsilon\to 0$. We expect from Exercise 7.1 that we will obtain boundary layers in some cases.

Let $\Omega=[0,1]^2$ and $\boldsymbol{\beta}=(1,0)$. Note that $\nabla\cdot\boldsymbol{\beta}=0$ and that

$$\Gamma_-=\{(0,y)\;:\;y\in[0,1]\},\quad \Gamma_+=\{(1,y)\;:\;y\in[0,1]\},$$

$$\Gamma_0=\{(x,0)\;:\;x\in[0,1]\}\cup\{(x,1)\;:\;x\in[0,1]\}.$$

Let u_ϵ denote the solution of (15.1), and in the case that $\epsilon\to 0$, we denote the limiting solution by u_0 (if it exists). We can solve (15.1) with $\epsilon=0$ formally for a possible limit u_0 via

$$u_0(x,y)=\int_0^x f(s,y)\,ds+u_0(0,y). \tag{15.13}$$

We know that the variational problem (15.12) is well-posed provided $\Gamma_-\subset\Gamma$ (and provided $\epsilon>0$). We assume that $u(x,y)=g(x,y)$ for $(x,y)\in\Gamma$. If it also holds that $u_0(x,y)=g(x,y)$ for $(x,y)\in\Gamma$, then (15.13) implies that the likely limit would be

$$u_0(x,y)=\int_0^x f(s,y)\,ds+g(0,y)\quad\forall y\in[0,1]. \tag{15.14}$$

We now examine this hypothesis in various cases.

degree	mesh number	ϵ	$\epsilon^{-1}\|u_\epsilon - u_0\|_{L^2(\Omega)}$
4	8	1.0e+00	0.27270
4	8	1.0e-01	0.71315
4	8	1.0e-02	0.86153
4	8	1.0e-03	0.87976
4	8	1.0e-04	0.88172
4	8	1.0e-05	0.88190
4	8	1.0e-06	0.88191
4	8	1.0e-07	0.88192
4	8	1.0e-08	0.88192

Table 15.1: The diffusion advection problem (15.1)–(15.2) defines u_ϵ with $\Gamma = \Gamma_-$, g given in (15.15) and $f(x,y) = 1 - x$; u_0 is given in (15.16).

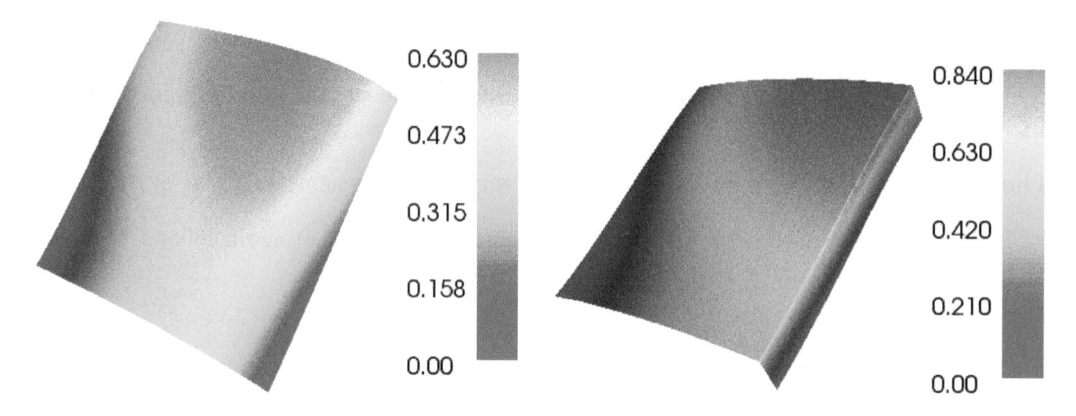

Figure 15.1: Diffusion-advection problem (15.1)–(15.2) with $\Gamma = \Gamma_- \cup \Gamma_+$ and g given in (15.15) and $f(x,y) = 1-x$. Left: $\epsilon = 0.1$, u_ϵ computed using piecewise linears on a 100×100 mesh. Right: $\epsilon = 0.001$, u_ϵ computed using piecewise linears on a 1000×1000 mesh.

15.4.1 First example

If $f \equiv 1$, and (15.14) holds, then $u_0(x,y) = x + g(0,y)$ for all $x, y \in [0,1]^2$. This solution has a chance of being compatible for $\epsilon > 0$ if, for example, $g(x,y) = a + by$, since $\Delta u_0 = 0$ in this case. However, we need to pick the right boundary conditions if we want to get this solution in the limit as $\epsilon \to 0$.

If we expect to converge to the limit $u_0(x,y) = x + g(y) = x + a + by$, then the boundary conditions should hold on u_0. We assume that $u_0(0,y) = g(y)$ is imposed on Γ_-. But on Γ_+, we have $(u_0)_{,x}(1,y) = 1$, so we would need inhomogeneous Neumann data there. On Γ_0, we have $(u_0)_{,y}(x,0) = g'(0) = b$ and $(u_1)_{,y}(x,0) = g'(1) = b$. So again we would need inhomogeneous Neumann data there.

We leave to Exercise 15.6 to explore this problem.

15.4.2 Second example

On the other hand, a Neumann condition $\frac{\partial u_0}{\partial x}(1,y) = 0$ holds if $f(1,y) = 0$, e.g., if $f(x,y) = 1 - x$. Then

$$u_0(x,y) = x - \tfrac{1}{2}x^2 + g(0,y)$$

when $\epsilon = 0$. Thus u_0 satisfies a homogeneous Neumann condition on Γ_+. If in addition, $\frac{\partial g}{\partial y}(0,0) = \frac{\partial g}{\partial y}(0,1) = 0$, then u_0 satisfies a homogeneous Neumann condition on Γ_0, that is, the top and bottom of $\Omega = [0,1]^2$. For example, we can take

$$g(x,y) = y^2\Big(1 - \frac{2}{3}y\Big). \tag{15.15}$$

In this case, we take $\Gamma = \Gamma_-$ and

$$u_0(x,y) = x - \tfrac{1}{2}x^2 + y^2\Big(1 - \frac{2}{3}y\Big). \tag{15.16}$$

When ϵ is small, u_ϵ should be a small perturbation of this. This problem has been explored using Program 15.1 and some resulting data is collected in Table 15.1.

From Table 15.1, we see that $u_\epsilon \to u_0$ as we had expected. More precisely, we can say that

$$\|u_\epsilon - u_0\|_{L^2(\Omega)} \approx C\epsilon, \tag{15.17}$$

where we are converging to $C = 0.88192\ldots$ as ϵ gets smaller. So we conclude that, if $\Gamma = \Gamma_-$ and the Neumann boundary conditions for the limiting solutions are appropriate, then the diffusion-advection problem is quite predictable for small ϵ.

The code to generate the data in Table 15.1 is given in Program 15.1. We leave as Exercise 15.2 to explore this problem further. We now consider a problem with more complex behavior.

15.4.3 Third example

In the previous example problem, we made the minimal assumption that $\Gamma_- \subset \Gamma$. If we also take $\Gamma_+ \subset \Gamma$ then we potentially obtain a constraint, in that (15.14) implies $g(1,y) = \int_0^1 f(s,y)\,ds + g(0,y)$, that is,

$$\int_0^1 f(s,y)\,ds = g(1,y) - g(0,y) \text{ for all } y \in [0,1]. \tag{15.18}$$

If the data does not satisfy the constraint (15.18), we might expect some sort of boundary layer for $\epsilon > 0$. In the case that g is given in (15.15) and $f(x,y) = 1 - x$, such a constraint holds, and we see in Figure 15.1 (right) that there is a sharp boundary layer for $\epsilon = 0.001$. For $\epsilon = 0.1$, Figure 15.1 (left) shows that the solution deviates from u_0 over a broader area. The middle ground, where $\epsilon = 0.01$, the boundary layer is still localized, as shown in Figure 15.2 (left). If we attempt to resolve this problem with too few grid points, as shown in Figure 15.2 (right), then we get spurious oscillations on the scale of the mesh.

15.4.4 Wrong boundary conditions

Let us now ask the question: what happens if $\Gamma_- \not\subset \Gamma$? Suppose that we take $\Gamma = \Gamma_+$, and we consider the problem (15.1)–(15.2) with g given in (15.15) and $f(x,y) = 1 - x$.

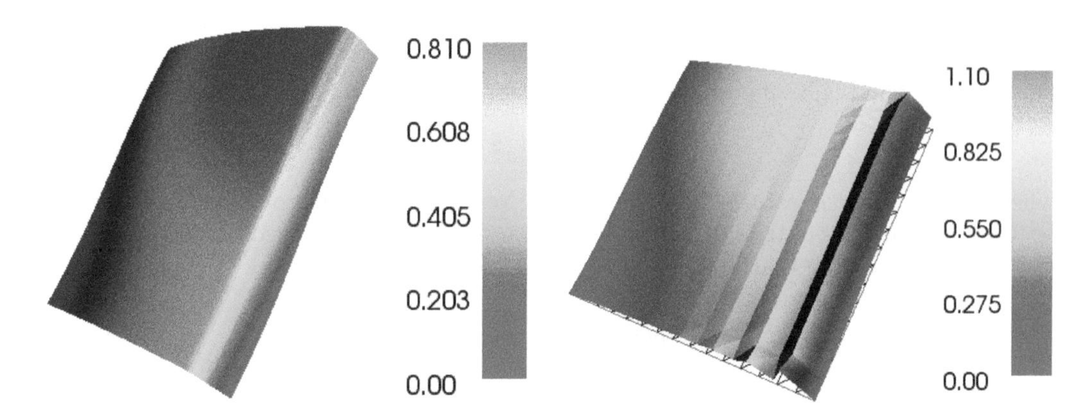

Figure 15.2: Diffusion-advection problem (15.1)–(15.2) with $\Gamma = \Gamma_- \cup \Gamma_+$, $\epsilon = 0.01$, g given in (15.15) and $f(x, y) = 1 - x$. Left: u_ϵ computed using piecewise linears on a 100×100 mesh. Right: u_ϵ computed using piecewise linears on a 15×15 mesh.

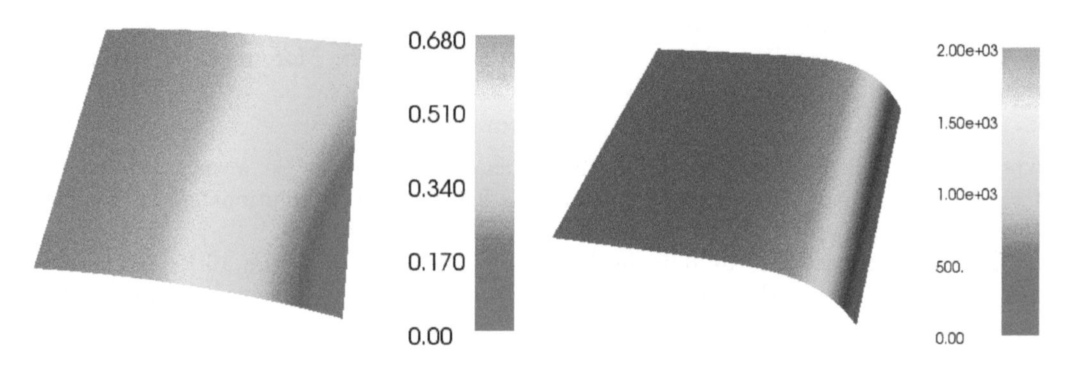

Figure 15.3: Diffusion-advection problem (15.1)–(15.2) with $\Gamma = \Gamma_+$ and g given in (15.15) and $f(x, y) = 1 - x$. The solution u_ϵ was computed using piecewise linears on a 100×100 mesh. Left: $\epsilon = 1.0$, Right: $\epsilon = 0.1$.

Numerical solutions for the variational problem (15.12) are depicted in Figure 15.3. These look at first to be reasonable. At least the case $\epsilon = 1.0$ looks plausible, and reducing ϵ by a factor of 10 produces something like the boundary layer behavior we saw previously. However, look at the scale. The solution is now extremely large. And if we continue to reduce ϵ (see Exercise 15.4), the solution size becomes disturbingly large. Picking different orders of polynomials and values for ϵ tends to give random, clearly spurious results. For example, Figure 15.4 shows what happens if we pick ϵ slightly smaller and use quadratics as well as linears. Now the scale of the solution is much larger, and the difference between the result for linears and quadratics is large, even though they are superficially similar. Thus we conclude that the coercivity condition provides good guidance regarding how to proceed.

15.5 Transport equation

In some cases, there is no natural diffusion in a system, and we are left with pure advection. The resulting equation is often called a **transport equation**. Equations of this type play

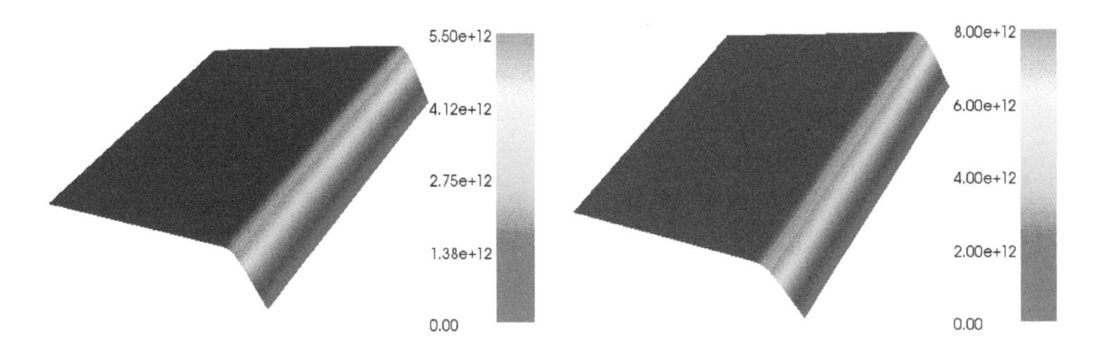

Figure 15.4: Diffusion-advection problem (15.1)–(15.2) with $\Gamma = \Gamma_+$ and g given in (15.15) and $f(x, y) = 1 - x$ and $\epsilon = 0.01$ on a 100×100. The solution u_ϵ was computed using piecewise linears (left) and piecewise quadratics (right).

a major role in non-Newtonian fluid models. As a model equation of this type, we consider

$$\tau u + \boldsymbol{\beta} \cdot \nabla u = f \text{ in } \Omega. \tag{15.19}$$

Here we assume for simplicity that τ is a positive constant. Without a diffusion term, it is not possible to pose Dirichlet boundary conditions arbitrarily. In the case where $\boldsymbol{\beta} \cdot \mathbf{n} = 0$ on $\partial\Omega$, the flow stays internal to Ω, and it has been shown [140, Proposition 3.7] that there is a unique solution $u \in L^2(\Omega)$ of (15.19) for any $f \in L^2(\Omega)$, provided that $\boldsymbol{\beta} \in H^1(\Omega)$. Such results are extended in [38, 39] to the general case in which boundary conditions are posed on Γ_-.

Unfortunately, the Lax-Milgram theorem does not apply to the transport equation (15.19). This equation is not coercive in standard spaces. On the other hand, more sophisticated theory [140, 38, 39] has been developed to prove well-posedness of this problem. Moreover, this theory justifies using a standard variational approach.

The variational formulation of (15.19) involves the bilinear form

$$a_\tau(u, v) = \int_\Omega \tau u v + (\boldsymbol{\beta} \cdot \nabla u) v \, d\mathbf{x}. \tag{15.20}$$

In this case, u can be characterized uniquely via

$$u \in V \text{ satisfies } a_\tau(u, v) = (f, v)_{L^2(\Omega)} \quad \forall v \in V. \tag{15.21}$$

In our simple example with $\boldsymbol{\beta} = (1, 0)$, (15.19) can be written

$$\tau u(x, y) + u_{,x}(x, y) = f(x, y) \; \forall y \in [0, 1].$$

Fix $y \in [0, 1]$ and write $v(x) = e^{\tau x} u(x, y)$. Then

$$v'(x) = e^{\tau x} \big(\tau u(x, y) + u_{,x}(x, y)\big) = e^{\tau x} f(x, y),$$

so that

$$v(x) = v(0) + \int_0^x v'(s) \, ds = v(0) + \int_0^x e^{\tau s} f(s, y) \, ds.$$

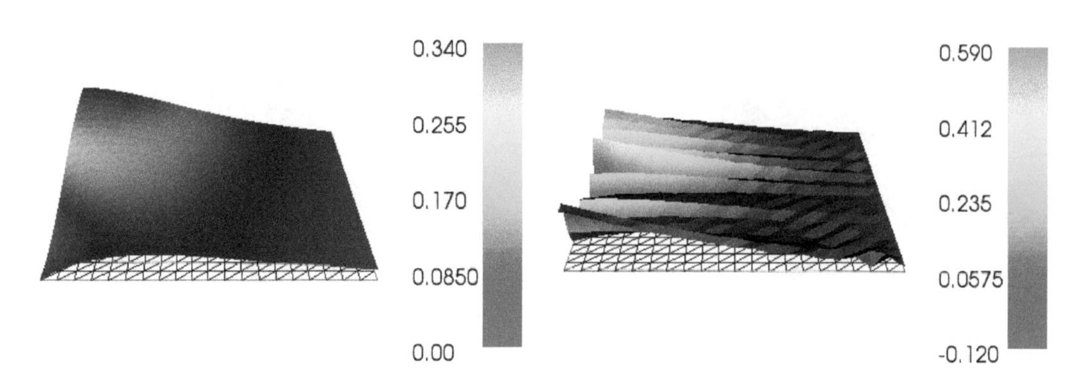

Figure 15.5: Transport problem with $\tau = 3.0$, with $f = e^{-\tau x_1}$, computed using piecewise linears on a 20×20 mesh. The boundary data g given in (15.15) was imposed on (left) Γ_- and (right) Γ_+. The code to generate this is given in Program 15.2.

Therefore

$$u(x,y) = e^{-\tau x} v(x) = e^{-\tau x}\Big(u(0,y) + \int_0^x e^{\tau s} f(s,y)\,ds\Big)\ \forall (x,y) \in [0,1] \times [0,1]. \qquad (15.22)$$

For example, if we take $f(x,y) = e^{-\tau x}$, then $u(x,y) = (g(y) + x)e^{-\tau x}$, where g represents the Dirichlet data posed on $\Gamma = \Gamma_-$.

The results of a numerical simulation for this problem are shown in Figure 15.5(a), with $\tau = 3.0$. In Figure 15.5(b), we contrast this with what happens if we pose boundary conditions instead on $\Gamma = \Gamma_+$. We see that a completely erroneous solution is obtained. Curiously, when the mesh is further refined in the case $\Gamma = \Gamma_+$, convergence does occur but with wiggles similar to those seen in Figure 15.5(b) that eventually get small. However, we have no explanation of this, nor do we have any guarantee that worse behavior will not occur with other data.

The code to implement the transport problem (15.20) is given in Program 15.2. We leave to Exercise 15.5 the further study of this problem.

15.6 Exercises

Exercise 15.1 *Consider the diffusion-advection problem (15.1) implemented via the variational formulation (15.12) using the bilinear form in (15.9), where Ω and $\boldsymbol{\beta}$ are as in Section 15.4 and $\Gamma = \Gamma_-$. In particular, take homogeneous Neumann data $g_N \equiv 0$. Take $f(x,y) \equiv 1$ and $g(y) = a + by$. Compare with the proposed limit $u_0(x,y) = x + g(y) = x + a + by$. Plot $u_h - u_0$ for various values of ϵ, mesh size, and polynomial degree. Experiment with different choices of a and b. Solve on various meshes and with various polynomial orders with $\epsilon = 1.0, 0.1, 0.001, 0.00001$ and other values of your choice. Explain what you see, and provide figures illustrating key conclusions. Also modify the problem to include inhomogeneous Neumann data as suggested in Section 15.4, one of which is $u_{,x}(1,y) = 1$ on Γ_+. (Also choose the corresponding Neumann data for Γ_0.) How does this change the solutions?*

Exercise 15.2 *Experiment further with the second example (in Section 15.4.2) by varying the mesh size and polynomial degree. Do you still get convergence as in (15.17)? What is* *the constant C? Does it vary with the mesh size and polynomial degree? Do you see any boundary layer?*

Exercise 15.3 *Consider the problem (15.1)–(15.2) implemented via the variational formulation (15.12). Explore the case $\Gamma = \Gamma_- \cup \Gamma_+$ with $\epsilon = 0.001$, data f and g as given in Figure 15.1, on a 100×100 mesh using piecewise linears. How large does the mesh need to be to eliminate the oscillations you see? What happens with higher degree approximations? How much smaller can you make the mesh? What gets the best balance of accuracy for time of computation?*

Exercise 15.4 *Consider the problem (15.1)–(15.2) implemented via the variational formulation (15.12). Explore the case $\Gamma = \Gamma_+$ for f and g as given in Figure 15.1. Solve with piecewise linears on a 100×100 mesh with $\epsilon = 0.01$. How big is the solution? Use quadratics and quartics and compare the size. But also is the solution negative in some cases?*

Exercise 15.5 *Consider the transport problem (15.19) implemented via the variational formulation (15.21) using the bilinear form in (15.20) where Ω and $\boldsymbol{\beta}$ are as in Section 15.4 and $\Gamma = \Gamma_-$. Take $f(x,y) = e^{-\tau x}$ and g is your choice. Modify your code for the diffusion-advection problem to implement this problem, or consult Program 15.2. Solve on various meshes and with various polynomial orders with $\tau = 10.0, 1.0, 0.1$ and other values of your choice. Use the exact solution (15.22) to test your code. Then switch to $\Gamma = \Gamma_+$ and see what happens as the mesh gets finer.*

Exercise 15.6 *Consider the transport problem (15.19) implemented via the variational formulation (15.21) using the bilinear form in (15.20) where Ω and $\boldsymbol{\beta}$ are as in Section 15.4 and $\Gamma = \Gamma_-$. Take $f(x,y) \equiv 1$ and $g(y) = a + by$. Compare with the proposed limit $u_0(x,y) = x + g(y) = x + a + by$ when $\tau \to 0$. Modify Program 15.2 or your code for the diffusion-advection problem to implement this problem. Experiment with different choices of a and b. Solve on various meshes and with various polynomial orders with $\tau = 10.0, 1.0, 0.1, 0.001$ and other values of your choice. Explain what you see, and provide figures illustrating key conclusions. Plot $u_h - u_0$ for various values of τ, mesh size, and polynomial degree.*

Exercise 15.7 *Consider the transport problem with Dirichlet conditions posed on*

$$\Gamma = \Gamma_- \cup \Gamma_+.$$

Pick boundary data for which you know the exact solution. What happens?

Exercise 15.8 *Consider the alternate variational formulation in which the bilinear form $b(\cdot,\cdot)$ in (15.6) is defined by integrating by parts. What are the coercivity conditions for this formulation? Experiment with this formulation following the outline of the chapter. (Hint: consider (15.8).)*

```
 1 from dolfin import *
 2 import sys,math
 3 from timeit import default_timer as timer
 4
 5 startime=timer()
 6 pdeg=int(sys.argv[1])
 7 meshsize=int(sys.argv[2])
 8 acoef=float(sys.argv[3])
 9
10 # Create mesh and define function space
11 mesh = UnitSquareMesh(meshsize, meshsize)
12 V = FunctionSpace(mesh, "Lagrange", pdeg)
13
14 # Define Dirichlet boundary (x = 0)
15 def boundary(x):
16   return x[0] < DOLFIN_EPS
17
18 # Define boundary condition
19 gee = Expression("x[1]*x[1]*(1.0-(2.0/3.0)*x[1])",degree=pdeg)
20 uex = Expression("(x[0]-(1.0/2.0)*x[0]*x[0])+ \
21                   (x[1]*x[1]*(1.0-(2.0/3.0)*x[1]))",degree=pdeg)
22 bee = Expression(("1.0","0.0"),degree=pdeg)
23 bc = DirichletBC(V, gee, boundary)
24
25 # Define variational problem
26 u = TrialFunction(V)
27 v = TestFunction(V)
28 f = Expression("1.0-x[0]",degree=pdeg)
29 a = (acoef*inner(grad(u), grad(v))+inner(bee,grad(u))*v)*dx
30 L = f*v*dx
31
32 # Compute solution
33 u = Function(V)
34 solve(a == L, u, bc)
35 aftersolveT=timer()
36 totime=aftersolveT-startime
37 ue=interpolate(uex,V)
38 ge=interpolate(gee,V)
39 uerr=errornorm(ue,u,norm_type='l2', degree_rise=0)
40 print " ",pdeg," ",meshsize," %.1e"%acoef," %.1e"%uerr, \
41       " %.5f"%(uerr/acoef)," %.3f"%totime
```

Program 15.1: Code to implement the advection problem (15.1)–(15.2).

```
 1 from dolfin import *
 2 import sys,math
 3 from timeit import default_timer as timer
 4
 5 startime=timer()
 6 pdeg=int(sys.argv[1])
 7 meshsize=int(sys.argv[2])
 8 acoef=float(sys.argv[3])
 9
10 # Create mesh and define function space
11 mesh = UnitSquareMesh(meshsize, meshsize)
12 V = FunctionSpace(mesh, "Lagrange", pdeg)
13
14 # Define Dirichlet boundary (x = 0)
15 def boundary(x):
16   return x[0] < DOLFIN_EPS
17
18 # Define boundary condition
19 gee = Expression("x[1]*x[1]*(1.0-(2.0/3.0)*x[1])",degree=pdeg)
20 uex = Expression("(x[0]+(x[1]*x[1]*(1.0-(2.0/3.0)*x[1]))) \
21                  *exp(-ac*x[0])",ac=acoef,degree=pdeg)
22 bee = Expression(("1.0","0.0"),degree=pdeg)
23
24 bc = DirichletBC(V, gee, boundary)
25
26 # Define variational problem
27 u = TrialFunction(V)
28 v = TestFunction(V)
29 f = Expression("exp(-ac*x[0])",ac=acoef,degree=pdeg)
30 a = (acoef*u*v+inner(bee,grad(u))*v)*dx
31 L = f*v*dx
32
33 # Compute solution
34 u = Function(V)
35 solve(a == L, u, bc)
36 aftersolveT=timer()
37 totime=aftersolveT-startime
38 uerr=errornorm(uex,u,norm_type='l2')
39 print " ",pdeg," ",meshsize," %.1e"%acoef," %.1e"%uerr," %.3f"%totime
40 # Plot solution
41 plot(u, interactive=True)
```

Program 15.2: Code to implement the transport problem (15.20). The solution is depicted in Figure 15.5.

Chapter 16

Mesh Adaptivity

We consider two approaches to mesh adaptivity. In Section 16.2, refined meshes are shown to improve approximation substantially. Such meshes are derived analytically based on *a priori* information about the singularities of the solution. This approach establishes the viability of adapting meshes to solutions. The second approach refines meshes automatically based on preliminary computations using techniques that estimate the size of the error for a given mesh. The feasibility of the latter approach is not at all obvious and requires some explanation.

One of the major advances of computational mathematics in the 20th century was the development of error indicators [57, Chapter 9]. Such indicators identify where the computational error is largest and thus suggest regions where the mesh should be refined. This concept was pioneered mathematically by Ivo Babuška [22], primarily by focusing on the residual error for the equation. Again, it is not at all obvious that the residual could indicate where the error is large, but this issue is now well understood. The subject has developed significantly in the subsequent decades [7, 241, 281]. Other approaches to error estimation have also been widely used, especially the Zienkiewicz–Zhu error estimators [187, 221, 234].

16.1 Mesh terminology

There are various terms used to describe families of meshes. These become particularly relevant in the case of mesh adaptivity because several meshes are typically generated and we need to know what properties hold uniformly for all of the meshes.

The weakest mesh restriction on a family of meshes $\{\mathcal{T}_h\}$ is that they be **nondegenerate**. We say that a mesh family is nondegenerate if there is a constant $C < \infty$ such that for each mesh, each element e in that mesh satisfies

$$\frac{\rho_{\min}(e)}{\rho_{\min}(e)} \leq C. \tag{16.1}$$

Here $\rho_{\min}(e)$ (respectively, $\rho_{\max}(e)$) is the radius of the largest ball contained in e (respectively, the radius of the smallest ball containing e).

A stronger notion of size restriction is that of **quasi-uniformity**. For simplicity, assume that for each mesh in the family, the parameter h satisfies

$$h = \max\{\rho_{\max}(e) : e \in \mathcal{T}_h\}. \tag{16.2}$$

That is, the mesh is labeled by its maximum element size. Then we say that a mesh family is **quasi-uniform** if there is a constant $C < \infty$ such that for each mesh, each element e in that mesh satisfies

$$\frac{h}{\rho_{\min}(e)} \leq C. \tag{16.3}$$

Note that any quasi-uniform family of meshes is necessarily nondegenerate.

In general, automatically refined meshes will often have the same maximal mesh size, so the parameter defined in (16.2) is not ideal as a label for the mesh. Instead, we define quasi-uniformity via the condition that there is a constant C such that for all h

$$\max\{\rho_{\max}(e) \,:\, e \in \mathcal{T}_h\} \leq C \min\{\rho_{\min}(e) \,:\, e \in \mathcal{T}_h\},$$

where now h is any appropriate label for the mesh. For example, we might start with an initial mesh $\mathcal{T}_0$ and generate further meshes $\mathcal{T}_1, \mathcal{T}_2, \ldots$.

There are important classes of meshes that **are** degenerate. One such class relates to problems with a large aspect ratio, and another involves problems where there is a discrepancy between the approximation needs in one direction versus others [47, 48, 134, 186, 220]. Significant work regarding error estimators in anisotropic contexts has been done [9, 43, 106, 107, 109, 112, 185, 187, 188, 221, 234, 235, 265]. However, the subsequent discussion here will be limited to the case of nondegenerate meshes.

16.2 Optimal mesh refinements

When the form of a singularity is known, it is possible to predict what an optimal mesh refinement should be. We have seen that the gradient of the solution of the L-shaped problem blows up like $|(x, y)|^{-1/3}$ near the re-entrant corner. So suppose that, in general,

$$|\nabla^k u(\mathbf{r})| \approx C|\mathbf{r} - \mathbf{r}_0|^{-k+\gamma} \text{ for } \mathbf{r} \in \Omega, \tag{16.4}$$

where $\nabla^k u$ denotes the tensor of partial derivatives of order k of u, and $|\nabla^k u|$ denotes the Euclidean norm of the tensor represented as a vector (the square root of the sum of squares of all entries). For the solution of the L-shaped problem, we have seen that this holds for $k = 1$ and $\gamma = 2/3$. It is possible to show that (16.4) holds for all $k \geq 1$ and $\gamma = \pi/\kappa$ for boundary vertices with angle κ. For simplicity, we assume that $\mathbf{r}_0 = \mathbf{0}$ from now on.

From (4.13) we have $\|u - u_h\|_{H^1(\Omega)} \leq C \inf_{v \in V_h} \|u - v\|_{H^1(\Omega)}$. For a non-uniform mesh, we need to use a more precise characterization of the interpolant (4.10) error:

$$\|u - \mathcal{I}_h u\|_{H^1(\Omega)}^2 \leq C \sum_e \left(h_e^{m-1} \|u\|_{H^m(e)}\right)^2, \tag{16.5}$$

where the summation is over all of the elements e of the mesh subdivision and h_e is the size of e. Here we assume that the meshes are non-degenerate (16.1), so the "size" of e can be defined in various ways that are equivalent up to a constant:

$$h_e = \rho_{\min}(e), \quad h_e = \rho_{\max}(e), \text{ or } \quad h_e = |e|^{1/d}, \tag{16.6}$$

where $|e|$ denotes the volume of an element e.

Since we are assuming that the derivatives of the solution degrade in a radial fashion, let us also assume that the mesh is refined in a radial fashion and is non-degenerate (16.1).

For each element e, let $\mathbf{r}_e$ denote its centroid. We assume that there is a monotonic mesh function μ such that

$$h_e \approx (1/n)\mu(|\mathbf{r}_e|), \tag{16.7}$$

where n is a parameter that we can use to refine the mesh. For example, we will consider $\mu(r) = r^\beta$ for $\beta > 0$. With such a mesh and under the assumption (16.4), the error expression (16.5) takes the form

$$n^{2-2m} \sum_e \left(\mu(|\mathbf{r}_e|)^{m-1} |\mathbf{r}_e|^{-m+\gamma} \sqrt{|e|}\right)^2 \approx n^{2-2m} \int_\Omega \left(\mu(|\mathbf{r}|)^{m-1} |\mathbf{r}|^{-m+\gamma}\right)^2 d\mathbf{r}. \tag{16.8}$$

Taking $\mu(r) = r^\beta$, the integrand in (16.8) simplifies to $|\mathbf{r}|^p$ where $p = 2(\beta(m-1) - m + \gamma)$. Such an expression is integrable in d dimensions if and only if $p > -d$, that is, if

$$\beta > \frac{m - \gamma - d/2}{m - 1}.$$

For example, if $d = 2$ and $m = 2$ (piecewise linears in two dimensions), then the requirement is $\beta > 1 - \gamma$. For the L-shaped domain, this means $\beta > \frac{1}{3}$. However, for higher-order approximations, the appropriate mesh conditions will be different. In addition, the other corners of the L-shaped domain can also require mesh refinement. For these, $\gamma = 2$, and so using cubics ($m = 4$) also requires $\beta > \frac{1}{3}$ at these convex right angles. In this case, $\beta > 7/9$ is required at the re-entrant corner (for $m = 4$).

Recall that $\frac{1}{2} \leq \gamma < \infty$ in general ($\gamma = \pi/\kappa$). Thus when γ is sufficiently large (comparable with $m - d/2$), we can take $\beta \approx 0$, meaning a mesh of essentially uniform size (quasi-uniform). For example, for piecewise linears ($m = 2$), at the convex corners of the L-shaped domain, no refinement is required, whereas for cubics such refinement would be required to achieve high accuracy for the least cost. This may seem strange until we turn the logic around. It says that there is no benefit to mesh refinement at the convex corners for lower-order approximation. For higher-order approximation, a much coarser mesh is allowed in the interior, but refinement is then required at all the corners.

The mesh parameter n can be related to the number of degrees of freedom N, at least asymptotically, as follows. We can write

$$N \approx c_1 \sum_e |e|^0 \approx c_2 \sum_e h_e^{-d} |e|^1 \approx c_3 n^d \int_\Omega |r|^{-\beta d}\, d\mathbf{x} \approx c_4 n^d,$$

provided that $\beta < 1$, as we now assume.

Thus we see that it is theoretically possible to refine a mesh to achieve a more effective approximation. Now we turn to the question of generating such meshes automatically.

16.3 Residual error estimators

Many successful error estimators are based on the **residual**. Consider the variational form

$$a_\alpha(v, w) = \int_\Omega \alpha(x) \nabla v(x) \cdot \nabla w(x)\, d\mathbf{x} \tag{16.9}$$

with α piecewise smooth, but not necessarily continuous. We will study the corresponding variational problem with Dirichlet boundary conditions on a polyhedral domain Ω in the

n dimensions, so that $V = H_0^1(\Omega)$. For simplicity, we take the right-hand side for the variational problem to be a piecewise smooth function, f.

As usual, let V_h be piecewise polynomials of degree less than k on a mesh $\mathcal{T}_h$, and assume that the discontinuities of α and f fall on mesh faces (edges in two dimensions) in $\mathcal{T}_h$. That is, both α and f are smooth on each $T \in \mathcal{T}_h$. However, we will otherwise assume only that the family of meshes $\mathcal{T}_h$ is non-degenerate, satisfying (16.1), since we will want to allow significant local mesh refinement.

Let u satisfy the usual variational formulation $a_\alpha(u,v) = (f,v)_{L^2(\Omega)}$ for all $v \in V$, and let $u_h \in V_h$ be the standard Galerkin approximation. The residual $R_h \in V'$ is defined by

$$R_h(v) = a_\alpha(u - u_h, v) \quad \forall v \in V. \tag{16.10}$$

Note that, by definition,

$$R_h(v) = 0 \quad \forall v \in V_h, \tag{16.11}$$

assuming $V_h \subset V$.

16.3.1 Why the residual?

The role of the residual in linear algebra is well known. Suppose that we want to solve a finite dimensional system

$$Ax = f. \tag{16.12}$$

Suppose also that y is some approximation to x. The residual r measures how close y is to solving (16.12):

$$r = f - Ay. \tag{16.13}$$

Define $e = x - y$, the error in the approximation. Then

$$Ae = Ax - Ay = f - Ay = r. \tag{16.14}$$

Thus the error e satisfies $e = A^{-1}r$, that is, knowing the residual gives an estimate of the error. We now return to the PDE case and show that a similar relationship holds.

16.3.2 Computing the residual

Let $\mathcal{A}$ denote the differential operator formally associated with the form (16.9), that is, $\mathcal{A}v := -\nabla\cdot(\alpha\nabla v)$. The residual can be represented by

$$\begin{aligned} R_h(v) &= \sum_T \int_T (f + \nabla\cdot(\alpha\nabla u_h))v\,dx + \sum_e \int_e [\alpha\mathbf{n}_e \cdot \nabla u_h]_{\mathbf{n}_e} v\,ds \\ &= \sum_T \int_T (f - \mathcal{A}u_h)v\,dx + \sum_e \int_e [\alpha\mathbf{n}_e \cdot \nabla u_h]_{\mathbf{n}_e} v\,ds \quad \forall v \in V, \end{aligned} \tag{16.15}$$

where $\mathbf{n}_e$ denotes a unit normal to e and $[\phi]_{\mathbf{n}}$ denotes the jump in ϕ across the face normal to $\mathbf{n}$:

$$[\phi]_{\mathbf{n}}(x) := \lim_{\epsilon\to 0} \phi(x + \epsilon\mathbf{n}) - \phi(x - \epsilon\mathbf{n}),$$

so that the expression in (16.15) is independent of the choice of normal $\mathbf{n}$ on each face. There are two parts to the residual. One is the integrable function R_A defined on each element T by

$$R_A|_T := (f + \nabla\cdot(\alpha\nabla u_h))\,|_T = (f - \mathcal{A}u_h)\,|_T, \tag{16.16}$$

and the other is the "jump" term

$$R_J(v) := \sum_e \int_e [\alpha \mathbf{n}_e \cdot \nabla u_h]_{\mathbf{n}_e} v \, ds \quad \forall v \in V. \tag{16.17}$$

The proof of (16.15) is derived by integrating by parts on each T, and the resulting boundary terms are collected in the term R_J.

Assuming that $a_\alpha(\cdot,\cdot)$ is coercive on $H^1(\Omega)$, and inserting $v = e_h$ in (16.10), we see that

$$\frac{1}{c_0}|e_h|^2_{H^1(\Omega)} \leq |a_\alpha(e_h, e_h)| = |R_h(e_h)|. \tag{16.18}$$

Therefore

$$\|e_h\|_{H^1(\Omega)} \leq c_0 \sup_{v \in H_0^1(\Omega)} \frac{|R_h(v)|}{\|v\|_{H^1(\Omega)}}. \tag{16.19}$$

The right-hand side of (16.19) is the $H^1(\Omega)'$ (dual) norm of the residual. This norm is not easily computable in terms of the data of the problem (f and α) and u_h. One typical approach is to estimate it using what is known as a Scott-Zhang [288] interpolant $\mathcal{I}_h$ which satisfies, for some constant γ_0,

$$\|v - \mathcal{I}_h v\|_{L^2(T)} \leq \gamma_0 h_T |v|_{H^1(\widehat{T})} \tag{16.20}$$

for all $T \in \mathcal{T}_h$, where $\widehat{T}$ denotes the union of elements that contact T, and

$$\|v - \mathcal{I}_h v\|_{L^2(e)} \leq \gamma_0 h_e^{1/2} |v|_{H^1(T_e)} \tag{16.21}$$

for all faces e in $\mathcal{T}_h$, where T_e denotes the union of elements that share the face e, where h_e (resp. h_T) is a measure of the size of e (resp. T). Dropping the subscript "e" when referring to a normal $\mathbf{n}$ to e, we get

$$\begin{aligned} |R_h(v)| &= |R_h(v - \mathcal{I}_h v)| \\ &= \Big| \sum_T \int_T R_A (v - \mathcal{I}_h v)\, dx + \sum_e \int_e [\alpha \mathbf{n} \cdot \nabla u_h]_{\mathbf{n}} (v - \mathcal{I}_h v)\, ds \Big|. \end{aligned} \tag{16.22}$$

Applying (16.20) and (16.21) to (16.22) we find

$$\begin{aligned} |R_h(v)| &= |R_h(v - \mathcal{I}_h v)| \\ &\leq \sum_T \|R_A\|_{L^2(T)} \|v - \mathcal{I}_h v\|_{L^2(T)} + \sum_e \| \, [\alpha \mathbf{n} \cdot \nabla u_h]_{\mathbf{n}} \, \|_{L^2(e)} \|v - \mathcal{I}_h v\|_{L^2(e)} \\ &\leq \sum_T \|R_A\|_{L^2(T)} \gamma_0 h_T |v|_{H^1(\widehat{T})} + \sum_e \| \, [\alpha \mathbf{n} \cdot \nabla u_h]_{\mathbf{n}} \, \|_{L^2(e)} \gamma_0 h_e^{1/2} |v|_{H^1(\widehat{T}_e)} \\ &\leq \gamma \Big(\sum_T \|R_A\|^2_{L^2(T)} h_T^2 + \sum_e \| \, [\alpha \mathbf{n} \cdot \nabla u_h]_{\mathbf{n}} \, \|^2_{L^2(e)} h_e \Big)^{1/2} |v|_{H^1(\Omega)}, \end{aligned} \tag{16.23}$$

where $\gamma = C\gamma_0$ for some constant C that depends only on the maximum number of elements in $\widehat{T}$ for each T. In view of (16.23), the **local error indicator** $\mathcal{E}_e$ is defined by

$$\mathcal{E}_e(u_h)^2 := \sum_{T \subset T_e} h_T^2 \|f + \nabla \cdot (\alpha \nabla u_h)\|^2_{L^2(T)} + h_e \| \, [\alpha \mathbf{n} \cdot \nabla u_h]_{\mathbf{n}} \, \|^2_{L^2(e)}. \tag{16.24}$$

With this definition, the previous inequalities can be summarized as

$$|R_h(v)| \leq \gamma\Big(\sum_e \mathcal{E}_e(u_h)^2\Big)^{1/2} |v|_{H^1(\Omega)}, \tag{16.25}$$

which in view of (16.19) implies that

$$|e_h|_{H^1(\Omega)} \leq \gamma c_0 \Big(\sum_e \mathcal{E}_e(u_h)^2\Big)^{1/2}, \tag{16.26}$$

where γ is a constant related only to interpolation error.

The key point of the above analysis is to identify the appropriate scaling to combine the two error terms (16.16) and (16.17), as given in (16.24), in order to get the error bound (16.26).

16.4 Local error estimates and refinement

In the previous section, the upper bound (16.26) for the global error $|u - u_h|_{H^1(\Omega)}$ was given in terms of locally defined, computable error estimators (16.24). If the data f and α are themselves piecewise polynomials of some degree, there is a lower bound for the local error [57, Section 9.3]

$$|e_h|_{H^1(T_e)} \geq c\,\mathcal{E}_e(u_h), \tag{16.27}$$

where $c > 0$ depends only on the nondegeneracy constant for $\mathcal{T}_h$. One corollary of this estimate is the reverse inequality to (16.26),

$$|e_h|_{H^1(\Omega)} \geq \frac{c}{\sqrt{2}}\Big(\sum_{e\in\mathcal{T}_h} \mathcal{E}_e(u_h)^2\Big)^{1/2}.$$

The $\sqrt{2}$ factor occurs because a sum over all edges (or faces) of integrals over T_e duplicates most of the elements in $\mathcal{T}_h$. A reverse inequality to (16.27) (a local *upper* bound) is not true in general. However, the local lower bound (16.27) suggests the strategy that

the mesh should be refined wherever the local error indicator $\mathcal{E}_e(u_h)$ is big.

Unfortunately, we cannot be sure that where it is small that the error will necessarily be small. Distant effects may pollute the error and make it large even if the error indicator $\mathcal{E}_e(u_h)$ is small nearby.

16.4.1 Other norms

It is possible to have error estimators for other norms. For example, the pointwise error $u - u_h$ at $\mathbf{x}$ can be represented using the Green's function (Section 6.2) $G^{\mathbf{x}}$ via

$$(u - u_h)(\mathbf{x}) = a_\alpha(u - u_h, G^{\mathbf{x}}) = a_\alpha(u - u_h, G^{\mathbf{x}} - v) = R_h(G^{\mathbf{x}} - v) \quad \forall v \in V_h. \tag{16.28}$$

Thus choosing v as the Scott-Zhang interpolant of $G^{\mathbf{x}}$ [110, page 719] leads to an error indicator of the form

$$\mathcal{E}^\infty(u_h) := \max_{T\in\mathcal{T}_h}\Big(h_T^2\|f + \nabla\cdot(\alpha\nabla u_h)\|_{L^\infty(T)} + h_e\|\,[\alpha\mathbf{n}\cdot\nabla u_h]_{\mathbf{n}}\,\|_{L^\infty(e)}\Big). \tag{16.29}$$

It can be proved [110] that there is a constant C such that

$$\|u - u_h\|_{L^\infty(\Omega)} \leq C\mathcal{E}^\infty(u_h).$$

The error estimators in [110] apply as well to nonlinear problems and to singular perturbation problems as in Exercise 7.1. An extension to anisotropic meshes is given in [181] for two-dimensional problems and piecewise linear approximation.

16.4.2 Other goals

Instead of attempting to estimate norms of the error, we can estimate linear functionals of the error. For example, the quantity of interest (C_6) in Section 7.2.1 is an integral (7.19). The strategy of **goal oriented error estimation** [249] (a.k.a. **dual weighted residual method** [33]) is to solve an adjoint problem to find $z \in V$ such that

$$a^*(z, v) = \mathcal{M}(v) \quad \forall v \in V, \tag{16.30}$$

where $\mathcal{M}$ is the linear functional to be optimized. That is, we seek meshes $\mathcal{T}_h$ such that $\mathcal{M}(u - u_h)$ is less than a given tolerance. Here, the adjoint form $a^*(\cdot,\cdot)$ is defined for any bilinear form $a(\cdot,\cdot)$ via

$$a^*(v, w) = a(w, v) \quad \forall v, w \in V. \tag{16.31}$$

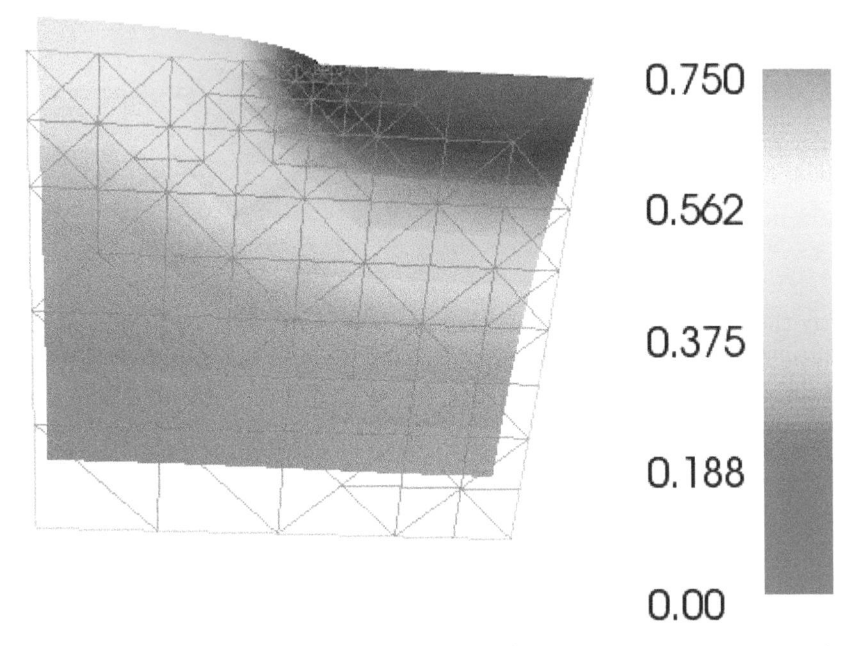

Figure 16.1: Adaptivity applied to the problem (6.10) using piecewise linears and an initial mesh of size 4 with a goal $\mathcal{M}(u) = \int_\Omega u^2\, d\mathbf{x}$. The initial, unrefined mesh is apparent in the lower-left corner of the domain.

If $a(\cdot,\cdot)$ is symmetric, then $a^*(\cdot,\cdot)$ is the same as $a(\cdot,\cdot)$. But it is different for a form like $a_\beta(\cdot,\cdot)$ defined in Section 15.2:

$$a_\beta(v, w) = \int_\Omega \nabla v(\mathbf{x}) \cdot \nabla w(\mathbf{x}) + \big(\boldsymbol{\beta}(\mathbf{x}) \cdot \nabla v(\mathbf{x})\big) w(\mathbf{x})\, d\mathbf{x}.$$

We see from (15.8) that, if $\nabla\cdot\boldsymbol{\beta}=0$ and Dirichlet conditions are imposed on the boundary wherever $\boldsymbol{\beta}\cdot\mathbf{n}\neq 0$, then

$$\begin{aligned} a_{\beta}^{*}(v,w)=a_{\beta}(w,v)&=\int_{\Omega}\nabla v(\mathbf{x})\cdot\nabla w(\mathbf{x})-\big(\boldsymbol{\beta}(\mathbf{x})\cdot\nabla v(\mathbf{x})\big)w(\mathbf{x})\,d\mathbf{x}\\ &=a_{-\beta}(v,w)\quad\forall v,w\in V. \end{aligned}\tag{16.32}$$

Suppose as usual that $u\in V$ satisfies $a(u,v)=F(v)$ for all $v\in V$, that $u_h\in V_h$ satisfies $a(u_h,v)=F(v)$ for all $v\in V_h$, and that $V_h\subset V$. Then $a(u-u_h,v)=0$ for all $v\in V_h$, and

$$\begin{aligned} \mathcal{M}(u-u_h)&=a^{*}(z,u-u_h)=a(u-u_h,z)\\ &=a(u-u_h,z-v)=R_h(z-v)\quad\forall v\in V_h. \end{aligned}\tag{16.33}$$

Note the analogy with (16.28), where instead of the Green's function $G^{\mathbf{x}}$ we have z.

It is helpful to re-write (16.22) by re-balancing the jump terms via

$$|R_h(v)|=\Big|\sum_T\int_T R_A(v-\mathcal{I}_hv)\,dx+\sum_{e\subset\partial T}\int_e[\alpha\mathbf{n}\cdot\nabla u_h]_{\mathbf{n}}^{*}(v-\mathcal{I}_hv)\,ds\Big|,\tag{16.34}$$

where $[\phi]_{\mathbf{n}}^{*}=\frac{1}{2}[\phi]_{\mathbf{n}}$ for interior edges (or faces) and $[\phi]_{\mathbf{n}}^{*}=\phi$ for boundary edges (or faces). Thus the local error indicator η_T is defined by

$$\eta_T(v)=\Big|\int_T R_A(v-\mathcal{I}_hv)\,dx+\sum_{e\subset\partial T}\int_e[\alpha\mathbf{n}\cdot\nabla u_h]_{\mathbf{n}}^{*}(v-\mathcal{I}_hv)\,ds\Big|.\tag{16.35}$$

Then (16.33) and (16.34) combine to give

$$|\mathcal{M}(u-u_h)|\leq\sum_T\eta_T(z).\tag{16.36}$$

The strategy then is to refine the mesh where $\eta_T(z)$ is large.

The difficulty now is that we do not know z, and we need to compute it. Moreover, if we simply use the same approximation space V_h to compute z_h, then we get a false impression (take $v=z_h$ in (16.33)). Thus there is a need to have a higher-order approximation of z than would normally be provided via V_h. Different approaches to achieving this have been studied [33], including simply approximating via a globally higher-order method.

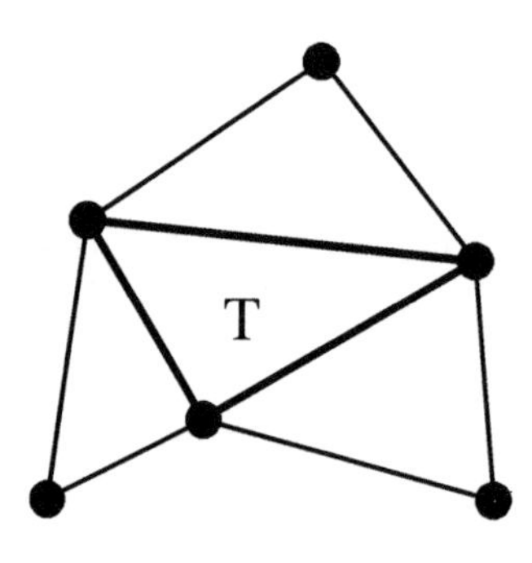

Figure 16.2: Nearby elements are used to construct a higher-order approximation to z.

What is done in `dolfin` [249] (see also [33]) is to first compute z_h using V_h, then interpolate it on patches around a given element using a higher-degree approximation, as indicated in Figure 16.2, using the interpolant as an approximation to z. In Figure 16.2, we see what would be done for a piecewise linear approximation, and we see that including three neighboring triangles gives exactly the data needed to construct a quadratic. This approach is effective and relatively inexpensive, but there is a philosophical conundrum: if this approach does give higher-order accuracy, why not simply use it instead of using error estimators? One answer to this is that the error estimator is trying to find only where $z - \mathcal{I}_h z$ is large, that is where the derivatives of z are large. This is a more restricted problem than trying to get higher accuracy in general.

The concept of adjoint form can also be extended [249] to the case where $a(\cdot,\cdot)$ is defined on a pair of spaces $V \times W$ instead of $V \times V$ as is the usual case considered so far. It is also possible to extend the theory to allow the goal functional $\mathcal{M}$ to be nonlinear.

16.4.3 Singularities

Another issue to consider is that there may be singularities in z that make its approximation poor. Fortunately, there is a duality between estimating the accuracy of u_h and the approximation of z [33] that can address this. However, there is a certain amount of art in goal-based error estimation that cannot be fully justified rigorously. In any case, it is clear from Figure 16.1 that the approach works. This figure depicts the solution of problem (6.10) using piecewise linears with an initial mesh of size 4 with a goal $\mathcal{M}(u) = \int_\Omega u^2 \, d\mathbf{x}$. The initial, unrefined mesh is apparent in the lower-left corner of the domain, and the adaptivity scheme clearly finds the right place to refine the mesh. The code used to generate this figure is given in Program 16.1.

16.4.4 The initial mesh

Mesh adaptivity employs a boot-strap process. That is, it uses an initial mesh to predict where refinement is needed. This information is then used to refine the mesh, and the process is iterated. But if the initial mesh is too coarse, the process can fail. Exploration of this is part of Exercise 16.1.

16.4.5 A special case

Suppose that $a(\cdot,\cdot)$ is symmetric, so that $a^*(\cdot,\cdot) = a(\cdot,\cdot)$, and that $\mathcal{M}(v) = F(v)$. Then $z = u$. Such a situation occurs in Section 7.2.1, and it is explored further in Exercise 16.3.

16.4.6 Mesh generation

Even when properties of desired meshes are known, it is still a difficult task to generate meshes with these properties [253].

16.5 Boundary layers

So far, we have been motivated by point singularities in the discussion of automated mesh refinement. However, the theoretical foundations of error estimation are insensitive to the nature of singularities. Another type of problem we have encountered has singularities near large segments (or all of) the domain boundary, so-called boundary layers, in Section 7.1 and Section 15.4. Thus it is of interest to see how automated techniques for mesh refinement perform in such cases.

To explore the use of how automated techniques for mesh refinement for boundary layer problems, we return to the boundary value problem considered in Section 7.1.1. The results obtained are depicted in Figure 16.3 for the case $\epsilon = 0.001$. We have chosen a representation where we plot the mesh on the contours of the solution. This should be compared with Figure 7.1 which represents the solution for a smaller ϵ computed with an unadapted mesh. It appears that the automated techniques have accurately determined where mesh refinement was needed. The computations were done with piecewise linears and a goal $\mathcal{M}(u) = \int_\Omega u^2\,d\mathbf{x}$. The remnants of the initial mesh are visible in the middle of the domain. The code used to generate Figure 16.3 is given in Program 16.2.

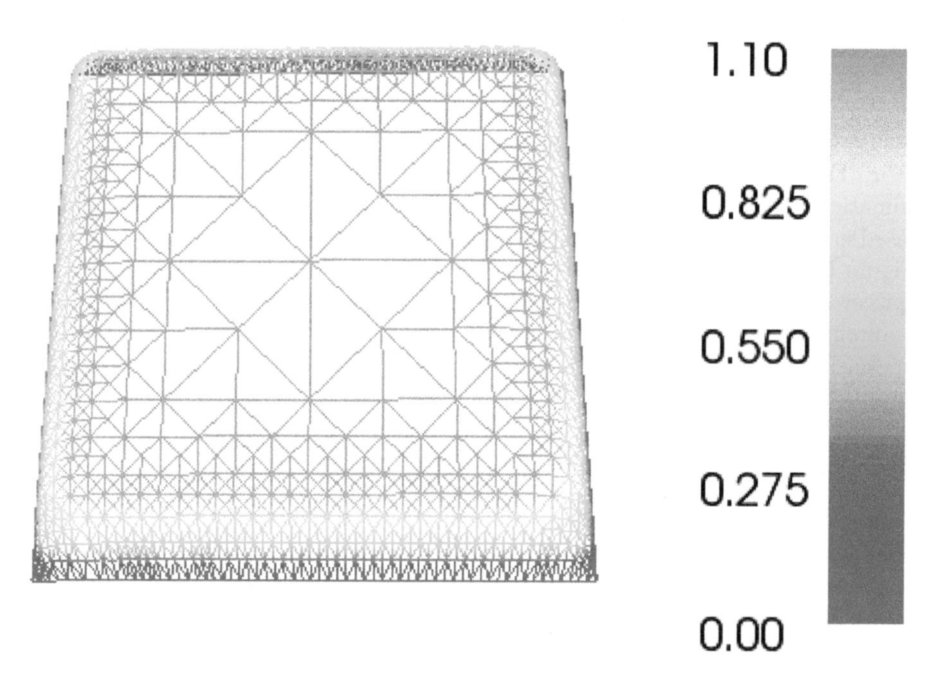

Figure 16.3: Adaptivity applied to the problem in Section 7.1.1 using piecewise linears and an initial mesh of size 2 with a goal $\mathcal{M}(u) = \int_\Omega u^2\,d\mathbf{x}$. The coarsest mesh elements are apparent in the middle of the domain, and the refinement is made all around the boundary, with a special concentration at the four corners of the square.

16.6 Exercises

Exercise 16.1 *Run Program 16.1 with* `meshsize` *=4,* `pdeg` *=1,* `qdeg` *=1, and* `mytol`*=0.01. How many mesh refinements are performed? Note that Newton's method is used since the goal functional is nonlinear. Can you verify this by looking at the final mesh? Try different parameters for* `meshsize`*,* `pdeg`*,* `qdeg`*, and* `mytol`*, and explain what you observe. How coarse can you take the initial mesh to be (see Section 16.4.4)?*

Exercise 16.2 *On page 171, we observe that our theoretical predictions of optimal mesh refinement suggest that there is no benefit to mesh refinement at convex corners for piecewise linear approximation, but for, say, cubic approximation, refinement at such corners would be seen for sufficiently small tolerances. Explore this dichotomy for automatically refined meshes via the problem in Exercise 6.7. Compare this with the problem* $-\Delta u = x(1-x) + y(1-y)$ *in the unit square* Ω *with* $u = 0$ *on* $\partial\Omega$ *which has the smooth solution* $u(x,y) = x(1-x)y(1-y)$.

Exercise 16.3 *Re-do the problem in Section 7.2.1 using adaptivity to compute* C_6 *via (7.19), with the goal*

$$\mathcal{M}(v) = \int_0^\infty \int_0^\infty r_1^2 r_2^2 e^{-(r_1+r_2)} v(r_1, r_2)\, dr_1 dr_2.$$

Truncate the integral in this definition appropriately to match the computational approach taken in Section 7.2.1.

Exercise 16.4 *Consider the variational form*

$$b_\beta(v,w) = \int_\Omega (\boldsymbol{\beta} \cdot \nabla v) w \, d\mathbf{x} + \oint_{\Gamma_-^\beta} u\, v\, \boldsymbol{\beta} \cdot \mathbf{n}\, ds,$$

where we define $\Gamma_\pm^\beta = \{\mathbf{x} \in \partial\Omega \,:\, \pm\boldsymbol{\beta}(\mathbf{x}) \cdot \mathbf{n}(\mathbf{x}) > 0\}$. *Suppose that* $\nabla \cdot \boldsymbol{\beta} = 0$. *Use (15.8) to show that* $b_\beta(v,w) = -b_{-\beta}(w,v)$. *(Hint: show that* $\Gamma_-^{-\beta} = \Gamma_+^\beta$.*)*

Exercise 16.5 *Consider the problem (6.10) using adaptivity with various goals. How coarse can the initial mesh be to obtain reasonable results?*

Exercise 16.6 *Define a goal function* $\mathcal{M}$ *via*

$$\mathcal{M}(v) = \int_\Omega \delta_{\mathbf{x}_0}^A \, v \, d\mathbf{x},$$

where $\delta_{\mathbf{x}_0}^A$ *is defined in (6.17) and* A *is sufficiently large. Explain what this goal is trying to do in words (hint: look at Section 6.2). Write a code to use this goal in the problem (6.16) with* $\mathbf{x}_0$ *near* $(\frac{1}{2}, \frac{1}{2})$, *and explain what happens. Compare this with having the goal* $\mathcal{M}(v) = \int_\Omega v(x)^2 \, d\mathbf{x}$.

```
1  from dolfin import *
2  import sys,math
3
4  parameters["form_compiler"]["quadrature_degree"] = 12
5
6  meshsize=int(sys.argv[1])
7  pdeg=int(sys.argv[2])
8  qdeg=int(sys.argv[3])
9  mytol=float(sys.argv[4])
10
11 # Create mesh and define function space
12 mesh = UnitSquareMesh(meshsize, meshsize)
13 V = FunctionSpace(mesh, "Lagrange", pdeg)
14
15 # Define Dirichlet boundary (x = 0 or x = 1 or y = 0 or y = 1)
16 def boundary(x):
17   return x[0] > 0.5 and x[1] < DOLFIN_EPS
18
19 # Define boundary condition
20 u0 = Constant(0.0)
21 bc = DirichletBC(V, u0, boundary)
22
23 # Define variational problem
24 u = Function(V)
25 v = TestFunction(V)
26 f = Expression("1.0",degree=pdeg)
27 J = u*u*dx
28 F = (inner(grad(u), grad(v)))*dx - f*v*dx
29
30 # Compute solution
31 solve(F == 0, u, bc, tol=mytol, M=J)
32 # Plot solution
33 plot(u.leaf_node(), interactive=True)
```

Program 16.1: Code to solve the stick-slip problem (6.10) and used to generate Figure 16.1.

```
1  from dolfin import *
2  import sys,math
3
4  meshsize=2
5  pdeg=1
6  acoef=0.001
7  mytol=0.001
8
9  # Create mesh and define function space
10 mesh = UnitSquareMesh(meshsize, meshsize)
11 V = FunctionSpace(mesh, "Lagrange", pdeg)
12
13 # Define boundary condition
14 u0 = Constant(0.0)
15 bc = DirichletBC(V, u0, "on_boundary")
16
17 # Define variational problem
18 u = Function(V)
19 v = TestFunction(V)
20 f = Expression("1.0",degree=pdeg)
21 F= (acoef*inner(grad(u), grad(v))+u*v)*dx - f*v*dx
22 J = u*u*dx
23
24 # Compute solution
25 solve(F == 0, u, bc, tol=mytol, M=J)
26 #plot(u, interactive=True)
27 plot(u.leaf_node(), interactive=True)
```

Program 16.2: Code to solve the problem in Section 7.1.1 and used to generate Figure 16.3.

Chapter 17

Scalar Elliptic Problems

The general scalar elliptic problem takes the form

$$-\sum_{i,j=1}^{d} \frac{\partial}{\partial x_j}\left(\alpha_{ij}(\mathbf{x})\frac{\partial u}{\partial x_i}(\mathbf{x})\right) = f(\mathbf{x}) \tag{17.1}$$

where the α_{ij} are given functions, together with suitable boundary conditions of the type considered previously.

To be elliptic, the functions $\alpha_{ij}(\mathbf{x})$ need to form a positive definite matrix at almost every point $\mathbf{x}$ in a domain Ω. Often, this is a symmetric matrix. More precisely, it is assumed that for some finite, positive constant C,

$$C^{-1} \leq |\xi|^{-2} \sum_{i,j=1}^{d} \alpha_{ij}(\mathbf{x})\, \xi_i\, \xi_j \leq C \quad \forall\, 0 \neq \xi \in \mathbb{R}^d, \text{ for almost all } \mathbf{x} \in \Omega. \tag{17.2}$$

Here the expression "for almost all" means the condition can be ignored on a set of measure zero, such as a lower-dimensional surface running through Ω. However, there is no need for the $\alpha_{ij}'s$ to be continuous, and in many important physical applications they are not.

An interpretation of the general scalar elliptic problem in classical terms is difficult when the α_{ij}'s are not differentiable. However, the variational formulation is quite simple. It is in divergence form (see Section 9.3.1), so we define

$$a_\alpha(u,v) := \int_\Omega \sum_{i,j=1}^{d} \alpha_{ij}(\mathbf{x})\frac{\partial u}{\partial x_i}(\mathbf{x})\frac{\partial v}{\partial x_j}\, d\mathbf{x}. \tag{17.3}$$

Using this bilinear form, the problem (17.1) can be posed (cf. (3.8)) as:

Find $u \in V$ such that

$$a_\alpha(u,v) = F(v) \quad \forall v \in V, \tag{17.4}$$

where the boundary conditions are incorporated in the space V as described in Section 2.2.

17.1 Discontinuous coefficients

It is frequently the case that the coefficients which arise in physical models vary so dramatically that it is appropriate to model them as discontinuous. These often arise due to a

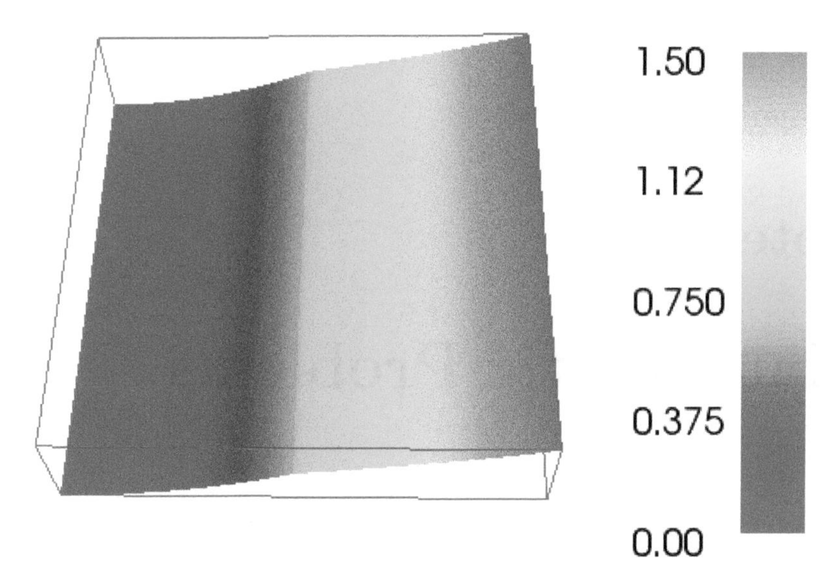

Figure 17.1: Scalar elliptic problem with "discontinuous" coefficient described in Section 17.1.3. Computed using piecewise linears on a 128×128 mesh and $\epsilon = 10^{-5}$ via Program 17.1.

change in materials or material properties. Examples can be found in the modeling of nuclear reactors [115], porous media [114], semiconductors [31], proteins in a solvent [24, 171] and on and on. However, the lack of continuity of the coefficients has less effect on the model than might be thought at first.

The critical factor is the *ellipticity* of the coefficients. We suppose that the coefficients form a positive definite matrix almost everywhere, that is, that

$$\sum_{i=1}^{d} \xi_i^2 \leq c_0 \sum_{i,j=1}^{d} \alpha_{ij}(\mathbf{x})\xi_i\xi_j \quad \forall \xi \in \mathbb{R}^d,\ \mathbf{x} \in \Omega_0 \tag{17.5}$$

for some positive constant c_0 and some set Ω_0 where the complementary set $\Omega\backslash\Omega_0$ has *measure zero*, that is, contains no sets of positive volume. Examples of such sets are ones which consist of sets of lower-dimensional surfaces. On the set $\Omega\backslash\Omega_0$ the coefficients may jump from one value to another and so have no precise meaning, and we are allowed to ignore such sets.

We also assume that the coefficients are bounded almost everywhere:

$$\sum_{i,j=1}^{d} \alpha_{ij}(\mathbf{x})\xi_i\nu_j \leq c_1 |\xi|\,|\nu| \quad \forall \xi, \nu \in \mathbb{R}^d,\ \mathbf{x} \in \Omega_0, \tag{17.6}$$

for some finite constant c_1, where $|\xi|^2 = \sum_{i=1}^{d} \xi_i^2$.

The ellipticity constant ε is the ratio

$$\varepsilon := \frac{1}{c_0\, c_1}. \tag{17.7}$$

For elliptic coefficients, the coercivity condition (3.3) and the corresponding stability result (3.6) both hold, where $C = c_0\, c_1 = \varepsilon^{-1}$.

There is a subtle dependence of the regularity of the solution in the case of discontinuous coefficients [219]. It is not in general the case that the gradient of the solution is bounded. However, from the variational derivation, we see that the gradient of the solution is always square integrable. A bit more is true, that is, the p-th power of the solution is integrable for $2 \le p \le P_\varepsilon$ where P_ε is a number bigger than two depending only on the ellipticity constant ε in (17.7) (as ε tends to zero, P_ε tends to two).

17.1.1 Coercivity and continuity

The assumption (17.5) immediately implies coercivity of the bilinear form (17.3). For each $\mathbf{x} \in \Omega$, we take $\xi_i = v_{,i}(\mathbf{x})$ and apply (17.5):

$$\int_\Omega |\nabla \mathbf{v}(\mathbf{x})|^2 \, d\mathbf{x} = \int_\Omega \sum_{i=1}^d v_{,i}(\mathbf{x})^2 \, d\mathbf{x} \le c_0 \int_\Omega \sum_{i,j=1}^d \alpha_{ij}(\mathbf{x}) v_{,i}(\mathbf{x}) v_{,j}(\mathbf{x}) \, d\mathbf{x} = a_\alpha(v,v). \tag{17.8}$$

Similarly, (17.6) implies that the bilinear form (17.3) is bounded:

$$\begin{aligned} a_\alpha(u,v) = \int_\Omega \sum_{i,j=1}^d \alpha_{ij}(\mathbf{x}) u_{,i}(\mathbf{x}) v_{,j}(\mathbf{x}) \, d\mathbf{x} &\le c_1 \int_\Omega |\nabla u(\mathbf{x})| \, |\nabla v(\mathbf{x})| \, d\mathbf{x} \\ &\le c_1 \|u\|_{H^1(\Omega)} \|v\|_{H^1(\Omega)}, \end{aligned} \tag{17.9}$$

using the Cauchy-Schwarz inequality (3.15).

17.1.2 Flux continuity

Using the variational form (17.3) of the equation (17.1), we will see that the *flux*

$$\sum_{i=1}^d \alpha_{ij}(\mathbf{x}) \frac{\partial u}{\partial x_i}(\mathbf{x}) n_j \tag{17.10}$$

is continuous across an interface normal to $\mathbf{n}$ even when the α_{ij}'s are discontinuous across the interface. This implies that the normal slope of the solution must have a jump (that is, the graph has a kink).

The derivation of (17.10) is just integration by parts. Suppose that $\Omega = \Omega_1 \cup \Omega_2$ and that the coefficients are smooth on the interiors of Ω_i, $i = 1,2$, but have a jump across $\Gamma = \overline{\Omega_1} \cap \overline{\Omega_2}$.[1] Suppose that $v = 0$ on $\partial\Omega$. Define $\mathbf{w} = v \boldsymbol{\alpha} \nabla \mathbf{u}$ and apply the divergence theorem on each Ω_i separately to get

$$\oint_\Gamma v \mathbf{n}_i \cdot \boldsymbol{\alpha} \nabla \mathbf{u} \, ds = \int_{\Omega_i} \nabla \cdot \mathbf{w} \, dx = \int_{\Omega_i} (\boldsymbol{\alpha} \nabla \mathbf{u}) \cdot \nabla v \, dx + \int_{\Omega_i} v \nabla \cdot (\boldsymbol{\alpha} \nabla \mathbf{u}) \, dx$$

Summing this over i and using (17.1) we get

$$\oint_\Gamma v [\mathbf{n} \cdot \boldsymbol{\alpha} \nabla \mathbf{u}]_\Gamma \, ds = a(u,v) - \int_\Omega f v \, d\mathbf{x} = 0, \tag{17.11}$$

[1] We are being a bit picky here about whether the sets Ω_i include their boundaries (that is, are closed) or not. To write $\Omega = \Omega_1 \cup \Omega_2$, one of the Ω_i's has to include the overlap Γ.

where the jump expression $[\phi]_\Gamma$ is defined by

$$[\phi(x)]_\Gamma = \lim_{h\to 0} \phi(x - h\mathbf{n}) - \lim_{h\to 0} \phi(x + h\mathbf{n})$$

and $\mathbf{n}$ is either $\mathbf{n}_1$ or $\mathbf{n}_2 = -\mathbf{n}_1$. Note that the expression $[\mathbf{n}\cdot\boldsymbol{\alpha}\nabla\mathbf{u}]_\Gamma$ is the same whether we define $\mathbf{n} = \mathbf{n}_1$ or $\mathbf{n} = \mathbf{n}_2$. We recognize $[\mathbf{n}\cdot\boldsymbol{\alpha}\nabla\mathbf{u}]_\Gamma$ as the jump in the flux (17.10) across Γ. Since (17.11) holds for all v vanishing on $\partial\Omega$, we conclude that $[\mathbf{n}\cdot\boldsymbol{\alpha}\nabla\mathbf{u}]_\Gamma = 0$ everywhere on Γ.

17.1.3 Piecewise constant example

Take $\boldsymbol{\alpha}(\mathbf{x})$ to be a scalar function times the identity matrix, that is, the diagonal matrix $\alpha_{ij}(\mathbf{x}) = \delta_{ij}\alpha(\mathbf{x})$, where δ_{ij} is the Kronecker delta. Assume that, for some constant $C > 0$,

$$(1/C) \geq \alpha(\mathbf{x}) \geq C \quad \text{for all } \mathbf{x} \in \Omega.$$

Let $\Omega = [0,1]^2$, let $\Omega_1 = [0,1/2]\times[0,1]$, and let $\Omega_2 = [1/2,1]\times[0,1]$. Thus

$$\Gamma = \left\{(x,y) \;:\; x = \tfrac{1}{2}\right\}.$$

Define

$$a(u,v) = \int_\Omega \alpha\nabla u\cdot\nabla v\,d\mathbf{x},$$

where we take

$$\alpha(x,y) = \begin{cases} 1 & x < 1/2 \\ 3 & x > 1/2. \end{cases} \tag{17.12}$$

Consider the problem (17.1), posed variationally as (17.4), with $f \equiv -6$ and with Dirichlet boundary conditions $u = 0$ on $\{(0,y) : y \in [0,1]\}$ and $u = 3/2$ on $\{(1,y) : y\in[0,1]\}$. Thus the variational space is

$$V = \left\{v \in H^1(\Omega) \;:\; v(x,y) = 0 \text{ if } x = 0 \text{ or } x = 1, \text{ for all } y\in[0,1]\right\}.$$

The exact solution u satisfies

$$u(x,y) = \begin{cases} 3x^2 & x \leq 1/2 \\ \frac{1}{2} + x^2 & x \geq 1/2. \end{cases} \tag{17.13}$$

Note that $\alpha\frac{\partial u}{\partial x} = 6$ for all $x \neq \frac{1}{2}$. The solution is depicted in Figure 17.1, and the "kink" in the solution across Γ is evident.

To render the computational problem simpler, we defined $\alpha(x) = 2 + \tanh(M(x - 0.5))$ for a large number M. The computation represented in Figure 17.1 was done with $M = 10^5$. This definition of α is actually more consistent with many applications where the coefficient is smooth but changes abruptly over a length scale of order $\mathcal{O}\left(M^{-1}\right)$. It is noteworthy that the computations do not depend significantly on M. This is implemented in Program 17.1, with `fudg`$=M$.

17.2 Dielectric models

One of the most important scalar elliptic equations with discontinuous coefficients is a model for the dielectric behavior of a protein in water. This takes the form

$$\begin{aligned} -\nabla\cdot(\mathcal{E}\nabla u) &= \sum_{i=1}^{N} c_i\,\delta_{\mathbf{x}_i} \quad \text{in } \mathbb{R}^3 \\ u(\mathbf{x}) &\to 0 \quad \text{as } \mathbf{x}\to\infty, \end{aligned} \tag{17.14}$$

where the dielectric constant $\mathcal{E}$ is small inside the protein, which we assume occupies the domain Ω, and large outside. Here, the point charges at $\mathbf{x}_i$ are modeled via Dirac δ-functions $\delta_{\mathbf{x}_i}$. The constant c_i corresponds to the charge at that point.

Confusion has arisen about the efficacy of error estimators due to the need for resolving point singularities $\mathbf{x}_i \in \Omega$ resulting from point charges [169]; this has limited the use of error estimators for such models. Error estimators necessarily indicate large errors anywhere there are fixed charges, thus throughout the protein, not primarily at the interface. Indeed, the singularity due to the point charges is more severe than that caused by the jump in the dielectric coefficient $\mathcal{E}$.

But we can introduce a splitting u=v+w where

$$v(\mathbf{x}) = \sum_{i=1}^{N} \frac{c_i}{|\mathbf{x}-\mathbf{x}_i|}. \tag{17.15}$$

Here we assume that units chosen so that fundamental solution of $-\mathcal{E}_0\Delta u = \delta_0$ is $1/|\mathbf{x}|$, where $\mathcal{E}_0$ is the dielectric constant in Ω.

17.2.1 Equation for w

By definition, w is harmonic in both Ω and $\mathbb{R}^3\backslash\Omega$, and $w(\mathbf{x})\to 0$ as $\mathbf{x}\to\infty$. But the jump in the normal derivative of w across the interface $B=\partial\Omega$ is not zero. Define

$$\left[\mathcal{E}\frac{\partial w}{\partial n}\right]_B = \mathcal{E}_0\frac{\partial w}{\partial n}\Big|_{B-} - \mathcal{E}_\infty\frac{\partial w}{\partial n}\Big|_{B+},$$

where $B-$ denotes the inside of the interface, $B+$ denotes the outside of the interface, and $\mathbf{n}$ denotes the outward normal to Ω. The solution u of (17.14) satisfies $\left[\mathcal{E}\frac{\partial u}{\partial n}\right]_B = 0$, so

$$\left[\mathcal{E}\frac{\partial w}{\partial n}\right]_B = (\mathcal{E}_\infty - \mathcal{E}_0)\frac{\partial v}{\partial n}\Big|_B.$$

From the integration-by-parts formula (2.10), we have

$$a(w,\phi) = \oint_B \left[\mathcal{E}\frac{\partial w}{\partial n}\right]_B \phi\,ds = (\mathcal{E}_\infty - \mathcal{E}_0)\oint_B \frac{\partial v}{\partial n}\phi\,ds$$

for all test functions ϕ. The linear functional F defined by

$$F(\phi) = (\mathcal{E}_\infty - \mathcal{E}_0)\oint_B \frac{\partial v}{\partial n}\phi\,ds \tag{17.16}$$

is clearly well defined for any test function, since v is smooth except at the singular points x_i, which we assume are in the interior of Ω, not on the boundary $B = \partial\Omega$. Thus w is defined by a standard variational formulation and can be computed accordingly, modulo the need to truncate the infinite domain at some distance from Ω. For example, we can define

$$B_R = \left\{\mathbf{x} \in \mathbb{R}^3 \ : \ |\mathbf{x}| < R\right\},$$

and define

$$a_R(\phi,\psi) = \int_{B_R} \mathcal{E}\nabla\phi\cdot\nabla\psi\,d\mathbf{x},$$

and solve for $w_R \in H_0^1(B_R)$ such that

$$a_R(w_R,\psi) = F(\psi) \quad \forall\psi \in H_0^1(B_R), \tag{17.17}$$

where F is defined in (17.16). Then $w_R \to w$ as $R \to \infty$.

17.2.2 Point-charge example

Let us consider a single point charge at the origin of a spherical domain

$$\Omega = \left\{\mathbf{x} \in \mathbb{R}^3 \ : \ |\mathbf{x}| < R\right\}$$

of radius $R > 0$. Let $\mathcal{E}_0$ denote the dielectric constant in Ω and $\mathcal{E}_\infty$ denote the dielectric constant in $\mathbb{R}^3\backslash\Omega$. Then the solution to (17.14) is

$$u(\mathbf{x}) = \begin{cases} \frac{1}{|\mathbf{x}|} - \frac{c}{R} & |\mathbf{x}| \le R \\ \frac{1-c}{|\mathbf{x}|} & |\mathbf{x}| \ge R, \end{cases} \tag{17.18}$$

where

$$c = 1 - \frac{\mathcal{E}_0}{\mathcal{E}_\infty}.$$

The verification is as follows. In Ω, we have $\Delta u = \delta_\mathbf{0}$. In $\mathbb{R}^3\backslash\Omega$, we have $\Delta u = 0$. At the interface $B = \partial\Omega = \left\{\mathbf{x} \in \mathbb{R}^3 \ : \ |\mathbf{x}| = R\right\}$,

$$\frac{\partial u}{\partial n}\Big|_{B-} = \frac{\partial u}{\partial r}(R-) = \frac{-1}{R^2}, \qquad \frac{\partial u}{\partial n}\Big|_{B+} = \frac{\partial u}{\partial r}(R+) = \frac{-(1-c)}{R^2},$$

where $B-$ denotes the inside of the interface and $B+$ denotes the outside of the interface. Thus the jump is given by

$$\left[\mathcal{E}\frac{\partial u}{\partial n}\right]_B = \mathcal{E}_0\frac{\partial u}{\partial n}\Big|_{B-} - \mathcal{E}_\infty\frac{\partial u}{\partial n}\Big|_{B+} = \frac{-\mathcal{E}_0 + (1-c)\mathcal{E}_\infty}{R^2} = 0.$$

In this case, $v(\mathbf{x}) = 1/|\mathbf{x}|$, so

$$w(\mathbf{x}) = -c\begin{cases} \frac{1}{R} & |\mathbf{x}| \le R \\ \frac{1}{|\mathbf{x}|} & |\mathbf{x}| \ge R. \end{cases} \tag{17.19}$$

Thus if we solve numerically for w, we have a much smoother problem. But as $R \to 0$, w becomes more singular.

17.2.3 Error estimators for electrostatic models

Error estimators used in models in which the numerical techniques must resolve the point singularities resulting from point charges [169] necessarily indicate large errors anywhere there are fixed charges, thus throughout the protein, not primarily at the interface. Indeed, the authors of [169, 26] considered a simplified algorithm to estimate errors due to the protein-solvent interface in the second paper. Further, in the subsequent paper [81], the authors considered the splitting advocated here and studied the corresponding improved error estimator.

When using the solution splitting that we advocate, one would expect that the primary numerical error would occur at the protein-water interface, due primarily to the jump in the dielectric coefficients at this interface. Specific studies of error estimators and adaptivity for elliptic problems with discontinuous coefficients have been an active area of research for over a decade [232, 233, 84, 268, 70, 282, 80, 82, 180].

If the error is dominated by the jump in the solution gradient at the interface, it is possible that the refinement necessary to represent the protein boundary already forces sufficient accuracy near the interface. In any case, it may well be that simple error indicators [26] are sufficient to obtain a good estimate of the errors. However, it seems prudent to examine this issue in detail as it has the potential to benefit a large class of codes that currently do not have a good way of determining appropriate resolution. Moreover, there is a reasonable chance that significant efficiencies can be obtained with a state-of-the-art approach to mesh refinement and coarsening [62].

17.3 Exercises

Exercise 17.1 *Verify the formula (17.13) for the exact solution of the problem in Section 17.1.3.*

Exercise 17.2 *Run Program 17.1 and describe how the solution depends on M.*

Exercise 17.3 *Use the variational formulation (17.17) to approximate the solution of (17.14) using the splitting $u = v+w$ where v is defined in (17.15). Use the example in Section 17.2.2 as a test case. Consider the impact of the approximation parameter R (see if the results stabilize as $R \to \infty$), as well as the choice of mesh and approximation space, on the results. Choose an appropriate norm in which to measure the error.*

Exercise 17.4 *Use the variational formulation (17.17) to approximate the solution of (17.14) directly via the approximation (6.17) to the Dirac δ-function developed in Section 6.2. That is, define the linear functional F^A ($A > 0$) by*

$$F^A(v) = \sum_{i=1}^{N} c_i \int_\Omega \delta^A_{\mathbf{x}_i}(\mathbf{x})\, v(\mathbf{x})\, d\mathbf{x},$$

and solve for $u^{A,R} \in H^1_0(B_R)$ satisfying

$$a_R(u^{A,R}, v) = F^A(v) \quad \forall v \in H^1_0(B_R).$$

Use the example in Section 17.2.2 as a test case. Consider the impact of the approximation parameters A and R (see if the results stabilize as $A, R \to \infty$), as well as the choice of mesh and approximation space, on the results. Choose an appropriate norm in which to measure the error. Compare with the approach in Exercise 17.3.

Exercise 17.5 *Let* $\Omega = [-R, R]^2$ *and consider the coefficient*

$$\mathcal{E}(\mathbf{x}) = 1 + 40(1 - \tanh(M(|\mathbf{x}| - 1))),$$

for $R > 1$ *and* $M >> 1$*. Compare the mesh refinements done by* `dolfin` *for the variational formulation (17.17) to approximate the solution of (17.14) directly via the approximation (6.17) to the Dirac* δ*-function developed in Section 6.2. That is, define the linear functional* F^A $(A > 0)$ *by*

$$F^A(v) = \sum_{i=1}^{N} c_i \int_\Omega \delta^A_{\mathbf{x}_i}(\mathbf{x})\, v(\mathbf{x})\, d\mathbf{x},$$

and solve for $u^{A,R} \in H^1_0(B_R)$ *satisfying*

$$a_R(u^{A,R}, v) = F^A(v) \quad \forall v \in H^1_0(B_R).$$

Use the example in Section 17.2.2 as a test case. Consider the impact of the approximation parameters A *and* R *(see if the results stabilize as* $A, R \to \infty$*), as well as the choice of mesh and approximation space, on the results. Choose an appropriate norm in which to measure the error. Compare with the approach in Exercise 17.3.*

```
from dolfin import *
import sys,math

meshsize=int(sys.argv[1])
pdeg=int(sys.argv[2])
fudg=int(sys.argv[3])

# Create mesh and define function space
mesh = UnitSquareMesh(meshsize, meshsize)
V = FunctionSpace(mesh, "Lagrange", pdeg)

#Dirichlet boundary (x = 0 or x = 1)
def boundary(x):
  return x[0] < DOLFIN_EPS or x[0] > 1- DOLFIN_EPS

# Define boundary condition
u0 = Expression("1.5*x[0]",degree=pdeg)
bc = DirichletBC(V, u0, boundary)

# Define variational problem
u = TrialFunction(V)
v = TestFunction(V)
f = Expression("-6.0",degree=pdeg)
alfa = Expression("2.0+tanh(fud*(x[0]-0.5))",fud=fudg,degree=pdeg)
a = (alfa*(inner(grad(u), grad(v))))*dx
L = f*v*dx

# Compute solution
u = Function(V)
solve(a == L, u, bc)

# Plot solution
plot(u, interactive=True)
```

Program 17.1: Code to implement the scalar elliptic problem with discontinuous coefficient described in Section 17.1.3. The solution is depicted in Figure 17.1.

Chapter 18

Mixed Methods

The name "mixed method" is applied to a variety of finite element methods which have more than one approximation space. Typically one or more of the spaces play the role of Lagrange multipliers which enforce constraints. The name and many of the original concepts for such methods originated in solid mechanics [15] where it was desirable to have a more accurate approximation of certain derivatives of the displacement. However, for the Stokes equations which govern viscous fluid flow, the natural Galerkin approximation is a mixed method.

Mixed methods have different features that make them attractive. When used for problems like (17.1), the most obvious is that the primary emphasis switches from approximating the solution to approximating its gradient. In addition, we will see that the role of essential and natural boundary conditions is reversed. Thus with mixed methods for (17.1), the Neumann condition becomes essential, whereas the Dirichlet condition is imposed only weakly through the variational equation.

One characteristic of mixed methods is that not all choices of finite element spaces will lead to convergent approximations. Standard approximability alone is insufficient to guarantee success, as we saw with the Stokes equations in Chapter 13. Thus significant care is required in using them.

18.1 Mixed formulations

We will focus in this chapter on mixed methods in which there are two bilinear forms and two approximation spaces. There are two key conditions that lead to the success of a mixed method. Both are in some sense coercivity conditions for the bilinear forms. One of these will look like a standard coercivity condition, while the other, often called the *inf-sup* condition, takes a new form.

To motivate the mixed method, we take a particular application in which the mixed method arises naturally.

18.1.1 Miscible displacement in a porous medium

A simplified model [125] for miscible displacement of a fluid in a porous medium, occupying a domain Ω, takes the form

$$-\sum_{i,j=1}^{d} \frac{\partial}{\partial x_i}\Big(\alpha_{ij}(\mathbf{x})\frac{\partial p}{\partial x_j}(\mathbf{x})\Big) = f(\mathbf{x}) \text{ in } \Omega, \tag{18.1}$$

where p is the pressure (we take an inhomogeneous right-hand-side for generality). Darcy's Law [284] postulates that the fluid velocity $\mathbf{u}$ is related to the gradient of p by

$$u_i(\mathbf{x}) = \sum_{j=1}^{d} \alpha_{ij}(\mathbf{x})\frac{\partial p}{\partial x_j}(\mathbf{x}) \quad \forall i = 1,\ldots,d. \tag{18.2}$$

Thus using matrix and vector notation, we have $\mathbf{u} = \boldsymbol{\alpha}\nabla p$. The coefficients α_{ij}, which we assume form a symmetric, positive-definite matrix $\boldsymbol{\alpha}$ (almost everywhere—frequently the coefficients are discontinuous so there are submanifolds where they are ill defined), are related to the porosity of the medium. Of course, numerous other physical models also take the form (18.1), as in Section 17.2.

Combining (18.1) and Darcy's Law (18.2), we find $-\nabla\cdot \mathbf{u} = f$ in Ω. A variational formulation for (18.1) can be derived by letting $\mathbf{A}(\mathbf{x})$ denote the (almost everywhere defined) inverse of the coefficient matrix $\boldsymbol{\alpha} = (\alpha_{ij})$ and by writing $\nabla p = \mathbf{A}\mathbf{u}$. Define

$$a(\mathbf{u},\mathbf{v}) := \sum_{i,j=1}^{d} \int_\Omega A_{ij}(\mathbf{x})u_i(\mathbf{x})v_j(\mathbf{x})\,d\mathbf{x}. \tag{18.3}$$

If we multiply (dot product) the equation $\nabla p = \mathbf{A}\mathbf{u}$ by $\mathbf{v}$, and integrate over Ω, we get

$$\int_\Omega \nabla p(\mathbf{x})\cdot \mathbf{v}(\mathbf{x})\,d\mathbf{x} = \int_\Omega \big(\mathbf{A}(\mathbf{x})\mathbf{u}(\mathbf{x})\big)\cdot \mathbf{v}(\mathbf{x})\,d\mathbf{x} = a(\mathbf{u},\mathbf{v}). \tag{18.4}$$

Define

$$b(\mathbf{w},q) = \int_\Omega \big(\nabla\cdot \mathbf{w}(\mathbf{x})\big)\,q(\mathbf{x})\,d\mathbf{x}. \tag{18.5}$$

Then integration by parts gives

$$\begin{aligned}\int_\Omega \mathbf{w}(\mathbf{x})\cdot\nabla q(\mathbf{x})\,d\mathbf{x} &= -\int_\Omega \big(\nabla\cdot \mathbf{w}(\mathbf{x})\big)\,q(\mathbf{x})\,d\mathbf{x} + \oint_{\partial\Omega} q(\mathbf{x})\,\mathbf{w}(\mathbf{x})\cdot\mathbf{n}(\mathbf{x})\,d\mathbf{x}\\ &= -b(\mathbf{w},q) + \oint_{\partial\Omega} q(\mathbf{x})\,\mathbf{w}(\mathbf{x})\cdot\mathbf{n}(\mathbf{x})\,d\mathbf{x}.\end{aligned} \tag{18.6}$$

The integration by parts in (18.6) follows from the divergence theorem:

$$\int_\Omega \nabla\cdot\big(\mathbf{w}(\mathbf{x})q(\mathbf{x})\big)\,d\mathbf{x} = \oint_{\partial\Omega} q(\mathbf{x})\,\mathbf{w}(\mathbf{x})\cdot\mathbf{n}(\mathbf{x})\,d\mathbf{x}, \tag{18.7}$$

together with the product formula

$$\nabla\cdot\big(\mathbf{w}(\mathbf{x})q(\mathbf{x})\big) = \mathbf{w}(\mathbf{x})\cdot\nabla q(\mathbf{x}) + \nabla\cdot\mathbf{w}(\mathbf{x})\,q(\mathbf{x}).$$

Combining (18.4) and (18.6), we get

$$a(\mathbf{u},\mathbf{v}) + b(\mathbf{v},p) = \oint_{\partial\Omega} p(\mathbf{x})\,\mathbf{v}(\mathbf{x})\cdot\mathbf{n}(\mathbf{x})\,d\mathbf{x}.$$

generic name	example	honorific name
natural	$u = 0$	Dirichlet
essential	$\frac{\partial u}{\partial n} = g$	Neumann

Table 18.1: Reversed nomenclature for different types of boundary conditions appropriate for mixed methods.

18.1.2 Mixed formulation of (18.1)

Define a new space $\mathbf{V}$ by

$$\mathbf{V} := \left\{ \mathbf{v} \in L^2(\Omega)^d \ : \ \nabla\!\cdot \mathbf{v} \in L^2(\Omega), \ \mathbf{v}\cdot\mathbf{n} = 0 \text{ on } \partial\Omega\backslash\Gamma \right\}.$$

Also define $\Pi = L^2(\Omega)$. Then the solution of (18.1), together with the boundary conditions $\mathbf{u}\cdot\mathbf{n} = 0$ on $\partial\Omega\backslash\Gamma$ and $p = g$ on Γ satisfies $\mathbf{u} \in \mathbf{V}$, $p \in \Pi$, and solves

$$\begin{aligned} a(\mathbf{u}, \mathbf{v}) + b(\mathbf{v}, p) &= \oint_\Gamma g(\mathbf{x})\, \mathbf{v}(\mathbf{x}) \cdot \mathbf{n}(\mathbf{x})\, d\mathbf{x} \quad \forall \mathbf{v} \in \mathbf{V}, \\ b(\mathbf{u}, q) &= F(q) \quad \forall q \in \Pi, \end{aligned} \tag{18.8}$$

where $F(q) = -\int_\Omega f(\mathbf{x})\, q(\mathbf{x})\, d\mathbf{x}$. Note that the boundary condition $p = g$ on Γ appears here as a natural boundary condition, imposed variationally, whereas it would be an essential boundary condition if a standard variational approach were taken to (18.1). To emphasize this, we list the reversed nomenclature in Table 18.1.

The space $\mathbf{V}$ is based on the space called $H(\text{div};\Omega)$ [273, Chapter 20, page 99] that has a natural norm given by

$$\|\mathbf{v}\|^2_{H(\text{div};\Omega)} = \|\mathbf{v}\|^2_{L^2(\Omega)^d} + \|\nabla\!\cdot \mathbf{v}\|^2_{L^2(\Omega)}; \tag{18.9}$$

$H(\text{div};\Omega)$ is a Hilbert space with inner-product given by

$$(\mathbf{u}, \mathbf{v})_{H(\text{div};\Omega)} = (\mathbf{u}, \mathbf{v})_{L^2(\Omega)^d} + (\nabla\!\cdot \mathbf{u}, \nabla\!\cdot \mathbf{v})_{L^2(\Omega)}.$$

The trace $\mathbf{v}\cdot\mathbf{n} = 0$ on $\partial\Omega$ is well defined for $\mathbf{v} \in H(\text{div};\Omega)$ [273], but the tangential derivatives of a general function $\mathbf{v} \in H(\text{div};\Omega)$ are not well defined. The meaning of the boundary condition $p = g$ on Γ must be interpreted carefully. If p is smooth enough, it will be defined pointwise, but otherwise its meaning is like that of the Neumann condition for the Laplace equation and will be enforced only weakly.

The bilinear form $a(\cdot,\cdot)$ is not coercive on all of $\mathbf{V}$, but it is coercive on the subspace $\mathbf{Z}$ of divergence-zero functions, since on this subspace the inner-product $(\cdot,\cdot)_{H(\text{div};\Omega)}$ is the same as the $L^2(\Omega)$ inner-product. In particular, this proves uniqueness of solutions. Suppose that F and g are zero. Then $\mathbf{u} \in \mathbf{Z}$ and $a(\mathbf{u}, \mathbf{u}) = 0$. Thus $\|\mathbf{u}\|_{L^2(\Omega)} = 0$, that is, $\mathbf{u} \equiv \mathbf{0}$. To show that $p = 0$, we need to invoke the inf-sup condition, as follows.

18.2 inf-sup for scalar mixed method

Existence and stability of solutions follows from the inf-sup condition. Recall the space $\Pi_0 = \left\{ q \in L^2(\Omega) \ : \ \int_\Omega q(\mathbf{x})\, d\mathbf{x} = 0 \right\}$. Then there is a finite, positive constant C such that for all $q \in \Pi_0$

$$\begin{aligned} \|q\|_{L^2(\Omega)} &\leq C \sup_{0\neq \mathbf{v}\in H^1_0(\Omega)} \frac{b(\mathbf{v},q)}{\|\mathbf{v}\|_{H^1(\Omega)}} \\ &\leq C' \sup_{0\neq \mathbf{v}\in \mathbf{V}} \frac{b(\mathbf{v},q)}{\|\mathbf{v}\|_{H(\mathrm{div};\Omega)}}, \end{aligned} \tag{18.10}$$

where the first inequality is the same as (13.19), and the second follows from the inclusion $H^1(\Omega)^d \subset H(\mathrm{div};\Omega)$ and the less restrictive boundary conditions on $\mathbf{v} \in \mathbf{V}$. The inclusion is bounded by

$$\|\mathbf{v}\|_{H(\mathrm{div};\Omega)} \leq \sqrt{d}\,\|\mathbf{v}\|_{H^1(\Omega)},$$

in view of Exercise 18.2. This means that the inf-sup condition determines the solution p in the mixed formulation (18.8) up to a constant. We could not expect more, since the solution of the pure Neumann problem (Section 2.4) can be determined only up to a constant. The mixed formulation of the pure Neumann problem has $\Gamma = \emptyset$. Thus to have a well posed problem, we must have $\Gamma \neq \emptyset$. This restriction is easy to motivate, as follows.

18.2.1 When $\Gamma = \emptyset$

If $\mathbf{V} = \{\mathbf{v} \in H(\mathrm{div};\Omega) : \mathbf{v}\cdot\mathbf{n} = 0 \text{ on } \partial\Omega\}$, which means that $\Gamma = \emptyset$, then the divergence theorem implies that

$$\int_\Omega \nabla\cdot \mathbf{v}(\mathbf{x})\,d\mathbf{x} = 0 \quad \forall \mathbf{v} \in \mathbf{V}.$$

Thus $b(\mathbf{v},p) = 0$ for any constant p. Therefore $(\mathbf{u},p) = (\mathbf{0}, \text{constant})$ provides a solution to the variational formulation (18.8) for $F = 0$ and $g = 0$. Thus it is essential to have $\Gamma \neq \emptyset$.

18.2.2 When $\Gamma \neq \emptyset$

When $\Gamma \neq \emptyset$, we can take any $\mathbf{w}$ such that

$$\mathbf{w}\cdot\mathbf{n} = 1 \text{ on } \Gamma$$

and by the divergence theorem we are assured that

$$\int_\Omega \nabla\cdot \mathbf{w}(\mathbf{x})\,d\mathbf{x} = |\Gamma|.$$

Let $\overline{q} = \frac{1}{|\Omega|}\int_\Omega q(\mathbf{x})\,d\mathbf{x}$. Then by (18.10)

$$\|q-\overline{q}\|_{L^2(\Omega)} \leq C \sup_{0\neq \mathbf{v}\in H^1_0(\Omega)} \frac{b(\mathbf{v},q-\overline{q})}{\|\mathbf{v}\|_{H^1(\Omega)}} = C \sup_{0\neq \mathbf{v}\in H^1_0(\Omega)} \frac{b(\mathbf{v},q)}{\|\mathbf{v}\|_{H^1(\Omega)}}.$$

because $\nabla\cdot\mathbf{v}$ has mean zero for $\mathbf{v} \in H^1_0(\Omega)$. Define B by

$$B = \sup_{0\neq \mathbf{v}\in \mathbf{V}} \frac{b(\mathbf{v},q)}{\|\mathbf{v}\|_{H^1(\Omega)}}. \tag{18.11}$$

So we have

$$\|q-\overline{q}\|_{L^2(\Omega)} \leq CB.$$

Therefore

$$\|q\|_{L^2(\Omega)} \le \|q-\overline{q}\|_{L^2(\Omega)} + \|\overline{q}\|_{L^2(\Omega)} \le CB + \|\overline{q}\|_{L^2(\Omega)}.$$

Also

$$\begin{aligned}\|\overline{q}\|_{L^2(\Omega)} &= |\Omega|^{1/2}\,|\overline{q}| = |\Omega|^{1/2}|\Gamma|^{-1}|b(\mathbf{w},\overline{q})| \\ &\le |\Omega|^{1/2}|\Gamma|^{-1}\big|b(\mathbf{w},q) - b(\mathbf{w},q-\overline{q})\big|.\end{aligned} \tag{18.12}$$

Let $c = |\Omega|^{1/2}|\Gamma|^{-1}$. Then

$$\begin{aligned}\|\overline{q}\|_{L^2(\Omega)} &\le c\big(|b(\mathbf{w},q)| + \|\nabla\cdot\mathbf{w}\|_{L^2(\Omega)}\|q-\overline{q}\|_{L^2(\Omega)}\big) \\ &\le c|b(\mathbf{w},q)| + c\|\nabla\cdot\mathbf{w}\|_{L^2(\Omega)}CB.\end{aligned} \tag{18.13}$$

Therefore

$$\|q\|_{L^2(\Omega)} \le CB\big(1 + c\|\nabla\cdot\mathbf{w}\|_{L^2(\Omega)}\big) + c|b(\mathbf{w},q)|. \tag{18.14}$$

Clearly

$$|b(\mathbf{w},q)| \le \|\mathbf{w}\|_{H^1(\Omega)}B.$$

So

$$\|q\|_{L^2(\Omega)} \le C'B.$$

Recalling the definition (18.11) of B, we have

$$\|q\|_{L^2(\Omega)} \le C' \sup_{0\neq\mathbf{v}\in\mathbf{V}} \frac{b(\mathbf{v},q)}{\|\mathbf{v}\|_{H^1(\Omega)}},$$

which is the desired inf-sup condition.

18.3 Discrete mixed formulation

Now let $\mathbf{V}_h \subset \mathbf{V}$ and $\Pi_h \subset \Pi$ and consider the variational problem to find $u_h \in \mathbf{V}_h$ and $p_h \in \Pi_h$ such that

$$\begin{aligned} a(u_h,v) + b(v,p_h) &= F(v) \quad \forall v \in \mathbf{V}_h\,, \\ b(u_h,q) &= 0 \quad \forall q \in \Pi_h\,. \end{aligned} \tag{18.15}$$

The case of an inhomogeneous right-hand-side in the second equation is considered in [57, Section 10.5] and in [256].

18.4 Choice of spaces

We have already seen two pairs of spaces that satisfy inf-sup conditions when we studied the Stokes equations in Chapter 13. After discussing these briefly, we consider a new pair of spaces.

18.4.1 What about Taylor-Hood?

One family of spaces that might seem plausible for mixed methods is the Taylor-Hood family described in Section 13.3. However, it appears that this method "converges but with a loss of convergence order and without convergence of the divergence of the velocities" [64]. For some computational experiments, see [163]. But it is of some interest to see why it fails, so we recall the details of the Taylor-Hood spaces.

Let the space W_h^k denote the space of continuous piecewise polynomials of degree k (with no boundary conditions imposed). Let the space $\mathbf{V}_h$ be defined by

$$\mathbf{V}_h = \left\{\mathbf{v} \in W_h^k \times W_h^k \ : \ \mathbf{v}\cdot\mathbf{n} = 0 \text{ on } \partial\Omega\right\}. \tag{18.16}$$

Let $\mathbf{V}_h^0 = \mathbf{V}_h \cap H_0^1(\Omega)$. Let the space Π_h be defined by

$$\Pi_h = \left\{q \in W_h^{k-1} \ : \ \int_\Omega q(\mathbf{x})\, d\mathbf{x} = 0\right\}. \tag{18.17}$$

Following (18.10), and recalling the inf-sup condition in Section 13.3, we have for $q \in \Pi_h$

$$\|q\|_{L^2(\Omega)} \le C \sup_{0\neq\mathbf{v}\in\mathbf{V}_h^0} \frac{b(\mathbf{v},q)}{\|\mathbf{v}\|_{H^1(\Omega)}} \le C \sup_{0\neq\mathbf{v}\in\mathbf{V}_h} \frac{b(\mathbf{v},q)}{\|\mathbf{v}\|_{H^1(\Omega)}} \le C\sqrt{d} \sup_{0\neq\mathbf{v}\in\mathbf{V}_h} \frac{b(\mathbf{v},q)}{\|\mathbf{v}\|_{H(\mathrm{div};\Omega)}}, \tag{18.18}$$

so the inf-sup condition holds.

To approximate the scalar elliptic problem (18.1) by a mixed method, we have to contend with the fact that the corresponding form $a(\cdot,\cdot)$ is not coercive on all of $\mathbf{V}$. It is clearly coercive on the space

$$\mathbf{Z} = \{\mathbf{v} \in H(\mathrm{div};\Omega) \ : \ \nabla\cdot\mathbf{v} = 0\}$$

so that (18.8) is well-posed. However, to apply our theory, it is required to assure that it is coercive as well on

$$\mathbf{Z}_h = \{\mathbf{v} \in \mathbf{V}_h \ : \ b(\mathbf{v},q) = 0 \quad \forall q \in \Pi_h\}.$$

The computational experience reported in [64] suggests that there is some form of degeneracy here, since the inf-sup condition is not the culprit. It is the lack of coercivity on $\mathbf{Z}_h$ that causes failure.

One simple solution is to insure that $\mathbf{Z}_h \subset \mathbf{Z}$, and we know from Chapter 13 that there are ways this can be done.

18.4.2 Scott-Vogelius spaces

Let $\mathbf{V}_h$ be as given in (18.16) and let $\Pi_h = \nabla\cdot\mathbf{V}_h$. Suppose that k satisfies one of the conditions in Table 14.1. Then (under certain mild restrictions on the mesh [256]) these spaces can be used. The iterated penalty method can be used to solve the linear system using $\Pi_h = \mathcal{D}\mathbf{V}_h$ without having explicit information about the structure of Π_h, as described in Section 14.2. For more information on mixed methods, see Section 13.2.

18.4.3 Subspaces with less regularity: BDM

Another pair of spaces of interest is BDM [60] for $\mathbf{V}_h$ and DG (discontinuous Galerkin) for Π_h. More precisely, the inf-sup stable pair of spaces is BDM(k) for u and DG($k-1$) for p. The space DG(k) consists of discontinuous polynomials of degree k. The BDM spaces are defined by

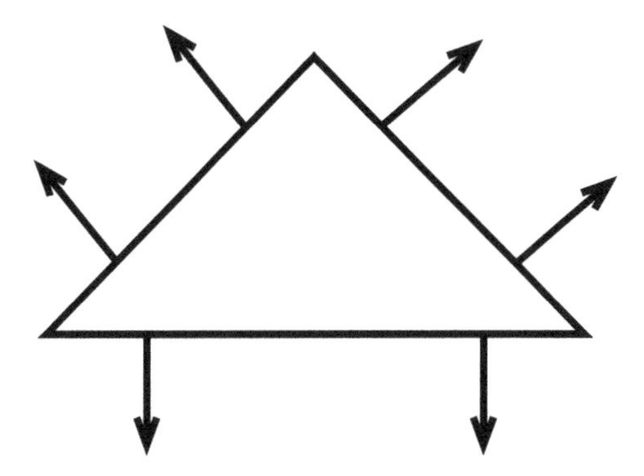

Figure 18.1: Nodal variables for BDM(1).

$$\mathrm{BDM}(k){=}\mathrm{DG}(k)\cap H(\mathrm{div};\Omega).$$

The BDM space is the largest subset of DG(k) which is suitable for the mixed method. The general case is more complicated to describe, so we limit our description to BDM(1).

The space BDM(1) consists of piecewise linear, vector-valued functions. We require that BDM(1)$\subset H(\mathrm{div};\Omega)$, so we must have the normal components of $\mathbf{v}\in$ BDM(1) continuous across edges. Thus we can define BDM(1) as the subset of vector-valued functions in DG(1)$\times$DG(1) whose normal components are continuous across edges.

It then remains to determine what this means in terms of nodal parameters to represent functions locally. On each triangle, a linear, vector-valued function has 6 degrees of freedom (3 for each component of the vector-valued function). On the other hand, continuity of the normal components of a linear function requires two constraints per edge, as shown in Figure 18.1. Thus we have 6 constraints and 6 degrees of freedom. Of course, this alone does not mean that the corresponding system of equations is invertible, but this can be proved as follows.

Let $\mathbf{v}$ be a linear, vector-valued function such that $\mathbf{v}\cdot\mathbf{n}=0$ at two points on each edge, and thus $\mathbf{v}\cdot\mathbf{n}=0$ on each edge of a triangle. Then by the divergence theorem, $\nabla\cdot\mathbf{v}=0$ in the triangle (see Exercise 18.5). Thus we can write $\mathbf{v}=\mathrm{curl}\, q$ for a quadratic (scalar) function q. But since $\mathbf{v}\cdot\mathbf{n}=0$ on each edge of the triangle, $\nabla q\cdot\mathbf{t}=0$ on each edge of the triangle, where $\mathbf{t}$ is tangent to each edge. Thus q is constant on each edge, and thus it must be constant on the entire triangle. Thus we conclude that $\mathbf{v}=0$.

18.4.4 Test problem

Let $\Omega=[0,1]^2$, and let $\Gamma=\{(x,y)\in\partial\Omega\ :\ x=0 \text{ or } x=1\}$. Consider the problem

$$\begin{aligned}-\Delta p &= 2\pi^2(\cos\pi x)(\cos\pi y)\\ \frac{\partial p}{\partial n} &= 0 \text{ on } \partial\Omega\backslash\Gamma\\ p &= (1-2x)(\cos\pi y) \text{ on } \Gamma\end{aligned}\tag{18.19}$$

whose exact solution is $p(x,y)=(\cos\pi x)(\cos\pi y)$ (see Exercise 18.1). We reformulate this using the variational equations in (18.8). Using the spaces BDM(1) for $\mathbf{V}_h$, together with the essential boundary condition $\mathbf{v}\cdot\mathbf{n}=0$ on $\partial\Omega\backslash\Gamma$, and DG(0) for Π_h, we obtained the result depicted in Figure 18.2 using Program 18.1.

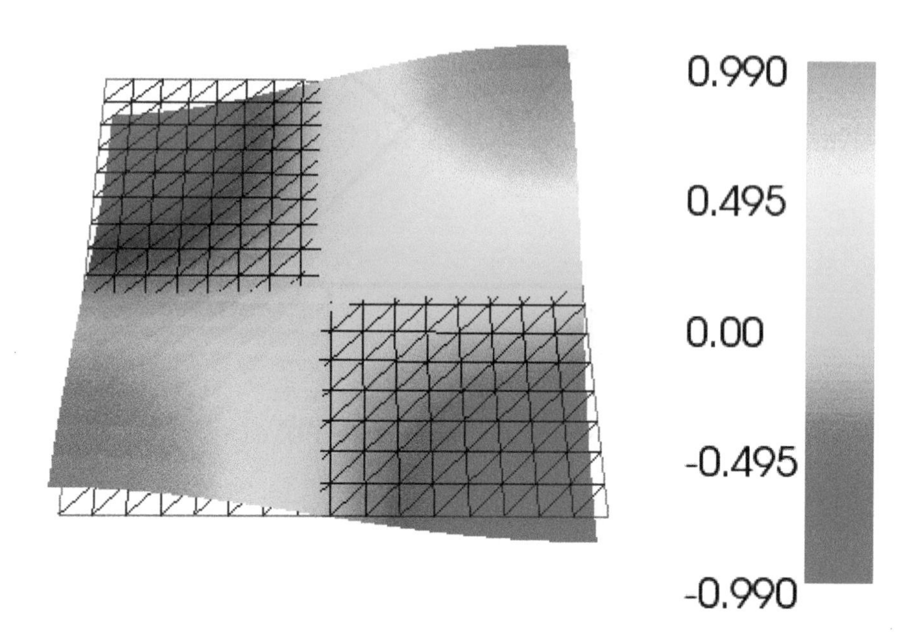

Figure 18.2: Mixed method using the spaces BDM(1) for $\mathbf{V}_h$ and DG(0) for Π_h to approximate the boundary value problem (18.19). The code to generate this is given in Program 18.1.

18.4.5 Numerical quadrature

The evaluation of forms having variable coefficients requires some sort of numerical quadrature. This presents an additional degree of approximation and potential cause for error.

18.5 Exercises

Exercise 18.1 *Prove that $p(x, y) = (\cos \pi x)(\cos \pi y)$ is the exact solution of the boundary value problem (18.19). (Hint: don't forget to check the boundary conditions.)*

Exercise 18.2 *Prove that for any domain $\Omega \subset \mathbb{R}^d$ and any $\mathbf{v} \in H^1(\Omega)^d$, $d = 2$ or 3,*

$$\|\mathbf{v}\|_{H(\mathrm{div};\Omega)} \leq \sqrt{d}\,\|\mathbf{v}\|_{H^1(\Omega)}.$$

Exercise 18.3 *Modify Program 18.1 to print the L^2 error between the exact solution $p(x, y) = (\cos \pi x)(\cos \pi y)$ and the computed p_h for mesh sizes 2^k for $k = 4, 5, 6, 7, 8$ and plot the error as a function of the mesh size. What is the order of accuracy of the BDM(1)/DG(0) method for the approximation of p?*

Exercise 18.4 *Compute the gradient ∇p for the expression $p(x, y) = (\cos \pi x)(\cos \pi y)$. Modify Program 18.1 to compute and print the L^2 error $\|\nabla p - \mathbf{u}_h\|_{L^2(\Omega)}$ for mesh sizes 2^k for $k = 4, 5, 6, 7, 8$ and plot the error as a function of the mesh size. What is the order of accuracy of the BDM(1)/DG(0) method for the approximation of ∇p? (Note that ∇p is approximated by $\mathbf{A}\mathbf{u}_h$, but here $\mathbf{A}$ is the identity matrix.)*

Exercise 18.5 *Use the divergence theorem to prove that*

$$\int_\Omega (\nabla\cdot \mathbf{v})^2\,d\mathbf{x} = \oint_{\partial\Omega} (\nabla\cdot \mathbf{v})(\mathbf{v}\cdot\mathbf{n})\,ds - \int_\Omega \mathbf{v}\cdot(\nabla\nabla\cdot \mathbf{v})\,d\mathbf{x}$$

for any Ω. *Use this with* $\Omega = T$ *to show that if* $\mathbf{v}$ *is a linear function on a triangle* T *such that* $\mathbf{v}\cdot\mathbf{n} = 0$ *on* ∂T, *then* $\nabla\cdot\mathbf{v} = 0$ *in* T. *(Hint: for the first step, let* $\mathbf{w} = (\nabla\cdot\mathbf{v})\mathbf{v}$ *and apply the divergence theorem to* $\mathbf{w}$.*)*

Exercise 18.6 *Solve the boundary value problem (18.19) by the standard variational approach using piecewise linears and compare with the mixed method using BDM(1) and DG(0).*

Exercise 18.7 *Solve the boundary value problem (18.19) by the mixed method using Taylor-Hood and compare this with using BDM(1) and DG(0).*

Exercise 18.8 *Solve the boundary value problem (18.19) by the mixed method using the Scott-Vogelius method, where the linear system is solved via the iterated penalty method. Compare this with using BDM(1) and DG(0).*

Exercise 18.9 *Experiment with the Taylor-Hood spaces for solving the boundary value problem (18.19) using the mixed method. What goes wrong? Compare this with (a) the Scott-Vogelius method, where the linear system is solved via the iterated penalty method, and (b) using BDM(1) and DG(0).*

```
1  from dolfin import *
2  import sys,math
3  meshsize=int(sys.argv[1])
4  # Create mesh
5  mesh = UnitSquareMesh(meshsize, meshsize)
6  n = FacetNormal(mesh)
7  # Define function spaces and mixed (product) space
8  BDM = FunctionSpace(mesh, "BDM", 1)
9  DG = FunctionSpace(mesh, "DG", 0)
10 W = BDM * DG
11 # Define trial and test functions
12 (uu, p) = TrialFunctions(W)
13 (vv, q) = TestFunctions(W)
14 # Define source function
15 f = Expression("2.0*mpi*mpi*(cos(mpi*x[0]))*(cos(mpi*x[1]))",\
16                     mpi=math.pi,degree=1)
17 pe = Expression("(cos(mpi*x[0]))*(cos(mpi*x[1]))",mpi=math.pi,degree=1)
18 glc = Expression("(1.0-2.0*x[0])*(cos(mpi*x[1]))",mpi=math.pi,degree=1)
19 G = Expression(("0.0","0.0"),degree=1)
20 # Define variational form
21 a = (dot(uu, vv) + div(vv)*p + div(uu)*q)*dx
22 L = - f*q*dx + glc*inner(vv,n)*ds
23 # Define essential boundary
24 def boundary(x):
25     return x[1] < DOLFIN_EPS or x[1] > 1.0 - DOLFIN_EPS
26 bc = DirichletBC(W.sub(0), G, boundary)
27 # Compute solution
28 w = Function(W)
29 solve(a == L, w, bc)
30 (uu, p) = w.split()
31 # Plot uu and p
32 #plot(uu)
33 plot(p)
34 interactive()
```

Program 18.1: Code to implement the mixed method for solving the boundary value problem (18.19). The solution is depicted in Figure 18.2.

Chapter 19

Solid Mechanics

The model equations for all solids take the form

$$\rho \mathbf{u}_{,tt} = \nabla\cdot \mathbf{T} + \mathbf{f},$$

where $\mathbf{u}(\mathbf{x}, t)$ is the displacement of the solid at the point $\mathbf{x}$ and time t, $\mathbf{T}$ is called the **Cauchy stress** and $\mathbf{f}$ is externally given data. This is just a version of Newton's Law: force is equal to mass times acceleration. Each point in a body accelerates at the rate $\mathbf{u}_{,tt}$, and $\nabla\cdot \mathbf{T} + \mathbf{f}$ is the force on it; ρ is the mass density.

Models of solids differ based on the way the stress $\mathbf{T}$ depends on the displacement $\mathbf{u}$. Time-independent models take the form

$$-\nabla\cdot \mathbf{T} = \mathbf{f}. \tag{19.1}$$

The divergence operator on a matrix function is defined by

$$(\nabla\cdot \mathbf{T})_i = \sum_{j=1}^{d} T_{ij,j}.$$

There is a strong analogy between models for fluids and solids. The main unknown in fluid models is the velocity $\mathbf{v}$, which corresponds to the time derivative of the displacement $\mathbf{u}_{,t}$. Thus the rate-of-strain tensor is the quantity related to stress in fluid models.

Many simplified models are used for solids. We derive some of them here to give an example of one way that new models are derived from existing ones.

19.1 Linear elasticity

The simplest expression for the stress is linear: $\mathbf{T} = \mathbf{C} : \epsilon$, where $\mathbf{C}$ is a material tensor, the **constitutive matrix**, and

$$\epsilon = \tfrac{1}{2}\big(\nabla \mathbf{u} + \nabla \mathbf{u}^t\big) \tag{19.2}$$

is called the **strain**. Such solids are called **elastic**. For **isotropic** models, that is, ones that are orientation independent,

$$C_{ijkl} = K\delta_{ij}\delta_{kl} + \mu\big(\delta_{ik}\delta_{jl} + \delta_{il}\delta_{jk} - \tfrac{2}{3}\delta_{ij}\delta_{kl}\big), \text{ for } i,j,k,l = 1,2,3, \tag{19.3}$$

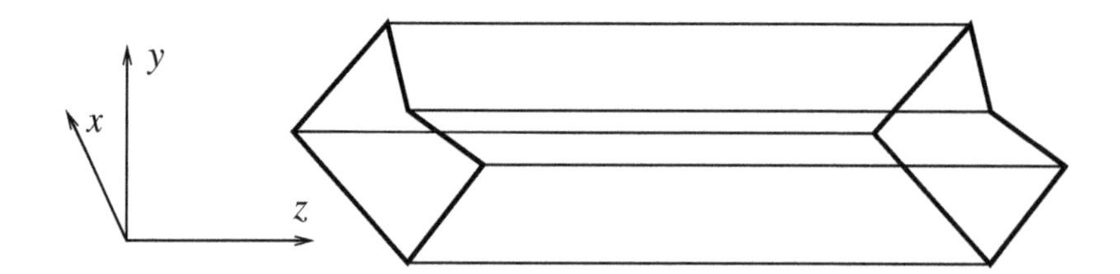

Figure 19.1: A domain that has constant x-y cross section in the z-direction.

where δ_{ij} is the Kronecker-δ, K is the **bulk modulus** (or incompressibility) of the material, and μ is the **shear modulus**. The tensor contraction $\mathbf{C}:\boldsymbol{\epsilon}$ is defined by

$$(\mathbf{C}:\boldsymbol{\epsilon})_{ij}=\sum_{k,l=1}^{d} C_{ijkl}\epsilon_{kl}.$$

Carrying out the tensor contraction, we have

$$\begin{aligned} T_{ij} &= K\delta_{ij}\epsilon_{kk}+2\mu\big(\epsilon_{ij}-\tfrac{1}{3}\delta_{ij}\epsilon_{kk}\big)=\lambda\delta_{ij}\epsilon_{kk}+2\mu\epsilon_{ij} \\ &= \lambda\delta_{ij}\nabla\cdot\mathbf{u}+\mu\big(\nabla\mathbf{u}+\nabla\mathbf{u}^t\big)_{ij}=\lambda\delta_{ij}\nabla\cdot\mathbf{u}+\mu\big(u_{i,j}+u_{j,i}\big), \end{aligned} \tag{19.4}$$

where $\lambda(=K-\frac{2}{3}\mu)$ and μ are known as the **Lamé parameters**, and the Einstein summation convention was used $\big(\epsilon_{kk}=\sum_{k=1}^{3}\epsilon_{kk}=\nabla\cdot\mathbf{u}\big)$. We can write (19.4) succinctly as

$$\mathbf{T}=\lambda(\nabla\cdot\mathbf{u})\mathcal{I}+\mu\boldsymbol{\epsilon}, \tag{19.5}$$

where $\mathcal{I}$ is the $d\times d$ identity matrix. The equations of elasticity are derived in $d=3$ dimensions, but they formally make sense in $d=2$ dimensions as well. The two-dimensional version arises via a modeling simplification that is presented in Section 19.3.2.

19.2 Elasticity variational formulation

The variational formulation of (19.1) takes the form: Find $\mathbf{u}$ such that $\mathbf{u}-\gamma\in V$ such that

$$a_C\left(\mathbf{u},\mathbf{v}\right)=F(\mathbf{v})\quad\forall\mathbf{v}\in V\,, \tag{19.6}$$

where $a(\cdot,\cdot)=a_\nabla(\cdot,\cdot)$ and $F(\cdot)$ are given by

$$a_C(\mathbf{u},\mathbf{v}):=\int_\Omega\mathbf{T}:\nabla\mathbf{v}\,d\mathbf{x}=\lambda\int_\Omega(\nabla\cdot\mathbf{u})(\nabla\cdot\mathbf{v})\,d\mathbf{x}+\mu\int_\Omega\left(\nabla\mathbf{u}+\nabla\mathbf{u}^t\right):\nabla\mathbf{v}\,d\mathbf{x}, \tag{19.7}$$

and

$$F(\mathbf{v}):=\int_\Omega\mathbf{f}\cdot\mathbf{v}\,d\mathbf{x}. \tag{19.8}$$

This is derived by multiplying (19.4) by $\mathbf{v}$ with a “dot” product, and integrating by parts as usual. The space V consists of the d-fold Cartesian product of the subset of $H^1(\Omega)$ of functions vanishing on the boundary.

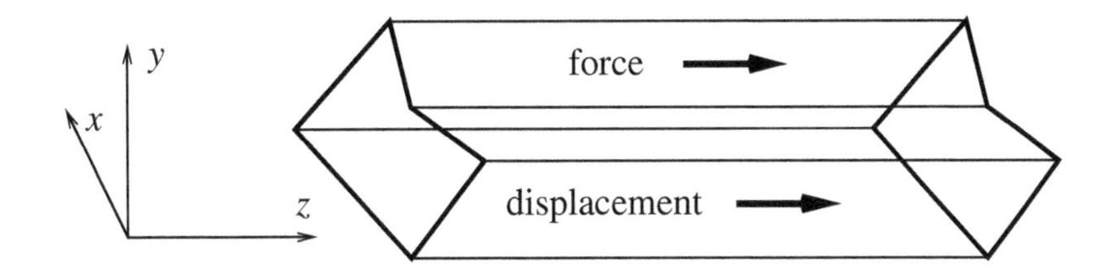

Figure 19.2: Force and displacement directions in anti-plane strain.

We see now that the analogy between solids and fluids is more than superficial. The variational form $a_C(\cdot,\cdot)$ is exactly what appears in the iterated penalty method for solving the Stokes equations in Section 14.2. In view of Exercise 19.3, we have

$$\mu\int_\Omega \left(\nabla\mathbf{u}+\nabla\mathbf{u}^t\right):\nabla\mathbf{v}\,d\mathbf{x}=\tfrac{1}{2}\mu a_\epsilon(\mathbf{u},\mathbf{v}),$$

where the latter form is defined in (13.11). Therefore

$$a_C(\mathbf{u},\mathbf{v})=\tfrac{1}{2}\mu\Big(a_\epsilon(\mathbf{u},\mathbf{v})+\frac{2\lambda}{\mu}\int_\Omega(\nabla\cdot\mathbf{u})(\nabla\cdot\mathbf{v})\,d\mathbf{x}\Big), \tag{19.9}$$

and we see that $\rho=2\lambda/\mu$ corresponds to the penalty parameter in Section 14.2.

19.3 Some two-dimensional models

There are two simplifications that can lead to a two-dimensional model. In both, it is assumed that the domain is longer in the z-direction than in the x and y dimensions, and further that the x-y cross section is the same for each z, as shown in Figure 19.1. More precisely, it is assumed that the domain

$$\Omega=\widehat{\Omega}\times[0,Z]$$

is a Cartesian product and Z is large with respect to the dimensions of the two-dimensional cross section $\widehat{\Omega}$. We identify coordinates $(x,y,z)\equiv(x_1,x_2,x_3)$ as convenient.

19.3.1 Anti-plane strain

In anti-plane strain [32], the component of strain normal to a particular plane (we will take it to be the (x_1,x_2) plane) is the only non-zero displacement, that is, $u_1=u_2=0$, and thus $\mathbf{u}=(0,0,w)$. This is an idealized state when the dimension of Ω is large in the x_3-direction, and the applied force is in that direction only, that is, $\mathbf{f}=(0,0,f)$. It is assumed that the displacement $w=u_3$ is independent of x_3, although it does depend on (x_1,x_2). In particular, $\nabla\cdot\mathbf{u}=0$. Thus

$$\nabla\mathbf{u}=\begin{pmatrix}0&0&0\\0&0&0\\w_{,1}&w_{,2}&0\end{pmatrix}\text{ and }\boldsymbol{\epsilon}=\frac{1}{2}\begin{pmatrix}0&0&w_{,1}\\0&0&w_{,2}\\w_{,1}&w_{,2}&0\end{pmatrix}.$$

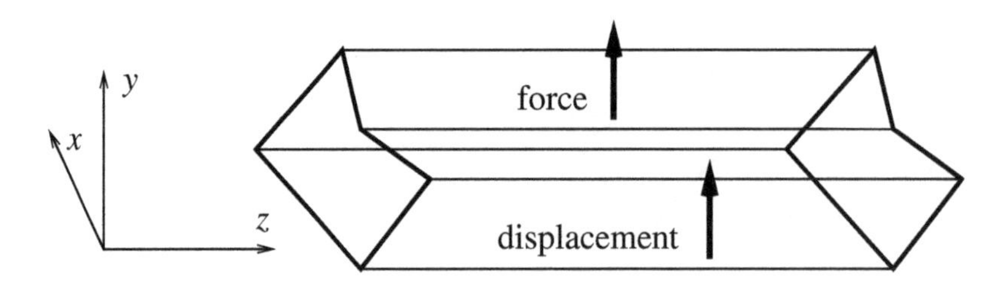

Figure 19.3: Force and displacement directions in plane strain.

Therefore

$$\mathbf{T} = \mu \begin{pmatrix} 0 & 0 & w_{,1} \\ 0 & 0 & w_{,2} \\ w_{,1} & w_{,2} & 0 \end{pmatrix}.$$

and so

$$\nabla\cdot \mathbf{T} = \mu \begin{pmatrix} 0 \\ 0 \\ w_{,11} + w_{,22} \end{pmatrix} = \mu \begin{pmatrix} 0 \\ 0 \\ \Delta w \end{pmatrix}.$$

Thus the problem of anti-plane strain reduces to the familiar Laplace equation, $-\mu\Delta w = f$.

19.3.2 Plane strain

In plane strain [32], the component of strain normal to a particular plane (we will take it to be the (x, y) plane) is zero. This is the idealized state when the dimension of Ω is large in the z-direction, and the applied forces in that direction are zero, that is, $\mathbf{f} = (f_1, f_2, 0)$. Thus $\mathbf{u} = (u, v, 0)$ and

$$\nabla\mathbf{u} = \begin{pmatrix} u_{,x} & u_{,y} & 0 \\ v_{,x} & v_{,y} & 0 \\ 0 & 0 & 0 \end{pmatrix} \text{ and } \boldsymbol{\epsilon} = \begin{pmatrix} u_{,x} & \frac{1}{2}(u_{,y} + v_{,x}) & 0 \\ \frac{1}{2}(u_{,y} + v_{,x}) & v_{,y} & 0 \\ 0 & 0 & 0 \end{pmatrix}.$$

and thus the variational problem (19.6) applies where we identify the integration in (19.7) and (19.8) as being just over a two-dimensional domain.

19.4 The plate-bending biharmonic problem

Plates and shells are thin structures for which simplified models are derived. A plate is planar, the simplest case. We will limit discussion to this case, although much of the description has an analog for shells. We give the details of the derivation of the plate model as an example of how many models are derived.

Let us suppose that $\widehat{\Omega}$ is some domain in the x, y plane, and

$$\Omega = \left\{(x, y, z) \ : \ (x, y) \in \widehat{\Omega},\ z \in [-\tau, \tau]\right\},$$

where we assume that τ is small with respect to the dimensions of $\widehat{\Omega}$. See Figure 19.4. When the structure is deformed, the behavior is different on each side of the midsurface $\tau = 0$, as indicated in Figure 19.5(a). Bending causes compression on one side and expansion on the other.

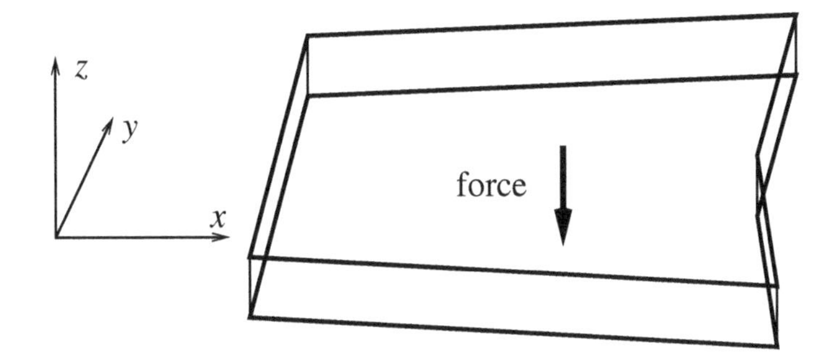

Figure 19.4: Another two-dimensional reduction. $\Omega = \widehat{\Omega} \times [-\tau, \tau]$.

19.4.1 Plate model assumptions

Using the **Kirchhoff hypothesis**,[1] the displacement $\mathbf{u} = (u, v, w)$ satisfies

$$u \approx -zw_{,x}, \quad v \approx -zw_{,y}.$$

See Figure 19.5(b) to see why this assumption is a good approximation.

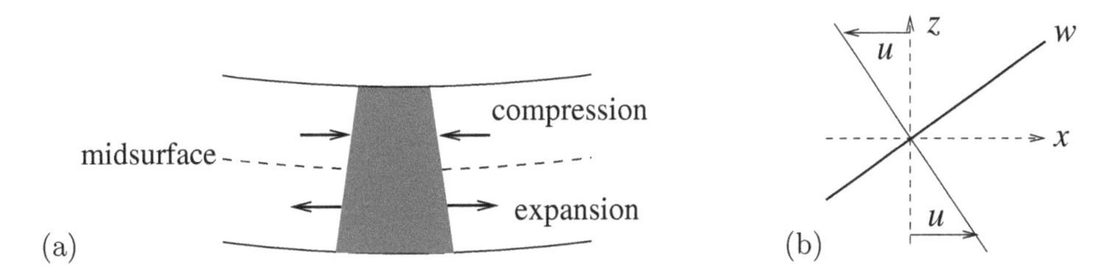

Figure 19.5: Relation between out-of-plane displacement and in-plane displacement leading to the Kirchhoff hypothesis. (a) Bending causes a combination of compression and expansion (or extension). (b) The slope of w causes a deformation in the (x, y) plane, that is, a change in (u, v), that depends on z. This is shown in the (x, z) plane.

Thus the equations of elasticity can be approximated as an equation for just the deflection w normal to the plane of the plate:

$$\nabla\mathbf{u} = \begin{pmatrix} u_{,x} & u_{,y} & u_{,z} \\ v_{,x} & v_{,y} & v_{,z} \\ w_{,x} & w_{,y} & w_{,z} \end{pmatrix} \approx \begin{pmatrix} -zw_{,xx} & -zw_{,xy} & -w_{,x} \\ -zw_{,xy} & -zw_{,yy} & -w_{,y} \\ w_{,x} & w_{,y} & 0 \end{pmatrix}.$$

Using this approximation, we obtain

$$\epsilon = \begin{pmatrix} -zw_{,xx} & -zw_{,xy} & 0 \\ -zw_{,xy} & -zw_{,yy} & 0 \\ 0 & 0 & 0 \end{pmatrix} \quad \text{and} \quad \nabla\cdot\mathbf{u} = -z\Delta w.$$

[1]Gustav Robert Kirchhoff (1824—1887) was a mathematical physicist, made famous by work done on electrical circuits as a graduate student. Kirchhoff coined the term "black body radiation" and, with Bunsen, discovered cesium and rubidium, among many other achievements.

Using (19.5), we get

$$\mathbf{T} = -z\lambda\Delta w \begin{pmatrix} 1 & 0 & 0 \\ 0 & 1 & 0 \\ 0 & 0 & 0 \end{pmatrix} + \mu \begin{pmatrix} -zw_{,xx} & -zw_{,xy} & 0 \\ -zw_{,xy} & -zw_{,yy} & 0 \\ 0 & 0 & 0 \end{pmatrix}. \tag{19.10}$$

19.4.2 Plate variational formulation

We want to see how this simplified model for the stress changes the variational formulation (19.7). Multiplying (19.10) by $\nabla\mathbf{v}$, where $\mathbf{v} = -z\nabla\phi$ and ϕ depends only on x, y, and integrating over Ω, we find

$$\lambda \int_\Omega z^2 \Delta w \Delta\phi \, d\mathbf{x} + \mu \int_\Omega z^2 \begin{pmatrix} w_{,xx} & w_{,xy} \\ w_{,xy} & w_{,yy} \end{pmatrix} : \begin{pmatrix} \phi_{,xx} & \phi_{,xy} \\ \phi_{,xy} & \phi_{,yy} \end{pmatrix} d\mathbf{x} = \int_\Omega \mathbf{f} \cdot \mathbf{v} \, d\mathbf{x},$$

since

$$\begin{pmatrix} 1 & 0 & 0 \\ 0 & 1 & 0 \\ 0 & 0 & 0 \end{pmatrix} : \nabla\mathbf{v} = -z\Delta w.$$

For simplicity, we consider the case where the body force $\mathbf{f} = \mathbf{0}$. We can expand to get

$$\begin{aligned} \begin{pmatrix} w_{,xx} & w_{,xy} \\ w_{,xy} & w_{,yy} \end{pmatrix} : \begin{pmatrix} \phi_{,xx} & \phi_{,xy} \\ \phi_{,xy} & \phi_{,yy} \end{pmatrix} &= w_{,xx}\phi_{,xx} + 2w_{,xy}\phi_{,xy} + w_{,yy}\phi_{,yy} \\ &= \Delta w \Delta\phi - w_{,xx}\phi_{,yy} - w_{,yy}\phi_{,xx} + 2w_{,xy}\phi_{,xy}. \end{aligned} \tag{19.11}$$

Note that the integral of z^2 with respect to z over the plate thickness is equal to $\frac{2}{3}\tau^3$. Then the above becomes

$$\tfrac{2}{3}\tau^3 \int_{\hat{\Omega}} (\lambda + \mu)\Delta w \Delta\phi + \mu(-w_{,xx}\phi_{,yy} - w_{,yy}\phi_{,xx} + 2w_{,xy}\phi_{,xy}) \, dxdy = 0.$$

Let $a_P(\cdot,\cdot)$ be the bilinear form defined on $H^2(\Omega)$ given by

$$a_P(u,v) := \int_\Omega \Delta u \, \Delta v - (1-\nu) \left(2u_{xx}v_{yy} + 2u_{yy}v_{xx} - 4u_{xy}v_{xy}\right) dxdy, \tag{19.12}$$

where ν is a physical constant known as Poisson's ratio, and $2(1-\nu) = \mu/(\lambda+\mu)$. In classical models for plate bending, ν is restricted to the range $[0, \frac{1}{2}]$, although negative values of ν correspond to **auxetic materials** [8].

19.4.3 Coercivity of the plate variational formulation

The variational form $a_P(\cdot,\cdot)$ satisfies a Gårding-type inequality,

$$a_P(v,v) + K\|v\|^2_{L^2(\Omega)} \geq \alpha \|v\|^2_{H^2(\Omega)} \quad \forall v \in H^2(\Omega) \tag{19.13}$$

for all $-3 < \nu < 1$, where $\alpha > 0$ and $K < \infty$ [4]. If $\nu = 1$, this inequality cannot hold since $a_P(v,v)$ then vanishes for all harmonic functions, v. Coercivity can be derived for

$0 < \nu < 1$, as follows. Write

$$
\begin{aligned}
a_P(v,v) &= \int_\Omega \nu\left(v_{xx}+v_{yy}\right)^2 + (1-\nu)\left(\left(v_{xx}-v_{yy}\right)^2 + 4v_{xy}^2\right)\,dxdy \\
&\geq \min\{\nu, 1-\nu\}\int_\Omega \left(v_{xx}+v_{yy}\right)^2 + \left(v_{xx}-v_{yy}\right)^2 + 4v_{xy}^2\,dxdy \\
&= 2\min\{\nu,1-\nu\}\int_\Omega v_{xx}^2 + v_{yy}^2 + 2v_{xy}^2\,dxdy \\
&= 2\min\{\nu,1-\nu\}|v|_{H^2(\Omega)}^2 .
\end{aligned}
\tag{19.14}
$$

Coercivity does not hold for functions v which have vanishing $H^2(\Omega)$ seminorm, that is, $|v|_{H^2(\Omega)} = 0$. Such functions must be linear polynomials, which we denote by $\mathcal{P}_1$. But (19.14) does imply that $a_P(\cdot,\cdot)$ is coercive over any closed subspace, $V \subset H^2(\Omega)$, such that $V \cap \mathcal{P}_1 = \emptyset$ (see [57, Section 5.9]). Thus, there is a constant $\alpha > 0$ such that

$$a_P(v,v) \geq \alpha\|v\|_{H^2(\Omega)}^2 \quad \forall v \in V. \tag{19.15}$$

For $V \subset H^2(\Omega)$ and $F \in V'$, we consider the problem: find $u \in V$ such that

$$a_P(u,v) = F(v) \quad \forall v \in V. \tag{19.16}$$

As a consequence of the Lax-Milgram theorem 3.1, we have the following.

Theorem 19.1 *If $V \subset H^2(\Omega)$ is a closed subspace such that $V \cap \mathcal{P}_1 = \emptyset$ and $0 < \nu < 1$, then* (19.16) *has a unique solution.*

19.4.4 Essential boundary conditions

Figure 19.6: Simply supported plate.

There are different boundary conditions relevant for physical applications. Let V^{ss} be defined by

$$V^{\mathrm{ss}} = \left\{v \in H^2(\Omega) \,:\, v = 0 \text{ on } \partial\Omega\right\}.$$

This is the subset of $H^2(\Omega)$ consisting of functions which vanish to first-order only on $\partial\Omega$. This variational space, used in (19.16), provides the model known as the **simply-supported plate** model. The displacement u is held at a fixed height but the plate is free to rotate ($\frac{\partial u}{\partial \nu} \neq 0$) at the boundary. This is depicted in Figure 19.6.

The **clamped plate** model uses the variational space

$$V^{\mathrm{c}} = \left\{v \in H^2(\Omega) \,:\, v = \frac{\partial v}{\partial \nu} = 0 \text{ on } \partial\Omega\right\},$$

the subset of $H^2(\Omega)$ consisting of functions which vanish to second order on $\partial\Omega$. In the clamped case, the rotation of the plate is constrained at the boundary.

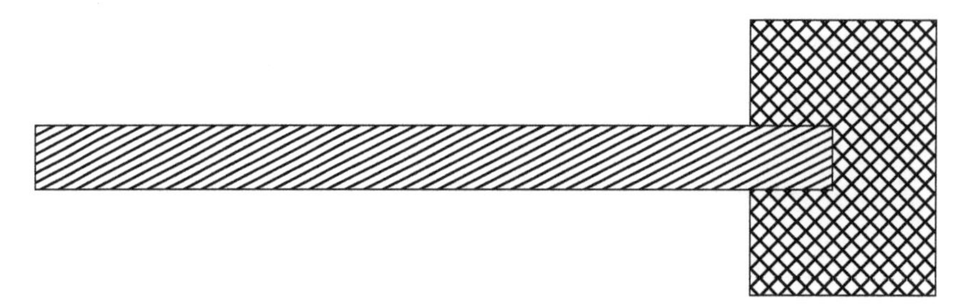

Figure 19.7: Plate clamped on right and free on left.

Finally, a mixture of clamped and simply supported boundary conditions can be imposed. Let $\Gamma_c \subset \partial\Omega$ denote the clamped region and $\Gamma_s \subset \partial\Omega$ denote the simply supported region. The region $\partial\Omega\backslash(\Gamma_c \cup \Gamma_s)$ is where the plate is left free, as indicated on the left side of Figure 19.7. The corresponding variational space is then

$$V = \Big\{ v \in H^2(\Omega) \; : \; v = 0 \text{ on } \Gamma_c \cup \Gamma_s \text{ and } \frac{\partial v}{\partial n} = 0 \text{ on } \Gamma_c \Big\}. \tag{19.17}$$

19.4.5 Natural boundary conditions

Let us derive a formula that indicates the natural boundary conditions associated with (19.12). We will see that, when integrating by parts, all of the terms multiplied by $1 - \nu$ cancel, as they all yield various versions of the cross derivative u_{xxyy}. Applying the divergence theorem to $\mathbf{w} = \mathbf{i}uv$, where $\mathbf{i}$ is either $(1, 0)$ or $(0, 1)$, we find

$$\int_\Omega u\, v_i \, d\mathbf{x} = -\int_\Omega u_i\, v \, d\mathbf{x} + \oint_{\partial\Omega} u\, v\, \mathbf{i} \cdot \mathbf{n} \, ds = -\int_\Omega u_i\, v \, d\mathbf{x} + \oint_{\partial\Omega} u\, v\, n_i \, ds.$$

Therefore

$$\begin{aligned} \int_\Omega u_{jj}\, v_{ii} \, d\mathbf{x} &= -\int_\Omega u_{jji}\, v_i \, d\mathbf{x} + \oint_{\partial\Omega} u_{jj}\, v_i\, n_i \, ds \\ &= \int_\Omega u_{jjii}\, v \, d\mathbf{x} + \oint_{\partial\Omega} u_{jj}\, v_i\, n_i \, ds - \oint_{\partial\Omega} u_{jji}\, v\, n_i \, ds. \end{aligned} \tag{19.18}$$

Similarly,

$$\begin{aligned} \int_\Omega u_{ji}\, v_{ji} \, d\mathbf{x} &= -\int_\Omega u_{jii}\, v_j \, d\mathbf{x} + \oint_{\partial\Omega} u_{ji}\, v_j\, n_i \, ds \\ &= \int_\Omega u_{jjii}\, v \, d\mathbf{x} + \oint_{\partial\Omega} u_{ji}\, v_j\, n_i \, ds - \oint_{\partial\Omega} u_{jii}\, v\, n_j \, ds. \end{aligned} \tag{19.19}$$

Therefore

$$\begin{aligned} &\int_\Omega \big(u_{11}\, v_{22} + u_{22}\, v_{11} - 2u_{12}\, v_{12}\big) \, d\mathbf{x} \\ &= \oint_{\partial\Omega} \big(u_{22}\, v_1\, n_1 + u_{11}\, v_2\, n_2\big) \, ds - 2\oint_{\partial\Omega} u_{12}\, v_1\, n_2 \, ds \\ &\quad - \oint_{\partial\Omega} v\big(u_{112}\, n_2 + u_{221}\, n_1 - 2u_{122}\, n_1\big) \, ds \\ &= \oint_{\partial\Omega} \big(u_{22}\, v_1\, n_1 + u_{11}\, v_2\, n_2 - 2u_{12}\, v_1\, n_2\big) \, ds - \oint_{\partial\Omega} v\big(u_{112}\, n_2 - u_{122}\, n_1\big) \, ds. \end{aligned} \tag{19.20}$$

Note that $u_{112}\, n_2 - u_{122}\, n_1 = u_{112}\, t_1 + u_{122}\, t_2 = \nabla u_{12} \cdot \mathbf{t} = u_{12t}$. Thus

$$\begin{aligned} &\int_\Omega \big(u_{11}\, v_{22} + u_{22}\, v_{11} - 2u_{12}\, v_{12}\big)\, d\mathbf{x} \\ &= \oint_{\partial\Omega} \big(u_{22}\, v_1\, n_1 + u_{11}\, v_2\, n_2 - u_{12}\, v_1\, n_2 - u_{12}\, v_2\, n_1\big)\, ds - \oint_{\partial\Omega} v\, u_{12t}\, ds. \end{aligned} \tag{19.21}$$

If a segment of the boundary is straight, then we can change coordinates so that the above simplifies to

$$\int_\Omega \big(u_{11}\, v_{22} + u_{22}\, v_{11} - 2u_{12}\, v_{12}\big)\, d\mathbf{x} = \oint_{\partial\Omega} \big(u_{tt}\, v_n - u_{ttn} v\big)\, ds.$$

Integration by parts for the other part of the bilinear form (19.12) is relatively simpler (see Exercise 19.4):

$$\begin{aligned} \int_\Omega \Delta u \Delta v\, d\mathbf{x} &= -\int_\Omega \nabla(\Delta u) \cdot \nabla v\, d\mathbf{x} + \oint_{\partial\Omega} \Delta u \frac{\partial v}{\partial n}\, ds \\ &= \int_\Omega (\Delta^2 u)\, v\, d\mathbf{x} - \oint_{\partial\Omega} \frac{\partial \Delta u}{\partial n}\, v\, ds + \oint_{\partial\Omega} \Delta u \frac{\partial v}{\partial n}\, ds. \end{aligned} \tag{19.22}$$

Therefore

$$\begin{aligned} a_P(u,v) = &\int_\Omega (\Delta^2 u)\, v\, d\mathbf{x} \\ &- \oint_{\partial\Omega} \Big(\frac{\partial \Delta u}{\partial n} - 2(1-\nu) u_{ttn}\Big)\, v\, ds + \oint_{\partial\Omega} \Big(\Delta u - 2(1-\nu) u_{tt}\Big)\, v_n\, ds. \end{aligned} \tag{19.23}$$

Thus, if $a_P(u,v) = (f,v)_{L^2(\Omega)}$ for all $v \in H_0^2(\Omega)$, we find that $\Delta^2 u = f$ holds in the L^2 sense, independent of the choice of ν.

In the simply-supported case ($V = V^{\mathrm{ss}}$), there is another, *natural* boundary condition that holds. In this sense, this problem has a mixture of Dirichlet and Neumann boundary conditions, but they hold on all of $\partial\Omega$. The natural boundary condition is found using integration by parts, but with v having an arbitrary, nonzero normal derivative on $\partial\Omega$. One finds [37] that the bending moment $\Delta u - 2(1-\nu)u_{tt}$ must vanish on $\partial\Omega$, where u_{tt} denotes the second directional derivative in the tangential direction. These results are summarized in the following.

Theorem 19.2 *Suppose that the space V is specified by (19.17) and satisfies $V \cap \mathcal{P}_1 = \emptyset$. If $f \in L^2(\Omega)$, and if $u \in H^4(\Omega)$ satisfies* (19.16) *with $F(v) = (f,v)$, then u satisfies*

$$\Delta^2 u = f$$

in the $L^2(\Omega)$ sense, and satisfies the following boundary conditions:

$$u = \frac{\partial u}{\partial \nu} = 0 \ \textit{on}\ \Gamma_c,$$

$$u = \Delta u - 2(1-\nu)u_{tt} = 0 \ \textit{on}\ \Gamma_s,$$

and

$$\Delta u - 2(1-\nu)u_{tt} = \frac{\partial \Delta u}{\partial n} - 2(1-\nu)u_{ttn} = 0 \ \textit{on}\ \partial\Omega \backslash (\Gamma_c \cup \Gamma_s).$$

19.4.6 Approximating plates

To approximate (19.16), we need a subspace V_h of $H^2(\Omega)$. For example, we could take a space based on the Argyris elements [57, Examples 3.2.10 and 3.2.11]. With either choice of V as above, if we choose V_h to satisfy the corresponding boundary conditions, we obtain the following.

Theorem 19.3 *If $V_h \subset V$ is based on Argyris elements of order $k \geq 5$ then there is a unique $u_h \in V_h$ such that*

$$a_P(u_h, v) = F(v) \quad \forall v \in V_h.$$

Moreover,

$$\begin{aligned} \|u - u_h\|_{H^2(\Omega)} &\leq C \inf_{v \in V_h} \|u - v\|_{H^2(\Omega)} \\ &\leq C h^{k-1} \|u\|_{H^{k+1}(\Omega)}. \end{aligned} \tag{19.24}$$

For more details regarding numerical methods for plate bending, see the survey [260]. Several mixed methods have been proposed [127, 129, 144] that reduce the biharmonic problem to a system of second-order problems. However, only recently has a mixed method been proposed that is faithful to the natural boundary conditions associated with the simply-supported plate model [240]. A related mixed method suitable for clamped plates appears in [183].

19.5 The Babuška paradox

The Babuška Paradox relates to the limit of polygonal approximations to a smooth boundary. For example, let Ω be the unit disc, and let Ω_n denote regular polygons inscribed in Ω with n sides. Then the Paradox is that the solutions w_n of the simply supported plate problems on Ω_n converge to the solution w of the clamped plate problem on Ω as $n \to \infty$ [215, Chapter 18, Volume II].

The reason for the paradox is that, at each vertex of Ω_n, the gradient of v must vanish for any sufficiently smooth function v that vanishes on $\partial\Omega_n$. This is illustrated in Figure 19.8. In particular, ∇w_n must vanish at all vertices of the polygon Ω_n. Thus in the limit, $\nabla w = 0$ at all points on the boundary, where $w = \lim_{n\to\infty} w_n$ and w_n denotes the solution of simply supported plate problem on Ω_n.

A corollary of this paradox is the following. Suppose we approximate a smooth domain Ω by polygons Ω_n and form the finite element approximation $w_{n,h}$ of the simply supported plate problem, say with $h = 1/n$. Then as $n \to \infty$ (equivalently, $h \to 0$), we expect that $w_{n,h}$ will converge to the solution w of the clamped plate problem on Ω, not the simply supported problem. This type of numerical error is the most insidious possible, in that the convergence is likely to be quite stable. There will be no red flags to indicate that something is wrong.

The Babuška Paradox has been widely studied [21, 218, 228, 243], and it is now generally known as the Babuška-Sapondzhyan Paradox [77, 217, 245]. Since the biharmonic equation arises in other contexts, including the Stokes equations, this paradox is of broader interest [280, 271, 111, 74].

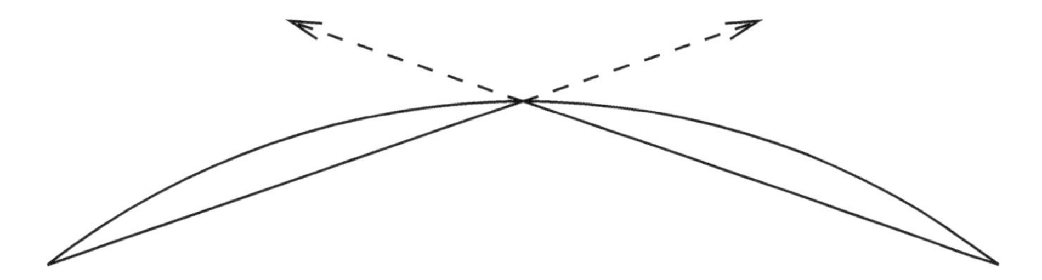

Figure 19.8: Polygonal approximation in the Babuška Paradox. At a vertex, the gradient of the simply supported solution must vanish as its tangential derivatives are zero in two independent directions.

19.6 Membranes

Membranes are thin elastic media that do not resist bending. Their models are similar in form to that of anti-plane strain (Section 19.3.1), but for different reasons. Membranes are similar to plates in that they are thin, but only the vertical deformation plays a role. Thus we assume that

$$\nabla \mathbf{u} \approx \begin{pmatrix} 0 & 0 & 0 \\ 0 & 0 & 0 \\ w_{,1} & w_{,2} & 0 \end{pmatrix} \text{ and } \boldsymbol{\epsilon} = \tfrac{1}{2} \begin{pmatrix} 0 & 0 & w_{,1} \\ 0 & 0 & w_{,2} \\ w_{,1} & w_{,2} & 0 \end{pmatrix}.$$

Therefore

$$\mathbf{T} = \mu \begin{pmatrix} 0 & 0 & w_{,1} \\ 0 & 0 & w_{,2} \\ w_{,1} & w_{,2} & 0 \end{pmatrix}.$$

and so

$$\nabla \cdot \mathbf{T} = \mu \begin{pmatrix} 0 \\ 0 \\ w_{,11} + w_{,22} \end{pmatrix} = \mu \begin{pmatrix} 0 \\ 0 \\ \Delta w \end{pmatrix}.$$

Thus the membrane problem reduces to the familiar Laplace equation, $-\mu \Delta w = f$.

19.7 Locking in elasticity

Locking is a numerical defect that can occur when Poisson's ratio $\nu \to \frac{1}{2}$ [23, 57]. The variational form for elasticity written as in (19.9) corresponds to the variational form in the iterated penalty method in Section 14.2, with

$$\rho = \frac{2\lambda}{\mu} = \frac{4\nu}{1 - 2\nu} = \frac{2\nu}{\frac{1}{2} - \nu},$$

in view of the conversions between different physical constants detailed in Table 19.1. Thus $\rho \to \infty$ when $\nu \to \frac{1}{2}$. It follows from the results in Section 14.2 that, if the constant κ in (14.19) satisfies $\kappa > 0$, $\mathbf{u}_h^\rho \to \mathbf{u}_h^\infty$ as $\rho \to \infty$ ($\nu \to \frac{1}{2}$). Of course, κ can depend on the mesh size h, so we write κ_h to indicate this. More precisely, it follows from (14.17) that

$$\|\mathbf{u}_h^\rho - \mathbf{u}_h^\infty\|_a \leq \frac{1}{1 + \rho \kappa_h} \|\mathbf{u}_h^\infty\|_a.$$

system	$K =$	$\mu =$	$\lambda =$	$\mu =$	$E =$	$\nu =$
K, μ	K	μ	$K - \frac{2}{3}\mu$	μ	$\frac{9K\mu}{3K+\mu}$	$\frac{3K-2\mu}{2(3K+\mu)}$
λ, μ	$\lambda + \frac{2}{3}\mu$	μ	λ	μ	$\mu\frac{3\lambda+2\mu}{\lambda+\mu}$	$\frac{\lambda}{2(\lambda+\mu)}$
E, ν	$\frac{E}{3(1-2\nu)}$	$\frac{E}{2(1+\nu)}$	$\frac{E\nu}{(1+\nu)(1-2\nu)}$	$\frac{E}{2(1+\nu)}$	E	ν

Table 19.1: Conversion guide for elasticity constants. E is Young's modulus. The shear modulus μ is sometimes denoted by G. Note that $\lambda \to \infty$ and $K \to \infty$ as $\nu \to \frac{1}{2}$.

Here $\mathbf{u}_h^\infty \in V_h$ satisfies $\nabla\cdot \mathbf{u}_h^\infty = 0$ and

$$\tfrac{1}{2}\mu a_\epsilon(\mathbf{u}_h^\infty, \mathbf{v}) = F(\mathbf{v}) \text{ for all } \mathbf{v} \in V_h,$$

which we recognize (Chapter 13) as an approximation to the solution of a Stokes system. Thus locking does **not** occur if the constant κ_h in (14.19) satisfies

$$\kappa_h > \kappa_0, \tag{19.25}$$

where $\kappa_0 > 0$ is independent of h. For example, we know that (19.25) holds for Lagrange elements of sufficiently high degree, as discussed in Chapter 13. We leave as Exercise 19.7 the exploration of the locking phenomenon.

19.8 Exercises

Exercise 19.1 *Show that for any smooth vector valued function* $\mathbf{u}$*, the following holds:*

$$\nabla\cdot \big(\nabla\mathbf{u} + (\nabla\mathbf{u})^t\big) = 2\Delta\mathbf{u}.$$

Exercise 19.2 *Let A and B be any $d \times d$ matrices. Prove that*

$$A : B^t = A^t : B.$$

(Hint: $A : B^t = \sum_{i,j=1}^d a_{ij}b_{ji}$.)

Exercise 19.3 *Let A be any $d \times d$ symmetric matrix, that is, $A^t = A$. Let B be any $d \times d$ matrix. Prove that*

$$A : B = A : \big(\tfrac{1}{2}(B + B^t)\big).$$

(Hint: use Exercise 19.2.)

Exercise 19.4 *Prove (19.22). (Hint: use (2.10) twice.)*

Exercise 19.5 *Let $\widehat{\Omega}$ be the unit square, and let*

$$\Omega = \big\{(x, y, z) \;:\; (x, y) \in \widehat{\Omega},\; z \in [0, Z]\big\}.$$

Compare the solution of the anti-plane strain problem on $\widehat{\Omega}$ to the solution of the full elasticity problem on Ω for various values of $Z > 0$. Take $f = 1$, so that $\mathbf{f} = (0, 0, 1)$.

Exercise 19.6 *Verify the tensor identity* $\Delta u = \nabla \cdot \epsilon(\mathbf{u})$, *where* ϵ *is defined in (19.2).*

Exercise 19.7 *Experiment with the phenomenon of locking [23, 57] for plane strain, that is, the two-dimensional equations of elasticity. In particular, solve them with piecewise linears and with* ν *approaching* $\frac{1}{2}$. *What happens? Then switch to piecewise quartics and compare.*

Chapter 20

Navier-Stokes Equations

In Chapter 13, we derived the Navier-Stokes equations under the assumption that the stress depends linearly upon the gradient of the fluid velocity. Here we develop the variational theory for these equations and present some computational algorithms for solving them.

20.1 The Navier-Stokes equations

The Navier-Stokes equations for the flow of a viscous, incompressible, Newtonian fluid can be written

$$\begin{aligned} -\Delta \mathbf{u} + \nabla p &= -R\left(\mathbf{u}\cdot\nabla\mathbf{u} + \mathbf{u}_t\right) \\ \nabla\cdot\mathbf{u} &= 0 \end{aligned} \tag{20.1}$$

in $\Omega \subset \mathbb{R}^d$, where $\mathbf{u}$ denotes the fluid velocity, p denotes the pressure, and R denotes the Reynolds number [190]. In our context, $R = 1/\eta$ where η denotes the fluid (kinematic) viscosity.

These equations must be supplemented by appropriate boundary conditions, such as the Dirichlet boundary conditions, $\mathbf{u} = \gamma$ on $\partial\Omega$.

A complete variational formulation of (20.1) takes the form: Find $\mathbf{u}$ such that $\mathbf{u} - \gamma \in V$ and $p \in \Pi$ such that

$$\begin{aligned} a\left(\mathbf{u},\mathbf{v}\right) + b\left(\mathbf{v},p\right) + R\big(c\left(\mathbf{u},\mathbf{u},\mathbf{v}\right) + \left(\mathbf{u}_t,\mathbf{v}\right)_{L^2(\Omega)}\big) = 0 \quad &\forall \mathbf{v}\in V\,, \\ b(\mathbf{u},q) = 0 \quad \forall q \in \Pi\,, & \end{aligned} \tag{20.2}$$

where e.g. $a(\cdot,\cdot)$, $b(\cdot,\cdot)$ and $c(\cdot,\cdot,\cdot)$ are given by

$$a(\mathbf{u},\mathbf{v}) := \int_\Omega \sum_{i,j=1}^n u_{i,j} v_{i,j}\, d\mathbf{x}, \tag{20.3}$$

$$b(\mathbf{v},q) := -\int_\Omega \sum_{i=1}^n v_{i,i}\, q\, d\mathbf{x}, \tag{20.4}$$

$$c(\mathbf{u},\mathbf{v},\mathbf{w}) := \int_\Omega (\mathbf{u}\cdot\nabla\mathbf{v})\cdot\mathbf{w}\, d\mathbf{x}, \tag{20.5}$$

and $(\cdot,\cdot)_{L^2(\Omega)}$ denotes the $L^2(\Omega)^d$-inner-product. The spaces V and Π are the same as for the Stokes equations (Chapter 13), as are the forms $a(\cdot,\cdot)$ and $b(\cdot,\cdot)$. As noted in Chapter 13, the $a(\cdot,\cdot)$ form can be either the gradient form (13.7) or the "epsilon" form (13.11).

20.1.1 Properties of the nonlinear term

The trilinear form (20.5) has some special properties that reflect important physical properties of fluid dynamics. To see these, we need to derive some calculus identities. For any vector-valued function $\mathbf{u}$ and scalar-valued function v, the product rule for derivatives gives (Exercise 20.2)

$$\nabla\cdot(\mathbf{u}\,v) = (\nabla\cdot\mathbf{u})v + \mathbf{u}\cdot\nabla v. \tag{20.6}$$

For any vector-valued function $\mathbf{u}$ and scalar-valued functions v and w, applying the product rule for derivatives again gives

$$\nabla\cdot(\mathbf{u}\,v\,w) = (\nabla\cdot\mathbf{u})v\,w + (\mathbf{u}\cdot\nabla v)w + (\mathbf{u}\cdot\nabla w)v.$$

Thus if we apply the divergence theorem we get

$$\oint_{\partial\Omega}(\mathbf{u}\cdot\mathbf{n})v\,w\,ds = \int_\Omega(\nabla\cdot\mathbf{u})v\,w\,d\mathbf{x} + \int_\Omega(\mathbf{u}\cdot\nabla v)w\,d\mathbf{x} + \int_\Omega(\mathbf{u}\cdot\nabla w)v\,d\mathbf{x}. \tag{20.7}$$

Thus if $\mathbf{u}$ satisfies the divergence constraint $\nabla\cdot\mathbf{u}=0$ in (20.1) and the product $(\mathbf{u}\cdot\mathbf{n})\,v\,w$ vanishes on $\partial\Omega$, we have

$$\int_\Omega(\mathbf{u}\cdot\nabla v)w\,d\mathbf{x} = -\int_\Omega(\mathbf{u}\cdot\nabla w)v\,d\mathbf{x}. \tag{20.8}$$

Suppose now that $\mathbf{v}$ and $\mathbf{w}$ are vector-valued functions, and $\mathbf{u}\cdot\mathbf{n}$ or $\mathbf{v}$ or $\mathbf{w}$ vanishes at each point on $\partial\Omega$. Applying (20.8), we find (Exercise 20.3)

$$\int_\Omega(\mathbf{u}\cdot\nabla\mathbf{v})\cdot\mathbf{w}\,d\mathbf{x} = -\int_\Omega(\mathbf{u}\cdot\nabla\mathbf{w})\cdot\mathbf{v}\,d\mathbf{x}. \tag{20.9}$$

Thus we have shown the following.

Lemma 20.1 *Suppose that* $\mathbf{u}$ *satisfies the divergence constraint* $\nabla\cdot\mathbf{u}=0$ *in (20.1) and that* $\mathbf{u}\cdot\mathbf{n}$ *or* $\mathbf{v}$ *or* $\mathbf{w}$ *vanishes at each point on* $\partial\Omega$. *Then the trilinear form (20.5) is antisymmetric in the last two arguments:*

$$c(\mathbf{u},\mathbf{v},\mathbf{w}) = -c(\mathbf{u},\mathbf{w},\mathbf{v}). \tag{20.10}$$

In particular, if $\mathbf{u}$ *satisfies the divergence constraint* $\nabla\cdot\mathbf{u}=0$ *and* $\mathbf{v}$ *vanishes on* $\partial\Omega$, *then* $c(\mathbf{u},\mathbf{v},\mathbf{v})=0$.

We think of the term $\mathbf{u}\cdot\nabla\mathbf{v}$ as a directional derivative, but it has another form that is more useful in other contexts:

$$\mathbf{u}\cdot\nabla\mathbf{v} = (\nabla\mathbf{v})\mathbf{u}, \tag{20.11}$$

where $\nabla\mathbf{v}$ is a matrix and $(\nabla\mathbf{v})\mathbf{u}$ denotes a matrix times a vector. The proof of (20.10) can be done by expanding in indices:

$$(\mathbf{u}\cdot\nabla\mathbf{v})_i = \sum_{j=1}^d u_j v_{i,j} = (\nabla\mathbf{v})_{ij}u_j = \big((\nabla\mathbf{v})\mathbf{u}\big)_i.$$

The interpretation (20.11) also means that

$$c(\mathbf{u},\mathbf{v},\mathbf{w})=\int_\Omega \sum_{i=1}^{d}(\nabla\mathbf{v})_{ij}u_iw_j\,d\mathbf{x}=\int_\Omega \mathbf{u}^t(\nabla\mathbf{v})\mathbf{w}\,d\mathbf{x}. \tag{20.12}$$

20.1.2 The nonlinear term with boundary conditions

When functions are nonzero on the boundary, the antisymmetry properties of the nonlinear form are more complex. If $\nabla\cdot\mathbf{u}=0$, then using (20.7) we can show that

$$\int_\Omega(\mathbf{u}\cdot\nabla\mathbf{v})\cdot\mathbf{w}\,d\mathbf{x}=-\int_\Omega(\mathbf{u}\cdot\nabla\mathbf{w})\cdot\mathbf{v}\,d\mathbf{x}+\oint_{\partial\Omega}(\mathbf{u}\cdot\mathbf{n})\mathbf{v}\cdot\mathbf{w}\,ds. \tag{20.13}$$

In particular,

$$c(\mathbf{u},\mathbf{v},\mathbf{v})=\int_\Omega(\mathbf{u}\cdot\nabla\mathbf{v})\cdot\mathbf{v}\,d\mathbf{x}=\frac{1}{2}\oint_{\partial\Omega}(\mathbf{u}\cdot\mathbf{n})\mathbf{v}\cdot\mathbf{v}\,ds=\frac{1}{2}\oint_{\partial\Omega}(\mathbf{u}\cdot\mathbf{n})|\mathbf{v}|^2\,ds. \tag{20.14}$$

20.2 Implicit time-stepping

The workhorse schemes for solving the time-dependent Navier-Stokes equations are implicit. The simplest of these is the implicit Euler scheme, which is the lowest-order backwards differentiation (BDF) scheme (Section 10.5.5). The implicit Euler time-stepping scheme for the Navier-Stokes equations can be defined as follows. Expressed in variational form, it is

$$\begin{aligned}a\left(\mathbf{u}^\ell,\mathbf{v}\right)+b\left(\mathbf{v},p^\ell\right)+R\,c\left(\mathbf{u}^\ell,\mathbf{u}^\ell,\mathbf{v}\right)+\frac{R}{\Delta t}\left(\mathbf{u}^\ell-\mathbf{u}^{\ell-1},\mathbf{v}\right)_{L^2(\Omega)}&=0,\\ b\left(\mathbf{u}^\ell,q\right)&=0,\end{aligned} \tag{20.15}$$

where $\mathbf{v}$ varies over all V (or V_h) and q varies over all Π (or Π_h) and Δt denotes the time-step size. More efficient time-stepping schemes will take a similar form, such as the backwards differentiation schemes. In particular, (20.15) is the first-order backwards differentiation scheme.

At each time step, one has a problem to solve for $(\mathbf{u}^\ell,p^\ell)$ with the form $\tilde{a}(\cdot,\cdot)$ is

$$\tilde{a}(\mathbf{u},\mathbf{v}):=a(\mathbf{u},\mathbf{v})+\tau\left(\mathbf{u},\mathbf{v}\right)_{L^2(\Omega)}, \tag{20.16}$$

where the constant $\tau=R/\Delta t$. It takes the form

$$\begin{aligned}\tilde{a}\left(\mathbf{u}^\ell,\mathbf{v}\right)+b\left(\mathbf{v},p^\ell\right)+R\,c\left(\mathbf{u}^\ell,\mathbf{u}^\ell,\mathbf{v}\right)&=\tau\left(\mathbf{u}^{\ell-1},\mathbf{v}\right)_{L^2(\Omega)},\\ b\left(\mathbf{u}^\ell,q\right)&=0.\end{aligned} \tag{20.17}$$

However, (20.17) is nonlinear, so an algorithm must be chosen to linearize it. We can use the default Newton solver in `dolfin`, the continuation algorithm in Section 9.4, or simple fixed-point iteration, as we now describe.

20.2.1 Fixed-point iteration

One of the simplest solution methods is fixed-point iteration, which takes the form:

$$\begin{aligned} \tilde{a}\left(\mathbf{u}^{\ell,k},\mathbf{v}\right)+b\left(\mathbf{v},p^{\ell,k}\right) &= -R\,c\left(\mathbf{u}^{\ell,k-1},\mathbf{u}^{\ell,k-1},\mathbf{v}\right)+\tau\left(\mathbf{u}^{\ell-1},\mathbf{v}\right)_{L^2(\Omega)}, \\ b\left(\mathbf{u}^{\ell,k},q\right) &= 0. \end{aligned} \tag{20.18}$$

This iteration can be started with an extrapolated value, e.g., $\mathbf{u}^{\ell,0} := 2\mathbf{u}^{\ell-1} - \mathbf{u}^{\ell-2}$, and once convergence is achieved, we set $\mathbf{u}^{\ell} = \mathbf{u}^{\ell,k}$.

Note that we have $\mathbf{u}^{\ell,k} = \gamma$ on $\partial\Omega$, that is, $\mathbf{u}^{\ell,k} = \mathbf{u}_0^{\ell,k} + \gamma$ where $\mathbf{u}_0^{\ell,k} \in V$. The variational problem for $\mathbf{u}^{\ell,k}$ can be written: Find $\mathbf{u}_0^{\ell,k} \in V$ and $p \in \Pi$ such that

$$\begin{aligned} \tilde{a}(\mathbf{u}_0^{\ell,k},\mathbf{v})+b(\mathbf{v},p) &= -\tilde{a}(\gamma,\mathbf{v}) - Rc(\mathbf{u}^{\ell,k-1},\mathbf{u}^{\ell,k-1},\mathbf{v})+\tau(\mathbf{u}^{\ell},\mathbf{v})_{L^2(\Omega)} \quad \forall \mathbf{v}\in V \\ b(\mathbf{u}_0^{\ell,k},q) &= -\,b(\gamma,q) \quad \forall q\in\Pi. \end{aligned} \tag{20.19}$$

This is of the form (13.21) with

$$\begin{aligned} F^{\ell,k}(\mathbf{v}) &= -\tilde{a}(\gamma,\mathbf{v}) - Rc(\mathbf{u}^{\ell,k-1},\mathbf{u}^{\ell,k-1},\mathbf{v})+\tau(\mathbf{u}^{\ell-1},\mathbf{v})_{L^2(\Omega)} \quad \forall \mathbf{v}\in V \\ G(q) &= -\,b(\gamma,q) \quad \forall q\in\Pi. \end{aligned} \tag{20.20}$$

Again, the inhomogeneous boundary data γ appears in both right-hand sides, $F^{\ell,k}$ and G.

20.2.2 Stability of the exact solution

The nonlinear time-stepping scheme (20.17) has excellent stability properties. To see why, let us assume for simplicity that the boundary data γ is zero. Then (20.10) implies

$$\tilde{a}(\mathbf{u}^{\ell},\mathbf{u}^{\ell}) = -Rc(\mathbf{u}^{\ell},\mathbf{u}^{\ell},\mathbf{u}^{\ell})+\tau(\mathbf{u}^{\ell-1},\mathbf{u}^{\ell})_{L^2(\Omega)} = \tau(\mathbf{u}^{\ell-1},\mathbf{u}^{\ell})_{L^2(\Omega)}. \tag{20.21}$$

Thus the Cauchy-Schwarz inequality (3.15) implies

$$\tilde{a}(\mathbf{u}^{\ell},\mathbf{u}^{\ell}) \le \tau\|\mathbf{u}^{\ell-1}\|_{L^2(\Omega)}\|\mathbf{u}^{\ell}\|_{L^2(\Omega)} \le \tfrac{1}{2}\tau\left(\|\mathbf{u}^{\ell-1}\|_{L^2(\Omega)}^2+\|\mathbf{u}^{\ell}\|_{L^2(\Omega)}^2\right)$$

Subtracting $\frac{1}{2}\tau\|\mathbf{u}^{\ell}\|_{L^2(\Omega)}^2$ from both sides yields

$$a(\mathbf{u}^{\ell},\mathbf{u}^{\ell})+\tfrac{1}{2}\tau\|\mathbf{u}^{\ell}\|_{L^2(\Omega)}^2 \le \tfrac{1}{2}\tau\|\mathbf{u}^{\ell-1}\|_{L^2(\Omega)}^2 \le a(\mathbf{u}^{\ell-1},\mathbf{u}^{\ell-1})+\tfrac{1}{2}\tau\|\mathbf{u}^{\ell-1}\|_{L^2(\Omega)}^2. \tag{20.22}$$

Thus $\mathbf{u}^{\ell}$ is non-increasing in the norm $\|\mathbf{v}\| = \sqrt{a(\mathbf{v},\mathbf{v})+\frac{1}{2}\tau\|\mathbf{v}\|_{L^2(\Omega)}^2}$.

20.2.3 Convergence of fixed-point iteration

The convergence of the iterative scheme (20.18) can be analyzed as follows. Subtracting two consecutive versions of (20.18), we find the following formula for $\mathbf{e}^k := \mathbf{u}^{\ell,k} - \mathbf{u}^{\ell,k-1}$:

$$\begin{aligned} \tilde{a}\left(\mathbf{e}^k,\mathbf{e}^k\right) &= R\Big(c\left(\mathbf{u}^{\ell,k-1},\mathbf{u}^{\ell,k-1},\mathbf{e}^k\right) - c\left(\mathbf{u}^{\ell,k-2},\mathbf{u}^{\ell,k-2},\mathbf{e}^k\right)\Big) \\ &= R\Big(c\left(\mathbf{u}^{\ell,k-1},\mathbf{u}^{\ell,k-1},\mathbf{e}^k\right) - c\left(\mathbf{u}^{\ell,k-2},\mathbf{u}^{\ell,k-1},\mathbf{e}^k\right) + \\ &\qquad c\left(\mathbf{u}^{\ell,k-2},\mathbf{u}^{\ell,k-1},\mathbf{e}^k\right) - c\left(\mathbf{u}^{\ell,k-2},\mathbf{u}^{\ell,k-2},\mathbf{e}^k\right)\Big) \\ &= R\Big(c\left(\mathbf{e}^{k-1},\mathbf{u}^{\ell,k-1},\mathbf{e}^k\right) + c\left(\mathbf{u}^{\ell,k-2},\mathbf{e}^{k-1},\mathbf{e}^k\right)\Big). \end{aligned} \tag{20.23}$$

From the Cauchy-Schwarz inequality (see Exercise 20.1), we find

$$|c\left(\mathbf{u}^{\ell,k-2},\mathbf{e}^{k-1},\mathbf{e}^{k}\right)| \leq \|\mathbf{u}^{\ell,k-2}\|_{L^\infty(\Omega)} \left(a\left(\mathbf{e}^{k-1},\mathbf{e}^{k-1}\right)\right)^{1/2} \left(\mathbf{e}^{k},\mathbf{e}^{k}\right)^{1/2}.$$

From (20.10) and the Cauchy-Schwarz inequality, we find

$$|c\left(\mathbf{e}^{k-1},\mathbf{u}^{\ell,k-1},\mathbf{e}^{k}\right)| = |c\left(\mathbf{e}^{k-1},\mathbf{e}^{k},\mathbf{u}^{\ell,k-1}\right)| \leq \|\mathbf{u}^{\ell,k-1}\|_{L^\infty(\Omega)} \left(\mathbf{e}^{k-1},\mathbf{e}^{k-1}\right)^{1/2} \left(a(\mathbf{e}^{k},\mathbf{e}^{k})\right)^{1/2}.$$

Thus (20.23) implies

$$\begin{aligned}
\tilde{a}\left(\mathbf{e}^{k},\mathbf{e}^{k}\right) &\leq R\|\mathbf{u}^{\ell,k-1}\|_{L^\infty(\Omega)} \left(\mathbf{e}^{k-1},\mathbf{e}^{k-1}\right)^{1/2} \left(a\left(\mathbf{e}^{k},\mathbf{e}^{k}\right)\right)^{1/2} \\
&\quad + R\|\mathbf{u}^{\ell,k-2}\|_{L^\infty(\Omega)} \left(a\left(\mathbf{e}^{k-1},\mathbf{e}^{k-1}\right)\right)^{1/2} \left(\mathbf{e}^{k},\mathbf{e}^{k}\right)^{1/2} \\
&\leq \tfrac{1}{2}\left(R\|\mathbf{u}^{\ell,k-1}\|_{L^\infty(\Omega)}\right)^2 \left(\mathbf{e}^{k-1},\mathbf{e}^{k-1}\right) + \tfrac{1}{2}a\left(\mathbf{e}^{k},\mathbf{e}^{k}\right) \\
&\quad + \frac{1}{2\tau}\left(R\|\mathbf{u}^{\ell,k-2}\|_{L^\infty(\Omega)}\right)^2 a\left(\mathbf{e}^{k-1},\mathbf{e}^{k-1}\right) + \frac{\tau}{2}\left(\mathbf{e}^{k},\mathbf{e}^{k}\right) \\
&= \tfrac{1}{2}\left(R\|\mathbf{u}^{\ell,k-1}\|_{L^\infty(\Omega)}\right)^2 \left(\mathbf{e}^{k-1},\mathbf{e}^{k-1}\right) \\
&\quad + \frac{1}{2\tau}\left(R\|\mathbf{u}^{\ell,k-2}\|_{L^\infty(\Omega)}\right)^2 a\left(\mathbf{e}^{k-1},\mathbf{e}^{k-1}\right) + \tfrac{1}{2}\tilde{a}\left(\mathbf{e}^{k},\mathbf{e}^{k}\right) \\
&\leq \frac{R^2}{2\tau}\left(\|\mathbf{u}^{\ell,k-1}\|^2_{L^\infty(\Omega)} + \|\mathbf{u}^{\ell,k-2}\|^2_{L^\infty(\Omega)}\right) \tilde{a}\left(\mathbf{e}^{k-1},\mathbf{e}^{k-1}\right) + \tfrac{1}{2}\tilde{a}\left(\mathbf{e}^{k},\mathbf{e}^{k}\right).
\end{aligned} \tag{20.24}$$

Therefore

$$\tilde{a}\left(\mathbf{e}^{k},\mathbf{e}^{k}\right) \leq \frac{R^2}{\tau}\left(\|\mathbf{u}^{\ell,k-1}\|^2_{L^\infty(\Omega)} + \|\mathbf{u}^{\ell,k-2}\|^2_{L^\infty(\Omega)}\right) \tilde{a}\left(\mathbf{e}^{k-1},\mathbf{e}^{k-1}\right). \tag{20.25}$$

Thus the fixed-point iteration for solving the nonlinear equations (20.17) for the time-stepping is convergent provided τ is large enough and $\|\mathbf{u}^{\ell,k-2}\|_{L^\infty(\Omega)}$ and $\|\mathbf{u}^{\ell,k-1}\|_{L^\infty(\Omega)}$ stay bounded. The latter can be monitored as the computation progresses. Note that the parameter $\frac{R^2}{\tau}$ appearing in (20.25) is equal to $R\Delta t$. Thus fixed-point iteration converges provided

$$R\Delta t\left(\|\mathbf{u}^{\ell,k-1}\|^2_{L^\infty(\Omega)} + \|\mathbf{u}^{\ell,k-2}\|^2_{L^\infty(\Omega)}\right) < 1. \tag{20.26}$$

20.2.4 Another time-stepping scheme

A more complex time-stepping scheme could be based on the variational equations

$$\begin{aligned}
a\left(\mathbf{u}^{\ell},\mathbf{v}\right) + b\left(\mathbf{v},p^{\ell}\right) + R\,c\left(\mathbf{u}^{\ell-1},\mathbf{u}^{\ell},\mathbf{v}\right) + \frac{R}{\Delta t}\left(\mathbf{u}^{\ell}-\mathbf{u}^{\ell-1},\mathbf{v}\right)_{L^2(\Omega)} &= 0, \\
b\left(\mathbf{u}^{\ell},q\right) &= 0,
\end{aligned} \tag{20.27}$$

in which the nonlinear term has been approximated in such a way that the linear algebraic problem changes at each time step. It takes the form (13.21) with a form $\tilde{a}(\cdot,\cdot)$ given by

$$\tilde{a}\left(\mathbf{u},\mathbf{v};\mathbf{U}\right) = a\left(\mathbf{u},\mathbf{v}\right) + \int_\Omega \left(\tau\mathbf{u}\cdot\mathbf{v} + \mathbf{U}\cdot\nabla\mathbf{u}\cdot\mathbf{v}\right)\,d\mathbf{x}, \tag{20.28}$$

where $\mathbf{U} = R\mathbf{u}^n$ arises from linearizing the nonlinear term.

Even though the addition of the $\mathbf{U}$ term makes it non-symmetric, $\tilde{a}(\cdot,\cdot)$ will be coercive for τ sufficiently large (i.e., for $\Delta t/R$ sufficiently small). In fact, when $\nabla\cdot\mathbf{U}\equiv 0$ then integrating by parts yields

$$\begin{aligned}\int_\Omega \mathbf{U}\cdot\nabla\mathbf{v}\cdot\mathbf{v}\,d\mathbf{x} &= \int_\Omega \sum_{i,j=1}^d U_i\, v_{j,i}\, v_j\,d\mathbf{x} = \int_\Omega \sum_{i,j=1}^d U_i\left(\tfrac{1}{2}\left(v_j^2\right)_{,i}\right)d\mathbf{x}\\ &= -\frac{1}{2}\int_\Omega \sum_{i,j=1}^d U_{i,i}\,v_j^2\,d\mathbf{x} = -\frac{1}{2}\int_\Omega \nabla\cdot\mathbf{U}\sum_{j=1}^d v_j^2\,d\mathbf{x} = 0\end{aligned} \tag{20.29}$$

for all $v\in V$ so that

$$\alpha\|\mathbf{v}\|_V^2 \le \tilde{a}(\mathbf{v},\mathbf{v}) \quad \forall\mathbf{v}\in V \tag{20.30}$$

for the same choice of $\alpha>0$ as before. Of course, $\tilde{a}(\cdot,\cdot)$ is continuous:

$$\tilde{a}(\mathbf{v},\mathbf{w}) \le C_a\|\mathbf{v}\|_V\|\mathbf{w}\|_V \quad \forall\mathbf{v},\mathbf{w}\in V \tag{20.31}$$

but now C_a depends on both τ and $\mathbf{U}$.

20.3 Time-independent solvers

Consider the time-independent Navier-Stokes equations in variational form:

$$F_\mathbf{v}(\mathbf{u}) = a(\mathbf{u},\mathbf{v}) + Rc(\mathbf{u},\mathbf{u},\mathbf{v}) = 0 \quad \forall\mathbf{v}\in Z, \tag{20.32}$$

using the notation introduced in Section 9.2.2 for a nonlinear system, together with the incompressibility constraint $\mathbf{u}\in Z$, that is, equivalently $\nabla\cdot\mathbf{u}=0$ or $b(\mathbf{u},q)=0$ for all $q\in\Pi$. In addition, we assume that we have Dirichlet boundary conditions $\mathbf{u}=\mathbf{g}$ on $\partial\Omega$. This is a nonlinear system of equations posed on the affine subspace $Z+\mathbf{g}$.

There are a variety of nonlinear solvers that can be applied. But it is useful to see what Newton's method looks like for this system. We compute the Jacobian of F by taking limits of difference quotients:

$$F_\mathbf{v}(\mathbf{u}+\epsilon\mathbf{w}) - F_\mathbf{v}(\mathbf{u}) = \epsilon\, a(\mathbf{w},\mathbf{v}) + R\big(c(\mathbf{u}+\epsilon\mathbf{w},\mathbf{u}+\epsilon\mathbf{w},\mathbf{v}) - c(\mathbf{u},\mathbf{u},\mathbf{v})\big).$$

Here, we note that we are differentiating in the affine space $Z+\mathbf{g}$, so the perturbation $\mathbf{w}$ satisfies homogeneous Dirichlet boundary conditions $\mathbf{w}=\mathbf{0}$ on $\partial\Omega$, as well as $\nabla\cdot\mathbf{w}=0$ (in short, $\mathbf{w}\in Z$). Expanding

$$\begin{aligned}c(\mathbf{u}+\epsilon\mathbf{w},\mathbf{u}+\epsilon\mathbf{w},\mathbf{v}) &= c(\mathbf{u},\mathbf{u}+\epsilon\mathbf{w},\mathbf{v}) + \epsilon\, c(\mathbf{w},\mathbf{u}+\epsilon\mathbf{w},\mathbf{v})\\ &= c(\mathbf{u},\mathbf{u},\mathbf{v}) + \epsilon\, c(\mathbf{u},\mathbf{w},\mathbf{v}) + \epsilon\big(c(\mathbf{w},\mathbf{u},\mathbf{v}) + \epsilon\, c(\mathbf{w},\mathbf{w},\mathbf{v})\big)\\ &= c(\mathbf{u},\mathbf{u},\mathbf{v}) + \epsilon\big(c(\mathbf{u},\mathbf{w},\mathbf{v}) + c(\mathbf{w},\mathbf{u},\mathbf{v})\big) + \epsilon^2 c(\mathbf{w},\mathbf{w},\mathbf{v}).\end{aligned} \tag{20.33}$$

Thus

$$F_\mathbf{v}(\mathbf{u}+\epsilon\mathbf{w}) - F_\mathbf{v}(\mathbf{u}) = \epsilon\big(a(\mathbf{w},\mathbf{v}) + R(c(\mathbf{u},\mathbf{w},\mathbf{v}) + c(\mathbf{w},\mathbf{u},\mathbf{v}))\big) + R\epsilon^2 c(\mathbf{w},\mathbf{w},\mathbf{v}).$$

Define a new variational form

$$\hat{c}(\mathbf{u},\mathbf{w},\mathbf{v}) = c(\mathbf{u},\mathbf{w},\mathbf{v}) + c(\mathbf{w},\mathbf{u},\mathbf{v}). \tag{20.34}$$

Note that $\hat{c}(\mathbf{u},\mathbf{w},\mathbf{v}) = \hat{c}(\mathbf{w},\mathbf{u},\mathbf{v})$, and in view of Lemma 20.1 and (20.11) we find

$$\hat{c}(\mathbf{u},\mathbf{w},\mathbf{w}) = c(\mathbf{u},\mathbf{w},\mathbf{w}) + c(\mathbf{w},\mathbf{u},\mathbf{w}) = c(\mathbf{w},\mathbf{u},\mathbf{w}) = \int_\Omega \mathbf{w}^t(\nabla\mathbf{u})\mathbf{w}\,d\mathbf{x}. \tag{20.35}$$

Therefore

$$J_F(\mathbf{u})_{\mathbf{v},\mathbf{w}} = \lim_{\epsilon\to 0}\epsilon^{-1}\big(F(\mathbf{u}+\epsilon\mathbf{w},\mathbf{v}) - F(\mathbf{u},\mathbf{v})\big) = a(\mathbf{w},\mathbf{v}) + R\,\hat{c}(\mathbf{u},\mathbf{w},\mathbf{v}).$$

Thus Newton's method takes the form

$$\begin{aligned} \text{Find }\ \mathbf{w}\in Z\ \ \text{ such that }\ a(\mathbf{w},\mathbf{v}) + R\,\hat{c}(\mathbf{u}^n,\mathbf{w},\mathbf{v}) &= F(\mathbf{u}^n,\mathbf{v}) \quad \forall\mathbf{v}\in Z,\\ \text{Set }\ \mathbf{u}^{n+1} &= \mathbf{u}^n - \mathbf{w}. \end{aligned} \tag{20.36}$$

The choice of $\mathbf{u}^0 \in Z + \mathbf{g}$ could come from a variety of sources. If we have an exact solution of the Stokes equations satisfying the boundary conditions, then we can use that. Alternatively, we could solve the Stokes equations for $\mathbf{u}^0 \in Z + \mathbf{g}$ satisfying the boundary conditions.

To solve for larger values of R, we could use the continuation method in Section 9.4 where we increase R successively. In that case, we take $\mathbf{u}^0$ at each step to be the solution for the previous value of R.

The system in (20.36) can be solved by the iterated penalty method. We leave as Exercise 20.11 to investigate the coercivity of the variational problem in (20.36).

20.4 Iterated penalty method

The iterated penalty method can be used to enforce the incompressibility constraint as was done for the Stokes system.

20.4.1 Iterated penalty method for Navier-Stokes

The iterated penalty method (14.9) (with $\rho' = \rho$) for (20.19) takes the following form:

Find $\mathbf{u}^{\ell,n} \in \mathbf{V} + \boldsymbol{\gamma}$ such that

$$\begin{aligned} \tilde{a}\left(\mathbf{u}^{\ell,n},\mathbf{v}\right) + \rho\left(\nabla\cdot\mathbf{u}^{\ell,n},\nabla\cdot\mathbf{v}\right)_{L^2} &= F^{\ell,k}(\mathbf{v}) - \left(\nabla\cdot\mathbf{w}^{\ell,n},\nabla\cdot\mathbf{v}\right)_{L^2} \quad \forall\mathbf{v}\in\mathbf{V}\\ \mathbf{w}^{\ell,n+1} &= \mathbf{w}^{\ell,n} - \rho\mathbf{u}^{\ell,n}, \end{aligned} \tag{20.37}$$

where $F^{\ell,k}(\mathbf{v})$ is defined in (20.20) and either $p^{\ell,0} = 0$ (i.e., $\mathbf{w}^{\ell,0} = 0$) or $\mathbf{w}^{\ell,0} = \mathbf{w}^{\ell-1,N}$ where N is the final value of n at time-step $\ell - 1$. If for some reason $p^\ell = p^{\ell,n} = P_{\Pi_h}\nabla\cdot\mathbf{w}^{\ell,n}$ were desired, it could be computed separately, projected onto continuous piecewise polynomials via the USA method in Section 14.1.2 if desired.

Note that the problem (20.36) has homogeneous Dirichlet conditions. Thus the iterated penalty method (14.9) (with $\rho' = \rho$) for (20.36) takes the following form:

Find $\mathbf{w}^\ell \in \mathbf{V}$ such that

$$\begin{aligned} a(\mathbf{w}^\ell,\mathbf{v}) + R\,\hat{c}(\mathbf{u}^n,\mathbf{w}^\ell,\mathbf{v}) + \rho(\nabla\cdot\mathbf{w}^\ell,\nabla\cdot\mathbf{v})_{L^2} &= F(\mathbf{u}^n,\mathbf{v})\\ &\quad - \left(\nabla\cdot\boldsymbol{\omega}^\ell,\nabla\cdot\mathbf{v}\right)_{L^2} \quad \forall\mathbf{v}\in\mathbf{V}\\ \boldsymbol{\omega}^{\ell+1} &= \boldsymbol{\omega}^\ell - \rho\mathbf{w}^\ell, \end{aligned} \tag{20.38}$$

where F is defined in (20.32), $\hat{c}(\cdot,\cdot,\cdot)$ is defined in (20.34), and $\boldsymbol{\omega}^0 = \mathbf{0}$. If for some reason the pressure is required, it can be computed separately, projected onto continuous piecewise polynomials via the USA method in Section 14.1.2 if desired.

We leave description of the iterated penalty method for the time-stepping scheme defined in Section 20.2.4 to Exercise 20.10.

20.4.2 Convergence and stopping criteria

The convergence properties of (20.37) follow from Section 20.2.2 since it is just a modified Stokes problem at each step.

20.5 Compatibility conditions

For the Navier-Stokes equations, there are compatibility conditions like those found for the heat equation in Section 10.3. Here we refer to these as "local" compatibility conditions since they can be determined by purely local considerations. We begin with a description of these. However, there are also non-local compatibility conditions for the Navier-Stokes equations, and we describe them subsequently.

20.5.1 Local compatibility conditions

There are local *compatibility conditions* for the boundary and initial data for the Navier-Stokes equations similar to the ones for the heat equation in order to have a smooth solution. These can be derived again from the observation that that the values of u on the spatial boundary have been specified twice at $t = 0$. The first condition is simply

$$\mathbf{u_0}(\mathbf{x}) = \gamma(\mathbf{x}) \quad \forall \mathbf{x} \in \partial\Omega. \tag{20.39}$$

Additional conditions arise by using the differential equation at $t = 0$ and for $x \in \partial\Omega$, but we post-pone temporarily deriving one of these. However, we find a new type of condition, namely,

$$\nabla\cdot \mathbf{u_0} = 0. \tag{20.40}$$

Although this condition is quite obvious, it does pose a significant constraint on the initial data.

If either of these compatibilities are not satisfied by the data (or by the approximation scheme), wild oscillations will result near $t = 0$ and $x \in \partial\Omega$. In such a nonlinear problem, this can cause completely wrong results to occur.

Another condition that arises due to the incompressibility (or divergence-free) condition is the following:

$$\oint_{\partial\Omega} \mathbf{n}\cdot\gamma = 0. \tag{20.41}$$

This arises simply from (2.10), and it says that the amount of fluid coming into the domain must balance the amount of fluid going out of the domain: the net mass flux into the domain is zero. If this compatibility condition is violated, then the solution can clearly not have divergence zero.

The compatibility conditions (20.39) and (20.40) do not have to be satisfied for the Navier-Stokes equations (20.1) to be well-posed in the usual sense. There is a unique solution in any case, but the physical model may be incorrect as a result if it is supposed to have a smooth solution. Compatibility conditions are a very subtle form of constraint on model quality.

The compatibility conditions (20.39) and (20.40) are described in terms of local differential-algebraic constraints. However, in Section 20.5.2 we will see that such compatibility conditions can lead to global constraints that may be extremely hard to verify or satisfy in practice.

20.5.2 A nonlocal compatibility condition

Simply applying the first equation in (20.1) on $\partial\Omega$ at $t = 0$ we find

$$-\Delta \mathbf{u_0} + \nabla p_0 = -R\,(\gamma \cdot \nabla \mathbf{u_0} + \gamma') \text{ on } \partial\Omega \tag{20.42}$$

where p_0 denotes the initial pressure. Since p_0 is not part of the data, it might be reasonable to assume that the pressure initially would just adjust to insure smoothness of the system, i.e., satisfaction of (20.42), which we can re-write as

$$\nabla p_0 = \Delta \mathbf{u_0} - R\,(\gamma \cdot \nabla \mathbf{u_0} + \gamma') \text{ on } \partial\Omega \tag{20.43}$$

However, taking the divergence of the first equation in (20.1) at $t = 0$ we find

$$\Delta p_0 = -R\nabla\cdot\,(\mathbf{u_0} \cdot \nabla \mathbf{u_0}) \text{ in } \Omega. \tag{20.44}$$

Thus p_0 must satisfy a Laplace equation with the full gradient specified on the boundary by (20.43). This is an over-specified system (one too many boundary conditions, see Section 27.1), so not all $\mathbf{u_0}$ will satisfy it. Note that

$$\nabla\cdot\,(\mathbf{v} \cdot \nabla \mathbf{v}) = \sum_{i,j} v_{i,j} v_{j,i} \text{ in } \Omega \tag{20.45}$$

if $\nabla\cdot\mathbf{v} = \mathbf{0}$.

The only simple way to satisfy both (20.43) and (20.44) is to have $\mathbf{u_0} \equiv \mathbf{0}$ and $\gamma = \gamma' = \mathbf{0}$, that is to start with the fluid at rest. For $R > 0$, it is easy to see that the system given by (20.43) and (20.44) is over-specified since γ' can be chosen arbitrarily.

20.6 Exercises

Exercise 20.1 *Prove that*

$$\left|\int_\Omega (\mathbf{u} \cdot \nabla \mathbf{v}) \cdot \mathbf{w}\, d\mathbf{x}\right| \leq \|\mathbf{u}\|_{L^\infty(\Omega)} \int_\Omega \|\nabla \mathbf{v}(x)\|_F |\mathbf{w}(x)|\, d\mathbf{x},$$

where $\|M\|_F := \sqrt{M : M}$ *denotes the Frobenius norm of any matrix* M *and* $|\mathbf{w}(x)|$ *denotes the Euclidean norm of* $\mathbf{w}(x)$. *(Hint: for any matrix* M *and vector* V, *write* $\sum_i (MV)_i^2 = \sum_i \left(\sum_j M_{ij} V_j\right)^2$ *and apply the Cauchy-Schwarz inequality for vectors to show that* $|MV| \leq \|M\|_F |V|$.*)*

Exercise 20.2 *Prove (20.6). (Hint: just write*

$$\nabla\cdot(\mathbf{u}\,v)=\sum_i \frac{\partial(u_i v)}{\partial x_i}$$

and apply the product rule to each term, using the fact that $\mathbf{u}\cdot\nabla v=\sum_i u_i\frac{\partial v}{\partial x_i}$*.)*

Exercise 20.3 *Prove (20.9). (Hint: write out the dot products and apply (20.8).)*

Exercise 20.4 *Prove that*

$$(1+ct/k)^k \le e^{ct} \quad \forall k\ge 1,$$

and show that in addition that

$$(1+ct/k)^k \to e^{ct} \;\; as \;\; k\to\infty.$$

(Hint: use the identity $x^k=e^{k\log x}$ *and prove the bound* $\log(1+y)\le y$ *for* $y>0$*.)*

Exercise 20.5 *The implicit Euler time-stepping scheme*

$$\begin{aligned} a\left(\mathbf{u}^\ell,\mathbf{v}\right)+b\left(\mathbf{v},p^\ell\right)+R\,c\left(\mathbf{u}^\ell,\mathbf{u}^\ell,\mathbf{v}\right)+\frac{R}{\Delta t}\left(\mathbf{u}^\ell-\mathbf{u}^{\ell-1},\mathbf{v}\right)_{L^2(\Omega)}&=0,\\ b\left(\mathbf{u}^\ell,q\right)&=0, \end{aligned} \tag{20.46}$$

has a nonlinear problem to be solved at each time step. Formulate Newton's method for solving the nonlinear problem (20.46) at each time step. How does the resulting linear algebraic problem change at each time step? How does it compare with (20.28)?

Exercise 20.6 *Consider the time-stepping scheme (20.46) in which the nonlinear term has been evaluated at the current time step. Formulate a fixed point iteration for solving the nonlinear problem (20.46) at each time step such that the resulting linear algebraic problem does not change at each time step.*

Exercise 20.7 *Identify the differential equations corresponding to the following variant of (20.2): Find* $\mathbf{u}$ *such that* $\mathbf{u}-\gamma\in V$ *and* $p\in\Pi$ *such that*

$$\begin{aligned} a\left(\mathbf{u},\mathbf{v}\right)+b\left(\mathbf{v},p\right)+R\big(c\left(\mathbf{v},\mathbf{u},\mathbf{u}\right)+\left(\mathbf{u}_t,\mathbf{v}\right)_{L^2(\Omega)}\big)&=0 \quad \forall\mathbf{v}\in V,\\ b(\mathbf{u},q)&=0 \quad \forall q\in\Pi, \end{aligned} \tag{20.47}$$

where we have switched the order of $\mathbf{u}$ *and* $\mathbf{v}$ *in the "c" form. How does it compare with (20.1)?*

Exercise 20.8 *Identify the differential equations corresponding to the following variant of (20.2): Find* $\mathbf{u}$ *such that* $\mathbf{u}-\gamma\in V$ *and* $p\in\Pi$ *such that*

$$\begin{aligned} a\left(\mathbf{u},\mathbf{v}\right)+b\left(\mathbf{v},p\right)+R\big(c\left(\mathbf{u},\mathbf{v},\mathbf{u}\right)+\left(\mathbf{u}_t,\mathbf{v}\right)_{L^2(\Omega)}\big)&=0 \quad \forall\mathbf{v}\in V,\\ b(\mathbf{u},q)&=0 \quad \forall q\in\Pi, \end{aligned} \tag{20.48}$$

where we have switched the order of $\mathbf{u}$ *and* $\mathbf{v}$ *in the "c" form. How does it compare with (20.1)?*

Exercise 20.9 *Consider the variant of (20.2) in which we switch the order of* $\mathbf{u}$ *and* $\mathbf{v}$ *in the "a" form. Does it change the equations from what appears in (20.1)? If so, to what? If not, why not?*

Exercise 20.10 *Describe the iterated penalty method for the time-stepping scheme defined in Section 20.2.4.*

Exercise 20.11 *Investigate the coercivity of the variational problem in (20.36). (Hint: use (20.35).)*

Exercise 20.12 *Any bilinear form* $a(u,v)$ *on a space* V *can be written as a sum of a symmetric bilinear form* $a_S(u,v)$ *and an antisymmetric bilinear form* $a_A(u,v)$*, where*

$$a_S(u,v) = \tfrac{1}{2}(a(u,v) + a(v,u)), \qquad a_A(u,v) = \tfrac{1}{2}(a(u,v) - a(v,u)), \qquad \forall u,v \in V.$$

Prove that

$$a(u,v) = a_S(u,v) + a_A(u,v) \quad \forall u,v \in V.$$

Show that the bilinear form $a(\mathbf{w},\mathbf{v}) = \hat{c}(\mathbf{u},\mathbf{w},\mathbf{v})$ *for fixed* $\mathbf{u}$ *is already split in this form in the definition (20.34). (Hint: show that the bilinear form* $a(\mathbf{w},\mathbf{v}) = c(\mathbf{u},\mathbf{w},\mathbf{v})$ *for fixed* $\mathbf{u}$ *is antisymmetric, and that the bilinear form* $a(\mathbf{w},\mathbf{v}) = c(\mathbf{w},\mathbf{u},\mathbf{v})$ *for fixed* $\mathbf{u}$ *is symmetric. For the latter, use (20.12).)*

Chapter 21

Navier-Stokes Examples

We give here some important examples of Navier-Stokes flow. The first ones are exact, but they are also the basis for many important applications. We begin with two exact solutions. Then we consider ones where no analytical form is available.

21.1 Exact solutions of Navier-Stokes

We begin with flow in a channel. Surprisingly, the solution is the same for all Reynolds numbers.

21.1.1 Poiseuille flow

Recall the notion of a two-dimensional channel Ω (a long rectangle) used as an idealization of a canal. The length is L and the depth is 1:

$$\Omega = \left\{(x, y) \in \mathbb{R}^2 \,:\, 0 \le x \le L,\, 0 \le y \le 1\right\}.$$

In the two dimensional model, it is assumed that flow is negligible in the third dimension across the width of the canal. Also recall Poiseuille flow, defined by (14.21), given by

$$\mathbf{u}(x, y) = (u(x, y), v(x, y)) = (\tfrac{1}{2}y(1 - y), 0), \quad \text{for } (x, y) \in \Omega.$$

Remarkably, this is also an exact solution of the Navier-Stokes equations, independent of the Reynolds number. This is because $v \equiv 0$ and the nonlinear term vanishes:

$$\mathbf{u} \cdot \nabla \mathbf{u} = u(\mathbf{u}_x) = \mathbf{0},$$

since $\mathbf{u}$ is independent of x. This $\mathbf{u}$ satisfies homogeneous Dirichlet boundary conditions on both the top and bottom of the channel. As before, the pressure is given by $p(x, y) = x$. Then

$$-\Delta \mathbf{u}(x, y) + \mathbf{u} \cdot \nabla \mathbf{u} + \nabla p(x, y) = -\Delta \mathbf{u}(x, y) + \nabla p(x, y) = 0 \quad \text{for } (x, y) \in \Omega.$$

Three-dimensional flow in a pipe (cylinder) is similar and also is named for Poiseuille. We can think of these flows as being driven by the non-zero pressure gradient.

Unfortunately, the Stokes cross in Section 14.3.2 does not generalize to the Navier-Stokes equations.

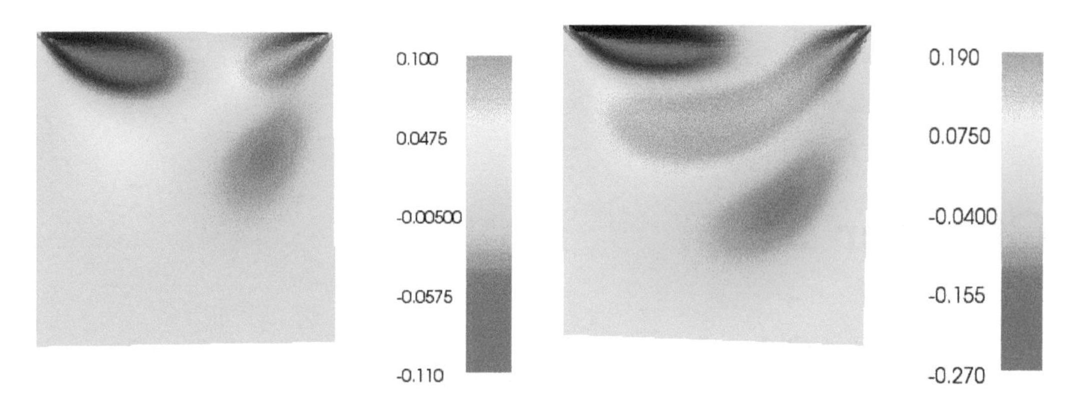

Figure 21.1: Driven cavity problem computed with quartics, horizontal component only. Difference between the Navier-Stokes and Stokes (Re=0) solutions. (left) Re = 50 and (right) Re = 200. The code is given in Programs 21.1 and 21.2.

21.1.2 Jeffrey-Hamel flow

In Section 9.2, we presented Jeffrey-Hamel flow. This is an exact solution of the Navier-Stokes equations in a converging or diverging duct. The flow is defined by (9.2), where u solves the ODE (9.1). The Reynolds number is related to C.

21.2 Driven cavity for Navier-Stokes

Let Ω be the unit square $[0,1]^2$ and let Γ denote the top of the square:

$$\Gamma = \{(x,1) \,:\, 0 \le x \le 1\}.$$

Define Dirichlet boundary conditions by (14.25), viz.,

$$\mathbf{u}(x,1) = 1 \text{ on } \Gamma, \quad \mathbf{u} = \mathbf{0} \text{ on } \partial\Omega\backslash\Gamma.$$

The resulting Navier-Stokes problem with boundary condition (14.25) is the driven cavity problem for Navier-Stokes, and we denote the solution by $\mathbf{u}_R$ where R is the Reynolds number. The solution of the Stokes driven cavity problem in Section 14.3.5 is the same as $\mathbf{u}_0$.

The solution of the driven cavity problem $\mathbf{u}_R$ is depicted in Figure 21.1, for two different values of R in (20.1), computed using the algorithm in Section 20.3. The discretization was done with the Scott-Vogelius iterated penalty method using quartics. Plotted is the horizontal component of the velocity differences $\mathbf{u}_R - \mathbf{u}_0$. Review Figure 14.2 to see the horizontal component of the velocity $\mathbf{u}_0$. We see a substantial change in the flow pattern as a function of the Reynolds number R.

The code to compute the driven cavity for Navier-Stokes is too lengthy for just one page, so it is given in Programs 21.1 and 21.2.

21.3 Sudden expansion

A common test problem for Navier-Stokes is a channel with a sudden expansion:

$$\Omega = \left\{(x, y) \in \mathbb{R}^2 \; : \; -L_1 \le x \le L_2, \; |y| \le 1 \text{ for } x \le 0, \quad |y| \le \delta^{-1} \text{ for } x \ge 0\right\},$$

for some $0 < \delta < 1$. The boundary conditions are specified by the function

$$\mathbf{g} = \begin{cases} \big((1-y^2), 0\big) & x = -L_1, \\ \big(\delta(1-\delta^2 y^2), 0\big) & x = L_2, \\ \mathbf{0} & \text{elsewhere.} \end{cases} \tag{21.1}$$

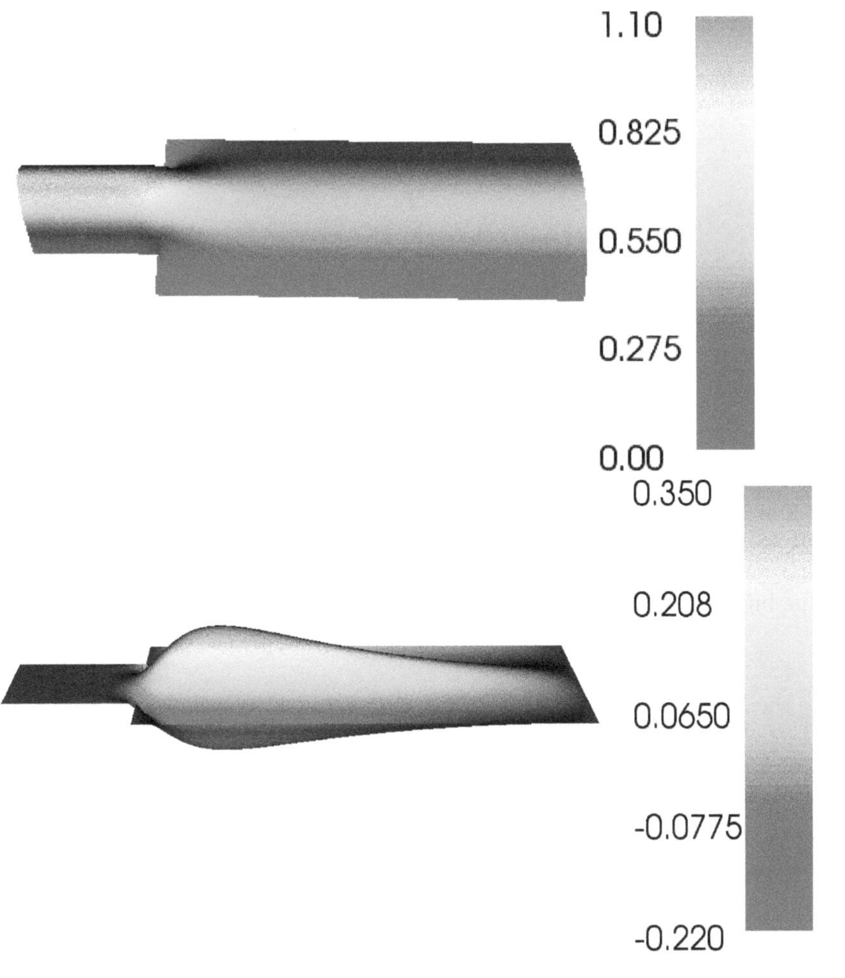

Figure 21.2: Sudden expansion problem computed with quartics, horizontal component only. Shown are (top) Stokes flow and (bottom) difference between the Navier-Stokes and Stokes (Re=0) solutions for Re = 50. The domain is defined with $L_1 = 3$, $L_2 = 10$, and $\delta = \frac{1}{2}$. Generated by code based on Programs 21.1 and 21.2.

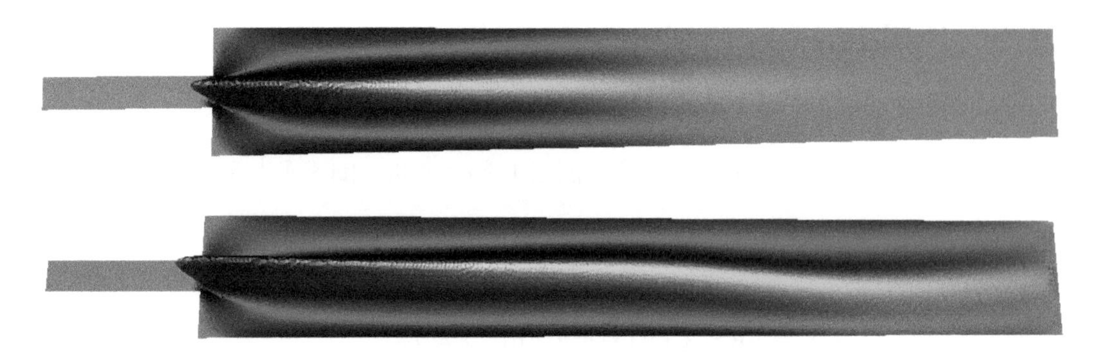

Figure 21.3: Sudden expansion problem computed with quartics, horizontal component only. Difference between the Navier-Stokes and Stokes (Re=0) solutions. The domain is defined with $L_1 = 10$, $L_2 = 60$, and $\delta = \frac{1}{4}$. Generated by code based on Programs 21.1 and 21.2. (top) $R = 50$ (bottom) $R = 100$.

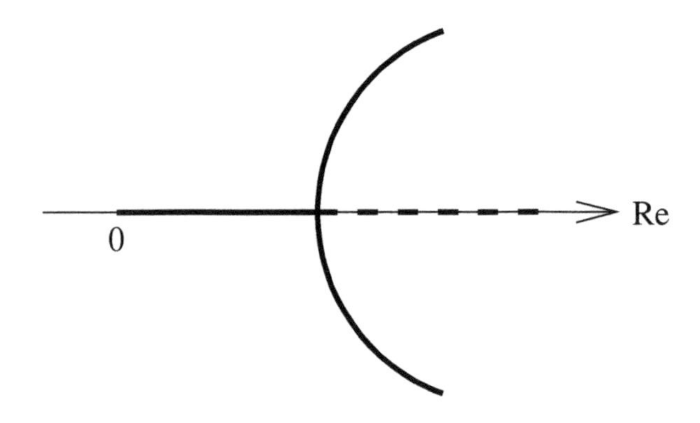

Figure 21.4: Idealization of the pitchfork bifurcation in the sudden-expansion problem for the Navier-Stokes equations. The dark solid lines indicate stable solutions of the Navier-Stokes equations as a function of the Reynolds number (Re). The dark dashed line indicates an unstable, symmetric solution of the Navier-Stokes equations. The unique solution indicated before the bifurcation is also symmetric.

Since the flow is going from the smaller channel to the larger one, it is necessary to take $L_2 >> L_1$ to get reliable results. It is easy to see (Exercise 21.3) that

$$\int_{\partial\Omega} \mathbf{g} \cdot \mathbf{n} \, ds = 0.$$

The Stokes flow is symmetric in the direction orthogonal to the direction of the channel. This can be proved by reflecting the solution around the centerline of the channel, and showing that the reflected function is also a solution. By uniqueness of Stokes flow we conclude that the reflection must reproduce the solution.

But for Navier-Stokes flow, symmetry is not guaranteed. It does hold for small enough Reynolds number, as indicated in Figure 21.3 on the left for $R = 50$. When the

21.4 Exercises

Exercise 21.1 *Modify Program 14.1 and Programs 21.1 and 21.2 to compute Navier-Stokes (Poiseuille) flow in a two-dimensional channel and compare with the exact solution (14.21) by computing the $L^2(\Omega)$ norm of the difference. Do this for various values of the Reynolds number. Take $L = 1$. Try this with both regular meshes generated by*

```
UnitSquareMesh(meshsize, meshsize)
```

and with crossed triangles using

```
UnitSquareMesh(meshsize, meshsize, "crossed")
```

Do this for various degrees k and values of `meshsize` *and report what you learn.*

Exercise 21.2 *Modify Program 14.1 and Programs 21.1 and 21.2 to compute Navier-Stokes (Poiseuille) flow in the Stokes cross in Section 14.3.2 and compare with the exact solution described there for the Stokes equations. Describe how the solutions differ for different values of the Reynolds number R in (20.1).*

Exercise 21.3 *Show that the function* $\mathbf{g}$ *defined in (21.1) satisfies*

$$\int_{\partial\Omega} \mathbf{g} \cdot \mathbf{n}\, ds = 0.$$

Exercise 21.4 *Implement the iterated penalty method for the time-stepping scheme defined in Section 20.2.4. Test it on a problem of your choice. (Hint: see Exercise 20.10.)*

```
 1 from dolfin import *
 2 import math,sys
 3 meshsize=int(sys.argv[1])
 4 pdeg=int(sys.argv[2])
 5 fudg=float(sys.argv[3])
 6 reno=float(sys.argv[4])
 7 # create mesh and define velocity and pressure function spaces
 8 mesh = UnitSquareMesh(meshsize, meshsize, "crossed")
 9 newmesh = refine(mesh)
10 newmesh = refine(newmesh)
11 V = VectorFunctionSpace(mesh, "Lagrange", pdeg)
12 W = VectorFunctionSpace(newmesh, "Lagrange", 1)
13 # define boundary condition
14 boundary_exp = Expression(("exp(-fu*(1.0-x[1])*(1.0-x[1]))","0"),\
15                             fu=fudg,degree=pdeg)
16 bc = DirichletBC(V, boundary_exp, "on_boundary",degree=pdeg)
17 # set the parameters
18 f = Expression(("0","0"),degree=pdeg)
19 bcz = DirichletBC(V, f, "on_boundary")
20 r = 1.0e3
21 # define test and trial functions, and function that is updated
22 uold = TrialFunction(V)
23 v = TestFunction(V)
24 w = Function(V)
25 asf = inner(grad(uold), grad(v))*dx + r*div(uold)*div(v)*dx
26 bs = -div(w)*div(v)*dx
27 uold = Function(V)
28 ust = Function(V)
29 pdes = LinearVariationalProblem(asf, - bs, uold, bc)
30 solvers = LinearVariationalSolver(pdes)
31 # Scott-Vogelius iterated penalty method
32 iters = 0; max_iters = 15; div_u_norm = 1
33 while iters < max_iters and div_u_norm > 1e-10:
34 # solve and update w
35     solvers.solve()
36     w.vector().axpy(-r, uold.vector())
37 # find the L^2 norm of div(u) to check stopping condition
38     div_u_norm = sqrt(assemble(div(uold)*div(uold)*dx(mesh)))
39     iters += 1
40 ust.vector().axpy(1.0, uold.vector())
```

Program 21.1: Part one of the code to implement the driven cavity problem for the Navier-Stokes equations. The solution is depicted in Figure 21.1.

```
 1 # second part: continuation of Navier-Stokes solver for driven cavity
 2 kters = 0; max_kters = 9; unorm = 1
 3 while kters < max_kters and unorm > 1e-9:
 4     u = TrialFunction(V)
 5     v = TestFunction(V)
 6     w = Function(V)
 7 #   uold = Function(V)
 8     a = inner(grad(u), grad(v))*dx + r*div(u)*div(v)*dx \
 9       +reno*inner(grad(uold)*u,v)*dx+reno*inner(grad(u)*uold,v)*dx
10     b = -div(w)*div(v)*dx
11     F = inner(grad(uold), grad(v))*dx+reno*inner(grad(uold)*uold,v)*dx
12     u = Function(V)
13     pde = LinearVariationalProblem(a, F - b, u, bcz)
14     solver = LinearVariationalSolver(pde)
15 # Scott-Vogelius iterated penalty method
16     iters = 0; max_iters = 11; div_u_norm = 1
17     while iters < max_iters and div_u_norm > 1e-10:
18     # solve and update w
19         solver.solve()
20         w.vector().axpy(-r, u.vector())
21     # find the L^2 norm of div(u) to check stopping condition
22         div_u_norm = sqrt(assemble(div(u)*div(u)*dx(mesh)))
23 #       print "   IPM iter_no=",iters,"div_u_norm=",div_u_norm
24         iters += 1
25     print "   IPM iter_no=",iters,"div_u_norm=",div_u_norm
26     kters += 1
27     uold.vector().axpy(-1.0, u.vector())
28 #   uold=uold-u
29     unorm=norm(u,norm_type='H1')
30     uoldnorm=norm(uold,norm_type='H1')
31     print "Newton iter_no=",kters,"Delta_u_norm=",unorm,"u_norm=",uoldnorm
32 uold.vector().axpy(-1.0, ust.vector())
33 plot(uold[0], interactive=True)
34 # Ultimate Stokes Algorithm (USA)
35 p_US = project(div(w), FunctionSpace(mesh, "Lagrange", pdeg - 1))
```

Program 21.2: Part two of the code to implement the driven cavity problem for the Navier-Stokes equations. The solution is depicted in Figure 21.1.

Chapter 22

Geometry Approximation

If the boundary $\partial\Omega$ of a domain Ω is curved, it is often necessary to approximate it in some way. For simplicity, we will consider the Laplace equation (2.1), viz.,

$$-\Delta u = f \text{ in } \Omega$$

together with homogeneous Dirichlet boundary conditions on all of $\partial\Omega$:

$$u = 0 \text{ on } \partial\Omega.$$

Such boundary conditions are easy to satisfy on polygonal boundaries with piecewise polynomials, provided only that the mesh match the vertices of the boundary (in two dimensions, but in three dimensions, edges must also be respected). However, for curved boundaries, exact satisfaction of boundary conditions is typically not possible. There are various ways in which this can be addressed:

- interpolate the boundary conditions [261] (a collocation approach)
- modify the polynomials via a change of coordinates (isoparametric elements)
- incorporate the boundary conditions into the variational form (Nitsche's method).

The name **isoparametric element** was coined by Bruce Irons[1] in part as a play on words, assuming that the audience was familiar with isoperimetric inequalities. The concept of employing a coordinate transformation to extend the applicability of finite elements was initiated by Ian Taig and later developed by Irons [2].

There are two, interconnected issues related to geometry approximation. One is to represent the boundary values accurately. The other is to compute the required quadrature related to elements with curved sides. The isoparametric method deals with this together, but it then requires the introduction of more complex technology to deal with the mappings. Nitsche's method addresses the issue of boundary conditions without dealing with the complexity related to quadrature on curved elements. However, a modification [50] of Nitsche's method solves this problem.

---

[1] Bruce Irons (1924—1983) is known for many concepts in finite element analysis, including the Patch Test for nonconforming elements [98] and frontal solvers, among others.

poly. order	mesh no.	γ	L^2 error
1	32	10	2.09e-03
2	8	10	5.16e-04
4	8	10	1.77e-06
4	128	10	4.96e-12
8	16	10	1.68e-11
16	8	10	2.14e-08

Table 22.1: L^2 errors for Nitsche's method for the problem in Section 2.3: effect of varying polynomial order and mesh size for fixed $\gamma = 10$. Here we take $h = N^{-1}$ where N is the mesh number.

22.1 Nitsche's method

The method of Nitsche[2] is useful for both curved and polygonal domains. It allows the use of functions that do not satisfy Dirichlet boundary conditions to approximate solutions which do satisfy Dirichlet boundary conditions. Define

$$a_\gamma(u,v) = \int_\Omega \nabla u \cdot \nabla v \, d\mathbf{x} + \gamma h^{-1} \oint_{\partial\Omega} uv \, ds - \oint_{\partial\Omega} \frac{\partial u}{\partial n} v \, ds - \oint_{\partial\Omega} \frac{\partial v}{\partial n} u \, ds, \tag{22.1}$$

where $\gamma > 0$ is a fixed parameter and h is the mesh size [173, 275].

22.1.1 Homogeneous Dirichlet boundary conditions

We claim that the solution to Poisson's equation satisfies the variational problem

$$u \in H_0^1(\Omega) \text{ such that } a_\gamma(u,v) = (f,v)_{L^2} \quad \forall v \in H_0^1(\Omega). \tag{22.2}$$

The reason is that, for $u, v \in H_0^1(\Omega)$, all the boundary terms vanish, and

$$a_\gamma(u,v) = a(u,v),$$

where $a(\cdot,\cdot)$ is the usual bilinear form for the Laplace operator:

$$a(u,v) = \int_\Omega \nabla u \cdot \nabla v \, d\mathbf{x}.$$

But more generally, we know from (2.10) that, for all $v \in H^1(\Omega)$,

$$\int_\Omega f v \, d\mathbf{x} = \int_\Omega (-\Delta u) v \, d\mathbf{x} = a(u,v) - \oint_{\partial\Omega} v \frac{\partial u}{\partial n} \, ds = a_\gamma(u,v), \tag{22.3}$$

since $u = 0$ on $\partial\Omega$. Thus if u solves (22.2), then it also satisfies

$$u \in H_0^1(\Omega) \text{ such that } a_\gamma(u,v) = (f,v)_{L^2} \quad \forall v \in H^1(\Omega). \tag{22.4}$$

Now consider the discrete problem

$$\text{find } u_h \in V_h \text{ such that } a_\gamma(u_h,v) = (f,v)_{L^2} \quad \forall v \in V_h, \tag{22.5}$$

[2] Joachim A. Nitsche (1926—1996) made major contributions to the mathematical theory of the finite element method. In addition to his method for enforcing boundary conditions, his name is often invoked in referring to the duality technique for proving error estimates in lower-order norms, as Nitsche's Trick.

```
meshsize=int(sys.argv[1])
pdeg=int(sys.argv[2])
gamma=float(sys.argv[3])
h=1.0/float(meshsize)
mypi=math.pi

# Create mesh and define function space
mesh = UnitSquareMesh(meshsize, meshsize)
n = FacetNormal(mesh)
V = FunctionSpace(mesh, "Lagrange", pdeg)

# Define variational problem
u = TrialFunction(V)
v = TestFunction(V)
f = Expression("(sin(mypi*x[0]))*(sin(mypi*x[1]))",mypi=math.pi,degree=pdeg)
a = inner(grad(u), grad(v))*dx -u*(inner(n,grad(v)))*ds- \
         v*(inner(n,grad(u)))*ds+(gamma/h)*u*v*ds
L = (2*mypi*mypi)*f*v*dx

# Compute solution
u = Function(V)
solve(a == L, u )

print pdeg,meshsize," %.2e"%gamma," %.2e"%errornorm(f,u,norm_type='l2',\
      degree_rise=3)
```

Program 22.1: Code to implement Nitsche's method for the problem (2.12).

where $V_h \subset H^1(\Omega)$ is not required to be a subset of $H^1_0(\Omega)$.

Nitsche's method can produce results of the same quality as are obtained with specifying Dirichlet conditions explicitly, as indicated in Table 22.1 (compare with Table 4.1). The code to generate Table 22.1 is given in Program 22.1. However, for particular values of γ, the behavior can be suboptimal, as indicated in Table 22.2. We will see that Nitsche's method can be guaranteed to work if γ is sufficiently large.

22.1.2 Analysis of Nitsche's method

Now let us analyze Nitsche's method. As a consequence of (22.4) and (22.5), we have

$$a_\gamma(u - u_h, v) = 0 \quad \forall v \in V_h. \tag{22.6}$$

Nitsche's method is of interest when $V_h \not\subset H^1_0(\Omega)$, for otherwise we could use the usual formulation. But the bilinear form $a_\gamma(v, v)$ is not defined for general $v \in H^1(\Omega)$. For example, take $\Omega = [0,1]^2$ and $v(x,y) = 1 + x^{2/3}$ for $(x,y) \in \Omega$. Then

$$v_{,x}(x,y) = \tfrac{2}{3}x^{-1/3} \text{ for all } x, y \in [0,1]^2.$$

Thus, $v_{,x}$ is square integrable on Ω, and since $v_{,y} = 0$, $|\nabla v|$ is square integrable on Ω. So $v \in H^1(\Omega)$. But, $v_{,x}(x,y) \to \infty$ as $x \to 0$ for all $y \in [0,1]$. In particular, this means that

poly. order	mesh no.	γ	L^2 error
1	8	100	3.23e-02
1	8	10	3.10e-02
1	8	2	2.76e-02
1	8	1.5	3.93e-02
1	8	1.1	6.00e-02
1	8	1.0	1.80e-01
1	32	1.0	1.81e-01

Table 22.2: L^2 errors for Nitsche's method for the problem in Section 2.3: effect of varying γ. For γ too small, the accuracy is limited.

$\frac{\partial v}{\partial n} = \infty$ on the part of the boundary $\{(0,y) : y \in [0,1]\}$. Therefore $a_\gamma(v,v) = \infty$. Thus we need a new theory to explain the behavior of Nitsche's method.

Since $a_\gamma(\cdot,\cdot)$ is not continuous on $H^1(\Omega)$, we cannot use our standard approach to analyze the behavior of the Nitsche method (22.5). Or at least we cannot use the standard norms. Instead we define

$$|\!|\!|\, v \,|\!|\!| = \Big(a(v,v) + h \oint_{\partial\Omega} \Big|\frac{\partial v}{\partial n}\Big|^2 \,ds + h^{-1} \oint_{\partial\Omega} v^2 \,ds \Big)^{1/2}. \tag{22.7}$$

The philosophy of this norm is that it penalizes departure from the Dirichlet boundary condition but it minimizes the impact of the normal derivative on the boundary. Correspondingly, we define V to be the subset of $H^1(\Omega)$ consisting of functions for which this norm is finite.

It is easy to see that this norm matches the different parts of the Nitsche bilinear form, so that

$$|a_\gamma(v,w)| \le C_\gamma |\!|\!|\, v \,|\!|\!| \; |\!|\!|\, w \,|\!|\!| \quad \forall v, w \in V. \tag{22.8}$$

One can show [275] that

$$|\!|\!|\, v \,|\!|\!| \le C_\gamma h^{-1} \|v\|_{L^2(\Omega)} \quad \forall v \in V_h, \tag{22.9}$$

for any space V_h of piecewise polynomials on a reasonable mesh. Moreover, for such spaces, there exist $\gamma_0 > 0$ and $\alpha > 0$ such that, for $\gamma \ge \gamma_0$,

$$\alpha |\!|\!|\, v \,|\!|\!|^2 \le a_\gamma(v,v) \quad \forall v \in V_h. \tag{22.10}$$

We assume that our solution u is sufficiently smooth that $|\!|\!|\, u \,|\!|\!| < \infty$. In this case, one can prove [275] that

$$|\!|\!|\, u - u_h \,|\!|\!| \le \Big(1 + \frac{C_\gamma}{\alpha}\Big) \inf_{v \in V_h} |\!|\!|\, u - v \,|\!|\!|_{L^2(\Omega)} \le C' h^k \|u\|_{H^{k+1}(\Omega)} \tag{22.11}$$

using piecewise polynomials of degree k. In particular, this guarantees that

$$\|u_h\|_{L^2(\partial\Omega)} \le C h^{k+1/2} \|u\|_{H^{k+1}(\Omega)},$$

so that the Dirichlet boundary conditions are closely approximated by Nitsche's method.

22.1.3 Inhomogeneous Dirichlet boundary conditions

Suppose now that we impose $u = g$ on $\partial\Omega$. From (2.10), for all $v \in H^1(\Omega)$,

$$\begin{aligned}\int_\Omega fv\,d\mathbf{x} &= \int_\Omega (-\Delta u)v\,d\mathbf{x} = a(u,v) - \oint_{\partial\Omega} v\frac{\partial u}{\partial n}\,ds \\ &= a_\gamma(u,v) - \gamma h^{-1}\oint_{\partial\Omega} gv\,ds + \oint_{\partial\Omega} \frac{\partial v}{\partial n} g\,ds,\end{aligned} \tag{22.12}$$

since $u = g$ on $\partial\Omega$. Thus the variational formulation of Nitsche's method with inhomogeneous Dirichlet boundary conditions g is: Find $u \in V$ such that

$$a_\gamma(u,v) = \int_\Omega fv\,d\mathbf{x} + \gamma h^{-1}\oint_{\partial\Omega} gv\,ds - \oint_{\partial\Omega} \frac{\partial v}{\partial n} g\,ds \tag{22.13}$$

for all $v \in V$.

22.2 Curved domains

When the boundary of a domain is not polygonal, for example, a circle, an error related to approximating $\partial\Omega$ must be made when using piecewise polynomials to approximate the solution of a PDE boundary-value problem. The simplest approach is to approximate the boundary $\partial\Omega$ by a simplicial surface (or, in two dimensions, polygonal curve), and an approximate domain Ω_h is constructed accordingly. If the domain Ω is not convex, then the approximate domain Ω_h may not be contained inside Ω.

Let us consider using the Nitsche form (22.1) to solve Poisson's equation with $f = 4$ on the unit circle, with Dirichlet boundary conditions. The exact solution is

$$u(x,y) = 1 - x^2 - y^2. \tag{22.14}$$

To deal with the curved boundary, we use the `mshr` system which includes a circle as a built-in domain type. We indicate how this is done in Program 22.2. What `mshr` does is to approximate the circle by a polygon, as seen on the left side of Figure 22.1. More information on `mshr` appears in Chapter 28.

Instructing `mshr` to use a finer mesh produces an approximation that is uniformly small, as seen on the right side of Figure 22.1, where the error only is plotted. The polygonal boundary approximation is a piecewise linear approximation of $\partial\Omega$, and we see that using piecewise linear approximation inside the approximate domain can be effective.

However, we might want more accuracy, and it is natural to consider using piecewise quadratic approximation inside the approximate domain. Thus we examine the use of piecewise quadratic approximation on a polygonal domain approximating the circle in Figure 22.2. We might have expected the error using quadratics for our test problem, whose solution is given in (22.14), would be essentially zero, since the exact solution is itself a quadratic polynomial. However, there is a significant geometric error due to the polygonal approximation of the domain, as shown on the left side of Figure 22.2. Using an even finer mesh as shown on the right side of Figure 22.2 indicates that the error is concentrated in a boundary layer around the polygonal boundary approximation. In the computations for the right side of Figure 22.2 we specified the `segments` parameter in the `Circle` function to be 18, instead of using the default value 32 as in all other computations. The corresponding code for this is

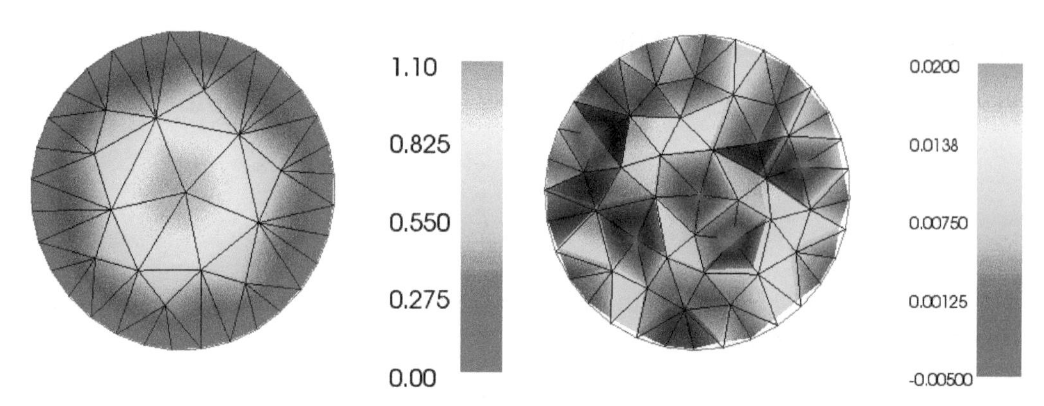

Figure 22.1: Using **mshr** to generate a mesh for a disc with piecewise linear approximation of the solution (22.14). The parameter $\gamma = 10$ in Nitsche's method. (left) Coarse mesh generated by using the **meshsize** parameter in Program 22.2 equal to 1. Values of the solution u_h are plotted. (right) Finer mesh generated by using the **meshsize** parameter in Program 22.2 equal to 5. Values of the error $u - u_h$ are plotted.

```
domain =  Circle(dolfin.Point(0.0, 0.0),1.0,segments)
```

We leave as Exercise 22.3 to experiment with changing the **segments** parameter in the `Circle` function in **mshr**.

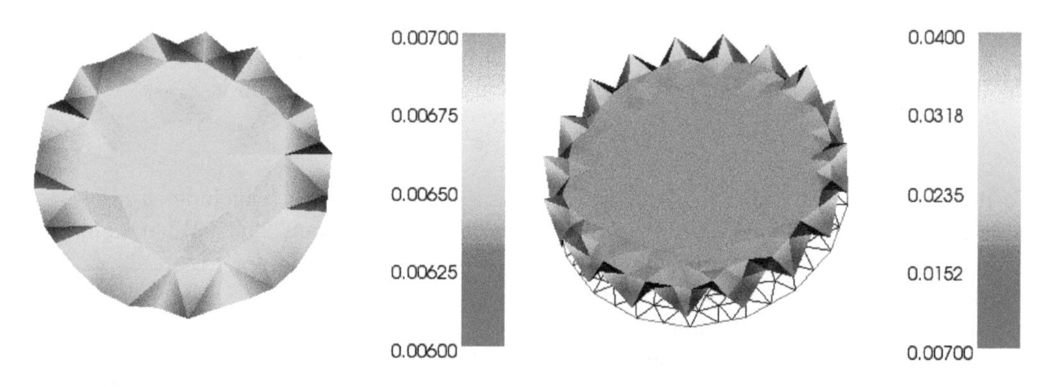

Figure 22.2: Using **mshr** to generate a mesh for a disc with piecewise quadratic approximation of the solution (22.14). Values of the error $u - u_h$ are plotted. The parameter $\gamma = 10$ in Nitsche's method. (left) Same mesh as used on the right-hand side of Figure 22.1. Mesh generated by using the **meshsize** parameter in Program 22.2 equal to 5. (right) Even more refined mesh. Mesh generated by using the **meshsize** parameter in Program 22.2 equal to 10 and **segments** parameter set to 18.

As shown in Table 22.3, neither reducing the mesh size, nor increasing the polynomial degree, can reduce the L^2 error substantially. However, increasing the number of **segments** in the approximation of the circle does allow the error to be decreased as desired. The limit on accuracy due to the geometry approximation has been known for some time [36], and it is known that the order of accuracy for quadratics and higher-order polynomials is restricted, essentially because the geometry approximation is piecewise linear. The exact

polynomial degree	`meshsize`	L^2 error	`segments`
1	1	5.11e-02	default
2	1	1.14e-02	default
1	5	2.88e-02	default
2	5	1.16e-02	default
1	10	1.55e-02	default
2	10	1.16e-02	default
3	10	1.16e-02	default
2	10	3.69e-02	18
2	10	9.17e-03	36
2	10	2.27e-03	72

Table 22.3: Geometric error as a function of mesh size and polynomial degree for the Poisson problem whose solution is given in (22.14). The parameter $\gamma = 10$ in Nitche's method. The default value for `segments` in `mshr` is 32.

(a)

k	M	L^2 error	H^1 error
1	4	2.93e-01	1.89e+00
1	8	9.55e-02	1.06e+00
1	16	2.47e-02	5.45e-01
2	4	9.44e-02	4.26e-01
2	8	2.30e-02	1.59e-01
2	16	5.62e-03	5.45e-02
3	4	8.81e-02	2.94e-01
3	8	2.22e-02	1.07e-01
3	16	5.53e-03	3.82e-02

(b)

k	M	γ	L^2 error	H^1 error
1	4	20	2.77e-01	1.80e+00
1	8	20	9.15e-02	1.04e+00
1	16	20	2.40e-02	5.42e-01
2	4	20	9.21e-02	3.70e-01
2	8	20	2.26e-02	1.27e-01
2	16	20	5.56e-03	3.94e-02
3	4	20	8.73e-02	2.41e-01
3	8	20	2.21e-02	8.40e-02
3	16	20	5.51e-03	2.97e-02

Table 22.4: Errors in $L^2(\Omega)$ and $H^1(\Omega)$ as a function of the `meshsize`, denoted by M, for the polygonal approximation for test problem whose exact solution is given by (22.15). The number of segments was chosen to be 5 times the `meshsize` in all cases. In (a), the standard finite element method was used with $u_h = 0$ on $\partial\Omega_h$. In (b), Nitsche's method was used on Ω_h.

solution (22.14) is quadratic, but the finite element approximation with quadratics does not match it due to the boundary approximation.

22.3 Accuracy limits

Let us examine more closely the accuracy limits related to polygonal approximation of the boundary. We continue with the circle as our test domain Ω, but we choose a higher-order polynomial manufactured solution. Using the method of manufactured solutions (Section 2.3), we take

$$u(x,y) = 1 - (x^2+y^2)^3 \text{ and } f(x,y) = 36(x^2+y^2)^2, \tag{22.15}$$

cf. Exercise 22.5. We start with the standard approximation in which we pose Dirichlet boundary conditions on $\partial\Omega_h$ [116]. Computational results are listed in Table 22.4(a).

Using Nitsche's method gives comparable results, even slightly better, as indicated in Table 22.4(b).

```
from mshr import *
from dolfin import *

# Create mesh and define function space
domain =  Circle(dolfin.Point(0.0, 0.0), 1.0)

# Create mesh and define function space
mesh   = generate_mesh(domain, meshsize)

n = FacetNormal(mesh)
V = FunctionSpace(mesh, "Lagrange", pdeg)

# Define boundary condition
u0 = Constant(0.0)
bc = DirichletBC(V, u0, "on_boundary")

# Define variational problem
u = TrialFunction(V)
v = TestFunction(V)
ue = Expression("1.0-x[0]*x[0]-x[1]*x[1]",degree=pdeg)
f = Expression("4.0",degree=pdeg)
a = inner(grad(u), grad(v))*dx -u*(inner(n,grad(v)))*ds \
              -v*(inner(n,grad(u)))*ds+(gamma/h)*u*v*ds
L = f*v*dx

# Compute solution
u = Function(V)
solve(a == L, u )
```

Program 22.2: Code to implement Nitche's method for the Dirichlet problem for Poisson's equation with $f \equiv 4$ on the unit circle whose solution is given by (22.14).

But in both cases, using piecewise cubics provides minimal improvement over piecewise quadratics. Thus to get higher-accuracy, something new has to be done. We explain one such approach in Section 22.5. But first we look in more detail at the effect of the parameter γ in Nitsche's method.

22.4 Limits on γ

Consider Nitsche's method as applied in the previous section, but with a variety of values of γ. In particular, fix meshsize $= 16$, segments $= 80$, and $k = 3$ (piecewise cubics). The corresponding errors are depicted in Figure 22.3 for $\gamma = 11$ and $\gamma = 12$. The errors on the left of Figure 22.3, with $\gamma = 11$, are a hundred times larger than on the right, where $\gamma = 12$, as indicated by the scale color bars for each figure. The values of corresponding norms are given in Table 22.5. Moreover, the error with $\gamma = 11$ is very localized near one part of the boundary. Hence we conclude computations for γ this small are spurious. In addition, the errors are very sensitive to the exact value of γ, as indicated in Table 22.5.

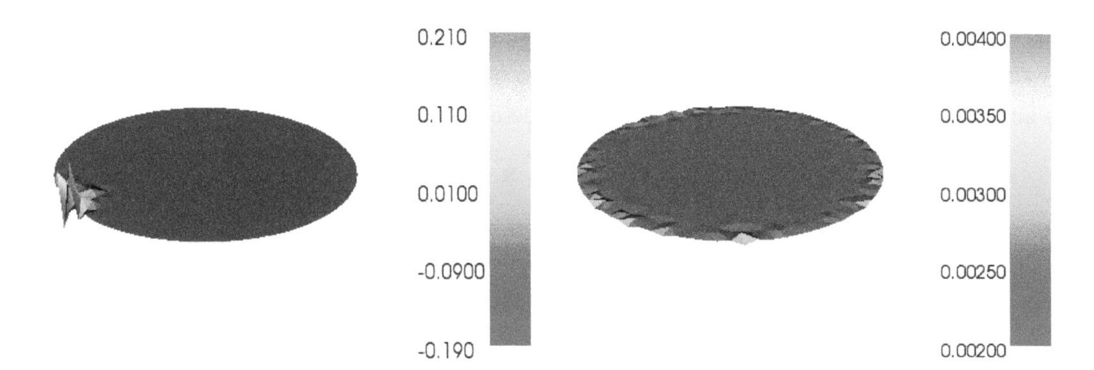

Figure 22.3: Solution using Nitsche's method with `meshsize` = 16, `segments` = 80, $k = 3$ (piecewise cubics), for the test problem whose exact solution is given by (22.15), with (left) $\gamma = 11$ and (right) $\gamma = 12$. The L^2 and H^1 errors are given for these values of γ and others in Table 22.5.

γ	L2 error	H1 error	γ	L2 error	H1 error
10.9	5.51e-03	6.24e-02	12.0	5.50e-03	2.92e-02
10.98	5.66e-03	2.64e-01	20.0	5.51e-03	2.97e-02
10.99	5.77e-03	3.61e-01	30.0	5.52e-03	3.21e-02
11.00	**2.03e-01**	**4.25e+01**	40.0	5.52e-03	3.35e-02
11.01	5.75e-03	3.59e-01	70.0	5.52e-03	3.54e-02
11.1	5.50e-03	4.88e-02	100	5.52e-03	3.62e-02

Table 22.5: Errors in $L^2(\Omega)$ and $H^1(\Omega)$ as a function of γ for the test problem whose exact solution is given by (22.15). Computed using Nitsche's method with `meshsize` = 16, `segments` = 80, $k = 3$ (piecewise cubics). The spatial error distributions for the cases $\gamma = 11$ and $\gamma = 12$ are visualized in Figure 22.3.

22.5 The BDT approach

The method [50] of Bramble-Dupont-Thomée (BDT) achieves high-order accuracy by modifying Nitsche's method [173] applied on Ω_h. In particular, in [50] the bilinear form

$$N_{1,h}(u,v) = a_h(u,v) - \oint_{\partial\Omega_h} \frac{\partial u}{\partial n} v\,ds - \oint_{\partial\Omega_h} \Big(u + \delta\frac{\partial u}{\partial n}\Big)\Big(\frac{\partial v}{\partial n} - \gamma h^{-1} v\Big)\,ds \tag{22.16}$$

is introduced, where $\mathbf{n}$ denotes the outward-directed normal to $\partial\Omega_h$ and

$$\delta(\mathbf{x}) = \min\{s > 0 \;:\; \mathbf{x} + s\mathbf{n} \in \partial\Omega\}.$$

Corrections of arbitrary order, involving terms $\delta^\ell \frac{\partial^\ell u}{\partial n^\ell}$ for $\ell > 1$ are studied in [50], but for simplicity we restrict attention to the first-order correction to Nitsche's method. If δ were 0 in (22.16), this would be Nitsche's method on Ω_h, that is,

$$N_{1,h}(u,v) = a_\gamma(u,v) - \oint_{\partial\Omega_h} \delta\frac{\partial u}{\partial n}\Big(\frac{\partial v}{\partial n} - \gamma h^{-1} v\Big)\,ds. \tag{22.17}$$

See Exercise 22.9 for a comparison between the BDT method and Nitsche's method (22.13) for problems with inhomogeneous boundary conditions.

Define W_h^k to be the set of piecewise polynomials of degree k on the mesh $\mathcal{T}_h$ that have no restriction on $\partial\Omega_h$. It is shown in [50] that the solution $u_h^* \in W_h^k$ of

$$N_{1,h}(u_h^*, v) = \int_{\Omega_h} f v\,dx \text{ for all } v \in W_h^k \tag{22.18}$$

satisfies

$$|||\, u - u_h^* \,||| \le C h^k \|u\|_{H^{k+1}(\Omega)} + C h^{7/2} \|u\|_{W^2_\infty(\Omega)},$$

where $|||\, v \,|||$ is defined in (22.7). Thus using the variational form (22.16) leads to an optimal-order approximation with quadratics and cubics and one that is only suboptimal for quartics by a factor of $h^{-1/2}$.

22.6 An example

Consider the case where Ω is the unit circle. We have $\mathbf{x} + \delta(\mathbf{x})\mathbf{n} \in \partial\Omega$ for $\mathbf{x} \in \partial\Omega_h$. We can write $\mathbf{x} = (\mathbf{x}\cdot\mathbf{n})\mathbf{n} + (\mathbf{x}\cdot\mathbf{t})\mathbf{t}$, and $(\mathbf{x}\cdot\mathbf{t})^2 = |\mathbf{x}|^2 - (\mathbf{x}\cdot\mathbf{n})^2$. Since $|\mathbf{x} + \delta(\mathbf{x})\mathbf{n}| = 1$, we have

$$1 = (\mathbf{x}\cdot\mathbf{t})^2 + (\mathbf{x}\cdot\mathbf{n} + \delta(\mathbf{x}))^2 = |\mathbf{x}|^2 - (\mathbf{x}\cdot\mathbf{n})^2 + ((\mathbf{x}\cdot\mathbf{n} + \delta(\mathbf{x}))^2.$$

Then

$$\delta(\mathbf{x}) = \sqrt{1 - |\mathbf{x}|^2 + (\mathbf{x}\cdot\mathbf{n})^2} - \mathbf{x}\cdot\mathbf{n}.$$

Note that for $\mathbf{x} \in \partial\Omega_h$, $|\mathbf{x}| \le 1$. Thus $\delta(\mathbf{x}) \ge 0$.

This expression for the function δ is simple to implement using `dolfin`:

```
x = SpatialCoordinate(mesh)
a = inner(grad(u),grad(v))*dx - (inner(n,grad(u)))*v*ds \
 -(u+(sqrt(1-inner(x,x)+inner(n,x)*inner(n,x))-inner(n,x))*inner(n,grad(u)))*\
       ((inner(n,grad(v)))-(gamma/h)*v)*ds
```

Computational experiments are summarized in Table 22.6 for Laplace's equation as described in Section 22.3. Accuracy in L^2 improves as k increases as long as $k \leq 3$, but the results for $k = 4, 5$ are essentially the same as for $k = 3$. Accuracy in H^1 improves as k increases as long as $k \leq 4$, but the results for $k = 5$ are essentially the same as for $k = 4$.

We see that a one-line change to Nitsche's method makes a very significant change in accuracy. The BDT method has been developed and applied in many ways [65].

22.7 Exercises

Exercise 22.1 *Experiment with Nitsche's method for imposing homogeneous Dirichlet conditions on the unit square. Choose different meshes, polynomial degrees, and parameter γ. Can you take $\gamma = 0$? Can you take $\gamma < 0$?*

Exercise 22.2 *Experiment with Nitsche's method for imposing homogeneous Dirichlet conditions on the unit circle. Choose different meshes (using* `mshr`*), polynomial degrees, and parameter γ. Do the results of Table 22.3 change substantially for larger γ? For smaller γ?*

Exercise 22.3 *Modify the code in Program 22.2 to specify the number of* `segments` *used to approximate the unit circle (using* `mshr`*). Verify the results of Table 22.3 and experiment with other values of the parameters.*

Exercise 22.4 *Modify the code in Program 22.2 to implement the BDT algorithm for the test problem (22.15).*

Exercise 22.5 *Verify that (22.15) is the exact solution to*

$$-\Delta u = f \text{ in } \Omega, \quad u = 0 \text{ on } \partial\Omega,$$

where $f(x, y) = 36(x^2 + y^2)^2$ and Ω is the unit circle.

Exercise 22.6 *Verify that the data in Table 22.4 is correct for cubics and give the corresponding result for quartics ($k = 4$).*

Exercise 22.7 *Show that all of the terms in Nitsche's form (22.1) have the same units, length to the power $d - 2$ in d dimensions.*

Exercise 22.8 *Solve Laplace's equation $\Delta u = 0$ in the unit square $\Omega = [0, 1]^2$ with boundary conditions $g(\mathbf{x}) = \log(\mathbf{x})$ on $\partial\Omega$ using Nitsche's method (22.13) for problems with inhomogeneous boundary conditions. Show that the exact solution solution is $u(\mathbf{x}) = \log(\mathbf{x})$, and compare your computational solution with this in various norms. Use automatic mesh refinement with a goal that emphasizes accuracy at the origin $\mathbf{0}$.*

Exercise 22.9 *Show that the BDT method for solving a problem with homogeneous Dirichlet data is equivalent to Nitsche's method (22.13) with inhomogeneous boundary conditions $g = -\delta\frac{\partial u}{\partial n}$. (Hint: see (22.17).)*

k	`meshsize`	γ	L2 error	H1 error	`segments`	hmax
1	2	100	1.84e+00	6.16e+00	10	1.05e+00
1	4	100	2.90e-01	1.87e+00	20	4.94e-01
1	8	100	9.47e-02	1.06e+00	40	2.61e-01
1	16	100	2.45e-02	5.44e-01	80	1.35e-01
1	32	100	6.39e-03	2.77e-01	160	6.88e-02
1	64	100	1.58e-03	1.37e-01	320	3.53e-02
2	2	100	2.04e-01	1.23e+00	10	1.05e+00
2	4	100	1.72e-02	3.06e-01	20	4.94e-01
2	8	100	2.81e-03	1.03e-01	40	2.61e-01
2	16	100	3.70e-04	2.77e-02	80	1.35e-01
2	32	100	4.77e-05	7.17e-03	160	6.88e-02
2	64	100	5.91e-06	1.79e-03	320	3.53e-02
3	2	100	4.92e-02	3.84e-01	10	1.05e+00
3	4	100	2.36e-03	3.08e-02	20	4.94e-01
3	8	100	1.56e-04	5.31e-03	40	2.61e-01
3	16	100	9.44e-06	7.06e-04	80	1.35e-01
3	32	100	5.81e-07	9.23e-05	160	6.88e-02
3	64	100	3.57e-08	1.15e-05	320	3.53e-02
4	2	100	3.75e-02	1.09e-01	10	1.05e+00
4	4	100	2.32e-03	7.95e-03	20	4.94e-01
4	8	100	1.49e-04	7.41e-04	40	2.61e-01
4	16	100	9.29e-06	6.63e-05	80	1.35e-01
4	32	100	5.80e-07	5.90e-06	160	6.88e-02
4	64	100	3.63e-08	5.22e-07	320	3.53e-02
5	2	100	3.30e-02	7.42e-02	10	1.05e+00
5	4	100	2.29e-03	7.55e-03	20	4.94e-01
5	8	100	1.47e-04	7.10e-04	40	2.61e-01
5	16	100	9.27e-06	6.44e-05	80	1.35e-01
5	32	100	5.80e-07	5.77e-06	160	6.88e-02
5	64	100	3.62e-08	5.12e-07	320	3.53e-02

Table 22.6: Errors in $L^2(\Omega)$ and $H^1(\Omega)$ as a function of mesh size (hmax) for the the BDT approximation for various polynomial degrees. Key: k is the polynomial degree, `meshsize` and `segments` (the number of boundary edges) are input parameters to the `mshr` function `circle` used to generate the mesh, γ is the parameter used in Nitsche's method, and hmax is the maximum mesh size for the mesh that `mshr` generates.

Chapter 23

Conservation Laws

Conservation laws are PDEs of the form

$$\mathbf{u}_t(\mathbf{x},t) + \nabla \cdot \mathbf{F}(\mathbf{u}(\mathbf{x},t)) = 0. \tag{23.1}$$

Here $\mathbf{x} \in \mathbb{R}^d$ for $d = 1, 2, 3$, $\mathbf{u} \in \mathbb{R}^n$ where n can be any positive integer, and $\mathbf{F}$ is a function defined on $\mathbb{R}^n$ with values in $\mathbb{R}^d$. Thus $\nabla \cdot \mathbf{F}$ means

$$(\nabla \cdot \mathbf{F}(\mathbf{v}))_j = \sum_{k=1}^{d} F_{j,k},\ j = 1, \ldots, n.$$

The simplest example is for $d = n = 1$, the **inviscid Burgers equation**

$$0 = u_t + \tfrac{1}{2}(u^2)_x = u_t + uu_x. \tag{23.2}$$

Here $F(v) = \frac{1}{2}v^2$.

23.1 Weak solutions

Following [193], let us restrict to the case $d = 1$ of functions of a single spatial variable. For simplicity, further restrict to the case of a scalar conservation law, $n = 1$. Thus (23.1) becomes

$$u_t(x,t) + f(u(x,t))_x = 0. \tag{23.3}$$

We can think of the pair $U = (u, f(u))$ as a vector function of x and t. In this notation, $u_t + f(u)_x = \nabla\cdot U$. Define $\mathbb{R}_\pm = \{t \in \mathbb{R} : \pm t \geq 0\}$. Multiplying by a test function v and integrating over $\mathbb{R} \times \mathbb{R}_+$ we get

$$0 = \int_{\mathbb{R}} \int_{\mathbb{R}_+} (\nabla\cdot U) v\, dt\, dx. \tag{23.4}$$

If we apply the divergence theorem (2.9) to Uv on the domain $\mathbb{R} \times \mathbb{R}_+$, we get

$$\begin{aligned} -\int_{\mathbb{R}} u_0 v\, dx &= \int_{\mathbb{R}} \int_{\mathbb{R}_+} \nabla\cdot (Uv)\, dt\, dx = \int_{\mathbb{R}} \int_{\mathbb{R}_+} (\nabla\cdot U) v\, dt\, dx + \int_{\mathbb{R}} \int_{\mathbb{R}_+} U \cdot (v_t, v_x)\, dt\, dx \\ &= \int_{\mathbb{R}} \int_{\mathbb{R}_+} (u_t + f(u)_x) v\, dt\, dx + \int_{\mathbb{R}} \int_{\mathbb{R}_+} (u, f(u)) \cdot (v_t, v_x)\, dt\, dx. \end{aligned} \tag{23.5}$$

Therefore

$$0 = \int_{\mathbb{R}} \int_{\mathbb{R}_+} (u_t + f(u)_x) v \, dt \, dx = - \int_{\mathbb{R}} \int_{\mathbb{R}_+} u v_t + f(u) v_x \, dt \, dx - \int_{\mathbb{R}} u_0 v \, dx.$$

This yields the weak formula for the conservation law:

$$\int_{\mathbb{R}} \int_{\mathbb{R}_+} u v_t + f(u) v_x \, dt \, dx + \int_{\mathbb{R}} u_0 v \, dx = 0 \tag{23.6}$$

for all smooth v that vanish outside a bounded set in $\mathbb{R} \times \mathbb{R}_+$. Functions u satisfying (23.6) are called **weak solutions**.

With elliptic equations, there is a strong correspondence between the weak solutions defined by the variational formulation and the strong form of the PDE. However, for conservation laws, the situation is more complicated. Indeed, the weak form of a conservation law does not fully specify their solution. It has been observed that the "class of weak solutions associated with a given system of equations depends on the form in which the equations are written" [193, page 161].

An example of the nonuniqueness for conservation laws is given in [193]: both

$$u(x,t) = \begin{cases} 0 & x < 0 \\ x/t & 0 < x < t \\ 1 & t < x \end{cases} \quad \text{and} \quad w(x,t) = \begin{cases} 0 & 2x < t \\ 1 & t < 2x \end{cases} \tag{23.7}$$

solve (23.6) for the inviscid Burgers equation.

We can verify that u is a solution:

$$u_t(x,t) = \begin{cases} 0 & x < 0 \\ -x/t^2 & 0 < x < t \\ 0 & t < x \end{cases} \quad \text{and} \quad u_x(x,t) = \begin{cases} 0 & x < 0 \\ 1/t & 0 < x < t \,. \\ 0 & t < x \end{cases}$$

Thus $u u_x = -u_t$ in each of the intervals $x < 0$, $0 < x < t$, and $x > t$. Thus $(u_t + u u_x, v)_{L^2(\Omega)} = 0$ for all smooth v. Since u is continuous, and piecewise linear, we can integrate by parts to obtain (23.6).

The verification that w is a weak solution is complicated by the fact that it is discontinuous. But the weak formula does not require continuity, and both $w w_x$ and w_t are zero on the intervals $2x < t$ and $2x > t$. We can revisit our application of the divergence theorem in (23.5). Let us be slightly more general and assume that we have a candidate solution w that is piecewise smooth, with a jump only across a curve $(\xi(t), t)$ in $\mathbb{R} \times \mathbb{R}_+$. For simplicity, assume that $\xi(0) = 0$. Define

$$\Omega_- = \{(x,t) \in \mathbb{R} \times \mathbb{R}_+ \, : \, x < \xi(t)\} \quad \text{and} \quad \Omega_+ = \{(x,t) \in \mathbb{R} \times \mathbb{R}_+ \, : \, x > \xi(t)\}.$$

Let $\Gamma = \{(x,t) \in \mathbb{R} \times \mathbb{R}_+ \, : \, x = \xi(t)\}$. As before, define $U = (w, f(w))$ and apply the divergence theorem to Uv separately on Ω_- and Ω_+ and add the result together:

$$\begin{aligned} - \int_{\mathbb{R}} u_0 v \, dx + \int_{\Gamma} [\mathbf{n} \cdot U] v \, ds &= \int_{\Omega_-} \nabla \cdot (Uv) \, dt \, dx + \int_{\Omega_+} \nabla \cdot (Uv) \, dt \, dx \\ &= \int_{\mathbb{R}} \int_{\mathbb{R}_+} (\nabla \cdot U) v \, dt \, dx + \int_{\mathbb{R}} \int_{\mathbb{R}_+} U \cdot (v_t, v_x) \, dt \, dx \\ &= \int_{\mathbb{R}} \int_{\mathbb{R}_+} (w_t + f(w)_x) v \, dt \, dx + \int_{\mathbb{R}} \int_{\mathbb{R}_+} (w, f(w)) \cdot (v_t, v_x) \, dt \, dx. \end{aligned} \tag{23.8}$$

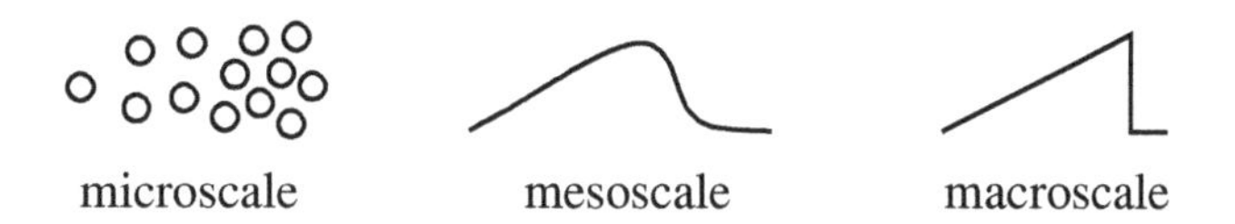

Figure 23.1: Different descriptions of matter. From the left: microscopic (e.g., molecules in a gas), mesoscopic (e.g., density of molecules described via continuum description), macroscopic (idealized limit of mesoscopic description).

Here $[\phi]$ denotes the jump of ϕ across Γ and arises because the boundary of $\Omega_\pm$ is $\Gamma \cup \mathbb{R}_\pm$, with the normals $\pm\mathbf{n}$ in the divergence theorem being equal and opposite for $\Omega_\pm$ on Γ. To be a weak solution, we must have

$$[\mathbf{n} \cdot U] = 0 \quad \text{on } \Gamma.$$

This is known as the **Rankine–Hugoniot** condition. The vector $(\xi'(t), 1)$ is tangent to Γ, so the normals to Γ are $\pm c(t)(-1, \xi'(t))$, where $c(t) = \sqrt{1 + \xi'(t)^2}$. Thus we can write the **jump condition** as

$$w_+ - w_- = \big(f(w_+) - f(w_-)\big)\xi'(t). \tag{23.9}$$

The proposed solution w satisfies $w_- = 0$ and $w_+ = 1$, and $\xi'(t) = 2$, so this reduces to

$$1 = f(1)\xi'(t) = \tfrac{1}{2} \cdot 2.$$

This completes the verification that w is a weak solution of the inviscid Burgers equation.

Since the variational equation does not define the solution, some rule must be adopted to sort things out. We present an approach in Section 23.2 that has been widely studied. However, there is no universal way to determine relevant weak solutions. Some have argued that there must be a solution determined by Nature. The thinking is that the conservation law models a natural phenomenon and thus it should have a unique, natural solution. But there could be many microscopic models of natural phenomenon leading to the same macroscopic model, so there is no "natural" criterion to choose one.

23.2 Diffusion limits

Conservation laws represent the macroscale level in a multiscale model for many physical systems [118, 252], as depicted in Figure 23.1. One such system models the dynamics of a gas [41, 202]. The microscale model in this case is a molecular model [118]. In many cases, the microscale model can be well approximated at a mesoscale as an advection–diffusion system. In the case of the Burgers equation, the resulting equation is

$$0 = u_t + uu_x - \epsilon u_{xx}. \tag{23.10}$$

This is called the **viscous Burgers equation**. In many cases, it makes sense to take the limit as $\epsilon \to 0$, obtaining what are called **viscosity solutions** [104].

Hamilton–Jacobi equations generalize the concept of conservation laws and take the form

$$u_t(\mathbf{x}, t) + H(\mathbf{x}, \mathbf{u}(\mathbf{x}, t), \nabla\mathbf{u}(\mathbf{x}, t)) = 0.$$

Viscosity solutions were first developed in this general framework [104] and then generalized to second-order PDEs [103].

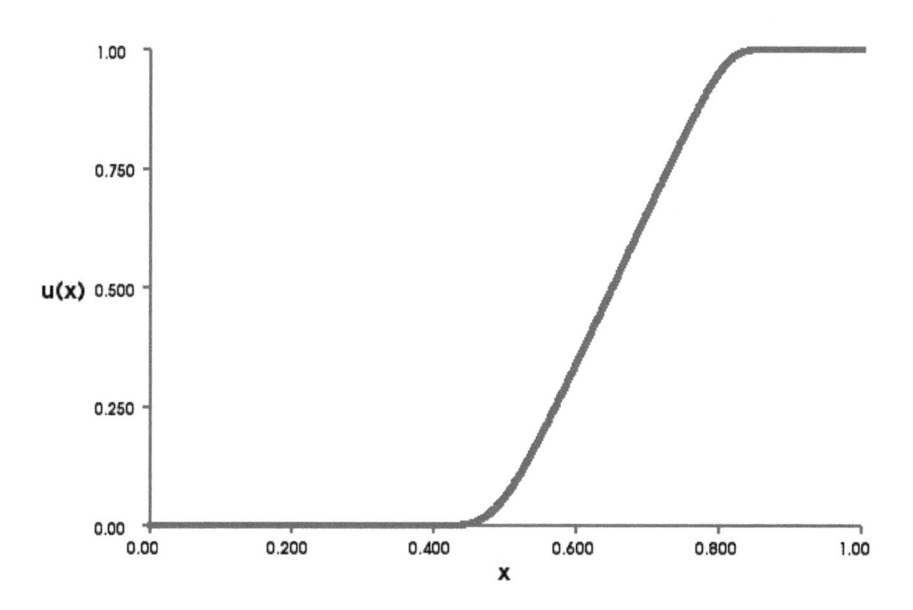

Figure 23.2: Solution of (23.10) on $[0,1]$ by piecewise linears using the algorithm (23.11) with 1000 mesh points, $\Delta t = 0.001$, and $\epsilon = 10^{-3}$. Initial condition $u_0(x) = \frac{1}{2}(1 + \tanh(10^5(x - \frac{1}{2}))$. Solution is shown at $T = 0.3$.

23.2.1 Solving the viscous Burgers equation

Let us consider solving (23.10) with initial conditions appropriate for the proposed solutions (23.7). We will shift the origin by one-half, and take the initial condition to be

$$u_0(x) = \tfrac{1}{2}(1 + \tanh(K(x - \tfrac{1}{2}))$$

for a suitably large value of K.

To simplify the approximation, we modified the implicit Euler scheme (10.34) for the heat equation to obtain

$$(u^{n+1}, v)_{L^2(\Omega)} + \Delta t\big(a_\epsilon(u^{n+1}, v) + (u^{n+1}u_x^n, v)_{L^2(\Omega)}\big) = (u^n, v)_{L^2(\Omega)} \quad \forall v \in V, \tag{23.11}$$

where

$$a_\epsilon(w, v) = \epsilon \int_\Omega w'(x)v'(x)\,dx = \epsilon \int_\Omega w_x(x)v_x(x)\,dx.$$

Here we have approximated the nonlinear term uu_x via $u^{n+1}u_x^n$. We see in Figure 23.2 that the viscosity method picks the solution u in (23.7) even though it has a more complex structure than w. The code to produce Figure 23.2 and Figure 23.3 is in Program 23.2.

23.2.2 Smooth initial data

Using (23.11), we can investigate the behavior of Burgers' equation for different initial data. In Figure 23.3, we show the solution with a Gaussian as initial data. What happens is

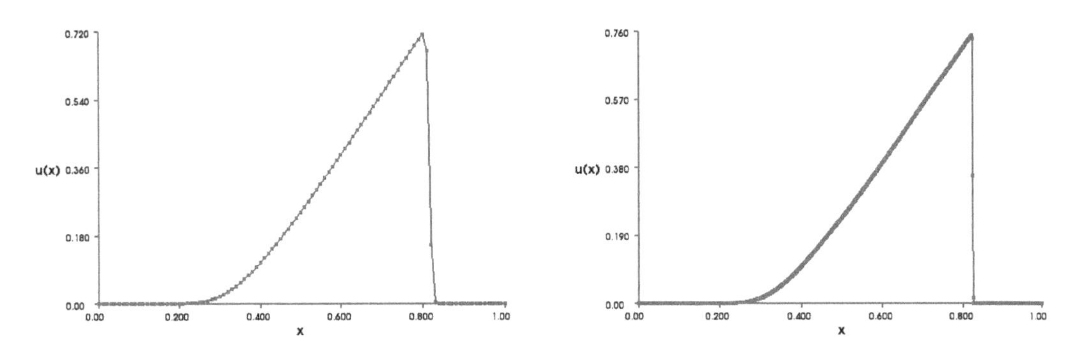

Figure 23.3: Solution of (23.10) on $[0,1]$ by piecewise quartics using the algorithm (23.11). Initial condition $u_0(x) = e^{-(10x)^2}$. Solution is shown at $T = 0.5$. (Left) 100 mesh intervals, $\Delta t = 0.0001$, and $\epsilon = 10^{-3}$. (Right) 1000 mesh intervals, $\Delta t = 0.00005$, and $\epsilon = 10^{-4}$.

quite different from what we saw with other wave equations. The solution is approaching a discontinuity on the front of the wave. The back side approaches a linear ramp as seen in Figure 23.2.

23.3 Numerical nonuniqueness

In Section 9.5, we saw that nonlinear equations can have solutions whose data agree to within round-off error yet are globally quite different. Consider the related problem

$$\begin{aligned} \frac{du}{dt}(t,x) - \epsilon\frac{d^2u}{dx^2}(t,x) + u(t,x)\frac{du}{dx}(t,x) = 0 \quad \text{for } x \in [0,1],\ t \in [0,T], \\ \frac{du}{dx}(t,0) = 0, \quad \frac{du}{dx}(t,1) = 0, \\ u(0,x) = \phi(x), \end{aligned} \tag{23.12}$$

where $\epsilon > 0$ is a fixed parameter. The corresponding time-independent problem (9.18) was studied in Section 9.5 on the interval $[-1,1]$. In [67], it was shown that, if u is a solution of (23.12) such that $u(t,x) \to v(x)$ as $t \to \infty$ then v is a constant. More precisely, they show that if $v \in L^2(0,1)$ satisfies

$$\|u(t,\cdot) - v\|_{L^2(0,1)} \to 0 \text{ as } t \to \infty,$$

then v is constant. Clearly, constants are time-independent solutions of (23.12). Compare the results of [182, 244].

On the other hand, numerical evidence is presented in [67] that there are solutions of (23.12) that appear to tend to time-independent solutions, for example, for $\phi(x) = 5\cos(\pi x)$ and $\phi(x) = 50(\frac{1}{2} - x)^3$, with $\epsilon = 0.1$. They show that the limiting numerical functions v are of the form

$$v_\beta(x) = -\beta \tanh((\beta/2\epsilon)(x - \tfrac{1}{2})), \tag{23.13}$$

where the coefficient β is determined based on the computed solution. Note that v does not satisfy the Neumann conditions in (23.12) exactly, but the discrepancy is exponentially small, as described in Section 9.5. We leave as Exercise 23.13 to explore this phenomenon further.

23.4 Review of wave equations

The simplest wave model (see Section 12.2) is

$$u_t + cu_x = 0, \tag{23.14}$$

where c is the wave speed. Solutions of this equation satisfy

$$u(t,x) = v(x - ct).$$

Solutions of nonlinear advection equations of the form

$$0 = u_t + f(u)_x = u_t + f'(u)u_x$$

no longer just translate to the right. Things move to the right at speeds $c(t,x) = f'(u(t,x))$ that depend on the size of u, and they can change shape, as seen in Figure 23.3. Thus linear and nonlinear conservation laws are very different in character.

23.4.1 Finite difference approximation

```
1  b=[ +1 -1 ];
2  a=[ 1 ];
3  bigx=10000;
4  dx=1/bigx
5  numeps=0.5*dx
6  r=dx*(1:bigx);
7  cfl=0.1
8  % results depend only on cfl
9  dt=cfl*dx
10 yo=exp(-(10*(r-0.5)).^2);
11 nts=25000;
12 bigt=4*nts*dt
13 yu=yo;
14 npics=2;
15 for k=1:nts
16     yu=yu-cfl*filter(b,a,0.5*(yu .* yu));
17 end
18 ymid=yu;
19 for k=1:nts
20     yu=yu-cfl*filter(b,a,0.5*(yu .* yu));
21 end
22 plot(r,yo,"linewidth",3,r,ymid+bigt,"linewidth",3,r,yu+2*bigt,"linewidth",3)
23 title('upwind scheme')
24 xlabel('x')
25 ylabel('pseudo time')
```

Program 23.1: octave code to implement the upwind scheme (23.15). The solution is depicted in Figure 23.4.

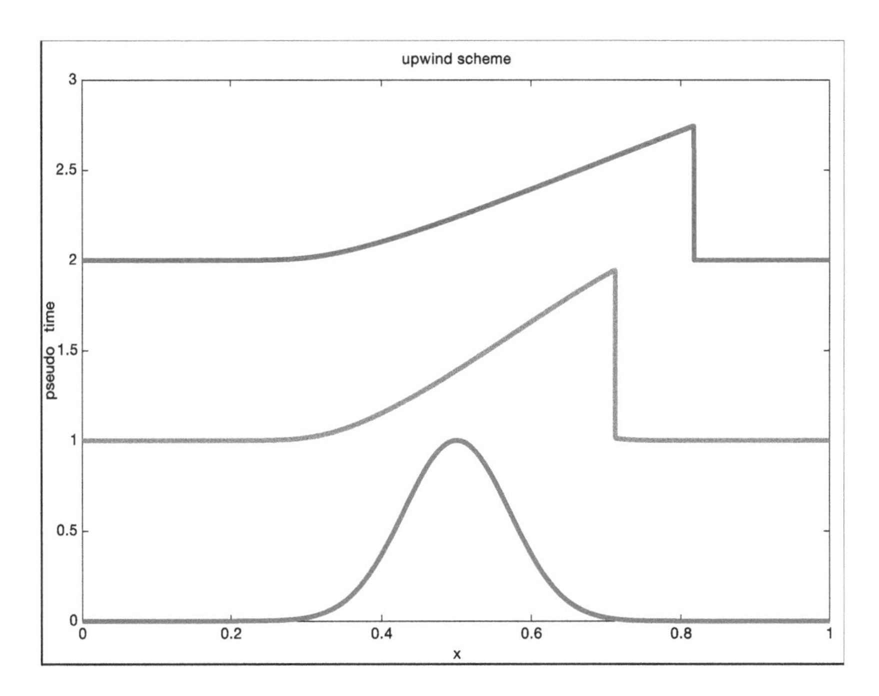

Figure 23.4: Solution of (23.2) on [0, 1] by the upwind scheme (23.15) with 10^4 mesh points and $\Delta t/\Delta x = 0.1$. Initial condition $u_0(x) = e^{-(10x)^2}$. Solution is shown at $T = 0, .25, .5$. The vertical axis represents a pseudo time give by $4T$ chosen to avoid intersection of the curves. The `octave` code to produce this plot is given in Program 23.1.

We can approximate u on a grid in space and time:

$$u(i\Delta t, j\Delta x) \approx u_{i,j}.$$

We write

$$u_t(i\Delta t, j\Delta x) \approx \frac{u_{i,j} - u_{i-1,j}}{\Delta t}$$

$$f(u)_x(i\Delta t, j\Delta x) \approx \frac{f(u)_{i,j} - f(u)_{i,j-1}}{\Delta x}.$$

Thus we obtain the **upwind scheme**

$$u_{i+1,j} = u_{i,j} - \frac{\Delta t}{\Delta x}\left(f(u)_{i,j} - f(u)_{i,j-1}\right). \tag{23.15}$$

This finite-difference approximation allows us to simulate nonlinear advection as easily as linear advection. Notice that the scheme depends only on the ratio $\Delta t/\Delta x$, often referred to as the **CFL number** in honor of a paper by Courant, Friedrichs, and Lewy [102]. In Figure 23.4 we show the solution of the inviscid Burgers equation (23.2),

$$0 = u_t + \tfrac{1}{2}(u^2)_x,$$

with the same Gaussian initial data as in Figure 23.3.

23.4.2 Integral invariants

Let us consider solutions of conservation laws with finite support in space. Although the wave shape changes with time, the integral of u is preserved: integrating the advection equation in space (and integrating by parts) gives

$$\frac{\partial}{\partial t}\int_{\mathbb{R}} u\,dx = \int_{\mathbb{R}} u_t\,dx = -\int_{\mathbb{R}} f(u)_x\,dx = 0. \tag{23.16}$$

Thus the area under the graph of u is constant. In Figure 23.4, we see that the initial wave forms convert to a long triangular form, and so its amplitude must decrease to maintain a constant area.

The integral of u^2 is also preserved: multiplying the advection equation by u and integrating in space (and integrating by parts) gives

$$\begin{aligned}\frac{1}{2}\frac{\partial}{\partial t}\int_{\mathbb{R}} u^2\,dx &= \int_{\mathbb{R}} uu_t\,dx = -\int_{\mathbb{R}} f(u)_x u\,dx \\ &= \int_{\mathbb{R}} f(u)u_x\,dx = \int_{\mathbb{R}} g(u)_x\,dx = 0,\end{aligned} \tag{23.17}$$

where $g' = f$, that is, g is an antiderivative of f, with $g(0) = 0$.

23.5 Shocks

Shocks can be described as discontinuities that can form and move, as shown in Figure 23.4, again with $f(u) = u^2$. Shock fronts stay sharp, but the back side of an advancing wave remains continuous, as shown in Figure 23.4. The amplitude has to decrease since the integrals of u and u^2 remain constant. Over time, the wave amplitude goes to zero. This is further illustrated on the left side of Figure 23.5 which has a step-function initial data.

23.5.1 Linear versus nonlinear shocks

In the linear case (23.14), even discontinuous solutions are propagated by translation:

$$u(t, x) = v(x - ct).$$

Even though the exact solution is trivial, let's see what our upwind difference method produces. On the right side of Figure 23.5 we show the result of the upwind difference method (23.15) for $f(u) = u$. In the case of linear advection, our numerical method produces waves that are no longer sharp at either the leading edge or trailing edge of a discontinuity. We examine why in Section 23.5.2. By contrast, the leading edge of the numerically computed nonlinear wave is sharp. On the other hand, since the wave speed is constant, the linear waves move much faster than the nonlinear waves. Thus difference methods treat linear and nonlinear waves quite differently.

23.5.2 Numerical dissipation

Numerical schemes for conservation laws introduce implicit dissipation. Taylor's approximation says

$$\frac{u_{i,j} - u_{i,j-1}}{\Delta x} \approx u_x(i\Delta t, j\Delta x) + \frac{\Delta x}{2} u_{xx}(i\Delta t, j\Delta x). \tag{23.18}$$

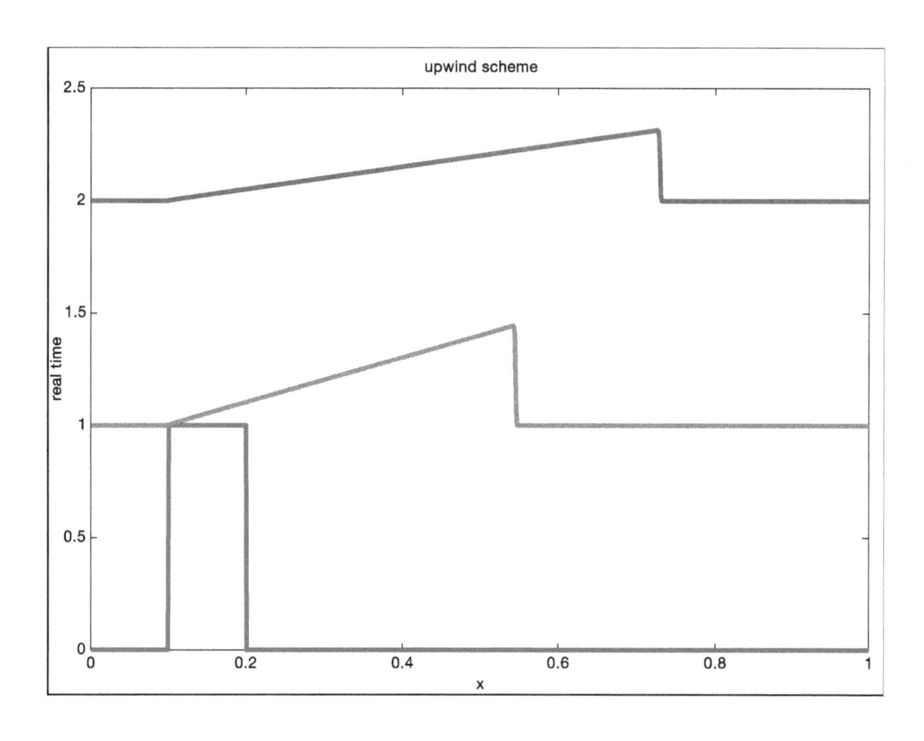

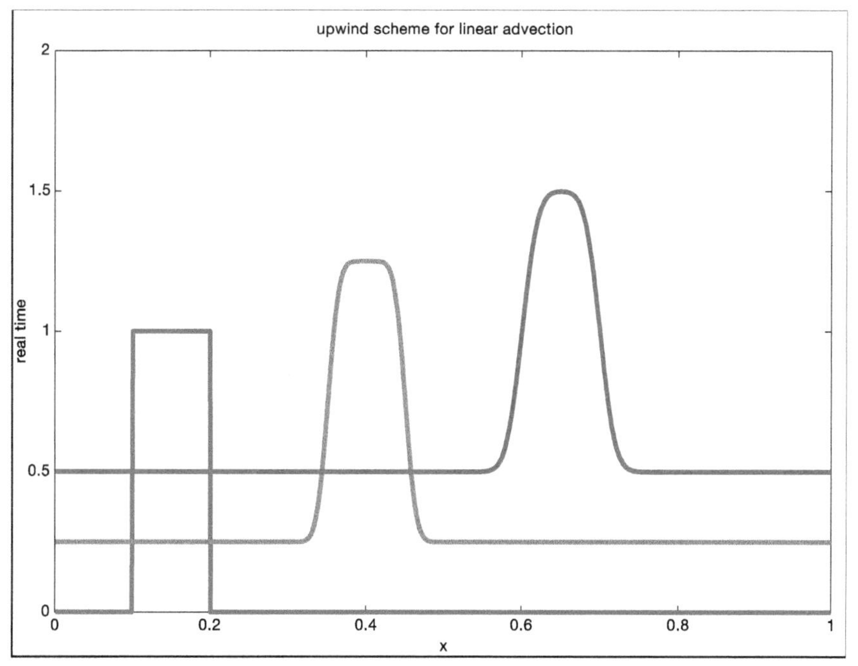

Figure 23.5: Upwind scheme with CFL=0.5, $\Delta x = 10^{-3}$ for (top) inviscid Burgers equation (23.2) and (bottom) linear advection (23.14) with speed $c = 1$.

Thus the difference scheme is actually a better approximation to

$$u_t + u_x - \frac{\Delta x}{2} u_{xx} = 0$$

than it is to the linear advection equation

$$u_t + u_x = 0.$$

In this case, we see [165, 85] that the difference method effectively introduces a diffusion or dissipation element, where the size of the diffusion constant depends on the mesh size. Thus the difference method naturally picks out the diffusion-limit solution.

In the nonlinear case, we have

$$0 = u_t + f(u)_x - \frac{\Delta x}{2} f(u)_{xx}.$$

For the inviscid Burgers equation, this becomes

$$0 = u_t + uu_x - \frac{\Delta x}{2} \big(uu_x\big)_x = u_t + uu_x - \frac{\Delta x}{2} \big((u_x)^2 + uu_{xx}\big). \tag{23.19}$$

The effect of the dissipation term is harder to predict in this case, but apparently it does not lead to excessive smoothing of shocks, contrary to the linear case. We leave as Exercise 23.3 to explore this further. One key point is that the dissipation term in variational form (Exercise 23.3) turns off when $u = 0$.

The second-order derivative term in

$$u_t + f(u)_x - \epsilon f(u)_{xx} = 0$$

is called a dissipation term due to the following. Multiply the equation by u, integrate in space and integrate by parts to get

$$0 = \frac{1}{2}\frac{\partial}{\partial t}\int_{\mathbb{R}} u^2\,dx - \epsilon \int_{\mathbb{R}} uf(u)_{xx}\,dx = 0 = \frac{1}{2}\frac{\partial}{\partial t}\int_{\mathbb{R}} u^2\,dx + \epsilon \int_{\mathbb{R}} (u_x)^2 f'(u)\,dx, \tag{23.20}$$

as in (23.17). Now we see that the integral of u^2 must dissipate to zero, since its time derivative is strictly negative (assuming that u is not identically constant and $f'(u) > 0$).

The behavior depicted in Figure 23.5 suggests that nonlinearity controls diffusion artifacts. Harten advocated artificial compression [266] as a means of reducing numerical dissipation.

23.5.3 Numerical dispersion

It is possible to alter numerical modifications in difference methods, but not eliminate them [85, 6]. For example, the Lax-Wendroff scheme for linear $f(u) = u$ [192, 194] is

$$u_{i+1,j} = \sum_{k=-1}^{1} b_k u_{i,j+k}, \tag{23.21}$$

where $b_{\pm 1} = \frac{1}{2}\alpha(\alpha \mp 1)$ and $b_0 = 1 - \alpha^2$, where $\alpha = \Delta t/\Delta x$ is the CFL number. The Lax-Wendroff scheme is second-order accurate in space, and it is a better approximation to

$$u_t + u_x - \gamma \Delta x^2 u_{xxx} = 0 \tag{23.22}$$

than it is to $u_t + u_x = 0$. We leave as Exercise 23.1 to compute γ.

The third-order derivative term in

$$u_t + f(u)_x - \epsilon u_{xxx} = 0 \tag{23.23}$$

is called a dispersion term, as discussed in Section 12.4. Multiply the dispersion term by u, integrate in space and integrate by parts to get

$$\int u u_{xxx}\, dx = -\int u_x u_{xx}\, dx = -\int \tfrac{1}{2}((u_x)^2)_x\, dx = 0. \tag{23.24}$$

In view of (23.17), we conclude that the integral of u^2 is conserved for the solution u of (23.23).

23.5.4 Numerical errors

There has been a long quest to achieve more accuracy in numerical methods for conservation laws. Although the upwind scheme (23.15) is quite effective, as we have seen, there has been significant interest in more accurate schemes. The Lax-Wendroff [192, 194] scheme (23.21) is an early example.

More recently, **discontinuous Galerkin** (DG) schemes have been widely studied [264]. DG schemes were first used in the context of models for advection terms in neutron transport (see references in [236]). Even more recently, Galerkin schemes using continuous finite elements have been studied [19, 153, 153, 152, 151, 150, 149].

Another new approach to conservation laws has been developed called **kinetic schemes** [11]. An example of their use is given in [88].

23.6 Exercises

Exercise 23.1 *Compute the constant γ in (23.22) for the Lax-Wendroff scheme (23.21).*

Exercise 23.2 *Use the Lax-Wendroff scheme (23.21) to solve the inviscid Burgers equation.*

Exercise 23.3 *Modify Program 23.2 to solve the PDE*

$$u_t + uu_x - \epsilon(uu_x)_x = 0$$

with a square wave initial condition. Explain what the solution looks like for various values of ϵ. (Hint: use the variational form

$$a_\epsilon(u, v) = \epsilon \int (u + \epsilon)\, u_x v_x\, dx$$

for the dissipation term to avoid a singularity.)

Exercise 23.4 *Modify Program 23.2 to solve the viscous Burgers equation (23.10) by changing (23.11) to the adjoint form*

$$(u^{n+1}, v)_{L^2(\Omega)} + \Delta t\big(a_\epsilon(u^{n+1}, v) - (u^{n+1}u_x^n, v_x)_{L^2(\Omega)}\big) = (u^n, v)_{L^2(\Omega)} \quad \forall v \in V.$$

Solve using the data in Figure 23.2. How do the two different methods compare?

Exercise 23.5 *Explore numerical dispersion for nonlinear conservation laws* $u_t + f(u)_x = 0$ *associated with the Lax-Wendroff scheme.*

Exercise 23.6 *Modify Program 23.2 to solve (23.12) with initial data (a)* $\phi(x) = 5\cos(\pi x)$ *and (b)* $\phi(x) = 50(\frac{1}{2} - x)^3$, *with* $\epsilon = 0.1$ *and* $T = \frac{1}{2}$. *Define* $v(x) = u(T, x)$. *Determine the value of* β *in (23.13) that gives the best fit to the computed* v *in* $L^2(0, 1)$. *Plot the error between* v *and* v_β.

```
1  from dolfin import *
2  import sys, math
3
4  dt=.00005
5  kluge=100
6  deg=4
7  mno=1000
8  enn=10000
9  eps=0.0001
10 # Create mesh and define function space
11 mesh = UnitIntervalMesh(mno)
12 V = FunctionSpace(mesh, "Lagrange", deg)
13 # Define Dirichlet boundary (x = 0 or x = 1)
14 def boundary(x):
15     return x[0] < DOLFIN_EPS or x[0] > 1.0 - DOLFIN_EPS
16 # Define boundary condition
17 u0 = Expression("exp(-(x[0]-0.5)*(x[0]-0.5)*kl)",kl=kluge,degree=deg)
18 #u0 = Expression("0.5 + 0.5*tanh((x[0]-0.5)*kl)",kl=kluge,degree=deg)
19 bc = DirichletBC(V, u0, boundary)
20 # Define variational problem
21 u = TrialFunction(V)
22 uold = Function(V)
23 v = TestFunction(V)
24 a = dt*eps*inner(grad(u), grad(v))*dx + dt*u*uold.dx(0)*v*dx + u*v*dx
25 F = uold*v*dx
26 u = Function(V)
27 T = enn*dt
28 t = 0
29 uold.interpolate(u0)
30 u.assign(uold)
31 plot(u)
32 time.sleep(1)
33 while t <= T:
34     # Compute solution
35     solve(a == F, u, bc)
36     uold.assign(u)
37     plot(u)
38     print t
39     t += dt
40 interactive()
```

Program 23.2: Code to implement the implicit Euler scheme (23.11) for the viscous Burgers equation (23.10). The solution is depicted in Figure 23.3.

Chapter 24

Hyperbolic Systems

Systems of hyperbolic conservation laws arise in many applications. Perhaps the simplest are the isentropic Euler equations. These consist of two equations, one for the density of a gas and the other for the velocity (or momentum). They are ostensibly defined in 3 space dimensions, but there are flows that are constant in some dimensions, so the system makes sense in 1 and 2 spatial dimensions as well. We begin with the one-dimensional case.

The primary new phenomenon with a system is that waves can propagate in multiple directions and with different speeds. Thus there may be no clear direction that is "upwind" in typical problems. Moreover, shocks can collide.

In the two-dimensional case, a complication arises that does not at the moment have a simple resolution. In short, there are multiple solutions which arise after shocks collide and there is no known way either to select one solution theoretically or to compute reliable solutions numerically. Thus our discussion is necessarily open-ended.

24.1 Gas dynamics in one dimension

The behavior of a gas moving in one direction at high speed can be modeled via

$$\begin{aligned} \rho_t + (\rho u)_x &= 0 \\ (\rho u)_t + (\rho u^2 + p(\rho))_x &= 0, \end{aligned} \tag{24.1}$$

where ρ is the density of the gas, u is the velocity in the x direction, and p is the pressure. It is assumed that the pressure depends in an explicit way on the density. A common choice for the pressure p is $p(\rho) = a\rho^\gamma$, where a and γ are constants satisfying $a > 0$ and $\gamma \geq 1$. In this setting, it is assumed that the density and velocity are independent of the y and z directions. Such behavior is approximated in a shock tube [279]. We assume that the domain of x is $\mathbb{R}$ and $t \geq 0$.

If we define $w = \rho u$, then the system (24.1) becomes

$$\begin{aligned} \rho_t + w_x &= 0 \\ w_t + (\rho^{-1} w^2 + p(\rho))_x &= 0, \end{aligned} \tag{24.2}$$

which is of the form (23.1), where

$$\mathbf{u} = \begin{pmatrix} \rho \\ w \end{pmatrix} \qquad \text{and} \qquad \mathbf{F} = \begin{pmatrix} w \\ \rho^{-1} w^2 + p(\rho) \end{pmatrix}.$$

This is often called the **conservation form** of the equations. It has the defect that the vacuum state $\rho = 0$ [202] corresponds to a singularity.

24.2 Example solution

In order to understand better key aspects of hyperbolic systems, we consider an example. If we take $\gamma = 3$, then (24.1) can be written [88] as two Burgers equations. In particular, assume that

$$p(\rho) = \tfrac{1}{12}\rho^3.$$

24.2.1 Equivalent formulation

Define

$$a(t,x) = u(t,x) + \tfrac{1}{2}\rho(t,x) \quad \text{and} \quad b(t,x) = u(t,x) - \tfrac{1}{2}\rho(t,x).$$

First rewrite (24.1) as

$$\rho_t = -(\rho u)_x \qquad - u(\rho u)_x + \rho u_t + (\rho u^2 + \tfrac{1}{12}\rho^3)_x = 0.$$

The second equation can be simplified to

$$0 = u\rho u_x + \rho u_t + \tfrac{1}{4}\rho^2\rho_x = \rho\big(uu_x + u_t + \tfrac{1}{4}\rho\rho_x\big).$$

Then

$$\begin{aligned} a_t + aa_x &= u_t + \tfrac{1}{2}\rho_t + \big(u + \tfrac{1}{2}\rho\big)\big(u_x + \tfrac{1}{2}\rho_x\big) \\ &= u_t - \tfrac{1}{2}(\rho u)_x + uu_x + \tfrac{1}{2}\big(\rho u_x + u\rho_x\big) + \tfrac{1}{4}\rho\rho_x \\ &= u_t + uu_x + \tfrac{1}{4}\rho\rho_x = 0, \end{aligned} \tag{24.3}$$

assuming $\rho > 0$. Similarly

$$\begin{aligned} b_t + bb_x &= u_t - \tfrac{1}{2}\rho_t + \big(u - \tfrac{1}{2}\rho\big)\big(u_x - \tfrac{1}{2}\rho_x\big) \\ &= u_t + \tfrac{1}{2}(\rho u)_x + uu_x - \tfrac{1}{2}\big(\rho u_x + u\rho_x\big) + \tfrac{1}{4}\rho\rho_x \\ &= u_t + uu_x + \tfrac{1}{4}\rho\rho_x = 0. \end{aligned} \tag{24.4}$$

Note that

$$\rho = a - b, \quad u = \tfrac{1}{2}(a+b), \quad \text{and} \quad w = \rho u = \tfrac{1}{2}\big(a^2 - b^2\big).$$

24.2.2 Equivalent solution

Following [88], define initial data

$$a_0(x) = \begin{cases} 1 & x \le -1 \\ -x & -1 \le x \le 0 \\ 0 & x \ge 0 \end{cases}, \quad \text{and} \quad b_0(x) = a_0(x-1) - 1 = \begin{cases} 0 & x \le 0 \\ -x & 0 \le x \le 1 \\ -1 & x \ge 1 \end{cases}.$$

This corresponds to initial data for ρ and u of the form

$$\rho_0(x) = \begin{cases} 1 & |x| \ge 1 \\ |x| & |x| \le 1 \end{cases} \qquad \text{and} \qquad u_0(x) = \begin{cases} \frac{1}{2} & x \le -1 \\ -\frac{1}{2}x & -1 \le x \le 1 \\ -\frac{1}{2} & x \ge 1 \end{cases}.$$

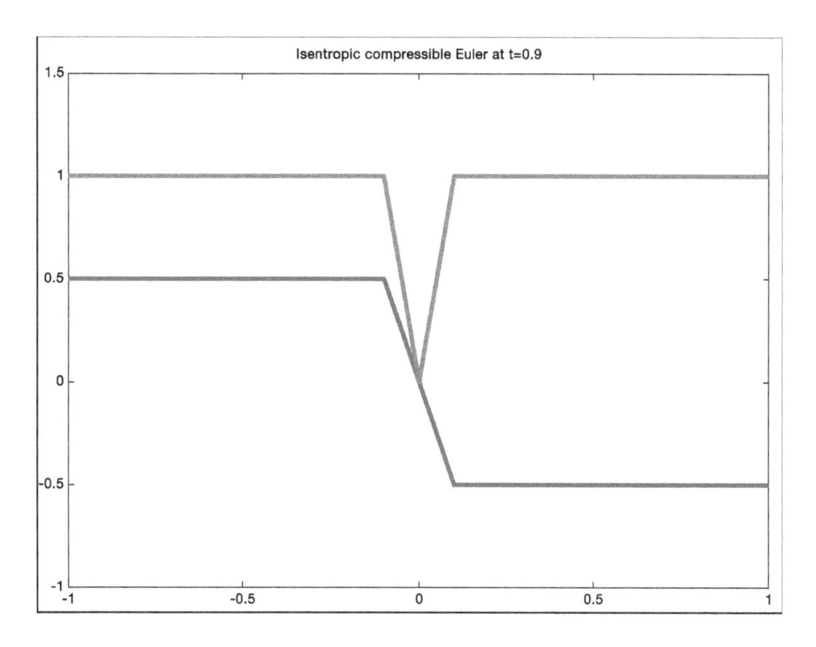

Figure 24.1: Solutions (24.9) at $t = 0.9$.

For $0 \leq t < 1$,

$$a(t,x) = \begin{cases} 1 & x \leq t-1 \\ -x/(1-t) & -1+t \leq x \leq 0 \\ 0 & x \geq 0, \end{cases} \tag{24.5}$$

and then for $t \geq 1$,

$$a(t,x) = \begin{cases} 1 & x \leq 2(t-1) \\ 0 & x > 2(t-1) \end{cases}. \tag{24.6}$$

We can verify that (24.5) satisfies $a_t = -aa_x$ as follows. Differentiating with respect to t and x, we get

$$a_t(t,x) = \begin{cases} 0 & x \leq t-1 \\ -x/(t-1)^2 & -1+t \leq x \leq 0\,, \\ 0 & x \geq 0, \end{cases} \qquad a_x(t,x) = \begin{cases} 0 & x \leq t-1 \\ 1/(t-1) & -1+t \leq x \leq 0\,. \\ 0 & x \geq 0, \end{cases}$$

Multiplying the formula for a_x times (24.5) yields the formula for $-a_t$. We leave as Exercise 24.1 to show that (24.6) satisfies the Rankine-Hugoniot (weak solution) jump condition (23.9). Similarly, for $0 \leq t < 1$,

$$b(t,x) = \begin{cases} 0 & x \leq 0 \\ -x/(1-t) & 0 \leq x \leq 1-t\,. \\ -1 & x \geq 1-t, \end{cases} \tag{24.7}$$

and for $t \geq 1$,

$$b(t,x) = \begin{cases} 0 & x \leq 2(1-t) \\ -1 & x > 2(1-t) \end{cases}. \tag{24.8}$$

Rewriting this in terms of u and ρ, we get for $0 \le t < 1$

$$u(t,x) = \begin{cases} \frac{1}{2} & x \le t-1 \\ -\frac{1}{2}x/(1-t) & t-1 \le x \le 1-t \\ -\frac{1}{2} & x \ge 1-t \end{cases}, \quad \rho(t,x) = \begin{cases} 1 & x \le t-1 \\ |x|/(1-t) & t-1 \le x \le 1-t \\ 1 & x \ge 1-t \end{cases}.$$

These solutions are depicted in Figure 24.1 at $t = 0.9$.

24.2.3 Getting past the shock

Unfortunately, the equivalence of (a, b) and (u, ρ) does not extend past $t = 1$ where the shocks collide, due to the discontinuity of u in x that appears at $t = 1$. Starting at $t = 1$, we have what is called a **Riemann problem**, with initial data

$$\rho_{\pm} = 1 \quad \text{and} \quad u_{\pm} = \pm\tfrac{1}{2}.$$

That is, we have

$$u(1,x) = u_1(x) = \begin{cases} \frac{1}{2} & x < 0 \\ -\frac{1}{2} & x > 0 \end{cases}, \qquad \rho(1,x) = \rho_1(x) = \begin{cases} 1 & x < 0 \\ 1 & x > 0 \end{cases}.$$

The solution [88] of this Riemann problem for $t \ge 1$ consists of piecewise constants dictated by the Rankine-Hugoniot conditions

$$u(t,x) = \begin{cases} \pm\frac{1}{2} & \mp x > c(1-t) \\ 0 & |x| < c(t-1) \end{cases}, \qquad \rho(t,x) = \begin{cases} 1 & |x| > c(1-t) \\ \rho_m & |x| < c(t-1) \end{cases}, \tag{24.9}$$

with $\rho_m \approx 1.93$ [88]. We leave as Exercise 24.4 the determination of the wave speed c in (24.9).

24.3 Nonuniqueness in systems of conservation laws

Now extend (24.1) to a system in two space dimensions. Write $\mathbf{v} = (u, v)$ for the flow variables. The isentropic, compressible Euler equations can be written as

$$\begin{aligned} \rho_t + \nabla\cdot(\rho\mathbf{v}) &= 0 \\ (\rho\mathbf{v})_t + \nabla\cdot(\rho\mathbf{v}\otimes\mathbf{v}) + \nabla p(\rho)) &= 0, \end{aligned} \tag{24.10}$$

where $\mathbf{v}\otimes\mathbf{v}$ is the matrix with entries $(\mathbf{v}\otimes\mathbf{v})_{ij} = v_i v_j$ and, for a matrix-valued function $M(\mathbf{x})$, $\nabla\cdot M$ is defined by

$$(\nabla\cdot M)_i = \sum_{j=1}^{d} M_{ij,j}.$$

Unfortunately "in more than one space dimension, a good theory for unique continuation of solutions after the formation of shocks is not available" [88]. In particular, [88, Theorem 4, page 125] proves that there are infinitely many "wild solutions" with nonvanishing vorticity

$$\omega(t,x,y) := u_y(t,x,y) - v_x(t,x,y) \ne 0,$$

where $\mathbf{v} = (u, v)$. The piecewise constant weak solution in (24.9), extended with $v = 0$, clearly has vorticity equal to zero. Explicit computations are also given in [88] illustrating the behavior of "wild" solutions. This can be described loosely as the creation of vortices after the collision of two shocks. Given that the conservation laws are highly idealized models, such an outcome is not surprising.

It should be noted that recent theoretical research on nonuniqueness [1, 58, 79, 86, 87, 88, 89, 90, 91, 214] has focused on weak solutions satisfying entropy conditions. Such conditions were assumed to select physically relevant solutions for systems of conservation laws. Now it appears that they do not limit the ambiguity as expected.

It has been known for a long time that general solutions of conservation laws can be described in terms of Young measures [53]. Roughly speaking, at each point in space, the solution set is described in terms of a probability distribution of values. A classical solution in this setting corresponds to the probability measure being a Dirac δ-function, meaning that only one (vector) value is attained. It is known [161] that, as long as a classical solution of a conservation law exists, the Young measure reduces to a δ-function. However, after the collision of two shocks, such results are not known, and possible behaviors in such situations could involve non-δ, Young-measure solutions [78]. Such a solution has a definite physical interpretation: the Young-measure puts expected limits on solution behavior. Thus it could be very useful to find ways of computing such measure-valued solutions [132].

This area of modeling by PDEs is not fully understood, so we do not attempt to say more about it here. It seems clear that further research is needed to determine useful simulation models to be used where simple conservation laws were considered sufficient in the past. But until such improvements are made, multi-dimensional systems of conservation laws must be considered incomplete models.

24.4 Exercises

Exercise 24.1 *Prove that the function $a(t, x)$ defined in (24.6) satisfies the Rankine-Hugoniot (weak solution) jump condition (23.9). (Hint: $\gamma(t) = 2(t - 1)$.)*

Exercise 24.2 *Prove that the function b defined in (24.7) satisfies $b_t = -bb_x$ for $0 \le t < 1$.*

Exercise 24.3 *Prove that the function b defined in (24.8) satisfies the Rankine-Hugoniot (weak solution) jump condition (23.9).*

Exercise 24.4 *Determine the wave speed c in (24.9).*

Exercise 24.5 *Consider the viscous Burgers equation (23.10) on the unit interval $[0, 1]$ with boundary conditions $u(j, t) = (-1)^j \gamma \tanh(\gamma/4\epsilon)$, $j = 0, 1$, where $\gamma > 0$ is a fixed parameter. Can you find a steady state solution? (Hint: such a solution solves $\frac{1}{2}u^2 = \epsilon u_x + c$ for some constant c. Consider the function $v(x) = \gamma \tanh(-\gamma(x - \frac{1}{2})/2\epsilon)$ defined in (9.20).)*

Exercise 24.6 *Solve the viscous Burgers equation (23.10) on the unit interval $[0, 1]$ with initial condition*

$$g(x) = -\tfrac{1}{2} \tanh\left(K(x - \tfrac{1}{2})\right)$$

and boundary conditions $u(j, t) = g(j)$, $j = 0, 1$. Experiment with various values of K and ϵ, as well as time step Δt, degree of approximation, and mesh size. Report all that you observe. What do you expect the limiting solution to be as $\epsilon \to 0$ and $K \to \infty$? Use the Rankine-Hugoniot conditions to verify your conjecture. (Hint: see Exercise 24.5.)

Chapter 25

Solvers

In large computations, the rate limiting step is often the solution of a linear system. In some cases, it is sufficient to use Gaussian elimination or its variants (such as Cholesky factorization). Such algorithms are called **direct methods**. However, for large, three-dimensional simulations, **iterative methods** are frequently more efficient.

25.1 Direct methods

Gaussian elimination is the basis for all direct methods for solving $Ax = f$, where A is an $n \times n$ matrix and x and f are vectors of length n. Its use can be traced to China centuries before the birth of Gauss, and it is now widely taught in the pre-highschool curriculum. But the modern view of Gaussian elimination is that it factors A into two triangular matrices: $A = LU$. More precisely, L is lower-triangular with 1's on the diagonal, and U is upper-triangular. This factorization was known to Doolittle[1] [113], and even Gauss [269]. Moreover, Doolittle's "contribution seems to have been to design a tableau in which the terms were expeditiously recorded" [269], meaning that the factorization was directly computed, not using the standard elimination method. The modern approach is to compute the factors first, and then solve $Ax = f$ by writing $f = L(Ux)$. This means that $f = Lg$ where $Ux = g$. So we first solve $Lg = f$ by forward substation [259], and then solve for x via backsubstition [259]: $Ux = g$.

Backsubstition, as well as the factorization process, involves the diagonal entries u_{ii} of U, which must be nonzero for the algorithm to work properly. This will hold under certain conditions on A, as indicated in Table 25.1. Since the ordering of variables and equations is arbitrary, we are allowed to do **pivoting**, meaning the rearrangement of the orderings. This is done very efficiently in the factorization process, but the details do not matter here. It is equivalent to think that the rearrangement has been done in advance. Partial pivoting means that either the variables or equations are reordered. Full pivoting means that both are reordered. The latter requires slightly more work than partial pivoting which in turn takes slightly more work than doing no pivoting.

Different factorizations are possible. The general factorization is $A = LDU$ where D is diagonal and both L and U have 1's on the diagonals. This factorization is unique [259].

[1] Myrick Hascall Doolittle (1830–1913) was a mathematician who worked at the U.S. Coast and Geodetic Survey in the Computing Division [59, 130].

type of pivoting	conditions on A that guarantee success
none	symmetric, positive definite
partial	A is invertible
full	A is any matrix

Table 25.1: Conditions for matrix factorization.

If A is symmetric, then it is easy to see that $A = LDL^t$ (Exercise 25.2). When A is also positive definite, the Cholesky factorization $A = \widetilde{L}\widetilde{L}^t$ holds, where the diagonal entries of $\widetilde{L}$ are equal to $\sqrt{d_{i,i}}$. The positivity of the diagonal entries $d_{i,i}$ of D is guaranteed by the condition that A is positive definite (Exercise 25.3).

25.1.1 Singular equations

Some explanation is required regarding the third line in Table 25.1. The elimination (or factorization) process with full pivoting can "solve" $Ax = f$ for even singular matrices A in the sense that it provides the information required to know if such a solution exists. More precisely, it may be that the diagonal entries u_{ii} of U are zero for $i > k$ for some $k < n$. Then there is a solution x to $Ax = f$ if and only if $g_i = 0$ for $i > k$, where g is the solution to $Lg = f$. More precisely, elimination with full pivoting will reduce the linear system after k steps to

$$\begin{pmatrix} u_{1,1} & u_{1,2} & \cdots & u_{1,k} & u_{1,k+1} & \cdots & u_{1,n} \\ 0 & u_{2,2} & \cdots & u_{2,k} & u_{1,k+1} & \cdots & u_{2,n} \\ \vdots & \vdots & \vdots & \vdots & \vdots & \vdots & \vdots \\ 0 & 0 & \cdots & u_{k,k} & u_{k,k+1} & \cdots & u_{k,n} \\ 0 & 0 & \cdots & 0 & 0 & \cdots & 0 \\ \vdots & \vdots & \vdots & \vdots & \vdots & \vdots & \vdots \\ 0 & 0 & \cdots & 0 & 0 & \cdots & 0 \end{pmatrix} \begin{pmatrix} x_1 \\ x_2 \\ \vdots \\ x_k \\ x_{k+1} \\ \vdots \\ x_n \end{pmatrix} = \begin{pmatrix} g_1 \\ g_2 \\ \vdots \\ g_k \\ g_{k+1} \\ \vdots \\ g_n \end{pmatrix}$$

Null solutions $Ax = 0$ are of the form $x_1 = \cdots = x_k = 0$ with $x_{k+1}, \ldots, x_n$ arbitrary. Code to implement the pure Neumann problem is given in Program 25.1.

25.1.2 Singular example

The pure Neumann problem is singular if we use the variational space $V = H^1(\Omega)$. The condition for existence of a solution is $\overline{f} = 0$, and the null space consists of all constant functions. In practice, the factorization of the associated matrix $A = LU$ will have round-off error, so that $u_{n,n} = \epsilon$. Similarly, it will happen that the discrete right-hand side will satisfy $\overline{f} = \epsilon'$. Therefore, the direct factorization method will produce a solution u_h such that $\overline{u_h} = C\epsilon'/\epsilon$ for some constant C. Thus we get an arbitrary, and potentially large, value for $\overline{u_h}$. However, we can subtract $\overline{u_h}$ from u_h to get a reliable approximation.

If $u_{n,n} = \epsilon$, then the system is not actually singular, so we do not really need the restriction $\overline{f} = 0$. But if we allow $\overline{f}$ to be large, then instead an added constant of size $C\epsilon'/\epsilon$, we will have an added constant of size C/ϵ, something of order of one divided by the size of round-off error, and this can potentially pollute the entire solution process. So it is essential to match the constraint on the right-hand side as nearly as possible.

```
# Create mesh and define function space
mesh = UnitSquareMesh(meshsize, meshsize)
V = FunctionSpace(mesh, "Lagrange", deg)

# Define variational problem
u = TrialFunction(V)
v = TestFunction(V)
f = Expression("(cos(mypi*x[0]))*(cos(mypi*x[1]))",mypi=math.pi,degree=deg)
a = inner(grad(u), grad(v))*dx
L = (2*(math.pi)*(math.pi))*f*v*dx

# Compute solution
u = Function(V)
solve(a == L, u)
meanu=assemble(u*dx)
mu = Expression("meanyou",meanyou=meanu,degree=deg)
mconstu = Function(V)
mconstu=interpolate(mu,V)
fo=interpolate(f,V)
um = Function(V)
um.assign(u - mconstu)
inteff=assemble(fo*dx)
print meshsize,degree," %.1e"%meanu," %.1e"%inteff," %.1e"%(meanu/inteff),\
      " %.2e"%errornorm(f,um,norm_type='l2', degree_rise=3)
```

Program 25.1: Code to implement the pure Neumann problem.

25.1.3 A nonsingular approach

It is possible to pose the pure Neumann problem in a way that is non-singular and still use the full space $V = H^1(\Omega)$ or subsets $V_h \subset V$. Consider a mixed method in which we define $\Pi = \mathbb{R}$. Define the variational form

$$b(v,q) = \int_\Omega v(\mathbf{x})\, q\, d\mathbf{x} = q \int_\Omega v(\mathbf{x})\, d\mathbf{x} \quad \forall v \in V,\ q \in \Pi.$$

Consider the variational problem to find $u \in V$ and $p \in \Pi$ such that

$$\begin{aligned} a(u,v) + b(v,p) &= F(v)\ \forall v \in V \\ b(u,q) &= 0\ \forall p \in \Pi. \end{aligned} \tag{25.1}$$

Assuming for the moment that this is well posed, the solution u has mean zero (by the second equation in (25.1)). That is, $u \in Z$, where

$$Z = \left\{ v \in H^1(\Omega)\ :\ \int_\Omega v(\mathbf{x})\, d\mathbf{x} = 0 \right\}$$

is the same as the space V in (2.15) for which the pure Neumann problem is well posed. Thus

$$a(u,v) = F(v) \quad \forall v \in Z, \tag{25.2}$$

meshsize	degree	$\overline{u_h}$	$\overline{f_h}$	$\overline{u_h}/\overline{f_h}$	$\|u-(u_h-\overline{u_h})\|_{L^2(\Omega)}$
16	1	1.1e+13	1.3e-03	8.1e+15	2.11e-02
16	2	-1.4e-03	-5.2e-18	2.6e+14	6.87e-05
16	1	1.1e+13	1.3e-03	8.1e+15	2.11e-02
32	1	6.5e+10	3.3e-04	2.0e+14	2.09e-03
64	1	2.8e+09	8.1e-05	3.4e+13	5.25e-04
128	1	1.5e+08	2.0e-05	7.2e+12	1.32e-04
256	1	8.4e+06	5.1e-06	1.7e+12	3.30e-05
16	2	-1.4e-03	-5.2e-18	2.6e+14	6.87e-05
16	4	2.0e-03	6.5e-18	3.1e+14	2.42e-08

Table 25.2: Results

since $b(v,q) = 0$ for all $v \in Z$ and $q \in \Pi$. So we obtain a solution to the pure Neumann problem. We leave as Exercise 25.4 to prove that the mixed method (25.1) is well posed. As with Taylor-Hood, we can form a single variational problem (13.32) and then solve this by Gaussian elimination. But again, the problem has lost the positive-definiteness of the linear system represented by (25.2). But we can use the iterated penalty method to solve (25.1) as we do for the Stokes equations.

25.1.4 A positive-definite approach

To conform to the presentation of the iterated penalty method described in Section 14.2, define the operator $\mathcal{D}$ by

$$\mathcal{D}v = \frac{1}{|\Omega|}\int_\Omega v(\mathbf{x})\,d\mathbf{x}, \qquad |\Omega| = \int_\Omega 1\,d\mathbf{x}. \tag{25.3}$$

Correspondingly, we define

$$(p,q)_\Pi = \int_\Omega p\,q\,d\mathbf{x} = p\,q\,|\Omega|. \tag{25.4}$$

Note that

$$b(v,q) = q\int_\Omega v(\mathbf{x})\,d\mathbf{x} = q\,|\Omega|\,\mathcal{D}v = (\mathcal{D}v,q)_\Pi.$$

Thus the iterated penalty method (14.9) (with $\rho = \rho'$) takes the form

$$\begin{aligned} a(u^n,v) + \rho\,(\mathcal{D}u^n,\mathcal{D}v)_\Pi &= F(v) - (\mathcal{D}v,\mathcal{D}w^n)_\Pi \quad \forall v \in V_h \\ w^{n+1} &= w^n + \rho u^n, \end{aligned} \tag{25.5}$$

since G is zero in this case. We again begin with $w^0 = 0$. Note that

$$(\mathcal{D}v,\mathcal{D}w)_\Pi = \mathcal{D}v\,\mathcal{D}w\,|\Omega| = \frac{1}{|\Omega|}\int_\Omega v(\mathbf{x})\,d\mathbf{x}\int_\Omega w(\mathbf{x})\,d\mathbf{x}.$$

We leave as Exercise 25.5 to implement the algorithm (25.5).

25.2 Stationary iterative methods

There are three important classes of iterative methods. The first of these are known equivalently as **stationary iterative methods** and **relaxation methods** [146, 175]. Examples

algorithm	sufficient conditions on A for convergence
Jacobi	generalized diagonally dominant
Gauss-Seidel	symmetric, positive definite
SOR	symmetric, positive definite

Table 25.3: Stationary iterative methods for solving $AX = F$ and conditions on A that guarantee convergence.

algorithm	matrices for which the method applies
CG	symmetric, positive definite
MINRES	symmetric
GMRES	invertible

Table 25.4: Krylov subspace based methods for solving $AX = F$ and conditions on A that guarantee convergence.

include Jacobi, Gauss-Seidel, SOR, SSOR, etc.; these basic techniques are still used in certain contexts, and many of the concepts behind them are frequently used in more complicated solvers. In particular, relaxation methods are frequently used as **smoothers** for multigrid methods. Typically, the simpler the iterative method, the easier it is to implement a parallel version.

Suppose that we are solving a linear system $AX = F$. The general form of a stationary iterative scheme is

$$Nx^{n+1} = PX^n + F,$$

where $A = N - P$ and N is chosen to be an easily invertible matrix, e.g., diagonal (Jacobi) or triangular (Gauss-Seidel, SOR). The error $E^n = X - X^n$ satisfies

$$x^{n+1} = MX^n,$$

where $M = N^{-1}P$. Thus convergence is equivalent to $\rho(M) < 1$ where ρ is the spectral radius. It is known [259] that Jacobi is convergent for generalized diagonally dominant matrices, and Gauss-Seidel and SOR are convergent for symmetric, positive definite matrices.

25.3 Krylov methods

Krylov[2] methods are a class of techniques based on projecting the solution onto an increasing subspace of vectors that is efficient to create.

Suppose that we are solving a linear system $AX = F$. Then the Krylov subspace of order k is the linear space spanned by

$$F, AF, \ldots, A^k F.$$

Such vectors are easily created iteratively via $A^i F = A(A^{i-1}F)$, where $A^0 F = F$.

[2]Alexei Nikolaevich Krylov (1863–1945) was very active in the theory and practice of shipbuilding and is commemorated by the Krylov Shipbuilding Research Institute.

The first of the Krylov methods is called **conjugate gradients** (a.k.a. **CG**) and was developed by Hestenes[3] and Stiefel[4]. Conjugate gradients converges for symmetric positive definite matrices, and it has an optimality property [259] that makes it extremely attractive.

The algorithm **MINRES** is applicable to symmetric but indefinite matrices [229]. Although CG and MINRES utilize the same Krylov space of vectors, they minimize different quantities. CG minimizes $\|X - X^k\|_A$, where $\|y\|_A = \sqrt{y^tAy}$, whereas MINRES minimizes $\|F - AX^k\|_{\ell^2}$, where $\|y\|_{\ell^2} = \sqrt{y^ty}$. It is easy to see that CG requires A to be positive definite, since $\|\cdot\|_A$ is not a norm otherwise. For symmetric, positive definite matrices, MINRES can outperform CG in some cases [133].

The algorithm **GMRES** [251, 147, 71] can be used for general matrices. The **Arnoldi** algorithm [61, 148] is closely related to GMRES.

25.4 Multigrid

Multigrid methods apply to problems posed on grids that are sufficiently structured to talk about coarse grids and fine grids. In a variational setting, this occurs if we have a sequence of subspaces $V^i \subset V$ with the property that $V^i \subset V^{i+1}$. The solutions to the variational problems

$$\text{Find } u^i \in V^i \text{ such that } a(u^i, v) = F(v) \quad \forall v \in V^i \tag{25.6}$$

are then increasingly accurate approximations to the solution u of the variational problem

$$\text{Find } u \in V \text{ such that } a(u, v) = F(v) \quad \forall v \in V. \tag{25.7}$$

But more importantly, u^i can be used as an initial guess for an iterative scheme for solving for u^{i+1}. However, the real power of multigrid is deeper than this. Suppose that we are trying to solve for $u^i \in V^i$ satisfying (25.6) and we have an approximate solution $w^i \in V^i$. Then the residual error $r^i = u^i - w^i$ satisfies

$$a(r^i, v) = a(u^i, v) - a(w^i, v) = F(v) - a(w^i, v) \quad \forall v \in V, \tag{25.8}$$

which does not involve knowing u^i. The magic of multigrid is to approximate (25.8) on a coarser space (V^{i-1}). Of course, we need to know that w^i is smooth enough that this is an effective strategy, but this can be achieved by using a variety of iterative methods, such as the stationary iterative methods, to remove high frequencies. For details, see [57].

It is not strictly required to have $V^i \subset V^{i+1}$. There are two ways in which $V^i \not\subset V^{i+1}$ occurs. One is when discontinuous finite element spaces are used [56]. Another is when the underlying grids are not nested [199, 291, 62, 145].

Multigrid methods were initiated by Bakhvalov[5] [27] in 1966. Achi Brandt [51] began popularizing and developing the method in 1977. Bank and Dupont [29, 30] gave one of the first proofs of convergence of the method, in research that initiated at the University of Chicago.

[3] Magnus Rudolph Hestenes (1906–1991) obtained a Ph.D. at the University of Chicago with Gilbert Bliss in 1932.

[4] Eduard L. Stiefel (1909–1978) is known both as a pure mathematician (for his work on the Stiefel-Whitney characteristic classes) and as a computational mathematician (he was also an early user and developer of computers [272]). Stiefel was the advisor of Peter Henrici as well as 63 other students over a period of 37 years. Henrici was the advisor of Gilbert Strang, one of the early pioneers of the mathematical theory of the finite element method.

[5] Nikolai Sergeevich Bakhvalov (1934—2005) studied with both Sobolev and Kolmogorov.

The linear system in the iterated penalty method for solving the Stokes problem described in Section 14.2 becomes ill-conditioned for ρ large. But there are multigrid methods available to solve such systems whose performance does not deteriorate for large ρ [195].

25.5 Preconditioners

The convergence rate of many iterative methods depends on the condition number of the linear system. For a symmetric, positive definite linear system, we can take the condition number to be defined as the ratio of the largest eigenvalue divided by the smallest eigenvalue. Linear systems associated with partial differential operators often have a condition number that grows inversely with the mesh resolution. This is because the PDE often has eigenvalues of unbounded size, and the finer the mesh the larger the eigenvalues that can be resolved. In particular, eigenfunctions often oscillate with a frequency roughly proportional to the eigenvalue. Thus the finer meshes resolve higher frequencies. Therefore iterative methods introduce a limit on our ability to resolve solutions based on mesh refinement.

We have seen that round-off is strongly amplified by the condition number of a linear system. One approach to this dilemma is to use higher-order approximations, but this is limited by the fact that the higher-order approximation resolves higher frequency eigenfunctions, so the condition number is not reduced. A better approach is to scale the linear system appropriately to control the size of the eigenvalues.

The simplest scaling is diagonal preconditioning. For a given matrix A, define $\operatorname{diag}(A)$ to be the diagonal matrix with the same diagonal entries as A. Then the diagonal preconditioning of A is the matrix $\operatorname{diag}(A)^{-1}A$. Fortunately, it is simple to compute the inverse of a diagonal matrix $P = \operatorname{diag}(A)^{-1}$. A more complex version of this idea is to produce a preconditioner by using an incomplete factorization of the system [155, 40] in which a sparsity condition is enforced autocratically. That is, Gaussian elimination (or other direct method) is performed in a way that only creates certain nonzero elements in the resulting factors. If for example we restrict the factors to be only diagonal, then the algorithm is equivalent to diagonal preconditioning. On the other hand, we make no restriction on sparsity, and allow arbitrary fill-in, then the algorithm produces the exact inverse (via forward and backward solution algorithms). The general case falls in between.

One common choice is to limit the sparsity of the factors to be the same as the sparsity pattern of the original matrix. Such a factorization is obtained by following an elimination algorithms (e.g., Gaussian elimination, Cholesky factorization, etc.), but when the algorithm calls for fill-in to occur, these additions to the original sparse structure of A are ignored. This yields a matrix P with the same sparsity pattern as A and yet P is in some sense an approximation to A^{-1}.

The benefit of preconditioning is that the iterative method performs as if the matrix condition number is that of the preconditioned system PA [119]. Thus significant benefit can occur. The main objective is to choose P to be as close to A^{-1} as possible.

The discrete Green's function provides a way to solve a system [255], and this can be used to create an efficient, parallel algorithm to implement a preconditioner [255].

A general understanding of preconditioners for linear systems arising in solving PDEs is given in [213]. They describe how to extend the concept of preconditioner to the PDE itself, and this in turn, when discretized, provides an effective preconditioner that can be robust with respect to mesh size and parameters in the PDE. In (25.9), we see two ways to construct preconditioners, and [213] advocates the bottom-left of the diagram.

$$\begin{array}{ccc} \text{PDE operator } A & \xrightarrow{\text{discretization}} & A_h \\ \Big\downarrow \begin{array}{l}\text{approx.}\\ \text{inverse}\end{array} & & \Big\downarrow \begin{array}{l}\text{approx.}\\ \text{inverse}\end{array} \\ \text{preconditioner } P \text{ for PDE} & \xrightarrow{\text{discretization}} & P_h\,. \end{array} \tag{25.9}$$

25.6 Exercises

Exercise 25.1 *Complete and execute the code in Program 25.1.*

Exercise 25.2 *Suppose that an $n \times n$ matrix A is symmetric: $A^t = A$. Suppose also that A has a factorization $A = LDU$. Show that $A = LDL^t$. (Hint: use the uniqueness of the factorization.)*

Exercise 25.3 *Suppose that an $n \times n$ matrix A is symmetric ($A^t = A$) has a factorization $A = LDL^t$ where L is lower triangular and has 1's on the diagonal. Prove that A is positive definite if and only if the diagonal entries of D are positive. (Hint: a matrix is positive definite if and only if $X^A X > 0$ for any vector $X \neq 0$. Use the factorization to expand $X^A X$.)*

Exercise 25.4 *Consider the mixed method in Section 25.1.3. Prove that the mixed method (25.1) is well posed, that is show that all the conditions in Section 13.2 are satisfied. In particular, the main ones to check are (13.28) and (13.29). (Hint: Π and Π_h are the same in this case, and $Z_h = V_h \cap Z$.)*

Exercise 25.5 *Implement the iterated penalty method in Section 25.1.4, that is, the algorithm (25.5). Solve the problem in Exercise 2.5. Compare with what is obtained via Gaussian elimination.*

Exercise 25.6 *Consider the iterated penalty method*

$$\begin{aligned} a(u^n, v) + \rho \int_\Omega u^n(\mathbf{x}) v(\mathbf{x})\, d\mathbf{x} &= F(v) - \int_\Omega v(\mathbf{x})\, d\mathbf{x} \int_\Omega w^n(\mathbf{x})\, d\mathbf{x} \quad \forall v \in V_h \\ w^{n+1} &= w^n + \rho u^n. \end{aligned} \tag{25.10}$$

How does this compare with the algorithm (25.5)? Solve the problem in Exercise 2.5. Compare with what is obtained via Gaussian elimination.

Chapter 26

Eigenvalues and Eigenvectors

Eigenvalues, and their associated eigenvectors, play a critical role in both theory and applications [12]. Thus we make a small detour here to talk about them, their role in various applications, and how to compute them.

26.1 Oscillations

We have seen two PDE systems, the wave equation in Chapter 12 and elasticity in Chapter 19, in which the governing equations are of the form

$$\mathbf{u}_{tt} + \mathbf{A}\mathbf{u} = \mathbf{f}, \tag{26.1}$$

where $\mathbf{u}$ is a vector in the discretized approximation. As we saw in detail with the wave equation in Chapter 12, such systems have oscillatory solutions as a function of t. But the amplitude of such oscillations can depend strongly on the frequency of oscillation of the forcing function $\mathbf{f}$. Such systems exhibit what is known as **resonance**, in which the amplitude becomes arbitrarily large as the frequency of $\mathbf{f}$ is tuned to characteristic frequencies of the system (26.1).

26.2 Resonance

Resonance is a phenomenon that children encounter when playing on a swing. They learn to tune their forcing (or pumping) to a natural frequency of the swing set. Fortunately, there is a simple algorithm for doing this, although some people are better at it than others. Basically, you pump at the same place in the cycle every time, and this makes $\mathbf{f}$ repeat at the natural frequency of the swing.

Resonance is a critical factor in engineering design. Resonance can lead to disasters such as the collapse of the original Tacoma Narrows bridge [12]. Thus it is considered in the design of all large structures: bridges, buildings, etc. Resonance is also a major factor in the amplification of the effects of earthquakes [277, 208]. And the amplitude of tidal motion is determined by resonance.

Acoustic resonance is critical in the design of musical instruments. Indeed, when you touch a violin string lightly at appropriate points, instead of holding it down to the fingerboard, and then bowing or plucking, you can generate higher harmonics, exploiting resonance.

26.2.1 Scalar resonance

To begin to understand resonance quantitatively, we simplify (26.1) even further by considering a scalar equation of the form

$$u'' + \mu u = f, \tag{26.2}$$

where $f(t) = \cos(\omega t)$ and ω is a constant. We can solve (26.1) as $u(t) = a\cos(\omega t)$, since for this function

$$u''(t) = -a\,\omega^2 \cos(\omega t) = -\omega^2 u(t).$$

Thus

$$u''(t) + \mu u(t) = (\mu - \omega^2)u(t) = a(\mu - \omega^2)\cos(\omega t) = a(\mu - \omega^2)f(t).$$

Therefore $u(t) = a\cos(\omega t)$ solves (26.1) if

$$a = \frac{1}{\mu - \omega^2}. \tag{26.3}$$

The fact that the amplitude a of u goes to infinity as $\omega \to \sqrt{\mu}$ is called **resonance**. That is, as the forcing frequency approaches the critical value $\sqrt{\mu}$, the solution gets arbitrarily big, even though f stays the same magnitude.

We can also solve (26.1) when $\mu = \omega^2$, although (26.3) is no longer valid. Instead, we find (Exercise 26.1) a solution

$$u(t) = t\sin(\omega t),$$

which grows without bound as time progresses. This provides one way to think about resonance in disasters: it causes the physical system to exceed its design limits, and then it fails.

Obviously, we want to avoid having the forcing frequency match this critical value. For a single equation, it is easy to see what the critical value is, but for a system of equations, we need a bit more notation.

26.2.2 Vector resonance

To solve (26.1) with $\mathbf{f}(t) = \mathbf{g}\cos(\omega t)$, let us try $\mathbf{u}(t) = \mathbf{a}\cos(\omega t)$ for some vector $\mathbf{a}$ to be determined. Following the previous steps, we find

$$\mathbf{u}_{tt}(t) + \mathbf{A}\mathbf{u}(t) = (\mathbf{A} - \omega^2\mathcal{I})\mathbf{u}(t) = (\mathbf{A} - \omega^2\mathcal{I})\mathbf{a}\cos(\omega t), \tag{26.4}$$

where $\mathcal{I}$ is the identity matrix. Thus we have a solution provided

$$(\mathbf{A} - \omega^2\mathcal{I})\mathbf{a} = \mathbf{g}. \tag{26.5}$$

So to understand resonance in this case, we need to know how big $\mathbf{a}$ can be for different values of ω. In particular, we want to avoid situations where $\mathbf{A} - \omega^2\mathcal{I}$ is nearly singular. This leads us to the study of **eigenvalues**.

26.3 Eigenvalues

Eigenvalues can take various forms. The simplest context is in terms of matrices.

26.3.1 Eigenvalues of matrices

The eigenvalue and eigenvector pair $(\lambda, \mathbf{X})$ for a matrix $\mathbf{A}$ is defined by the equation

$$\mathbf{AX} = \lambda\mathbf{X}. \tag{26.6}$$

The fine print requires $\mathbf{X} \neq \mathbf{0}$, for otherwise $(\lambda, \mathbf{0})$ would always be a solution for any λ. But moreover, $\mathbf{X}$ is not unique: if $\mathbf{X}$ is a solution so is $c\mathbf{X}$ for any scalar c. So we have to think of $\mathbf{X}$ as only prescribing a direction, not a magnitude.

So eigenvalues are ideal for answering the questions raised about resonance in (26.5). If ω^2 is not near an eigenvalue, then resonance does not occur. Thus we see why it is of interest to determine the eigenvalues of systems.

Even if we are only interested in real-valued matrices, the eigenpair $(\lambda, \mathbf{X})$ may be complex. However, if $\mathbf{A}$ is symmetric ($\mathbf{A}^t = \mathbf{A}$) then both are real. As we have seen, there are many applications for which $\mathbf{A}$ is symmetric, so we focus primarily on such systems.

26.3.2 Variational eigenproblems

Variational problems have eigenvalues too. They take the form

$$a(u, v) = \lambda\, (u, v)_{L^2(\Omega)} \quad \forall\, v \in V. \tag{26.7}$$

Here u is the eigenvector and λ is the eigenvalue. Again, u is defined only up to a constant multiple, and so it is natural to constrain it in some way.

The variational formulation is appropriate for the Rayleigh[1] characterization of eigenvalues. Define the Rayleigh quotient

$$\mathcal{R}(v) = \frac{a(v, v)}{(v, v)_{L^2(\Omega)}}, \qquad v \in V, \tag{26.8}$$

where V is one of our finite element spaces.

In particular, eigenvalues are critical points of $\mathcal{R}$. For example, the smallest eigenvalue is given by

$$\lambda_{\min} = \min_{0 \neq v \in V} \mathcal{R}(v). \tag{26.9}$$

Here the notation $0 \neq v \in V$ means that $v \in V$ is not identically zero, so in particular $\|v\|_{L^2(\Omega)} > 0$. Note that $\mathcal{R}(cv) = \mathcal{R}(v)$ for any scalar c, due to the homogeneity of $\mathcal{R}$ (it is quadratic in both the numerator and denominator). Thus it is equivalent to write

$$\lambda_{\min} = \min_{v \in V,\ \|v\|_{L^2(\Omega)} = 1} \mathcal{R}(v). \tag{26.10}$$

Writing out the Rayleigh quotient, we have

$$\lambda_{\min} = \min_{0 \neq v \in V} \frac{a(v, v)}{(v, v)_{L^2(\Omega)}} = \min_{0 \neq v \in V} \frac{a(v, v)}{\|v\|^2_{L^2(\Omega)}}.$$

[1] John William Strutt, 3rd Baron Rayleigh (1842–1919) was a student of Stokes.

Thus

$$\lambda_{\min} \leq \frac{a(v,v)}{\|v\|^2_{L^2(\Omega)}} \quad \forall\, 0 \neq v \in V.$$

Multiplying by $\|v\|_{L^2(\Omega)}$, we find

$$\lambda_{\min}\|v\|^2_{L^2(\Omega)} \leq a(v,v) \quad \forall\, v \in V. \tag{26.11}$$

Note that this holds trivially for $v \equiv 0$. We recognize (26.11) as a statement of coercivity if $\lambda_{\min} > 0$. This demonstrates a theoretical role for eigenvalues, in addition to the phenomenological role with regard to resonance discussed at the beginning of Section 26.2.

26.3.3 Computing eigenproblems

One simple algorithm for approximating eigenvalues is **Rayleigh quotient iteration**:

$$\begin{aligned} a(w^k,v) - \lambda^k (w^k,v)_{L^2(\Omega)} &= (u^k,v)_{L^2(\Omega)} \quad \forall\, v \in V, \\ u^{k+1} &= \|w^k\|^{-1}_{L^2(\Omega)}\, w^k, \\ \lambda^{k+1} &= \mathcal{R}\big(u^{k+1}\big). \end{aligned} \tag{26.12}$$

Note that

$$\|u^{k+1}\|_{L^2(\Omega)} = \|w^k\|^{-1}_{L^2(\Omega)}\|w^k\|_{L^2(\Omega)} = 1,$$

so that $\mathcal{R}\big(u^{k+1}\big) = a(u^{k+1},u^{k+1})$.

We need to start with some u^0 and λ^0, and the quality of the guesses we make will affect the efficiency of the algorithm. Some care needs to be taken regarding solving for w^k since the system used is approaching singularity. However, this is part of the magic of the algorithm [259, Section 15.2.1].

If we know that $a(v,v) \geq 0$ for all $v \in V$, then we could take any $\lambda^0 < 0$ to approximate the lowest eigenvalue. For the lowest eigenvalue, the corresponding eigenvector is often nonnegative, so that information could also be used. For example, we might take $u^0 \equiv 1$.

26.3.4 Characteristic values

The eigenvalues of a given operator, such as the Laplacian, will depend on the domain. Moreover, they can be characteristic of the domain, allowing the identification of the domain from the eigenvalues [174]. The word "eigen" is German for "characteristic," and one thus often sees the term **characteristic values** instead of eigenvalues.

26.4 Review of the Helmholtz problem

The Helmholtz problem in Section 12.3 involves solving

$$-k^2 u(\mathbf{x}) - \Delta u(\mathbf{x}) = f(\mathbf{x}), \tag{26.13}$$

as indicated in (12.15). But we know that there can be eigenvalues $\lambda = k^2$ where the corresponding eigenvector u_λ satisfies

$$-\Delta u_\lambda(\mathbf{x}) = \lambda u_\lambda(\mathbf{x}), \tag{26.14}$$

leading to a null solution u_λ of (26.13). For k near $\sqrt{\lambda}$ we thus expect a resonance phenomenon, and if $\lambda = k^2$ the character of the solution can change completely. In particular, f must satisfy constraints. If λ is a simple eigenvalue [270], then the constraint is that $(f, u_\lambda)_{L^2(\Omega)} = 0$.

26.5 Meaning of Gårding's inequality

The inequality (10.21) can be interpreted as follows. Let $\rho = \gamma_2/\gamma_1$. Then dividing by γ_1, (10.21) can be rewritten

$$\gamma_1^{-1}\|v\|_{H^1(\Omega)}^2 \leq a(v,v) + \rho\|v\|_{L^2(\Omega)}^2 \quad \forall v \in V.$$

This is the coercivity inequality for the new bilinear form

$$a_\rho(u,v) := a(u,v) + \rho(u,v)_{L^2(\Omega)} \quad \forall u, v \in V.$$

If λ is an eigenvalue for $a_\rho(\cdot,\cdot)$, then $\lambda - \rho$ is an eigenvalue for $a(\cdot,\cdot)$ (Exercise 26.4). Since coercivity is a statement about positivity of eigenvalues, this means that the eigenvalues of $a(\cdot,\cdot)$ are bounded below by $-\rho$.

26.6 Estimating the inf-sup constant

Several papers have addressed the issue of estimating computationally the inf-sup constant (β in (13.29)) for various spaces and variational problems [238, 247, 16]. We show here that this can be thought of as an eigenvalue problem [137]. Define κ by

$$\kappa = \min_{0\neq v\in V_h,\, v\perp_a Z_h} \frac{(\nabla\cdot v, \nabla\cdot v)_{L^2}}{a(v,v)} = \min_{0\neq v\in Z_h^\perp} \frac{(\nabla\cdot v, \nabla\cdot v)_{L^2}}{a(v,v)}, \tag{26.15}$$

where $Z_h^\perp = \{\mathbf{v} \in V_h : a(\mathbf{v},\mathbf{w}) = 0 \;\forall \mathbf{w} \in Z_h\}$. We have $\beta \geq \sqrt{\kappa}$, where β is the constant in the inf-sup condition provided we define $\|v\|_V = \sqrt{a(v,v)}$.

Lemma 26.1 *Suppose that $\|v\|_V = \sqrt{a(v,v)}$ and $Q_h = \nabla\cdot V_h$. Then*

$$\beta = \inf_{0\neq q\in Q_h} \sup_{0\neq v\in V_h} \frac{b(v,q)}{\|v\|_V\|q\|_{L^2}} = \inf_{0\neq q\in Q_h} \sup_{0\neq v\in Z_h^\perp} \frac{b(v,q)}{\|v\|_V\|q\|_{L^2}} \geq \sqrt{\kappa},$$

where κ is defined in (26.15).

Proof. Take $q = \nabla\cdot w$ where $w \in Z_h^\perp$. Then

$$\inf_{0\neq w\in Z_h^\perp} \sup_{0\neq v\in Z_h^\perp} \frac{(\nabla\cdot v, \nabla\cdot w)_{L^2}}{\|\nabla\cdot w\|_{L^2}\|v\|_V} \geq \inf_{0\neq w\in Z_h^\perp} \frac{(\nabla\cdot w, \nabla\cdot w)_{L^2}}{\|\nabla\cdot w\|_{L^2}\|w\|_V} = \inf_{0\neq w\in Z_h^\perp} \frac{\|\nabla\cdot w\|_{L^2}}{\|w\|_V} = \sqrt{\gamma}$$

by taking $v = w$.

On the other hand, [57, (13.1.16)] implies that

$$\sqrt{\kappa} \geq \beta\Big(\frac{\alpha}{\alpha + C_a}\Big).$$

With the choice of norm $\|v\|_V = \sqrt{a(v,v)}$, then $C_a = \alpha = 1$. Thus β and $\sqrt{\kappa}$ are essentially equivalent parameters measuring the stability of the Stokes approximation.

26.6.1 An eigenproblem

Consider the eigenproblem: find $0 \neq \mathbf{u}_h \in Z_h^\perp$ such that

$$(\nabla\cdot \mathbf{u}_h, \nabla\cdot \mathbf{v}) = \lambda a(\mathbf{u}_h, \mathbf{v})\ \forall \mathbf{v} \in Z_h^\perp.$$

Let $\lambda_{\min}$ be the smallest eigenvalue, which is given by the Rayleigh quotient

$$\lambda_{\min} = \min_{\mathbf{v}\in Z_h^\perp} \frac{(\nabla\cdot \mathbf{v}, \nabla\cdot \mathbf{v})}{a(\mathbf{v}, \mathbf{v})} > 0. \tag{26.16}$$

Note that $\lambda_{\min} > 0$ since $\lambda = 0$ leads to the contradiction $\nabla\cdot \mathbf{u}_h = 0$, that is, $\mathbf{u}_h \in Z_h \cap Z_h^\perp$.

We can solve for $\mathbf{u}_h$ via Rayleigh quotient iteration (**RQI**), namely to find $\mathbf{u}^k \in Z_h^\perp$ such that

$$\begin{aligned} (\nabla\cdot \mathbf{u}^{k-1}, \nabla\cdot \mathbf{v}) &= \lambda^k a(\mathbf{u}^k, \mathbf{v})\ \forall \mathbf{v} \in Z_h^\perp \\ \lambda^{k+1} &= \frac{(\nabla\cdot \mathbf{u}^k, \nabla\cdot \mathbf{u}^k)}{a(\mathbf{u}^k, \mathbf{u}^k)} \geq \lambda_{\min}. \end{aligned} \tag{26.17}$$

Now we consider how to compute this despite the fact that the space $Z_h^\perp$ is not explicitly known.

In the case that $a(\cdot,\cdot)$ is coercive on all of V_h, we can implement (26.17) by solving

$$a(\mathbf{u}^k, \mathbf{v}) = (\lambda^k)^{-1}(\nabla\cdot \mathbf{u}^{k-1}, \nabla\cdot \mathbf{v})\ \forall \mathbf{v} \in V_h.$$

Then $a(\mathbf{u}^k, \mathbf{v}) = 0$ for all $\mathbf{v} \in Z_h$, so that $\mathbf{u}^k \in Z_h^\perp$ for all $k > 0$.

26.6.2 Comparison with earlier techniques

The approach advocated in [238, 247, 16] requires working with a larger space than $\nabla\cdot V_h$, and it thus finds spurious modes in addition to estimating the constant $\kappa = \lambda_{\min}$. By contrast, our approach has no spurious modes, since $\kappa = \lambda_{\min} > 0$, and it identifies concretely an approximation of the extrema of (26.15). Thus there is a fundamental philosophical difference regarding spurious modes. Using our approach, the concept of spurious modes itself becomes spurious.

26.7 Exercises

Exercise 26.1 *Consider (26.2) in the case that $\omega = \sqrt{\mu}$. In this case, the formula (26.3) is no longer valid. Show that instead, there is a solution of the form*

$$u(t) = \frac{t}{2\omega}\sin(\omega t).$$

(Hint: write $u = tv$ and show that $u'' = 2v' + tv''$. Be sure to say what the formula for v is. Next show that $tv'' = -\omega^2 u$, so that $u'' + \omega^2 u = 2v'$. Finally, verify that $2v' = \cos(\omega t)$.)

Exercise 26.2 *Consider the Laplacian on the square with homogeneous Dirichlet conditions. Show that it has an eigenvalue $2\pi^2$ with corresponding eigenvector $u(x, y) = (\sin \pi x)(\sin \pi y)$.*

Exercise 26.3 *Consider the Laplacian on the square. Approximate its lowest eigenvalue using the Rayleigh quotient iteration starting with* $\lambda^0 = 0$ *and* $u^0 \equiv 1$. *Compare your answer with* $\lambda = 2\pi^2$. *Do you get close if you take the degree of approximation high enough and the mesh fine enough?*

Exercise 26.4 *Suppose that* $a(\cdot,\cdot)$ *is a bilinear form on a space* V *and* $\rho \in \mathbb{R}$. *Define a new bilinear form*

$$a_\rho(u,v) := a(u,v) + \rho(u,v)_{L^2(\Omega)} \quad \forall u,v \in V.$$

Suppose λ *is an eigenvalue for* $a_\rho(\cdot,\cdot)$. *Show that* $\lambda - \rho$ *is an eigenvalue for* $a(\cdot,\cdot)$

Chapter 27

Pitfalls in Modeling using PDEs

Systems of partial differential equations provide the basis for some of the most powerful models of physical and social phenomena. The formalism of such models allows a remarkable level of automation of the process of simulating complex systems. Leveraging this potential for automation has been developed to the greatest extent by the FEniCS Project. However, using partial differential equation models, and numerical methods to solve them, involves numerous *pitfalls*. We highlight many of these pitfalls and discuss ways to circumvent them.

It is simply not possible to provide a solution to all systems of differential equations. Any given differential equation may be *ill-posed*, meaning that it does not make sense to talk about the solution for one reason or another. At the moment, there is no simple criterion to determine if a system of differential equations is well-posed. As a result, it is not possible to provide software that solves all systems of differential equations automagically. The first step, then, is to determine if a system being studied is *well-posed*.

There are several ways in which a differential equation can fail to be well-posed. The most serious potential pitfall for a differential equation is the lack of a solution regardless of any boundary conditions or initial conditions. In Section 27.4, we give an example of such an equation with this extreme behavior. Although it may be quite rare, such a pitfall does exist if one tries to solve arbitrary systems of partial differential equations.

If a physical system is supposed to have a unique state given suitable determining conditions, then a mathematical model having multiple solutions is seriously flawed. The typical cause of a system of partial differential equations to have too many solutions is a lack of boundary conditions. It is not at all trivial to determine what the right number of boundary conditions might be for an arbitrary system of partial differential equations, and getting it wrong could lead to either too many solutions or too few! In section Section 27.1 we present a case where both of these can be seen.

Equally damaging, but often more subtle to detect, is the lack of continuous dependence of the solution on the data of a mathematical model, at least when the physical problem should have this property. Continuous dependence of the solution on the data will be verified for many systems of partial differential equations using various techniques subsequently. However, it is not always required that a physical problem have this property. One such "ill-posed" problem is considered in Section 10.6.

All of these shortcomings of models can be summarized as a lack of *well-posedness*. We will discuss some techniques to determine if a particular differential equation is well-posed, but this is generally beyond the scope of the book. Rather, it is assumed that the reader is trying to solved a well-posed problem.

Equally difficult to insure, even for differential equations that are well-posed, is the stability and consistency (and equivalently, convergence) of the numerical approximations. Even for well-posed systems of differential equations, there is no automatic way to define a discrete approximation scheme that will always converge to the solution of the differential equation as the approximation is refined. We discuss various pitfalls and examine in depth many of the most critical. However, we make no attempt to be exhaustive. We are mainly concerned with the implementation of convergent algorithms using structured programming techniques. It is assumed that the reader is trying to solved a well-posed problem with a stable and consistent numerical approximation.

A basic language we frequently employ is that of the variational formulation of differential equations. This is a powerful formulation that allows a simple proof of well-posedness in many cases. Moreover, it leads to stable and consistent numerical schemes through the use of appropriate approximation spaces of functions. In this way, finite element methods, spectral methods, spectral element methods, boundary element methods, collocation methods, variational difference methods and other discretization methods can be derived and analyzed with respect to stability and consistency.

27.1 Right-sizing BCs

Differential equations typically have too many solutions of the equations themselves to specify a solution in any reasonable sense. A unique solution, required by most physical models, is typically determined by boundary conditions and, for time-dependent problems, initial conditions. We will use the following notation of partial differential equations for the "Laplacian" operator

$$\Delta := \sum_{i=1}^{d} \frac{\partial^2}{\partial {x_i}^2}. \tag{27.1}$$

Consider the Laplace equation

$$-\Delta u = f \tag{27.2}$$

Then for $f \equiv 0$ the solutions are *harmonic* functions, and the real part of any complex analytic function in the plane (in two space dimensions) is harmonic. For any solution to (27.2), we can get another by adding any harmonic function. Thus there are way too many solutions to (27.2) without any further restrictions.

We will see in Chapter 2 that specifying the value of u on the boundary of some open set Ω makes the solution of (27.2) unique in Ω. That is, the system of equations

$$\begin{aligned} -\Delta u =& f \text{ in } \Omega \\ u =& g \text{ on } \partial\Omega \end{aligned} \tag{27.3}$$

has a unique solution, under suitable smoothness conditions on f, g and the boundary $\partial\Omega$.

There is no unique type of boundary condition that is appropriate for a given system of differential equations. For example, the system

$$\begin{aligned} -\Delta u =& f \text{ in } \Omega \\ \frac{\partial u}{\partial n} =& g \text{ on } \partial\Omega \end{aligned} \tag{27.4}$$

also has a solution, under suitable smoothness conditions on f, g and the boundary $\partial\Omega$, provided in addition that a simple compatibility condition exists between f and g, namely,

$$\int_\Omega f(\mathbf{x})\,d\mathbf{x} + \oint_{\partial\Omega} g(s)\,ds = 0. \tag{27.5}$$

This compatibility condition is a consequence of the divergence theorem (2.9) together with the observations that $\frac{\partial u}{\partial n} = (\nabla u)\cdot\mathbf{n}$ and $\Delta u = \nabla\cdot(\nabla u)$. Here, $\mathbf{n}$ is the outward-directed normal to $\partial\Omega$.

For any solution u to (27.4), $u + c$ is also a solution for any constant c. Thus there is a certain degree of non-uniqueness here, but it can be seen (Section 2.4) that this is all there is. That is, solutions to (27.4) exist and are unique up to an additive constant, provided the single compatibility condition (27.5) holds.

If some is good, then one might think more is better. However, it is easy to see that the system of equations

$$\begin{aligned} -\Delta u =& f \text{ in } \Omega \\ u =& g_0 \text{ on } \partial\Omega \\ \frac{\partial u}{\partial n} =& g_1 \text{ on } \partial\Omega \end{aligned} \tag{27.6}$$

has too many boundary conditions. Since the condition $u = g_0$ on $\partial\Omega$ already uniquely determines the solution u, it will only be a miracle that $\frac{\partial u}{\partial n} = g_1$ also holds on $\partial\Omega$. More precisely, there is a linear mapping A defined on functions on $\partial\Omega$ such that (27.6) has a solution if and only if $g_1 = Ag_0$ (see Exercise 27.4). Similarly, the system

$$\begin{aligned} -\Delta u =& f \text{ in } \Omega \\ \nabla u =& \mathbf{g} \text{ on } \partial\Omega \end{aligned} \tag{27.7}$$

is over-specified. It is closely related to (27.6) if we observe that the second equation says that the tangential derivative of u is equal to that of g_0. The over-determined boundary-value problem (27.7) appears in a non-local compatibility condition for the Navier-Stokes equations (Section 20.5.2).

27.2 Numerical stability

The simplest differential equation to solve is an ordinary differential equation

$$\frac{du}{dt} = f(u,t) \tag{27.8}$$

with initial value

$$u(0) = u_0 \tag{27.9}$$

where we are interested in solving on some interval $[0,T]$.

The definition of the derivative as a limit of difference quotients suggests a method of discretization:

$$\frac{du}{dt}(t) \approx \frac{u(t+\Delta t) - u(t)}{\Delta t} \tag{27.10}$$

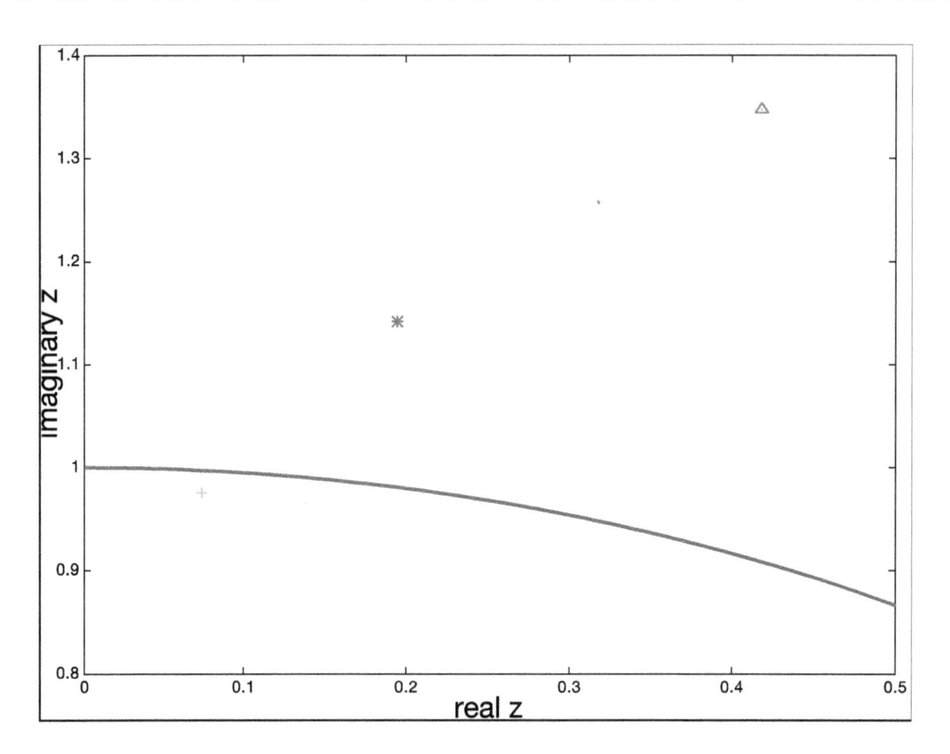

Figure 27.1: Roots of polynomials (27.20) with the smallest modulus are plotted for degrees $k = 5$ (triangle), $k = 6$ (asterisk), and $k = 7$ (plus). The solid line indicates the unit circle in the complex plane.

where Δt is a small positive parameter. This suggests an algorithm for generating a sequence of values $u_n \approx u(n\Delta t)$ given by (for example)

$$u_n = u_{n-1} + \Delta t f(u_n, t_n) \tag{27.11}$$

where $t_n = n\Delta t$.

The algorithm (27.11) is called the **implicit Euler** method, and it can be shown that it generates a sequence with the property that

$$|u(t_n) - u_n| \leq C_{f,T}\Delta t \quad \forall t_n \leq T \tag{27.12}$$

provided that we solve the implicit equation (27.11) for u_n exactly and we compute with exact arithmetic. The issue of solving the nonlinear equation at each step is important but not a show-stopper. However, the requirement of using finite-precision arithmetic means that the best error behavior we could expect is

$$|u(t_n) - u_n| \leq C_{f,T}\Delta t + n\epsilon \quad \forall t_n \leq T \tag{27.13}$$

where ϵ measures the precision error that occurs at each step in (27.11). It is useful to re-write (27.13) using the fact that $n = t_n/\Delta t$ as

$$|u(t_n) - u_n| \leq C_{f,T}\Delta t + \frac{t_n\epsilon}{\Delta t} \tag{27.14}$$

which shows that the error reaches a minimum and cannot be reduced by reducing Δt.

One way to increase the accuracy in (27.13) is to use a more accurate approximation of the derivative than (27.10), such as given by the backwards differentiation formulæ (BDF) defined in Section 10.5.5

$$\frac{du}{dt}(t) \approx \frac{1}{\Delta t}\sum_{i=0}^{k} a_i u_{n-i} \tag{27.15}$$

where the coefficients $\{a_i \,:\, i = 0, \ldots k\}$ are chosen so that (27.15) is exact for polynomials of degree k. The BDF for $k = 1$ is the same as implicit Euler. Using the approximation (27.15), we get an algorithm of the form

$$\sum_{i=0}^{k} a_i u_{n-i} = \Delta t f(u_n, t_n) \tag{27.16}$$

which can be solved for u_n provided $a_0 \neq 0$. In this case, the final error estimate would be

$$|u(t_n) - u_n| \leq C_{f,T,k}\Delta t^k + \frac{t_n \epsilon}{\Delta t}. \tag{27.17}$$

Ultimate accuracy is still limited, but smaller absolute errors (with larger Δt) can be achieved with higher values of k. For example, suppose that

- $\epsilon = 10^{-6}$ (which corresponds to single precision on a 32-bit machine)
- $T = 1$ and
- (for the sake of argument) $C_{f,T,k} = 1$.

Then with implicit Euler ($k = 1$) the smallest error we can get is 10^{-3} with $\Delta t = 10^{-3}$. On the other hand, with $k = 2$ we get an error of size 10^{-4} with $\Delta t = 10^{-2}$. Not only is this a smaller error but less work needs to be done to achieve it. In practice, the constant $C_{f,T,k}$ would depend on k and the exact error behavior would likely be different in detail, but the general conclusion that a higher-order scheme may be better still holds. The BDF methods for $k = 2$ and 3 are extremely popular schemes.

We see that higher-order schemes can lead to more manageable errors and potentially less work for the same level of accuracy. Thus it seems natural to ask whether there are limits to choosing the order to be arbitrarily high. Unfortunately, not all of the BDF schemes are viable. Beyond degree six, they become **unconditionally unstable**. Let us examine the question of stability via a simple experiment. Suppose that, after some time T_0, it happens that $f(u,t) = 0$ for $t \geq T_0$. Then the solution u remains constant after T_0, since $\frac{du}{dt} \equiv 0$. What happens in the algorithm (27.16) is that we have

$$\sum_{i=0}^{k} a_i u_{n-i} = 0 \tag{27.18}$$

for $n \geq T_0/\Delta t$. However, this does not necessarily imply that u_n would tend to a constant. Let us examine what the solutions of (27.18) could look like.

Consider the sequence $u_n := \xi^{-n}$ for some number ξ. Plugging into (27.18) we find

$$0 = \sum_{i=0}^{k} a_i \xi^{-n+i} = \xi^{-n}\sum_{i=0}^{k} a_i \xi^i \tag{27.19}$$

If we define the polynomial p_k by

$$p_k(\xi) = \sum_{i=0}^{k} a_i \xi^i \tag{27.20}$$

we see that we have a null solution to (27.18) if and only if ξ is a root of p_k. If there is a root ξ of p_k where $|\xi| < 1$ then we get solutions to (27.18) which grow like

$$u_n = \xi^{-n} = \left(\frac{1}{\xi}\right)^{t_n/\Delta t}. \tag{27.21}$$

Not only does this blow up exponentially, the exponential rate goes to infinity as $\Delta t \to 0$. This clearly spells disaster. On the other hand, if $|\xi| > 1$, then the solution (27.21) goes rapidly to zero, and more rapidly as $\Delta t \to 0$. For roots ξ with $|\xi| = 1$ the situation is more complicated, and $\xi = 1$ is always a root because the sum of the coefficients a_i is always zero. Instability occurs if there is a multiple root on the unit circle $|\xi| = 1$. In general, one must consider all complex (as well as real) roots ξ.

Given this simple definition of the general case of BDF, it is hard to imagine what could go wrong regarding stability. Unfortunately, the condition that $|\xi| \geq 1$ for roots of $p_k(\xi) = 0$ restricts k to be six or less for the BDF formulæ. In Figure 27.1, complex roots with the smallest modulus are plotted for degrees $k = 5$ (triangle), $k = 6$ (asterisk), and $k = 7$ (plus). The solid line indicates the unit circle in the complex plane. Unfortunately, for $k = 7$ there is a pair of complex conjugate roots $z_{\pm} = 0.0735 \pm 0.9755\iota$ with (the same) complex modulus less than 1: $|z_{\pm}| \approx 0.97827$.

In Chapter 13, the inf-sup condition for mixed methods encapsulates another type of numerical stability that effects the choice of finite element spaces suitable for fluid flow problems.

27.3 The right box

The variational formulation of PDEs is not only a convenient way to describe a model, it also provides a way to ensure that a model is well-posed. One of the critical ingredients in the variational formulation is the space of functions in which one seeks the solution. We can see that this is just the right size to fit the needs of most modeling problems.

We can think of the space of functions in the variational formulation of PDEs as a box in which we look for a solution. If the box were too big, we might get spurious solutions. If it is too small, then we may get no solutions. We have indicated possible boxes in Figure 2.2.

A box too small is easy to describe: it would be natural to think we could just work with the space C^m of functions whose derivatives up through order m are continuous. If the number of derivatives in the PDE is less than or equal to m, then all derivatives are classically defined, and the equation itself makes sense as a equation among numbers at all points in the model domain. However, many problems naturally arise that do not fit into this box. For example, when the geometry of the boundary of a domain in two-dimensions has an interior angle that is greater than π (and hence the domain is not convex), a singularity arises even for the Laplace equation (Chapter 2).

A box too big can be described already in one-dimension. The famous Cantor "middle-

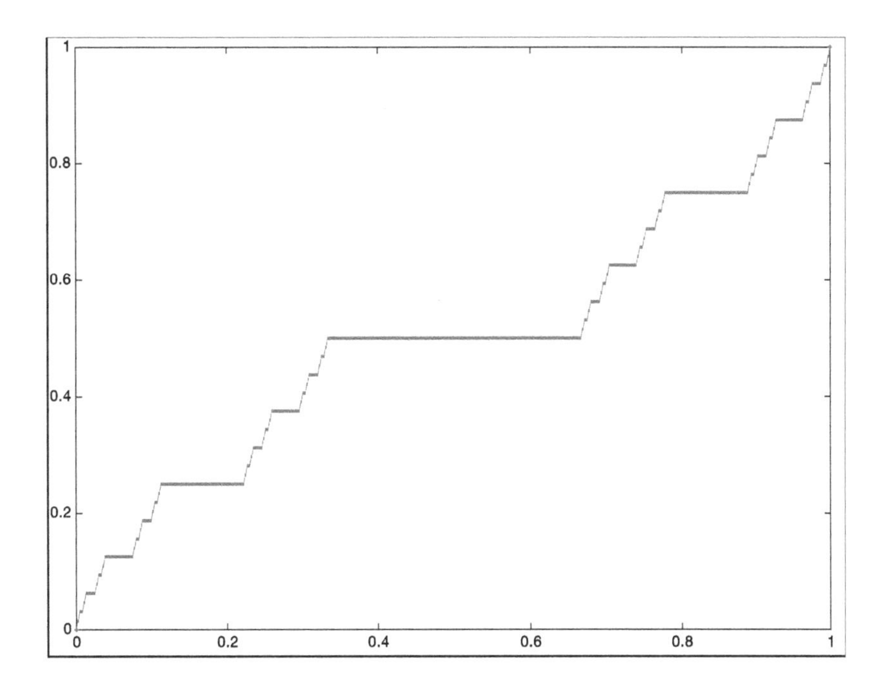

Figure 27.2: Cantor function (27.22).

thirds" function is defined as follows on the unit interval $[0,1]$:

$$\mathcal{C}(x) := \begin{cases} \frac{1}{2} & \frac{1}{3} \le x < \frac{2}{3}, \\ \frac{1}{2}\mathcal{C}(3x) & 0 \le x < \frac{1}{3}, \\ \frac{1}{2}(1+\mathcal{C}(3x-2)) & \frac{2}{3} \le x < 1. \end{cases} \tag{27.22}$$

The recursive nature of this definition means that it can easily be computed. Any programming language allowing recursion is suitable for implementation. By definition, the derivative of $\mathcal{C}$ is zero at almost every point (a notion made precise by Lebesgue measure theory [57].)

This is problematic, since we expect solutions of linear PDEs to be unique in most cases. But the simplest equation $u' = f$ would have $u + \mathcal{C}$ as a solution for any given solution u. However, the derivative of $\mathcal{C}$ does not qualify as a Lebesgue integrable function.

Thus the choice of spaces V of functions whose derivatives are Lebesgue integrable functions provides just the right size box in the variational formulation. These are called Sobolev spaces, and they are reviewed in Chapter 30.

27.4 Local solvability

When we state an equation such as $\Delta u = f$, we presume that it is possible to specify u, at least locally, by giving a combination of its derivatives $(u_{,11} + u_{,22} + \cdots)$. What is it that makes this possible? That is, should we always assume that an arbitrary combination of derivatives can be specified without any internal consistency required?

It is easy to see one kind of partial differential equation that would make little sense:

$$\frac{\partial^2 u}{\partial x\,\partial y} = -\frac{\partial^2 u}{\partial y\,\partial x}, \tag{27.23}$$

since we know that for smooth functions, the order of cross derivatives does not matter. Thus (27.23) corresponds to an equation of the form $t = -t$ and has only the zero solution.

There are some differential equations that simply have no solution even locally, independent of any boundary conditions. A famous example is due to Hans Lewy. Consider the equation

$$\frac{\partial u}{\partial x_1} - \iota\frac{\partial u}{\partial x_2} + 2(\iota x_1 - x_2)\frac{\partial u}{\partial x_3} = f, \tag{27.24}$$

where ι is the imaginary unit, $\iota = \sqrt{-1}$. Then for most infinitely differentiable functions f there is no solution of this equation in *any* open set in three-space. Note that this has nothing to do with boundary conditions, just with satisfying the differential equation. This equation is a complex equation ($\iota = \sqrt{-1}$) but it can easily be written as a system of two real equations for the real and imaginary parts of u respectively (see Exercise 27.3).

27.4.1 Multi-index notation

There is a general condition that must be satisfied in order that linear partial differential equations have a local solution. This condition is known as the **local solvability condition.** To explain the condition, we need to introduce some notation. Let $D = -\iota\left(\frac{\partial}{\partial x_1}, \ldots, \frac{\partial}{\partial x_j}, \ldots, \frac{\partial}{\partial x_d}\right)$ stand for the vector of complex partial differentials, and let $\alpha = (\alpha_1, \ldots, \alpha_j, \ldots, \alpha_d)$ be a **multi-index** (i.e., a vector of non-negative integers), so that

$$D^\alpha u := (-\iota)^{|\alpha|}\frac{\partial^{\alpha_1}}{\partial x_1^{\alpha_1}}\cdots\frac{\partial^{\alpha_j}}{\partial x_j^{\alpha_j}}\cdots\frac{\partial^{\alpha_d}}{\partial x_d^{\alpha_d}}u\,, \tag{27.25}$$

where $|\alpha| := \alpha_1 + \cdots \alpha_j + \cdots \alpha_d$. For any d-dimensional variable ξ, we can form the monomial

$$\xi^\alpha := {\xi_1}^{\alpha_1}\cdots{\xi_j}^{\alpha_j}\cdots{\xi_d}^{\alpha_d} \tag{27.26}$$

so that D^α is the same as ξ^α with the substitution $\xi_j = -i\partial/\partial x_j$. In this notation, the Lewy equation (27.24) becomes

$$-\iota D_1 u + D_2 u + 2(x_1 + \iota x_2)D_3 u = f \tag{27.27}$$

The reason for the factor $-\iota$ in the definition of D is so that the Fourier transform of D works out nicely; if $\hat{u}$ denotes the Fourier transform of u, then $\widehat{D^\alpha u}(\xi) = \xi^\alpha\hat{u}(\xi)$.

27.4.2 Symbology

Suppose that the differential operator in question takes the form

$$P(\mathbf{x}, D) = \sum_{|\alpha|\le m} a_\alpha(\mathbf{x})D^\alpha\,, \tag{27.28}$$

that is, suppose that we want to consider linear partial differential equations of the form

$$P(\mathbf{x}, D)u = \sum_{|\alpha|\le m} a_\alpha(\mathbf{x})D^\alpha u = f \tag{27.29}$$

for some f. We can form the corresponding **symbol** $P(\mathbf{x}, \xi)$ of the linear partial differential operator

$$P(\mathbf{x}, \xi) = \sum_{|\alpha| \le m} a_\alpha(\mathbf{x}) \xi^\alpha \,. \tag{27.30}$$

Define the **principal part** of the symbol, P_m, by

$$P_m(\mathbf{x}, \xi) = \sum_{|\alpha| = m} a_\alpha(\mathbf{x}) \xi^\alpha \,, \tag{27.31}$$

and correspondingly the complex conjugate of the principal part of the symbol, $\overline{P}_m$, by

$$\overline{P}_m(\mathbf{x}, \xi) = \sum_{|\alpha| = m} \overline{a_\alpha(\mathbf{x})} \xi^\alpha \,. \tag{27.32}$$

Also define the following partial derivatives of the principal part of the symbol:

$$P_m^{(j)}(\mathbf{x}, \xi) := \frac{\partial P_m}{\partial \xi_j}(\mathbf{x}, \xi) \,, \quad P_{m,j}(\mathbf{x}, \xi) := \frac{\partial P_m}{\partial x_j}(\mathbf{x}, \xi) \tag{27.33}$$

and define their complex conjugates analogously. Finally, define the **commutator** $C_{2m-1}(\mathbf{x}, \xi)$ of the principal part of the symbol via

$$C_{2m-1}(\mathbf{x}, \xi) := \iota \sum_{j=1}^{d} \left(P_m^{(j)}(\mathbf{x}, \xi) \overline{P}_{m,j}(\mathbf{x}, \xi) - \overline{P}_m^{(j)}(\mathbf{x}, \xi) P_{m,j}(\mathbf{x}, \xi) \right) \tag{27.34}$$

which is a polynomial of degree $2m - 1$ in ξ with real coefficients.

Theorem 27.1 *If the differential equation (27.29) has a solution in a set Ω for every smooth f that vanishes near the boundary of Ω, then*

$$C_{2m-1}(\mathbf{x}, \xi) = 0 \tag{27.35}$$

for all ξ and all $x \in \Omega$ such that $P_m(\mathbf{x}, \xi) = 0$.

27.4.3 The Lewy example

We can now examine the Lewy example (27.27) in terms of this theorem. The operator

$$P(x, D) = -\iota D_1 + D_2 + 2(x_1 + \iota x_2) D_3$$

has principal symbol

$$P_1(x, \xi) = -\iota \xi_1 + \xi_2 + 2(x_1 + \iota x_2) \xi_3.$$

Regarding the derivatives of the symbol, we have

$$P_1^{(j)}(x, \xi) = \frac{\partial P_1}{\partial \xi_j} = \begin{cases} -\iota & j = 1 \\ 1 & j = 2 \\ 2(x_1 + \iota x_2) & j = 3 \end{cases} \quad \text{and} \quad P_{1,j}(x, \xi) = \frac{\partial P_1}{\partial x_j} = \begin{cases} 2\xi_3 & j = 1 \\ 2\iota \xi_3 & j = 2 \\ 0 & j = 3 \end{cases}.$$

Similarly

$$\overline{P}_1^{(j)}(x,\xi) = \frac{\partial \overline{P}_1}{\partial \xi_j} = \begin{cases} \iota & j=1 \\ 1 & j=2 \\ 2(x_1 - \iota x_2) & j=3 \end{cases} \quad \text{and} \quad \overline{P}_{1,j}(x,\xi) = \frac{\partial \overline{P}_1}{\partial x_j} = \begin{cases} 2\xi_3 & j=1 \\ -2\iota\xi_3 & j=2 \\ 0 & j=3 \end{cases}.$$

Therefore

$$P_1^{(j)}(\mathbf{x},\xi)\overline{P}_{1,j}(\mathbf{x},\xi) - \overline{P}_1^{(j)}(\mathbf{x},\xi)P_{1,j}(\mathbf{x},\xi) = \begin{cases} -2\iota\xi_3 - 2\iota\xi_3 & j=1 \\ -2\iota\xi_3 - 2\iota\xi_3 & j=2 \\ 0 & j=3 \end{cases}.$$

Thus

$$C_1(x,\xi) = 8\xi_3.$$

On the other hand, $P_1(x,\xi) = 0$ means

$$0 = -\iota\xi_1 + \xi_2 + 2(x_1 + \iota x_2)\xi_3.$$

which means that P_1 vanishes for

$$\xi_3 = \frac{\iota\xi_1 - \xi_2}{2(x_1 + \iota x_2)} \neq 0$$

if $\iota\xi_1 \neq \xi_2$. Thus the condition (27.35) is violated for the Lewy PDE.

27.4.4 Laplace operator

Suppose that $P(x,D) = \Delta$. Then $P_2(x,\xi) = |\xi|^2$. Thus

$$P_2^{(j)}(x,\xi) = \frac{\partial P_2}{\partial \xi_j} = \frac{\partial \overline{P}_2}{\partial \xi_j} = 2\xi_j \quad \text{and} \quad P_{2,j}(x,\xi) = \frac{\partial P_2}{\partial x_j} = \frac{\partial \overline{P}_2}{\partial x_j} = 0.$$

Therefore, for all $j = 1, \ldots, d$,

$$P_2^{(j)}(\mathbf{x},\xi)\overline{P}_{2,j}(\mathbf{x},\xi) - \overline{P}_2^{(j)}(\mathbf{x},\xi)P_{2,j}(\mathbf{x},\xi) = 0.$$

Therefore

$$C_3(x,\xi) = 0$$

for all $x \in \mathbb{R}^d$ and $\xi \in \mathbb{R}^d$. On the other hand, $P_2(x,\xi) = |\xi|^2 = 0$ only for $\xi = \mathbf{0}$. Thus certainly $C_3(x,\xi) = 0$ whenever $P_2(x,\xi) = 0$. Indeed we see that the local solvability condition will be satisfied by any constant-coefficient operator $P(D)$, since the commutator vanishes.

27.4.5 Meaning of local solvability

Partial differential equation problems may be described in optimization terms as having a feasible set of solutions and boundary conditions to specify a desired solution in the feasible set. For example, a particular solution of $-\Delta u = f$ is the starting point for the feasible set of all solutions $u + v$ where v is harmonic ($\Delta v = 0$). Boundary (or other) conditions pick the v of interest in each case. PDEs that are not locally solvable have an empty set for the feasible set. So such PDEs are nonstarters, lacking the first requirement for an optimization problem.

Here, the notion of "solution" is very weak; it need not be a smooth solution. Thus the result provides a very stringent condition on the symbol in order to expect any sort of solution at all. For a complete description of this and other examples see [170]; see [49] for more recent results and references. The most striking feature of the local solvability condition (27.35) is that it is a "closed" condition. Otherwise said, "non-solvability" is an open condition: if $C_{2m-1}(\mathbf{x},\xi) \neq 0$ then small perturbations would not be expected to make it vanish. Moreover, even if (27.35) holds for one set of coefficients a_α, it may fail to hold for a small perturbation. Finally, we will be interested in nonlinear partial differential equations; if these have a solution, then the solution can be viewed as solutions to linear partial differential equations with appropriate coefficients (which depend on the particular solution).

Despite the pessimism implied by the local solvability condition (27.35), we will see that there are indeed broad classes of nonlinear partial differential equations which can be proved to have solutions. But this should not be taken for granted in general. In proposing a new model for a new phenomenon, the first question to ask is whether it makes sense at this most fundamental level.

27.5 PDE's in classical spaces

We have emphasized working with PDEs in Sobolev spaces via examples where the solutions have singularities. But even when everything is smooth, Sobolev spaces are essential. The usual C^k spaces of functions with k-th order continuous derivatives are not appropriate for characterizing PDEs even in the best case. We will just give an extended example to explain this and leave it to references [123, 139] for more details. Consider the Laplace equation

$$-\Delta u = f, \tag{27.36}$$

for the moment in all of $\mathbb{R}^d$ without regard for boundary conditions. Then a solution can be generated by convolution with the fundamental solution G:

$$u = G * f, \tag{27.37}$$

where the convolution operator is defined by

$$v * w(\mathbf{x}) = \int_{\mathbb{R}^d} v(\mathbf{x}-\mathbf{y})w(\mathbf{y})\,d\mathbf{y}$$

and

$$G(\mathbf{x}) = \begin{cases} c_2 \log|\mathbf{x}| & d=2 \\ c_d|\mathbf{x}|^{2-d} & d \geq 3. \end{cases} \tag{27.38}$$

To have a classical solution of (27.36), we would demand that $u \in C^2$, and we might expect this to be true for $f \in C^0$. We will see that this is not the case.

We can differentiate the expression (27.38) to represent derivatives of u in terms of f via

$$D^\alpha u = (D^\alpha G) * f, \tag{27.39}$$

using a well-known property of convolution, where D^α is defined in (27.25). It is not hard to show that

$$D^\alpha G(\mathbf{x}) = A_\alpha(\mathbf{x})|\mathbf{x}|^{-d} \text{ for } |\alpha| = 2,\ \mathbf{x} \neq \mathbf{0}, \tag{27.40}$$

where A_α is homogeneous of degree zero, that is, $A_\alpha(r\mathbf{x}) = A_\alpha(\mathbf{x})$ for any $r \in \mathbb{R}$. Thus we can think of A_α as just being defined on the surface of the unit ball and extended by the homogeneity relation to $\mathbb{R}^d \backslash \mathbf{0}$. Moreover, it is easy to see that A_α is smooth on the surface of the unit ball. See Exercise 27.6 for an example.

Thus $D^\alpha G$ is what is known as a Calderón-Zygmund singular kernel, and the mapping $f \to (D^\alpha G) * f$ is a singular integral operator. Such operators are known [139, Section 9.4] to be bounded on L^p for $1 < p < \infty$, but they are not bounded for the extreme values of p, as we will see shortly.

The key property of singular kernels that supports this is that A_α has mean zero when integrated over the boundary of a ball centered on the origin. This cancellation property allows the singular integral to be controlled in a natural way, but only in a mean sense. If we take

$$f(\mathbf{x}) = \frac{A_\alpha(\mathbf{x})}{|\log|\mathbf{x}||}\chi(|\mathbf{x}|), \quad \chi(r) = \begin{cases} 1 & r \leq \frac{1}{4} \\ 2 - 4r & \frac{1}{4} \leq r \leq \frac{1}{2} \\ 0 & r \geq \frac{1}{2} \end{cases}, \tag{27.41}$$

we get a divergent integral for $D^\alpha u = (D^\alpha G) * f$,

$$D^\alpha u(0) = \int_{|\mathbf{x}| \leq \frac{1}{2}} \frac{A_\alpha(\mathbf{x})^2 \chi(|\mathbf{x}|)}{|\mathbf{x}|^d |\log|\mathbf{x}||} d\mathbf{x} = C_{\alpha,d} \int_0^{\frac{1}{2}} \frac{\chi(r)\, dr}{r|\log r|} = \infty, \tag{27.42}$$

indicating that $D^\alpha u(\mathbf{x}) \to \infty$ as $\mathbf{x} \to 0$. Thus we see that bounded f can lead to solutions u of (27.36) whose second derivatives are not bounded. We leave as Exercise 27.6 to explore this.

Our example shows why the Calderón-Zygmund theorem fails for $p = \infty$, since f is bounded and the second derivatives of u are not bounded. But it also does more, as the function f is both bounded and continuous, since $f(\mathbf{x}) \to 0$ as $\mathbf{x} \to 0$. Our example shows that, not only is $u \notin C^2$, its second derivatives are not even bounded, that is, $u \notin W^2_\infty$. In [139, exercise 4.9(a)], a different example is given in which f is continuous but $u \notin C^2$. Thus our example shows that the mapping $f \to u$ is not even bounded as a map of C^0 to W^2_∞. The root cause of this behavior is the fact that the solution operator for the Laplace equation involves an aggregation of values. Thus if f has bad behavior over an extended region, this can add up to yield unexpected behavior of the solution.

27.6 Exercises

Exercise 27.1 *Consider the example following (27.17). How small can the error in (27.17) be made using a 5-th order ($k = 5$) BDF formula? What value of Δt yields the smallest error?*

Exercise 27.2 *Compute the solution of an ordinary differential equation using the 7-th order ($k = 7$) BDF formula. What happens after a few times steps?*

Exercise 27.3 *Write (27.24) as a system of two real equations for the real and imaginary parts of u respectively.*

Exercise 27.4 *Give a precise definition of the "Dirichlet to Neumann" map A such that (27.6) has a solution if and only if $g_1 = Ag_0$.*

Exercise 27.5 *Prove that the local solvability condition (27.35) does not hold for the equation (27.24).*

Exercise 27.6 *Compute $A_{(2,0)}$ in (27.40) for $d = 2$, that is,*

$$A_{(2,0)}(x, y) = c_2\big(x^2 + y^2\big)\frac{\partial^2}{\partial x^2}\log|(x, y)|.$$

Take f as defined in (27.41) and solve $-\Delta u = f$ in a domain containing the origin, with your choice of boundary conditions. Compute the second derivatives of u near the origin. Do they blow up as the mesh is made finer? (Hint: since the problem is linear, you do not need to compute c_2 to determine the smoothness of u at $\mathbf{0}$. As a first step, verify that $\nabla \log|\mathbf{x}| = |\mathbf{x}|^{-2}\mathbf{x}$. So $(\log|\mathbf{x}|)_x = x/(x^2 + y^2)$.)

Exercise 27.7 *Evaluate the integral*

$$\int_{\epsilon}^{\frac{1}{4}} \frac{dr}{r|\log r|}$$

and determine what happens as $\epsilon \to 0$. (Hint: let $s = |\log r|$, so that for $a < b$

$$\int_a^b \frac{dr}{r|\log r|} = \int_{|\log b|}^{|\log a|} \frac{ds}{s} = |\log a| - |\log b|.$$

What happens as $a \to 0$?)

Chapter 28

Tutorial on mshr

mshr is the mesh and domain generation component of FEniCS. It generates simplicial meshes in 2D and 3D that can be used in dolfin from geometries (domains) described by using constructive solid geometry (CSG). CSG creates complicated geometries from simpler ones using Boolean operations. The set-theoretic aspect of CSG allows arbitrary points in space to be classified as being either inside or outside the geometry created by CSG. This avoids issues related to other approaches in which it is possible to have topological inconsistencies [92].

The main author of mshr is Benjamin Kehlet (benjamik@simula.no) and contributors include Anders Logg (logg@chalmers.se), Johannes Ring (johannr@simula.no), and Garth N. Wells (gnw20@cam.ac.uk). mshr is hosted at

https://bitbucket.org/benjamik/mshr

and the documentation for mshr is currently under development at

https://bitbucket.org/benjamik/mshr/wiki

For bug reports and feature requests, visit mshr's issue tracker at BitBucket:

https://bitbucket.org/benjamik/mshr/issues

We begin by describing primitives that construct geometries in two dimensions using input parameters. Then we describe unary operators (rotation, translation, scaling) that can be applied to a given geometry. Finally, we consider the fundamental binary operators required to make complex geometries.

28.1 2D built-in geometries

The following geometries can be generated from parameters. They can be subsequently combined via the geometry algebra as desired.

28.1.1 Circle

```
Circle(c, r[, segments])
```

This function creates a domain in the plane whose boundary is a circle centered at `c` with radius `r`.

Parameters

- `c`: center (a `dolfin.Point`)
- `r`: radius (a positive real number)
- `segments`: number of segments when computing the polygonal approximation of the curved boundary [optional].

Optional parameters are enclosed in square brackets. The default size for the number of segments in `Circle` is 32.

Examples:

```
domain =  Circle(dolfin.Point(0.0, 0.0), 1.0)
domain =  Circle(dolfin.Point(0.0, 0.0), 1.0, 33)
```

28.1.2 2D axis-aligned rectangle

`Rectangle(a,b)`

This function creates a domain in the plane whose boundary is a 2-dimensional, axis-aligned rectangle, specified by its lower-left and upper-right corners.

Parameters

- `a`: lower-left corner (a `dolfin.Point`)
- `b`: upper-right corner (a `dolfin.Point`)

Example:

```
domain = Rectangle(dolfin.Point(0., 0.), dolfin.Point(1., 1.))
```

28.1.3 2D ellipse

`Ellipse(c, a, b[, segments])`

This function creates a two-dimensional ellipse centered at `c` with horizontal semi-axis `a` and vertical semi-axis `b`.

Parameters

- `c`: the center (a `dolfin.Point`)
- `a`: the horizontal semi-axis (a positive real number)
- `b`: the vertical semi-axis (a positive real number)

- `segments`: number of segments when computing the polygonal approximation of the curved boundary [optional].

Optional parameters are enclosed in square brackets. The default size for the number of segments in `Ellipse` is 32.

Example:

```
domain = Ellipse(dolfin.Point(0.0,0.0), 2.0, 1.0, 16)
```

28.1.4 2D polygon

`Polygon(vertices)`

This function creates a polygon defined by the given vertices. Vertices must be in counter-clockwise order, and the resulting edges must be free of self-intersections.

Parameters

- `vertices`: A vector of `dolfin.Points`.

Example: The code

```
from mshr import *
import dolfin

domain =  Polygon([dolfin.Point(0.0, 0.0),\
                   dolfin.Point(1.0, 0.0),\
                   dolfin.Point(0.0, 1.0)])
```

generates a unit right triangle.

28.2 Unary operators on geometries

Once a geometry has been created, there are some simple operations that can be performed to derive new geometries from given ones.

28.2.1 Translation

`CSGTranslation(geometry, tvec)`

This function translates an input `geometry` by a vector `tvec`.

Parameters

- `geometry`: a CSG geometry
- `tvec`: translation vector (a `dolfin.Point`)

28.2.2 Scaling

`CSGScaling(geometry, sfak)`

This function scales an input `geometry` by a scaling factor `sfak`.

Parameters

- `geometry`: a CSG geometry
- `sfak`: scaling factor (a real number).

28.2.3 2D rotation

`CSGRotation(geometry, [center,] theta)`

This function rotates an input `geometry` by an angle `theta` in two dimensions; optionally, the rotation can be about a `center` other than the origin.

Parameters

- `geometry`: a CSG geometry
- `center`: center-point for the rotation [optional] (a `dolfin.Point`)
- `theta`: rotation angle in radians (a real number).

The default value for `center` is the origin **0**.

Example: The code

```
from mshr import *
import dolfin

square =  Rectangle(dolfin.Point(0., 0.), dolfin.Point(1., 1.))
diamond = CSGRotation(square,math.pi/4)
```

rotates the unit square by 45 degrees.

28.3 Geometry algebra

CSG geometries can be defined by combining geometric primitives through the boolean operations intersection, union and difference. Here are some small 2D examples.

28.3.1 Set difference

Consider the code

```
from mshr import *
import dolfin

domain = Rectangle(dolfin.Point(0., 0.), dolfin.Point(1., 1.)) -
         Circle(dolfin.Point(0.5, 1.0), 0.5)
```

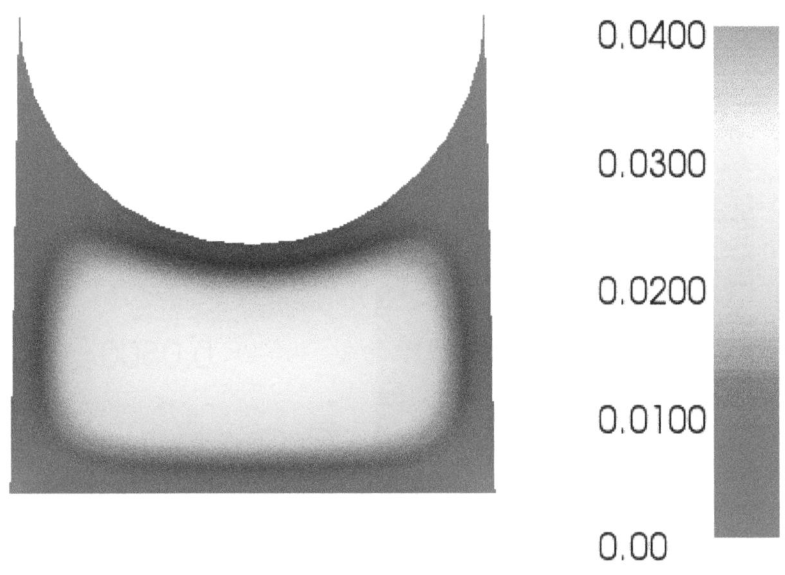

Figure 28.1: Laplace's equation on the set difference of two domains.

The geometry consists of a square with a circle removed. The minus sign (-) represents the boolean **set difference**:

$$\mathtt{A} - \mathtt{B} = \{x \in \mathtt{A} \ : \ x \notin \mathtt{B}\}.$$

The functions `Rectangle` and `Circle` are built-in `mshr` functions to be described subsequently. This yields the domain with cusps shown in Figure 28.1.

The construct `dolfin.Point(0., 1.)` creates a two-dimensional vector recognized by `mshr` from two real number inputs.

28.3.2 Set union

Similarly, the plus sign (+) in the context of geometries represents the boolean **set union**:

$$\mathtt{A} + \mathtt{B} = \{x \ : \ \text{either } x \in \mathtt{A} \text{ or } x \in \mathtt{B}\}.$$

For example,

```
domain = Rectangle(dolfin.Point(0., 0.), dolfin.Point(1., 1.)) + \
         Circle(dolfin.Point(0.5, 1.0), 0.5)
```

creates a box with a circular disc on top, which looks like a gravestone, as shown in Figure 28.2.

28.3.3 Set intersection

Finally, the multiplication sign (*) in the context of geometries represents the boolean **set intersection**:

$$\mathtt{A} * \mathtt{B} = \{x \in \mathtt{A} \ : \ x \in \mathtt{B}\}.$$

For example,

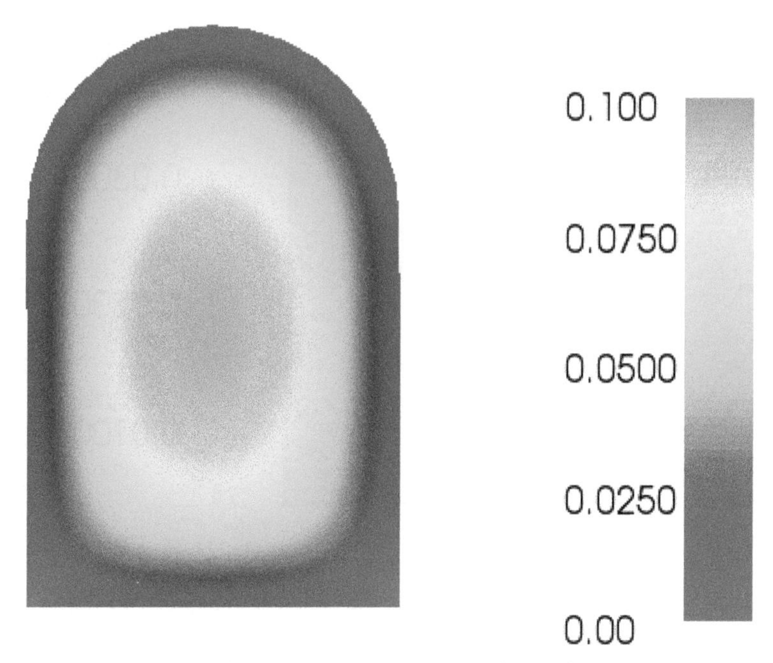

Figure 28.2: Laplace's equation on the sum (union) of two domains.

```
domain = Rectangle(dolfin.Point(0., 0.), dolfin.Point(1., 1.)) * \
         Circle(dolfin.Point(0.5, 1.0), 0.5)
```

creates a bowl, as shown in Figure 28.3.

28.4 Meshes vs. geometries

A geometry (what we typically refer to as a domain Ω) describes the extent of an object. A mesh is a subdivision of that object. Simple objects such as a unit square, together with its mesh, can be defined in one statement such as

```
mesh = UnitSquareMesh(16, 16)
```

Having a mesh, one can construct a function space via

```
V = FunctionSpace(mesh, "Lagrange", 2)
```

So far, we have seen how to create many domains (geometries) using constructive solid geometry. To create an associated mesh, we can use the operation

```
mesh = generate_mesh(domain, 1)
```

The general syntax of this command is as follows.

```
generate_mesh(geometry, howfine)
```

This function creates a mesh for an input `geometry` where the extent of refinement of the mesh is determined by the integer `howfine`.

Parameters

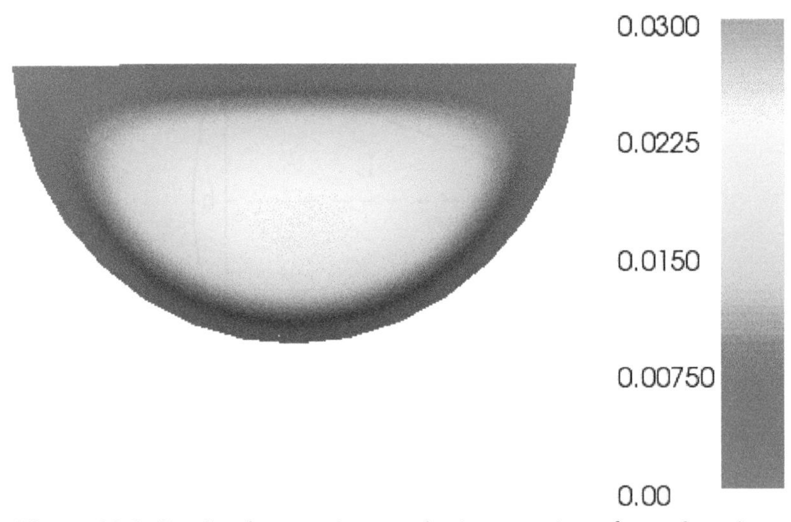

Figure 28.3: Laplace's equation on the intersection of two domains.

- `geometry`: a CSG geometry
- `howfine`: integer ≥ 1 defining the extent of refinement.

Example: The code

```
from mshr import *
import dolfin

domain =  Circle(dolfin.Point(0.0, 0.0),1.0,segmnts)

mesh   = generate_mesh(domain, meshsize)
```

yields a polygonal approximation to a circle with the number of boundary edges specified by `segments` and a fairly balanced mesh if we specify

```
segmnts=5*meshsize
```

Obviously, the size of `segments` determines the element size at the boundary, so it is necessary to use an associated `meshsize` to get a balanced mesh. The statement

```
hmax=mesh.hmax()
```

provides the value `hmax` corresponding to the largest element (triangle) size in this mesh.

28.5 Domain validation

One simple check of software to generate a particular domain is to compute the area of the domain and see if it agrees with what we expect. The `mshr` function for a circle actually generates a regular polygon that is inscribed in the specified circle. We describe how to compute the area of such a domain.

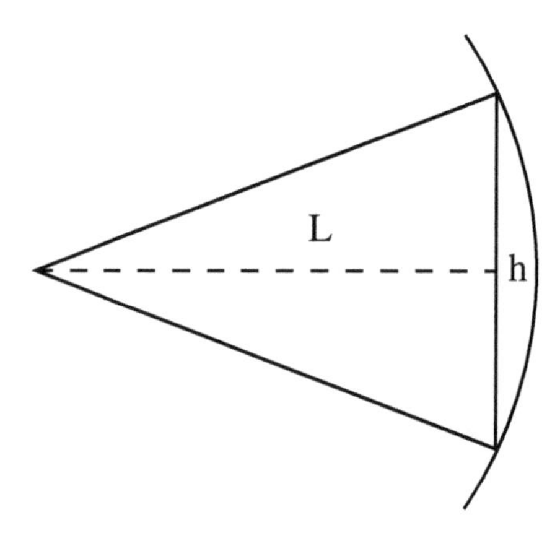

Figure 28.4: A typical triangle at the boundary for a triangulation of a regular s-gon.

The vertices of a regular polygon inscribed in a unit circle are $z_j = e^{2\pi\iota j/s}$ for $j = 0,\ldots,s-1$, where s is the number of segments on the polygon. The length h of each segment on the boundary $\partial\Omega_h$ is given by

$$\begin{aligned} h_s &= |z_1 - z_0| = |z_1 - (1,0)| = \sqrt{(1-\cos(2\pi/s))^2 + (\sin(2\pi/s))^2 x} \\ &= \sqrt{1 - 2\cos(2\pi/s) + (\cos(2\pi/s))^2 + (\sin(2\pi/s))^2} = \sqrt{2 - 2\cos(2\pi/s)}. \end{aligned} \tag{28.1}$$

The distance from the origin to the middle of a segment is

$$\begin{aligned} L_s &= |\tfrac{1}{2}(z_1 + z_0)| = \tfrac{1}{2}|z_1 + (1,0)| = \tfrac{1}{2}\sqrt{(1+\cos(2\pi/s))^2 + (\sin(2\pi/s))^2} \\ &= \tfrac{1}{2}\sqrt{2 + 2\cos(2\pi/s)}. \end{aligned} \tag{28.2}$$

Thus

$$|\Omega_s| = \tfrac{1}{2} s h_s L_s = \tfrac{1}{4} s \sqrt{2 - 2\cos(2\pi/s)}\sqrt{2 + 2\cos(2\pi/s)} = \tfrac{1}{2} s\sqrt{1 - (\cos(2\pi/s))^2}. \tag{28.3}$$

The integral $|\Omega_s| = \int_{\Omega_s} 1\, d\mathbf{x}$ can be computed by Program 28.1.

```
1  from mshr import *
2  from dolfin import *
3  import sys,math
4
5  domain =  Circle(dolfin.Point(0.0, 0.0),circsiz,segmnts)
6  mesh   = generate_mesh(domain, meshsize)
7  W = FunctionSpace(mesh, "Lagrange", 1)
8  eone = Expression("1.0",degree=1)
9  eoni=interpolate(eone,W)
10 areaomega= assemble(eoni*dx)
```

Program 28.1: Code to find the area of a domain.

In Exercise 28.8 we propose checking Program 28.1 against (28.3).

28.6 Exercises

Exercise 28.1 *Implement Laplace's equation with homogeneous Dirichlet boundary conditions on the "gravestone" domain*

```
domain = Rectangle(dolfin.Point(0., 0.), dolfin.Point(1., 1.)) +
         Circle(dolfin.Point(0.5, 1.0), 0.5)
```

with right-hand side $f \equiv 1$.

Exercise 28.2 *Use the* `Polygon` *function to create a rectangle aligned with the axes. Implement Laplace's equation with homogeneous Dirichlet boundary conditions with right-hand side* $f \equiv 1$ *on this domain and compare with using the built-in* `Rectangle` *primitive. (Hint: start with the triangle example and fill in the blanks*

```
rectangul =  Polygon([dolfin.Point(0.0, 0.0), dolfin.Point(1.0, 0.0),\
                    ......................., dolfin.Point(0.0, 1.0)])
```

Exercise 28.3 *Make a diamond domain in two ways: 1) rotate a* `Rectangle` *and 2) using the* `Polygon` *function. Compare the results by implementing Laplace's equation with homogeneous Dirichlet boundary conditions with right-hand side* $f \equiv 1$ *on these domains.*

Exercise 28.4 *Make a circular domain in two ways: 1) using the* `Circle` *function. 2) using the* `Ellipse` *function with* `a` *and* `b` *the same. Compare the results by implementing Laplace's equation with homogeneous Dirichlet boundary conditions with right-hand side* $f \equiv 1$ *on these domains.*

Exercise 28.5 *Implement Laplace's equation with homogeneous Dirichlet boundary conditions on the non-simply connected domain*

```
domain = Rectangle(dolfin.Point(0., 0.), dolfin.Point(1., 1.)) - \
         Circle(dolfin.Point(0.5, 0.5), 0.25)
```

with right-hand side $f \equiv 1$.

Exercise 28.6 *Implement Laplace's equation with homogeneous Dirichlet boundary conditions on the non-simply connected domain given by the unit square with your initials (font optional) remove.*

Exercise 28.7 *Using two* `Circle` *functions, create an annular domain*

$$\Omega = \left\{ \mathbf{x} \in \mathbb{R}^2 \; : \; \tfrac{1}{2} < |\mathbf{x}| < 1 \right\}.$$

Implement Laplace's equation with appropriate Dirichlet boundary conditions on the non-simply connected domain Ω *so that the exact solution is* $\log |\mathbf{x}|$. *Determine the accuracy as a function of mesh size and polynomial degree. (Hint: see Program 6.2.)*

Exercise 28.8 *Implement a program as in Program 28.1 to compute the area of the domain and compare this with the formula (28.3). Does it depend on the mesh size?*

Exercise 28.9 *Modify the program in Program 28.1 to compute the area of a domain as in Figure 28.1 that is the difference of a square and a circle. What is the exact area of this domain? What does the computational program give for the area? Does it depend on the mesh size?*

Exercise 28.10 *Modify the program in Program 28.1 to compute the area of a domain as in Figure 28.2 that is the union of a square and a circle. What is the exact area of this domain? What does the computational program give for the area? Does it depend on the mesh size?*

Chapter 29

Visualization Techniques

Visualization of computed results is critical part of the simulation process. It is valuable at many levels. Often the one most emphasized is the role it plays in presentation of achievements for a project. These "pretty pictures" are very important, but visualization has a much broader scope.

One application of visualization is in debugging. Debugging can refer to the code being written, to the choice of numerical method being made, or the model that is being proposed. At each step, we apply (as seen here) a mixture of visual representations and more quantitative measures (e.g., function-space norms, linear functionals, convergence assessments, etc.). It is critical to have both views of computed solutions, qualitative and quantitative. Unfortunately, visualization is a complex subject, so some understanding is required to use it effectively.

One feature of most current visualization software is that triangular facets are used to represent surfaces. This can cause a variety of misinterpretations. A key feature of finite elements is the ability to used higher-order representations, quadratics, cubics, quartics, quintics, and so forth. But to represent, say, a quadratic surface, something must be done to transform the data into triangular facets. This is easy to describe with finite-element terminology, since triangular facets correspond to piecewise linear representations.

The default technique in `dolfin` for converting higher-order representations into triangular facets is to do a projection onto a piecewise linear representation, on the same mesh. This means that information gets modified by the projection. An interpolant could be used instead, where we simply ignore any nodal values not related to vertices, but this has the obvious drawback of ignoring some data. One way to preserve all nodal values but retain interpolation, as opposed to projection (averaging), is to invoke a mesh refinement.

29.1 Mesh refinement

The `dolfin` code provides a simple way to refine a mesh. Consider the code

```
coarsemesh = UnitSquareMesh(2,3)
finermesh = refine(coarsemesh)
```

We can then have two different spaces

```
V = FunctionSpace(coarsemesh, "Lagrange", 2)
```

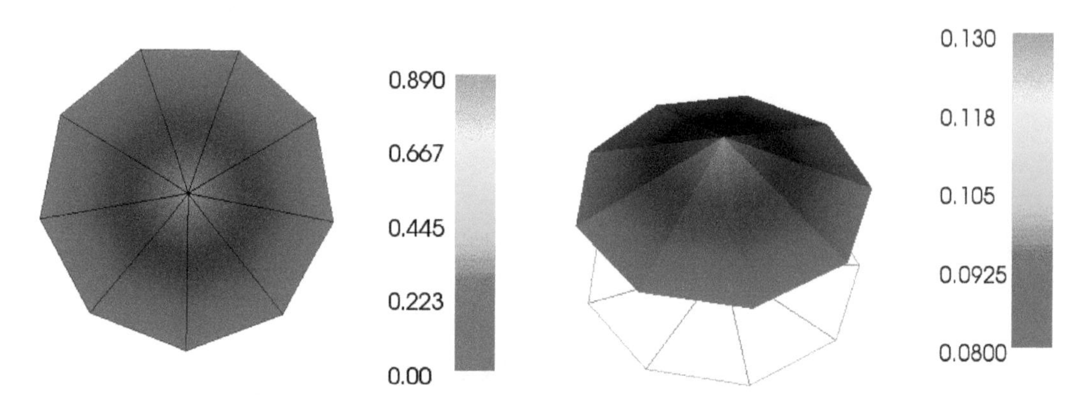

Figure 29.1: (left) Computed approximation of the problem whose exact solution is given in (22.14) using piecewise quadratics. We see that the Dirichlet conditions are imposed on $\partial\Omega_h$. (right) Plot of the error $u - u_h$ on the same mesh. This suggests that the error on the approximate boundary $\partial\Omega_h$ is a constant, which we know is wrong. Moreover, it indicates that the error on the approximate boundary $\partial\Omega_h$ is not zero, and again we know that it is zero at vertices.

```
W = FunctionSpace(finermesh, "Lagrange", 1)
```

We can now interpolate a (piecewise quadratic) function **u** in `V` to obtain a piecewise linear function in `W` using the command

```
wu=interpolate(u,W)
wu.interpolate(u)
```

or equivalently

```
wu=Function(W)
wu.interpolate(u)
```

The piecewise linear function **wu** retains the information found in internal nodes of the piecewise quadratic function **u**.

Consider the example from Section 22.2 in which the Dirichlet problem Laplace's equation on a circle Ω is considered. First, the circle Ω is approximated by a polygon Ω_h, and then a piecewise quadratic variational approximation is constructed. This is depicted in Figure 29.1 where, on the left side of the figure, we see the numerical approximation of the problem in Section 22.2 whose exact solution u is given in (22.14) (note that u is a quadratic polynomial). On the right side of Figure 29.1 we see what happens if we plot the error $u - u_h$ on the given mesh. What we obtain is a piecewise linear representation of the piecewise quadratic error function $u - u_h$. We know that $u - u_h$ is zero at the boundary vertices, but we do not see that in the visualization on the right side of Figure 29.1. Instead, we see a constant error that is small but nonzero. This could easily lead us to think that there is a bug in the code, and this could send us off on the wrong tack and lead to a significant waste of time (as it did for the author). Now consider a fix to this feature.

The mesh in Figure 29.1 is defined by

```
domain = Circle(dolfin.Point(0.0, 0.0),1.0,9)
mesh   = generate_mesh(domain, 1)
```

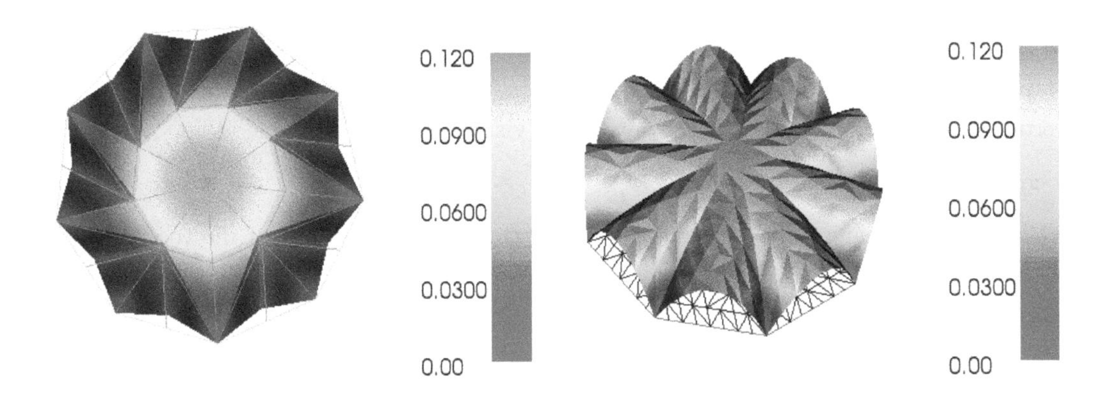

Figure 29.2: (left) Plot of the error $u - u_h$ on a refined mesh. Now the error on the approximate boundary $\partial\Omega_h$ is visible, but the character of the function is hard to discern. (right) Plot of the error $u - u_h$ on a much more refined mesh. Now the quadratic character of the error function is clear, although the triangular facets are still visible.

and this `mesh` is refined by

```
plotmesh=refine(mesh)
```

and the solution is interpolated on the finer mesh `plotmesh`, as described above, to create the error plot on the left side of Figure 29.2.

Now we can see that the error is zero at the vertices of $\partial\Omega_h$ as intended and the error is nonzero at the midpoints of the edges of $\partial\Omega_h$. However, the facets used for visualization make it confusing to interpret, whereas further mesh refinements as depicted on the right side of Figure 29.2 make it clear that the error is a piecewise quadratic function.

Note that the linear facets are still visible on the right side of Figure 29.2 even after substantial mesh subdivision. We leave it as Exercise 29.1 to see how many refinements make this go away.

There is one small issue that has to be addressed when interpolating functions from one mesh to another. Due to round-off error, it may be that there are points in one mesh outside the domain of the other mesh, even if the domains are essentially the same. Thus we have to use extrapolation in such cases to define the interpolant. On the other hand, there may be reasons *not* to extrapolate, and for safety it is a good idea to flag an error when the requested information for an interpolant is formally undefined. Thus `dolfin` takes a conservative point of view and requires the user to decide whether or not such extrapolation is allowed. This is expressed in the command

```
u.set_allow_extrapolation(True)
```

This allows `u` to be extrapolated so that the command

```
wu=interpolate(u,W)
```

can be successful, even if vertices in the space `W` do not fall within the domain of definition of `u`.

29.2 Visualizing derivatives

In Program 6.3, a technique was introduced to compute the derivative of a solution so that certain boundary conditions can be more easily visualized. The key code is

```
v=grad(u)[0]
```

which creates a scalar function v equal to the 0-th (or x-) component of the vector-valued function ∇u, that is, $u_{,x}$. Similarly,

```
v=grad(u)[1]
```

would create a scalar function v equal to y-component of ∇u, that is, $u_{,y}$.

In Figure 6.2, it might be of interest to check the boundary conditions. The problem visualized in Figure 6.2 comes from Section 6.1.3, and the boundary conditions are homogeneous Neumann conditions for much of the boundary. Indeed, the normal derivative of the solution would be expected to be nonzero only on the part Γ of the boundary where homogeneous Dirichlet conditions are posed in (6.10). We leave as Exercise 29.2 to check the natural boundary conditions using the visualization of derivatives technique described here.

In Section 17.1.3, a problem with a discontinuous coefficient α was studied. For such problems, the solution has a kink, that is, a discontinuity in slope (see Figure 17.1). In that particular problem, the locus of the kink is a straight line, and the slope is just $u_{,x}$. On the other hand, the product $\alpha\, u_{,x}$ is known to be continuous. This can be verified by plotting the product of the computed $u_{,x}$ times the computationally implemented coefficient α. (In Program 17.1, the discontinuous coefficient was implemented by a function that is mathematically smooth but jumps over a very small interval.) We leave as Exercise 29.3 to examine this behavior.

29.3 Exercises

Exercise 29.1 *Experiment with the problem described in Section 29.1 to see how many mesh refinements are needed to remove the visual effect of the facets used by visualization software.*

Exercise 29.2 *Modify Program 6.1 as described in Section 29.2 to determine if the natural boundary conditions in (6.10) are satisfied pointwise. Explain.*

Exercise 29.3 *Consider the problem posed in Section 17.1.3. The solution has a kink as shown in Figure 17.1, but the product $\alpha\, u_{,x}$ is continuous across the kink. (Recall that α is by definition discontinuous.) Modify Program 17.1 as described in Section 29.2 to plot the quantity $\alpha\, u_{,x}$ for the computed solution u to determine the extent to which this is computationally continuous. Explain.*

Chapter 30

Tutorial on Sobolev Spaces

The coercivity result (3.3) is the key to well-posedness of boundary-value problems for elliptic problems. It implicitly encodes both a statement of stability and a confirmation of the suitability of boundary conditions. Here, we offer a tutorial on some of the details underpinning why this is true. In addition, we provide some results in approximation theory that explain some details regarding stated orders of approximation. It is intriguing that some concepts of approximability and coercivity can be closely linked.

For simplicity, let us assume that Ω is convex, so that for any two points in Ω, all points on the line joining them is also in Ω. Most of the results derived in this simple setting can be proved for more general domains [57].

The presentation is not fully rigorous, but the main ideas are faithfully represented. The main shortcoming of the arguments is that we have not explained precisely what we mean by derivatives. There is a formal definition [57] of **weak derivatives** that is appropriate for Sobolev spaces. But formally, all operations are the same as would be expected. They just allow for defining derivatives for a broader class of functions.

Some tools are used here that go beyond typical advanced calculus. A notable one is the Hölder's inequality, which generalizes the Cauchy-Schwarz inequality. We leave these and other technicalities to be pursued by the interested reader, as desired.

30.1 Traces

The concept of the **trace** (on the boundary) of a function in a Sobolev is key to understanding well-posed boundary value problems. Suppose that we have a subset $\Gamma \subset \Omega$ and a function v in $H^1(\Omega)$. We have discussed posing boundary conditions $v = g$ on Γ, but what exactly does this mean? That is, how do we interpret the *trace* $u|_\Gamma$? Is it in a Sobolev space itself? The answer is yes, but the details are complicated. We can get good guidance by considering a simple example where Ω is the unit circle

$$\Omega = \left\{(x, y) \in \mathbb{R}^2 \,:\, x^2 + y^2 < 1\right\}.$$

The example here is taken from [201]. For simplicity, we take

$$\Gamma = \partial\Omega = \left\{(x, y) \in \mathbb{R}^2 \,:\, x^2 + y^2 = 1\right\}.$$

Using polar coordinates, $\Omega = \{(r\cos\theta, r\sin\theta) \,:\, 0 < r < 1,\ 0 \le \theta < 2\pi\}$. Let v be a smooth function defined on Ω. Define $\phi(r,\theta) = r^2\, v(r\cos\theta, r\sin\theta)$. Then using Cauchy-Schwarz (3.15) we find

$$\begin{aligned} v(\cos\theta,\sin\theta)^2 = \phi(1,\theta)^2 &= \int_0^1 2\phi(s,\theta)\frac{\partial\phi}{\partial r}(s,\theta)\,ds \\ &\le 2\Big(\int_0^1 \phi(s,\theta)^2\,ds\Big)^{1/2}\Big(\int_0^1 \Big(\frac{\partial\phi}{\partial r}(s,\theta)\Big)^2 ds\Big)^{1/2}. \end{aligned} \tag{30.1}$$

Therefore, using Cauchy-Schwarz (3.15) again, we have

$$\begin{aligned} \|v\|_{L^2(\partial\Omega)}^2 &= \int_0^{2\pi} v(\cos\theta,\sin\theta)^2\,d\theta \\ &\le 2\int_0^{2\pi}\Big(\int_0^1 \phi(s,\theta)^2\,ds\Big)^{1/2}\Big(\int_0^1 \Big(\frac{\partial\phi}{\partial r}(s,\theta)\Big)^2 ds\Big)^{1/2} d\theta \\ &\le 2\Big(\int_0^{2\pi}\int_0^1 \phi(s,\theta)^2\,ds\,d\theta\Big)^{1/2}\Big(\int_0^{2\pi}\int_0^1 \Big(\frac{\partial\phi}{\partial r}(s,\theta)\Big)^2 ds\,d\theta\Big)^{1/2}. \end{aligned} \tag{30.2}$$

We have

$$\begin{aligned} \int_0^{2\pi}\int_0^1 \phi(s,\theta)^2\,ds\,d\theta &= \int_0^{2\pi}\int_0^1 v(s\cos\theta, s\sin\theta)^2 s^4\,ds\,d\theta \\ &\le \int_0^{2\pi}\int_0^1 v(s\cos\theta, s\sin\theta)^2 s\,ds\,d\theta = \|v\|_{L^2(\Omega)}^2. \end{aligned} \tag{30.3}$$

Recall that $\phi(r,\theta) = r^2\, v(r\cos\theta, r\sin\theta)$, so

$$\begin{aligned} \Big(\frac{\partial\phi}{\partial r}(s,\theta)\Big)^2 &= \Big(2r\, v(r\cos\theta, r\sin\theta) + r^2\,(\cos\theta,\sin\theta)\cdot\nabla v(r\cos\theta, r\sin\theta)\Big)^2 \\ &\le 2\Big(2r\, v(r\cos\theta, r\sin\theta)\Big)^2 + 2\Big(r^2\,(\cos\theta,\sin\theta)\cdot\nabla v(r\cos\theta, r\sin\theta)\Big)^2 \end{aligned} \tag{30.4}$$

Thus

$$\int_0^{2\pi}\int_0^1 \Big(\frac{\partial\phi}{\partial r}(s,\theta)\Big)^2 ds\,d\theta \le 8\|v\|_{H^1(\Omega)}^2. \tag{30.5}$$

Combining (30.5), (30.3), and (30.2), we get

$$\|v\|_{L^2(\partial\Omega)}^2 \le 4\sqrt{2}\|v\|_{L^2(\Omega)}\|v\|_{H^1(\Omega)}. \tag{30.6}$$

Therefore

$$\|v\|_{L^2(\partial\Omega)} \le 3\|v\|_{L^2(\Omega)}^{1/2}\|v\|_{H^1(\Omega)}^{1/2}. \tag{30.7}$$

Thus we see that if $v \in H^1(\Omega)$, the restriction of v to $\partial\Omega$ is well defined as a square integrable function. In particular, the linear functional F defined in (2.25) is bounded on $H^1(\Omega)$, by the Cauchy-Schwarz inequality (3.15).

What (30.7) says is that the norm in $L^2(\partial\Omega)$ is halfway between the norms in $L^2(\Omega)$ and $H^1(\Omega)$. You can define fractional derivatives, ∇_s, for $0 < s < 1$, and these have significant applications [83] as well as being of theoretical interest [3]. Fractional Sobolev spaces are defined by

$$\|v\|^2_{H^s(\partial\Omega)} = \|\nabla_s v\|^2_{L^2(\partial\Omega)} + \|v\|^2_{L^2(\partial\Omega)}.$$

The general trace theorem reads

$$\|v\|_{H^{1/2}(\partial\Omega)} \le C_\Omega \|v\|_{H^1(\Omega)}, \tag{30.8}$$

and this holds in any dimension d.

30.2 An integral representation

We now consider an integral representation that will be useful in multiple contexts. We begin with a very simple representation using integral calculus. Suppose that x and y are two points in some domain Ω in d-dimensional space, and observe that we can write

$$u(\mathbf{y}) - u(\mathbf{x}) = \int_0^1 (\mathbf{y} - \mathbf{x}) \cdot \nabla u(\mathbf{x} + s(\mathbf{y} - \mathbf{x}))\, ds\,. \tag{30.9}$$

This is just the multi-dimensional version of the calculus theorem

$$f(1) - f(0) = \int_0^1 f'(s)\, ds\,. \tag{30.10}$$

We can obtain (30.9) from (30.10) by defining $f(s) := u(\mathbf{x} + s(\mathbf{y} - \mathbf{x}))$.

Let us now integrate (30.9) with respect to y over Ω, to get

$$|\Omega|(\overline{u} - u(\mathbf{x})) = \int_\Omega \int_0^1 (\mathbf{y} - \mathbf{x}) \cdot \nabla u(\mathbf{x} + s(\mathbf{y} - \mathbf{x}))\, ds\, d\mathbf{y}\,, \tag{30.11}$$

where $|\Omega|$ is the measure of Ω and $\overline{u}$ denotes the mean of u:

$$\overline{u} := \frac{1}{|\Omega|} \int_\Omega u(\mathbf{y})\, d\mathbf{y}\,. \tag{30.12}$$

Make the change of variables $\mathbf{z} = \mathbf{x} + s(\mathbf{y} - \mathbf{x})$, so that $\mathbf{y} = \mathbf{x} + s^{-1}(\mathbf{z} - \mathbf{x})$ and $d\mathbf{y} = s^{-d} d\mathbf{z}$; see Figure 30.1. With this representation, the variable $\mathbf{z}$ also ranges over all of Ω, but not independently of s. The range of values of s is restricted by the fact that $\mathbf{y} = \mathbf{x} + s^{-1}(\mathbf{z} - \mathbf{x})$ must remain in Ω; and for each $\mathbf{z} \in \Omega$, there is a $\sigma(\mathbf{z})$ such that $x + \sigma(\mathbf{z})^{-1}(\mathbf{z} - \mathbf{x}) \in \partial\Omega$. In fact, $\sigma(\mathbf{z})$ is just $|\mathbf{z} - \mathbf{x}|$ divided by the distance from $\mathbf{x}$ to $\partial\Omega$ along a line passing through $\mathbf{z}$. Since $\mathbf{z} \in \Omega$, this description of $\sigma(\mathbf{z})$ shows that it is always less than one. More importantly, $\sigma(\mathbf{z})^{-1} \le \operatorname{diam}(\Omega)|\mathbf{z} - \mathbf{x}|^{-1}$, where $\operatorname{diam}(\Omega)$ denotes the diameter of Ω (the largest distance between any two points in Ω).

Plugging and chugging, we get via Fubini's Theorem that

$$\begin{aligned} u(\mathbf{x}) =& \overline{u} - \frac{1}{|\Omega|} \int_\Omega \int_{\sigma(\mathbf{z})}^1 (\mathbf{z} - \mathbf{x}) \cdot \nabla u(\mathbf{z}) s^{-1-d}\, ds\, d\mathbf{z}\,, \\ =& \overline{u} - \frac{1}{|\Omega|} \int_\Omega \frac{1}{d} \left(\sigma(\mathbf{z})^{-d} - 1\right) (\mathbf{z} - \mathbf{x}) \cdot \nabla u(\mathbf{z})\, d\mathbf{z}\,, \\ =& \overline{u} + \int_\Omega k(\mathbf{x}, \mathbf{z}) \cdot \nabla u(\mathbf{z})\, d\mathbf{z}\,, \end{aligned} \tag{30.13}$$

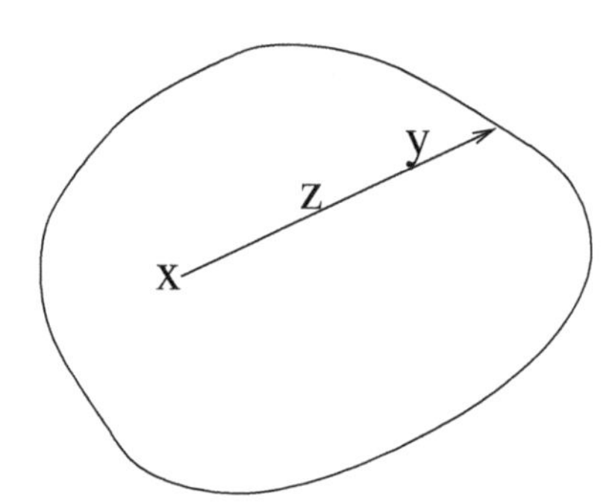

Figure 30.1: Notation for integral representation.

where $k(\mathbf{x},\mathbf{z}) := \frac{1}{|\Omega|d}\left(\sigma(\mathbf{z})^{-d}-1\right)(\mathbf{x}-\mathbf{z})$. Note that

$$|k(\mathbf{x},\mathbf{z})| \le \frac{\mathrm{diam}(\Omega)^d}{|\Omega|d}|\mathbf{x}-\mathbf{z}|^{1-d} \tag{30.14}$$

is integrable in $\mathbf{z}$ for $\mathbf{x}$ fixed.

30.3 Riesz potentials and applications

The kernel in (30.14) is bounded by what are called Riesz potentials which have simple properties. In this section, we derive various bounds for such potentials. Our main results will include an inclusion relation of the form

$$W_p^m(\Omega) \subset W_q^k(\Omega) \tag{30.15}$$

for suitable indices m,k,p,q. Here we are generalizing Sobolev spaces by defining

$$|v|_{W_p^m(\Omega)} = \left(\int_\Omega |\nabla^m v(\mathbf{x})|^p\, d\mathbf{x}\right)^{1/p}, \quad \|v\|_{W_p^m(\Omega)} = \left(\sum_{j=0}^m |v|^p_{W_p^j(\Omega)}\right)^{1/p} \tag{30.16}$$

for p being any real number such that $p \ge 1$. Of course, when $p=2$ we get the usual Sobolev space: $H^m(\Omega) = W_2^m(\Omega)$.

We can anticipate (and remember) the appropriate relationship (30.15) among these indices by considering units of the seminorms

$$|\cdot|_{W_p^m(\Omega)} \quad \text{and} \quad |\cdot|_{W_q^k(\Omega)}. \tag{30.17}$$

These units can be determined either by a dimensional analysis, or by scaling the spatial variable by a dilation. In either case, it is easy to see that the dimensions are

$$L^{-m+d/p} \quad \text{and} \quad L^{-k+d/q} \tag{30.18}$$

respectively, since each differentiation contributes a factor of L^{-1}, and the Lebesgue measure contributes a factor of $L^{n/p}$ (due to the fact that the $1/p$-th root is taken: note that the derivatives are raised to the p-th power first). Comparing these exponents suggests that we should have

$$m - \frac{d}{p} \ge k - \frac{d}{q} \tag{30.19}$$

in order for (30.15) to hold. That is, the way to count Sobolev derivatives is to take the number of L^p derivatives and subtract d/p from that. It is clear that if we can prove (30.15) for $m=1$ and $k=0$ then the general result obtains by iterating on the indices, as follows. It immediately follows for $k=m-1$ by applying the first case to derivatives of order $m-1$. Applying this result together with the corresponding result for $m \leftarrow m-1$ and $k \leftarrow m-2$ yields the desired result when $m-k=2$, with appropriate "p" indices. The general result is obtained by continuing in this way.

Now let us show how (30.15) can be verified, and explain the fine print on exactly when it applies.

Lemma 30.1 *If $f \in L^p(\Omega)$ for $1<p<\infty$ and $m>d/p$, then*

$$g(\mathbf{x}) := \int_\Omega |\mathbf{x}-\mathbf{z}|^{-n+m}\,|f(\mathbf{z})|\,d\mathbf{z} \le C\|f\|_{L^p(\Omega)} \quad \forall \mathbf{x}\in\Omega. \tag{30.20}$$

This inequality also holds for $p=1$ if $m \ge d$.

Proof. First assume that $1<p<\infty$ and $m>d/p$. Let $1/p+1/q=1$. By Hölder's inequality, we have

$$\begin{aligned}\int_\Omega |\mathbf{x}-\mathbf{z}|^{-n+m}\,|f(\mathbf{z})|\,d\mathbf{z} &\le \left(\int_\Omega |\mathbf{x}-\mathbf{z}|^{(-n+m)q}\,d\mathbf{z}\right)^{1/q} \|f\|_{L^p(\Omega)} \\ &\le C\left(\int_0^{\mathrm{diam}(\Omega)} r^{(-n+m)q+d-1}\,dr\right)^{1/q} \|f\|_{L^p(\Omega)} \\ &= C\,\|f\|_{L^p(\Omega)}\,.\end{aligned} \tag{30.21}$$

If $m \ge d$, then $|\mathbf{x}-\mathbf{z}|^{-n+m}$ is bounded, and

$$\int_\Omega |\mathbf{x}-\mathbf{z}|^{-n+m}\,|f(\mathbf{z})|\,d\mathbf{z} \le C\|f\|_{L^1(\Omega)}. \tag{30.22}$$

In view of (30.13), (30.14) and (30.20), we get the following result.

Corollary 30.1 *For $u \in W_p^1(\Omega)$,*

$$\|u-\overline{u}\|_{L^\infty(\Omega)} \le C|u|_{W_p^1(\Omega)},$$

provided that $d<p\le\infty$ or $d=1$ and $p\ge 1$.

30.3.1 Sobolev's inequality

Sobolev's inequality connects the H^s norms with the usual notion of pointwise smoothness.

Lemma 30.2 (Sobolev's Inequality) *Suppose Ω is bounded and convex. If u is in $W_p^m(\Omega)$ where either (i) $1<p<\infty$ and $m>d/p$ or (ii) $p=1$ and $d=1$, then u is continuous on Ω and*

$$\|u\|_{L^\infty(\Omega)} \le C\|u\|_{W_p^m(\Omega)}.$$

Proof. The inequality holds because

$$\begin{aligned}\|u\|_{L^\infty(\Omega)} &\leq \|u-\overline{u}\|_{L^\infty(\Omega)} + \|\overline{u}\|_{L^\infty(\Omega)}\\ &\leq |u|_{W^1_p(\Omega)} + \|u\|_{L^1(\Omega)}\\ &\leq C\|u\|_{W^1_p(\Omega)}.\end{aligned} \tag{30.23}$$

The proof that u is continuous on Ω follows by a density argument.

Applying Sobolev's inequality to derivatives, we obtain the following.

Corollary 30.2 *Suppose Ω is bounded and convex. If u is in $W^m_p(\Omega)$ where either (i) $1 < p < \infty$ and $m > k + d/p$ or (ii) $p = 1$ and $d = k+1$, then $u \in C^k(\Omega)$ and*

$$\|\nabla^k u\|_{L^\infty(\Omega)} \leq C\|u\|_{W^m_p(\Omega)}.$$

30.3.2 L^p bounds on Riesz potentials

We can think of the Riesz potentials as arising just by convolution. That is, we can define g in (30.20) as $g = K * |f|$ where we extend f by zero outside Ω and

$$K(\mathbf{x}) = |\mathbf{x}|^{m-n} \tag{30.24}$$

on a ball of radius diam(Ω) and zero outside. Strictly speaking, the definitions (30.20) and (30.24) of g agree only on Ω. Thus by Young's inequality we have

$$\begin{aligned}\|g\|_{L^r(\Omega)} &\leq \|K\|_{L^q(\Omega)}\|f\|_{L^p(\Omega)}\\ &\leq C\|f\|_{L^p(\Omega)}\end{aligned} \tag{30.25}$$

(provided that $K \in L^q(\Omega)$) where

$$\frac{1}{r} = \frac{1}{p} + \frac{1}{q} - 1 = \frac{1}{p} - \frac{1}{q'} \tag{30.26}$$

and $1/q + 1/q' = 1$. Then it is easy to see that $K \in L^q(\Omega)$ provided $q(m-n)+n-1 > -1$. This is equivalent to $m > n/q'$, or $-1/q' > -m/n$. Thus we have $g \in L^r(\Omega)$ provided

$$\frac{1}{r} = \frac{1}{p} - \frac{1}{q'} > \frac{1}{p} - \frac{m}{n}. \tag{30.27}$$

By more precise arguments, it is possible to prove [216] that the Riesz potential (30.24) maps $L^p(\Omega)$ to $L^r(\Omega)$ precisely for $\frac{1}{r} = \frac{1}{p} - \frac{m}{n}$.

Thus the following holds, known as Poincaré's inequality.

Theorem 30.1 *For $u \in W^1_p(\Omega)$,*

$$\|u - \overline{u}\|_{L^r(\Omega)} \leq C|u|_{W^1_p(\Omega)}, \tag{30.28}$$

provided that

$$\frac{1}{r} \geq \frac{1}{p} - \frac{1}{n}. \tag{30.29}$$

Choosing $p = r = 2$, we obtain the coercivity of the bilinear form

$$a(u, v) = \int_\Omega \nabla u(\mathbf{x}) \cdot \nabla v(\mathbf{x})\, d\mathbf{x}$$

on the space V defined in (2.15). More precisely, (30.28) becomes

$$\|u\|_{L^2(\Omega)} \leq C|u|_{H^1(\Omega)} = C\sqrt{a(u,u)},$$

for $u \in V$ (because $\overline{u} = 0$). But then for such u,

$$\|u\|^2_{H^1(\Omega)} = a(u,u) + \|u\|^2_{L^2(\Omega)} \leq \left(1 + C^2\right) a(u,u).$$

This is precisely the statement of coercivity for the bilinear form $a(\cdot,\cdot)$ on the space V defined in (2.15).

30.4 Compactness in Sobolev spaces

In Section 30.3 we saw that Sobolev spaces with one set of indices are naturally included in another, eg. (30.15). We now want to show that this inclusion is a compact mapping, that is, a bounded set in the stronger norm is **compact** in the weaker norm. We will not define this concept generally, but the following theorem captures the main essence.

Theorem 30.2 *Suppose that*

$$\frac{1}{r} > \frac{1}{p} - \frac{1}{n}.$$

Let K be a closed, bounded subset of $W^1_p(\Omega)$ and $\epsilon > 0$. Then there is a finite set of functions $v_j \in L^r(\Omega)$ such that

$$K \subset \cup_{j=1}^J \left\{ v \in L^r(\Omega) \;:\; \|v - v_j\|_{L^r(\Omega)} < \epsilon \right\}.$$

In words, this says that K can be covered by a finite set of balls of radius ϵ, no matter how small $\epsilon > 0$ gets. We take this as our operational definition of compactness. Our main ingredient in the proof of the theorem is Theorem 30.1. We apply that theorem on a triangulation $\mathcal{T}_h$ of Ω of size h to get the following approximation result for piecewise constant approximation.

Lemma 30.3 *For $u \in W^1_p(\Omega)$, let u_h denote the piecewise constant approximation of u on a triangulation $\mathcal{T}_h$ of Ω of size h. Then*

$$\|u - u_h\|_{L^r(\Omega)} \leq C h^{1-n/p+n/r} |u|_{W^1_p(\Omega)},$$

provided that

$$\frac{1}{r} > \frac{1}{p} - \frac{1}{n}.$$

Using this lemma, we prove Theorem 30.2 as follows. Let K be a bounded subset of $W^1_p(\Omega)$; that is, assume that $\|u\|_{W^1_p(\Omega)} \leq \gamma$ for all $u \in K$. Let $\epsilon > 0$. For any $h > 0$, the set of values u_h are bounded: $\|u_h\|_{L^\infty(\Omega)} \leq B$. Define piecewise constant functions v_j by

$$v_j\big|_e = -B + \frac{\epsilon\, \ell_{j,e}}{|\Omega|^{1/r}}, \quad \ell_{j,e} = 0, 1, \ldots, L,$$

where L is the smallest integer such that $L \geq 2B|\Omega|^{1/r}/\epsilon$. Let T be the number of elements $e \in \mathcal{T}_h$. Then the number of functions v_j is at most T^L. For a given u_h, pick j so that

$$\left| u_h|_e - (-B + \epsilon \ell_{j,e}/|\Omega|^{1/r}) \right| \leq \epsilon/(2|\Omega|^{1/r})$$

for all $e \in \mathcal{T}_h$. Then

$$\begin{aligned} \|u - v_j\|_{L^r(\Omega)} &\leq \|u - u_h\|_{L^r(\Omega)} + \|u_h - v_j\|_{L^r(\Omega)} \\ &\leq Ch^{1-n/p+n/r}\gamma + \epsilon/2 \leq \epsilon, \end{aligned} \tag{30.30}$$

provided that we choose h small enough. Thus we have shown that, for any $\epsilon > 0$, we can cover K by a finite number of balls of radius ϵ in $L^r(\Omega)$. Thus K is compact in $L^r(\Omega)$ [250]. Thus we have proved the following result for $m = 1$ and $k = 0$. The general result follows by iterating on the indices.

Theorem 30.3 *Let K be a bounded subset of $W_p^m(\Omega)$. Then K is a compact subset of $W_r^k(\Omega)$ if*

$$k - \frac{n}{r} < m - \frac{n}{p}. \tag{30.31}$$

One major application of compactness is the following statement.

If K is compact and $\{v_j \in K \,:\, j = 1, \ldots, \infty\}$ is an infinite sequence in K, then there is a subsequence $\{v_{j_k} \,:\, k = 1, \ldots, \infty\}$ and a limit $v \in K$ such that $v_{j_k} \to v$ as $k \to \infty$.

The proof of this statement is simple. Let $0 < \epsilon < 1$ and choose balls $B_1^1, \ldots, B_{J_1}^1$ of radius ϵ covering K. One of them, say B_{ℓ_1}, must contain an infinite number of v_j. Then the closure of $B_{\ell_1} \cap K$ is also compact, and it can be covered by a finite set of balls $B_1^2, \ldots, B_{J_2}^2$ of radius ϵ^2. One of them, say $B_{\ell_2}^2$, must contain an infinite number of v_j. Continuing in this way, we get balls of decreasing size with

$$(K \cap B_{\ell_1}) \supset (K \cap B_{\ell_1}^1 \cap B_{\ell_2}^2) \supset (K \cap B_{\ell_1}^1 \cap B_{\ell_2}^2 \cap B_{\ell_3}^3) \supset \cdots,$$

where each of these sets contains an infinite number of v_j's and the radius of $B_{\ell_j}^j$ is less than ϵ^j. The intersection of these sets contains the limit point v, and picking one point from each of them gives the required subsequence.

30.5 More on coercivity

The Poincaré inequality implies coercivity for the variational formulation of Poisson's equation with Neumann boundary conditions, using the space V defined in (2.15). We show now that it also implies coercivity for more general boundary conditions, using the concept of compactness.

Suppose that we want to show coercivity of the bilinear form

$$a(u, v) = \int_\Omega \nabla u(\mathbf{x}) \cdot \nabla v(\mathbf{x})\, d\mathbf{x}$$

on the space V defined by (2.6) with $\Gamma \neq \emptyset$. By Poincaré's inequality, there is an $\alpha > 0$ such that

$$\alpha \|v - \overline{v}\|_{H^1(\Omega)}^2 \leq a(v - \overline{v}, v - \overline{v})$$

for all $v \in H^1(\Omega)$, where $\overline{v}$ is the mean of v on Ω. But expanding, we find

$$a(v-\overline{v},v-\overline{v}) = a(v,v-\overline{v}) - a(\overline{v},v-\overline{v}) = a(v,v) - a(v,\overline{v}) - a(\overline{v},v) + a(\overline{v},\overline{v}) = a(v,v),$$

since $\overline{v}$ is a constant. Thus

$$\alpha\|v-\overline{v}\|^2_{H^1(\Omega)} \le a(v,v) \tag{30.32}$$

for all $v \in H^1(\Omega)$, where $\overline{v}$ is the mean of v on Ω.

If coercivity did not hold, it would mean that there are $v_j \in H^1(\Omega)$ with the properties that (see Exercise 30.3)

$$\|v_j\|_{H^1(\Omega)} = 1, \quad a(v_j,v_j) \le \frac{1}{j}. \tag{30.33}$$

This would imply in particular that

$$\|v_j\|^2_{L^2(\Omega)} = \|v_j\|^2_{H^1(\Omega)} - a(v_j,v_j) = 1 - a(v_j,v_j) \to 1$$

as $j \to \infty$. By compactness, we conclude that there is a subsequence v_{j_k} that converges to a limit v in $L^2(\Omega)$, and we therefore must have $\|v\|^2_{L^2(\Omega)} = 1$. Since $v_{j_k} \to v$ in $L^2(\Omega)$, we must have $\overline{v}_{j_k} \to \overline{v}$ as $k \to \infty$ (Exercise 30.4). From (30.32), we have

$$\begin{aligned}\alpha\|v_{j_k}-\overline{v}\|^2_{H^1(\Omega)} &\le \alpha\|v_{j_k}-\overline{v}_{j_k}\|^2_{H^1(\Omega)} + \alpha\|\overline{v}_{j_k}-\overline{v}\|^2_{H^1(\Omega)} \\ &\le a(v_{j_k},v_{j_k}) + C\left|\overline{v}_{j_k}-\overline{v}\right|^2 \to 0 \text{ as } k \to \infty.\end{aligned} \tag{30.34}$$

Thus $v_{j_k} \to \overline{v}$ in $H^1(\Omega)$ as $k \to \infty$, and since $v_{j_k} = 0$ on Γ, we conclude that $\overline{v} = 0$. That is $\|v_{j_k}\|_{H^1(\Omega)} \to 0$ as $k \to \infty$. But this contradicts the assumption that $\|v_j\|_{H^1(\Omega)} = 1$ for all j. Thus by contradiction, we have proved coercivity.

This technique of proof extends to other situations, such as the plate problem in Section 19.4.3. Instead of constants, linear functions must be subtracted to get an inequality similar to (30.32). But otherwise the arguments are similar (see Exercise 30.5).

30.6 Polynomial approximation in Sobolev spaces

We can think of Theorem 30.1 as an approximation result, which applied to a set of elements of a subdivision of size h yields a result like Lemma 30.3 for piecewise constant approximation. It is useful to ask about higher-order approximation, and we can use Theorem 30.1 to generate such a result.

30.6.1 Using averages

Suppose we apply Theorem 30.1 to a derivative $u^{(\alpha)}$. For simplicity, we take $r = p = 2$. Then we have

$$\|u^{(\alpha)} - \overline{u^{(\alpha)}}\|_{L^2(\Omega)} \le C|u|_{H^{|\alpha|+1}(\Omega)}. \tag{30.35}$$

Let $c_\alpha = \overline{u^{(\alpha)}}/\alpha!$. Note that

$$\partial^\alpha \mathbf{x}^\beta = \delta_{\alpha,\beta}\alpha!\,, \tag{30.36}$$

where $\delta_{\alpha,\beta}$ is the Kronecker δ: equal to one if $\alpha = \beta$ and zero otherwise. Thus $\partial^\alpha c_\alpha \mathbf{x}^\alpha = \overline{u^{(\alpha)}}$. Therefore

$$\|\partial^\alpha(u - c_\alpha\mathbf{x}^\alpha)\|_{L^2(\Omega)} \le C|u|_{H^{|\alpha|+1}(\Omega)}\,. \tag{30.37}$$

Now apply this for all α such that $m = |\alpha|$ and set

$$q_m(\mathbf{x}) = \sum_{|\alpha|=m} c_\alpha \mathbf{x}^\alpha. \tag{30.38}$$

Observe that (30.37) implies that

$$|u - q_m|_{H^m(\Omega)} \le C|u|_{H^{m+1}(\Omega)}. \tag{30.39}$$

Write $q_m = Q^m u$ where Q^m is the (bounded linear) operator which takes u to q_m. Then we have

$$|u - Q^m u|_{H^m(\Omega)} \le C|u|_{H^{m+1}(\Omega)}. \tag{30.40}$$

Iterating (30.40), we find

$$\begin{aligned} |(u - Q^m u) - Q^{m-1}(u - Q^m u)|_{H^{m-1}(\Omega)} &\le C|u - Q^m u|_{H^m(\Omega)} \\ &\le C|u|_{H^{m+1}(\Omega)} \end{aligned} \tag{30.41}$$

Define $Q_1^m u = Q^m u + Q^{m-1}(u - Q^m u)$ and $Q_0^m = Q^m$ for completeness. Then (30.41) says that

$$|u - Q_1^m u|_{H^{m-1}(\Omega)} \le C|u|_{H^{m+1}(\Omega)}.$$

Since $Q^{m-1}v$ is a polynomial of degree $\le m-1$ for any v, $|Q^{m-1}(u - Q^m u)|_{H^m(\Omega)} = 0$ since the derivatives of order m vanish on Q^{m-1}. So

$$\begin{aligned} |u - Q_1^m u|_{H^m(\Omega)} &= |(u - Q^m u) - Q^{m-1}(u - Q^m u)|_{H^m(\Omega)} \\ &= |u - Q^m u|_{H^m(\Omega)} \\ &\le C|u|_{H^{m+1}(\Omega)}. \end{aligned} \tag{30.42}$$

Thus we have

$$|u - Q_1^m u|_{H^m(\Omega)} + |u - Q_1^m u|_{H^{m-1}(\Omega)} \le C|u|_{H^{m+1}(\Omega)}. \tag{30.43}$$

Iterating, we can show that there exists a mapping Q_m^m onto polynomials of degree m such that

$$\|u - Q_m^m u\|_{H^m(\Omega)} \le C|u|_{H^{m+1}(\Omega)}. \tag{30.44}$$

This is the basic approximation result used to verify the corresponding estimate for the interpolant. Since derivatives of $Q_m^m u$ of order $m+1$ vanish, we can similarly write (30.44) as

$$\|u - Q_m^m u\|_{H^{m+1}(\Omega)} \le C|u|_{H^{m+1}(\Omega)}. \tag{30.45}$$

30.6.2 Interpolants

The operator Q_m^m provides a good approximation, according to (30.44). We can apply this locally on each element to guarantee a good approximation, but we need to see how this can be helpful in estimating an interpolant. The difficulty is that using Q_m^m on each element will only produce a discontinuous piecewise polynomial approximation. The interpolant is designed not only to provide good approximation on each element but also to link up adjoining elements to provide some level of continuity.

On each element, $\left(Q_m^m u\right)_I = Q_m^m u$, provided that our finite element space includes all piecewise polynomials of degree m. Thus on each element,

$$u - u_I = u - Q_m^m u + Q_m^m u - u_I = u - Q_m^m u + \left(Q_m^m u - u\right)_I. \tag{30.46}$$

It is possible [57] in most cases to show that the interpolation operator is bounded:

$$\|v_I\|_{H^{m+1}(e)} \leq C\|v\|_{H^{m+1}(e)} \tag{30.47}$$

for a reference elements e. For example, this is true for Lagrange piecewise polynomials of degree m provided that functions in $H^{m+1}(\Omega)$ are continuous. This is true by Sobolev's inequality (Lemma 30.2) if $m+1 > d/2$. For $d \leq 3$, this holds for all $m \geq 1$. To be more precise, the interpolant is defined on each element by

$$u_I = \sum_{i=1}^{N} \delta_i(u)\phi_i,$$

where $\{\phi_i : i = 1, \ldots, N\}$ is the local basis for the finite element space and each δ_i is a linear functional such that $\delta_i(\phi_j)$ is equal to the Kronecker delta. For Lagrange elements, each δ_i is just point evaluation corresponding to some node in the reference element.

The key to proving (30.47) is showing that each δ_i is a bounded linear functional:

$$|\delta_i(v)| \leq C\|v\|_{H^{m+1}(e)}.$$

If this holds, (30.47) follows by summing for $i = 1, \ldots, N$, provided that $\|\phi_i\|_{H^{m+1}(e)} \leq C$, which is almost always the case.

Once the bound (30.47) is established for the reference element e, we have

$$\|u - u_I\|_{H^k(e)} \leq \|u - u_I\|_{H^{m+1}(e)} \leq C\|u - Q^m_m u\|_{H^{m+1}(e)} \leq C|u|_{H^{m+1}(e)}. \tag{30.48}$$

Scaling the reference element, we see that for an element e_h of size h, we must have

$$\|u - u_I\|_{H^k(e_h)} \leq h^{m+1-k}|u|_{H^{m+1}(e_h)}. \tag{30.49}$$

Squaring this and summing over all elements gives

$$\|u - u_I\|_{H^k(\Omega)} \leq h^{m+1-k}|u|_{H^{m+1}(\Omega)}, \tag{30.50}$$

as well as the more sophisticated estimated (16.5).

30.7 Exercises

Exercise 30.1 *Explain what is being used to justify the inequality in the middle of (30.3).*

Exercise 30.2 *Verify the equality in the middle of (30.4).*

Exercise 30.3 *Prove that a lack of coercivity implies (30.33).*

Exercise 30.4 *Suppose that v_j represents a sequence of functions in $L^2(\Omega)$ converging to $v \in L^2(\Omega)$, that is $\|v - v_j\|_{L^2(\Omega)} \to 0$ as $j \to \infty$. Prove that $\overline{v}_{j_k} \to \overline{v}$ as $j \to \infty$, where $\overline{v}$ denotes the mean of v over Ω.*

Exercise 30.5 *Prove coercivity of the bilinear form in (19.14) for the plate problem in Section 19.4.3 for any space V such that the only linear function must be zero. (Hint: instead of constants, linear functions must be subtracted to get an inequality similar to (30.32). Use (30.45) instead of Poincaré's inequality.)*

Chapter 31

Notation

Here we collect different kinds of notation used in the book for reference and review.

31.1 Sets and logic

We write sets as

$$\{x \,:\, x \text{ satisfies some property}\}\,.$$

The empty set is denoted $\emptyset$.

31.1.1 $=$ versus $:=$ versus $\equiv$

The equal sign ($=$) is overloaded in technical usage. In many programming languages, it is used to mean *assignment*. We sometimes use the expression $:=$ to mean *is defined to be*, as in $A := B$ means that A is, by definition, equal to B, as opposed to the usual use of $=$ to mean that they can be shown to be equal.

If we want to define B to be A, we write $A =: B$.

The expression $u \equiv 0$ is used for emphasis to say that the function u is identically zero at every point.

31.1.2 $a \in A$ and $\forall a \in A$

For any set A, we use the short-hand $a \in A$ to mean that a is an element of the set A.

The notation $\forall a \in A$ means *for all* $a \in A$.

31.1.3 Subsets: $A \subset B$

Let A and B be subsets of $\mathbb{R}^d$. Then we write $A \subset B$ if $a \in B$ for all $a \in A$ ($\forall a \in A$).

31.1.4 Set restriction: $f|_B$

When a function is defined on a set A, and B is a subset of A, we write $f|_B$ to denote the function restricted to the subset B. Thus we can say $f|_B = 0$ as a shorthand to mean that f is zero on the subset B.

31.1.5 Set complements: $A\backslash B$

Let A and B be subsets of $\mathbb{R}^d$. Then we write $A\backslash B$ for the set of points in A that are not in B:

$$A\backslash B = \{a \in A \ : \ a \notin B\}.$$

31.1.6 inf and sup, min and max

We often write

$$\min_{a\in A} \cdots, \quad \max_{a\in A} \cdots,$$

to mean the minimum or maximum of something over a set A. This presumes that the minimum or maximum is attained over the set when it is an infinite set. To be cautious for infinite sets, we replace min by inf (max by sup) to allow for the possibility that the extreme value is not attained within the set. For example, $\max_{0<x<\pi/2} \sin x$ is not well defined, but

$$\sup_{0<x<\pi/2} \sin x = 1$$

is well defined.

31.1.7 Summation $\sum$

The summation of n things a_i, $i = 1, \ldots, n$, is written

$$\sum_{i=1}^{n} a_i = a_1 + a_2 + \cdots + a_n.$$

31.1.8 Cartesian product of sets

If we have two sets A and B, the Cartesian product of A and B is the set of pairs

$$A \times B = \{(a,b) \ : \ a \in A, \ b \in B\}.$$

When $A = B$, we write A^2 for $A \times A$. Or $A^d = A \times A \times \cdots A \times A$ (d copies).

31.2 Geometry

31.2.1 Cartesian space

We use the notation $\mathbb{R}^d$ to denote d-dimensional space, where $\mathbb{R}$ denotes real numbers.

31.2.2 Domains Ω

We use Ω to denote a subset of $\mathbb{R}^d$. For example, the unit disc Ω in $\mathbb{R}^2$ can be defined as

$$\Omega := \left\{\mathbf{x} \in \mathbb{R}^2 \ : \ |\mathbf{x}| < 1\right\}.$$

The unit interval is $[0,1] = \{x \in \mathbb{R} \ : \ 0 < x < 1\}$, and the unit square is

$$[0,1]^2 = \left\{(x,y) \in \mathbb{R}^2 \ : \ 0 < x < 1, \ 0 < y < 1\right\}.$$

Here the exponent indicates the Cartesian product.

It is important to distinguish between open and closed sets, but with domains Ω we will sometimes be flexible. But we will always assume that Ω has a non-empty interior.

31.2.3 Boundary $\partial\Omega$

The domain $\partial\Omega$ is the boundary of Ω and has one lower dimension than Ω. It is the intersection of the closure of Ω and the closure of the complement of Ω.

31.2.4 Distance $d(x, S)$

For any subset $S \subset \Omega$, define, for $x \in \Omega$,

$$d(x, S) = \inf \{|x - y| \ : \ y \in S\}.$$

For example, we could have $S = \partial\Omega$.

31.2.5 Complex numbers $x + \iota y$

We use $\iota = \sqrt{-1}$. The complex modulus $|x + \iota y| = \sqrt{x^2 + y^2}$ for all $x, y \in \mathbb{R}$.

We can think of complex numbers as equivalent spatially to $\mathbb{R}^2$.

31.3 Vectors and matrices

31.3.1 Vector dot product $\mathbf{u} \cdot \mathbf{v}$

If $\mathbf{u} = (u_1, \ldots, u_d)$ and $\mathbf{v} = (v_1, \ldots, v_d)$ are d-dimensional vectors, then the dot product is defined by

$$\mathbf{u} \cdot \mathbf{v} = \sum_{i=1}^{d} u_i v_i = u_1 v_1 + \cdots + u_d v_d.$$

The dot product is often written as $\mathbf{u}^t\mathbf{v}$. Here the superscript means *transpose*. We then think of $\mathbf{u} = (u_1, \ldots, u_d)$ and $\mathbf{v} = (v_1, \ldots, v_d)$ as $d \times 1$ matrices, so that $\mathbf{u}^t$ is a $1 \times d$ matrix, and $\mathbf{u}^t\mathbf{v}$ is interpreted as a matrix product.

31.3.2 Euclidean norm $|\mathbf{u}|$

The Euclidean norm of a vector is its length in d-dimensional space:

$$|\mathbf{u}| = \left(\sum_{i=1}^{d} u_i^2 \right)^{1/2} = \sqrt{\mathbf{u} \cdot \mathbf{u}}.$$

31.3.3 Matrix-vector product $\mathbf{Mv}$

If $\mathbf{M}$ is a $d \times d$ matrix

$$\mathbf{M} = \begin{pmatrix} m_{11} & \cdots & m_{1d} \\ \vdots & \ldots & \vdots \\ m_{d1} & \cdots & m_{dd} \end{pmatrix}$$

and $\mathbf{v} = (v_1, \ldots, v_d)$ is a d-dimensional vector, then the matrix-vector product $\mathbf{Mv}$ is a d-dimensional vector whose entries are defined by

$$\left(\mathbf{Mv}\right)_i = \sum_{j=1}^{d} m_{ij} v_j.$$

31.3.4 Frobenius product of matrices $\mathbf{M} : \mathbf{N}$

If $\mathbf{M}$ and $\mathbf{N}$ are $d \times d$ matrices, then $\mathbf{M} : \mathbf{N}$ is the number

$$\mathbf{M} : \mathbf{N} = \sum_{i,j=1}^{d} m_{ij} n_{ij}.$$

This is the same as the dot product of $\mathbf{M}$ and $\mathbf{N}$ if we think of them as d^2-dimensional vectors.

31.3.5 Frobenius norm of a matrix $|\mathbf{M}|$

If $\mathbf{M}$ is a $d \times d$ matrix, then $|\mathbf{M}|$ is the number

$$|\mathbf{M}| = \sqrt{M : M} = \Big(\sum_{i,j=1}^{d} m_{ij}^2 \Big)^{1/2}.$$

This is the same as the Euclidean norm of $\mathbf{M}$ if we think of it as a d^2-dimensional vector.

31.4 Notation for derivatives

31.4.1 Partial derivatives

The notation $\frac{\partial u}{\partial x_j}$ denotes the (partial) derivative of the scalar function u with respect to the jth coordinate x_j, with the other coordinates being held fixed. We similarly use the notation u_{x_j}, $u_{,x_j}$ and $u_{,j}$ as shorthand for $\frac{\partial u}{\partial x_j}$. When we make the coordinates explicit, e.g., (x, y, z), we will similarly write u_x (or $u_{,x}$), u_y (or $u_{,y}$) and so forth for $\frac{\partial u}{\partial x}$, $\frac{\partial u}{\partial y}$, etc.

31.4.2 Higher-order derivatives

Higher-order derivatives are defined by compounding them:

$$\frac{\partial^2 u}{\partial x_j^2} = \frac{\partial}{\partial x_j}\Big(\frac{\partial u}{\partial x_j}\Big).$$

The derivatives can be mixed:

$$\frac{\partial^2 u}{\partial x_i \partial x_j} = \frac{\partial}{\partial x_i}\Big(\frac{\partial u}{\partial x_j}\Big).$$

31.4.3 Multi-index notation

In a small number of places, we need to refer to derivatives more abstractly. Since we are dealing with problems of dimension d, the number of partial derivatives of order m increases rapidly. We use the **multi-index** notation to simplify this. A multi-index $\boldsymbol{\alpha} = (\alpha_1, \ldots, \alpha_d)$ is a vector of dimension d consisting of non-negative integers. We write

$$\Big(\frac{\partial}{\partial \mathbf{x}}\Big)^{\boldsymbol{\alpha}} u = \frac{\partial^{\alpha_1}}{\partial x_1^{\alpha_1}} \cdots \frac{\partial^{\alpha_d}}{\partial x_d^{\alpha_d}} u.$$

Similarly, we can define a monomial term

$$\mathbf{x}^{\boldsymbol{\alpha}} = x_1^{\alpha_1} \cdots x_d^{\alpha_d}.$$

For each multi-index, we define $|\boldsymbol{\alpha}| = \alpha_1 + \cdots + \alpha_d$. This measures the number of derivatives, often called the order of the derivative operator. The multi-index notation allows a compact notation both for derivatives and polynomials. For example, a general polynomial p of degree m can be written as

$$p(\mathbf{x}) = \sum_{|\boldsymbol{\alpha}| \le m} c_{\boldsymbol{\alpha}} \mathbf{x}^{\boldsymbol{\alpha}},$$

where $c_{\boldsymbol{\alpha}}$ denotes the appropriate coefficient of the monomial term $\mathbf{x}^{\boldsymbol{\alpha}}$.

31.4.4 Tensor notation

It is useful to have a notation for all derivatives of a given order, say m. We can write this using the notation in Section 31.4.3 as a set, but we also use a succinct tensor notation $\nabla^m u$, that is,

$$\nabla^m u = \left\{ \left(\frac{\partial}{\partial \mathbf{x}} \right)^{\boldsymbol{\alpha}} u \ : \ |\boldsymbol{\alpha}| = m \right\}.$$

31.4.5 Vector functions

For a vector valued function $\mathbf{w} = (w_1, \ldots, w_d)$, we use the notation $w_{i,j}$ to denote $\frac{\partial w_i}{\partial x_j}$.

31.5 Notation for integrals

The notation

$$\int_\Omega f(\mathbf{x})\, d\mathbf{x}$$

denotes the integral of the scalar valued function f over the domain Ω in d-dimensional space. Similarly,

$$\oint_{\partial\Omega} f(s)\, ds$$

denotes the integral of the scalar valued function f over the boundary of the domain Ω, which is denoted by $\partial\Omega$. The measure of Ω is the length, area, or volume of Ω, depending on the dimension of Ω:

$$\text{measure}(\Omega) = |\Omega| = \int_\Omega 1\, d\mathbf{x}.$$

Similarly,

$$\text{measure}(\partial\Omega) = |\partial\Omega| = \oint_{\partial\Omega} 1\, ds.$$

31.6 Some calculus identities

31.6.1 Gradient ∇

The gradient of a scalar function u is the vector-valued function

$$\nabla u = (u_{x_1}, \ldots, u_{x_d}) = (u_{,x_1}, \ldots, u_{,x_d}) = \left(\frac{\partial u}{\partial x_1}, \ldots, \frac{\partial u}{\partial x_d} \right).$$

31.6.2 Divergence $\nabla\cdot$

The divergence of a vector-valued function $\mathbf{w}$ is the scalar-valued function given by

$$\nabla\cdot\mathbf{w} = \sum_{i=1}^{d} \frac{\partial w_i}{\partial x_i} = \sum_{i=1}^{d} w_{i,i}.$$

31.6.3 Laplace operator Δ

The Laplace operator is defined by

$$\Delta u = \sum_{i=1}^{d} \frac{\partial^2 u}{\partial x_i^2} = u_{11} + \cdots + u_{dd} = u_{,11} + \cdots + u_{,dd}.$$

31.6.4 div, grad, and all that

The Laplace operator is sometimes written as ∇^2. We prefer this notation for something else (Section 31.7.5). But

$$\Delta u = \nabla\cdot(\nabla u)$$

(Exercise 2.2).

31.6.5 Directional derivative

The directional derivative $\mathbf{u}\cdot\nabla$ can be defined for any tensor-valued function, and it does not change the arity of the tensor. For a scalar-valued function v, the definition is a syntactic tautology:

$$\mathbf{u}\cdot\nabla v := \mathbf{u}\cdot(\nabla v) = \sum_{i=1}^{d} u_i v_{,i} = \sum_{i=1}^{d} u_i \frac{\partial v}{\partial x_i}.$$

For a vector-valued function $\mathbf{v}$, $\mathbf{u}\cdot\nabla\mathbf{v}$ is a vector-valued function whose components are defined by

$$(\mathbf{u}\cdot\nabla\mathbf{v})_i = \mathbf{u}\cdot\nabla v_i,\ i = 1,\ldots,d.$$

31.6.6 Symmetric gradient $\epsilon(\mathbf{u})$

For $\mathbf{u}$ a vector-valued function, $\nabla\mathbf{u}$ is a matrix-valued function, but that matrix is usually not symmetric. The symmetric part of that matrix is defined by

$$\epsilon(\mathbf{u})_{ij} = \tfrac{1}{2}\left(u_{i,j} + u_{j,i}\right)$$

and appears in several places, e.g., in (13.10).

31.6.7 Divergence of a tensor

In Section 31.6.2, the divergence of a vector-valued function is defined. This can be extended to any tensor-valued function. In particular, if $\mathbf{M}$ is a matrix-valued function, then $\nabla\cdot\mathbf{M}$ is a vector-valued function defined by

$$(\nabla\cdot\mathbf{M})_i = \sum_{j=1}^{d} m_{ij,j}.$$

Then

$$\nabla\cdot \epsilon(\mathbf{u}) = \Delta \mathbf{u}$$

(Exercise 19.6).

31.6.8 Normal derivative

The derivative of u in the direction normal to the boundary $\partial\Omega$ is written $\frac{\partial u}{\partial n}$, and it can be defined by

$$\frac{\partial u}{\partial n} = \mathbf{n} \cdot \nabla u,$$

where $\mathbf{n}$ is the outward-directed normal to $\partial\Omega$.

31.7 Function spaces

31.7.1 The space $C^k(\Omega)$

The space $C^k(\Omega)$ consists of functions all of whose derivatives up through order k are continuous on Ω.

31.7.2 The space $L^2(\Omega)$

The $L^2(\Omega)$ inner-product is defined by

$$(u, v)_{L^2(\Omega)} = \int_\Omega u(\mathbf{x})v(\mathbf{x})\, d\mathbf{x}.$$

The corresponding norm is

$$\|v\|_{L^2(\Omega)} = \sqrt{(v,v)_{L^2(\Omega)}} = \Big(\int_\Omega v(\mathbf{x})^2\, d\mathbf{x} \Big)^{1/2}.$$

For vector-valued functions, we have

$$(\mathbf{u}, \mathbf{v})_{L^2(\Omega)} = \int_\Omega \mathbf{u}(\mathbf{x}) \cdot \mathbf{v}(\mathbf{x})\, d\mathbf{x},$$

and

$$\|\mathbf{w}\|_{L^2(\Omega)} = \|\, |\mathbf{w}|\, \|_{L^2(\Omega)} = \Big(\int_\Omega |\mathbf{w}(\mathbf{x})|^2\, d\mathbf{x} \Big)^{1/2}.$$

The space $L^2(\Omega)$ is defined by

$$L^2(\Omega) = \left\{ v \,:\, \|v\|_{L^2(\Omega)} < \infty \right\},$$

and the space $L^2(\Omega)^d$ is defined by

$$L^2(\Omega)^d = \left\{ \mathbf{v} \,:\, \|\mathbf{v}\|_{L^2(\Omega)} < \infty \right\}.$$

31.7.3 The space $H^1(\Omega)$

The $H^1(\Omega)$ inner-product is defined by

$$(u,v)_{H^1(\Omega)} = \int_\Omega u(\mathbf{x})v(\mathbf{x}) + \nabla u(\mathbf{x}) \cdot \nabla v(\mathbf{x})\, d\mathbf{x}$$

The corresponding norm is

$$\|v\|_{H^1(\Omega)} = \sqrt{(v,v)_{H^1(\Omega)}} = \Big(\int_\Omega v(\mathbf{x})^2 + |\nabla v(\mathbf{x})|^2\, d\mathbf{x}\Big)^{1/2}.$$

For vector-valued functions, $\nabla \mathbf{u}$ and $\nabla \mathbf{v}$ are matrices, so

$$(\mathbf{u},\mathbf{v})_{H^1(\Omega)} = \int_\Omega \mathbf{u}(\mathbf{x}) \cdot \mathbf{v}(\mathbf{x}) + \nabla \mathbf{u}(\mathbf{x}) : \nabla \mathbf{v}(\mathbf{x})\, d\mathbf{x}.$$

$$\|\mathbf{w}\|_{H^1(\Omega)} = \Big(\int_\Omega |\mathbf{w}(\mathbf{x})|^2 + |\nabla \mathbf{w}(\mathbf{x})|^2\, d\mathbf{x}\Big)^{1/2},$$

where $|\nabla \mathbf{w}(\mathbf{x})|$ is the Frobenius norm (Section 31.3.5) of the matrix $\nabla \mathbf{w}(\mathbf{x})$. The space $H^1(\Omega)$ is defined by

$$H^1(\Omega) = \big\{v \,:\, \|v\|_{H^1(\Omega)} < \infty\big\},$$

and the space $H^1(\Omega)^d$ is defined by

$$H^1(\Omega)^d = \big\{\mathbf{v} \,:\, \|\mathbf{v}\|_{H^1(\Omega)} < \infty\big\}.$$

31.7.4 The space $H^1_0(\Omega)$

This is the set of functions in $H^1(\Omega)$ that vanish on the boundary:

$$H^1_0(\Omega) = \big\{v \in H^1(\Omega) \,:\, v = 0 \text{ on } \partial\Omega\big\}.$$

31.7.5 The space $H^m(\Omega)$

We define $\nabla^m u$ to be the tensor of all mth order derivatives of u. For $m = 1$, $\nabla^m u = \nabla u$. The **arity** of a tensor is the number of indices it has. So a scalar has arity 0, a vector has arity 1, and a matrix has arity 2. We can define $\nabla^m u$ inductively by $\nabla^m u = \nabla\big(\nabla^{m-1} u\big)$.

For a tensor $\mathbf{T}$ of any arity $(T_{ijk\ldots\ell})$, we can generalize the Frobenius norm (Section 31.3.5) for matrices to define

$$|\mathbf{T}| = \Big(\sum_{ijk\ldots\ell} \big(T_{ijk\ldots\ell}\big)^2\Big)^{1/2}.$$

Then

$$\|v\|_{H^m(\Omega)} = \Big(\int_\Omega \sum_{j=0}^{m} |\nabla^j v(\mathbf{x})|^2\, d\mathbf{x}\Big)^{1/2},$$

and the space $H^m(\Omega)^d$ is defined by

$$H^m(\Omega)^d = \big\{\mathbf{v} \,:\, \|\mathbf{v}\|_{H^m(\Omega)} < \infty\big\}.$$

This definition of $H^m(\Omega)^d$ is equivalent to the one where

$$\|v\|_{H^m(\Omega)} = \Big(\int_\Omega v(\mathbf{x})^2 + |\nabla^m v(\mathbf{x})|^2\, d\mathbf{x}\Big)^{1/2},$$

in the sense that each of the two norms can be bounded by a constant times the other.

31.8 Variational forms

Here we collect some of the key variational forms defined previously.

31.8.1 Laplace form (2.8)

$$a(u,v) = \int_{\Omega} \nabla u \cdot \nabla v \, d\mathbf{x}.$$

31.8.2 Robin form (5.11)

$$a_{\text{Robin}}(u,v) = \int_{\Omega} \nabla u(\mathbf{x}) \cdot \nabla v(\mathbf{x}) \, d\mathbf{x} + \oint_{\partial\Omega} \alpha(s) \, v(s) \, u(s) \, ds,$$

where $\alpha > 0$ is required for coercivity.

31.8.3 Laplace plus potential (7.3)

$$a_Z(u,v) = \int_{\Omega} \nabla u(\mathbf{x}) \cdot \nabla v(\mathbf{x}) + Z(\mathbf{x})u(\mathbf{x})v(\mathbf{x}) \, d\mathbf{x},$$

where Z is a given function.

31.8.4 van der Waals form (7.10)

$$a_\kappa(u,v) = \int_{\Omega} \tfrac{1}{2}\nabla u(r_1,r_2) \cdot \nabla v(r_1,r_2) + \big(\kappa(r_1) + \kappa(r_2)\big)u(r_1,r_2) \, v(r_1,r_2) \, dr_1 dr_2,$$

where $\kappa(r) = r^{-2} - r^{-1} + \frac{1}{2}$ and $\Omega = [0,\infty] \times [0,\infty]$.

31.8.5 One-dimensional Laplace forms (8.5) and (8.42)

$$a(u,v) = \int_0^1 u'(x)v'(x) + \alpha(x)u'(x)v(x) + \beta(x)u(x)v(x) \, dx.$$

The form (8.5) corresponds to $\alpha = \beta \equiv 0$.

31.8.6 Jeffrey-Hamel (nonlinear) (9.6)

$$a(u,v) + n(u,v) = \int_0^\alpha u'v' + 4uv + 6u^2 v \, dx$$

31.8.7 p-Laplacian (nonlinear) (9.17)

$$a_p(u,v) = \int_{\Omega} \big(\epsilon^2 + |\nabla u(\mathbf{x})|^2\big)^{(p-2)/2} \nabla u(\mathbf{x}) \cdot \nabla v(\mathbf{x}) \, d\mathbf{x},$$

where $1 < p < \infty$.

31.8.8 Heat equation (10.35)

$$a_{\Delta t}(v,w) = \int_\Omega v(\mathbf{x})w(\mathbf{x})\,d\mathbf{x} + \Delta t \int_\Omega \nabla v(\mathbf{x}) \cdot \nabla w(\mathbf{x})\,d\mathbf{x},$$

where $\Delta t > 0$ is the time step. This is the general form in d-dimensions; in (10.35) it is defined for $d = 1$.

31.8.9 Wave equation (12.12)

The θ scheme requires

$$a_\theta(v,w) = \int_\Omega v(\mathbf{x})w(\mathbf{x})\,d\mathbf{x} + \theta(\Delta t)^2 \int_\Omega \nabla v(\mathbf{x}) \cdot \nabla w(\mathbf{x})\,d\mathbf{x},$$

where $\Delta t > 0$ is the time step. This is the general form in d-dimensions; in (10.35) it is defined for $d = 1$.

31.8.10 Stokes' equations ∇ form (13.7)

$$a_\nabla(\mathbf{u},\mathbf{v}) = \int_\Omega \nabla\mathbf{u} : \nabla\mathbf{v}\,d\mathbf{x} = \int_\Omega \sum_{i,j=1}^d u_{i,j}v_{i,j}\,d\mathbf{x}.$$

31.8.11 Stokes' equations divergence form (13.8)

$$b(\mathbf{v},q) = -\int_\Omega \sum_{i=1}^d v_{i,i}q\,d\mathbf{x}.$$

31.8.12 Stokes' equations ϵ form (13.11)

$$a_\epsilon(\mathbf{u},\mathbf{v}) = 2\int_\Omega \sum_{i,j=1}^d \epsilon(\mathbf{u})_{ij}\epsilon(\mathbf{v})_{ij}\,d\mathbf{x} = 2\int_\Omega \epsilon(\mathbf{u}) : \epsilon(\mathbf{v})\,d\mathbf{x},$$

where

$$\epsilon(\mathbf{u})_{ij} = \tfrac{1}{2}\left(u_{i,j} + u_{j,i}\right)$$

was defined in (13.10) (also see Section 31.6.6).

31.8.13 Stokes iterated penalty form (14.13)

$$a_\rho(\mathbf{u},\mathbf{v}) = a(\mathbf{u},\mathbf{v}) + \rho\int_\Omega (\nabla\cdot\mathbf{u})(\nabla\cdot\mathbf{v})\,d\mathbf{x},$$

where $a(\cdot,\cdot)$ can be either (13.7) or (13.11), and $\rho > 0$.

31.8.14 Advection-diffusion form (15.9)

$$a_\beta(u,v) = \int_\Omega \nabla u(\mathbf{x}) \cdot \nabla v(\mathbf{x})\,d\mathbf{x} + \int_\Omega (\boldsymbol{\beta}(\mathbf{x}) \cdot \nabla u(\mathbf{x}))v(\mathbf{x})\,d\mathbf{x},$$

where $\boldsymbol{\beta}$ is a given function.

31.8.15 Transport form (15.20)

$$a_\tau(u,v) = \int_\Omega \tau uv + (\boldsymbol{\beta}\cdot\nabla u)v\,d\mathbf{x}.$$

where $\tau > 0$ and $\boldsymbol{\beta}$ is a given function.

31.8.16 Scalar elliptic form (17.3)

$$a_\alpha(u,v) = \int_\Omega \sum_{i,j=1}^{d} \alpha_{ij}(\mathbf{x})\frac{\partial u}{\partial x_i}(\mathbf{x})\frac{\partial v}{\partial x_j}\,d\mathbf{x},$$

where α_{ij} is a given matrix-valued function.

31.8.17 Darcy's Law (18.3) and (18.6)

$$a(\mathbf{u},\mathbf{v}) = \sum_{i,j=1}^{d} \int_\Omega A_{ij}(\mathbf{x})u_i(\mathbf{x})v_j(\mathbf{x})\,d\mathbf{x},$$

where A_{ij} is a given matrix-valued function.

$$b(\mathbf{w},q) = \int_\Omega \mathbf{w}(\mathbf{x})\cdot\nabla q(\mathbf{x})\,d\mathbf{x} = -\int_\Omega \nabla\cdot\mathbf{w}(\mathbf{x})\,q(\mathbf{x})\,d\mathbf{x} + \oint_{\partial\Omega} q(\mathbf{x})\,\mathbf{w}(\mathbf{x})\cdot\mathbf{n}(\mathbf{x})\,d\mathbf{x},$$

where $\mathbf{n}$ is the unit (outer) normal to $\partial\Omega$.

31.8.18 Elasticity form (19.7)

Under the assumption that the material is isotropic,

$$a_C(\mathbf{u},\mathbf{v}) = \int_\Omega \mathbf{T}:\nabla\mathbf{v}\,d\mathbf{x} = \lambda\int_\Omega (\nabla\cdot\mathbf{u})(\nabla\cdot\mathbf{v})\,d\mathbf{x} + \mu\int_\Omega \left(\nabla\mathbf{u}+\nabla\mathbf{u}^t\right):\nabla\mathbf{v}\,d\mathbf{x},$$

where μ and ν are the Lamé parameters.

31.8.19 Plate bending form (19.12)

$$a_P(u,v) = \int_\Omega \Delta u\,\Delta v - (1-\nu)\left(2u_{xx}v_{yy} + 2u_{yy}v_{xx} - 4u_{xy}v_{xy}\right)\,dxdy,$$

where ν is Poisson's ratio, and $2(1-\nu) = \mu/(\lambda+\mu)$, where μ and ν are the Lamé parameters.

31.8.20 Navier-Stokes nonlinear form (20.5)

$$c(\mathbf{u},\mathbf{v},\mathbf{w}) = \int_\Omega (\mathbf{u}\cdot\nabla\mathbf{v})\cdot\mathbf{w}\,d\mathbf{x}.$$

The directional derivative $\mathbf{u}\cdot\nabla\mathbf{v}$ is defined in Section 31.6.5.

31.8.21 Navier-Stokes time-stepping form (20.16)

$$\tilde{a}(\mathbf{u},\mathbf{v}) = a(\mathbf{u},\mathbf{v}) + \tau\,(\mathbf{u},\mathbf{v})_{L^2(\Omega)},$$

where $a(\cdot,\cdot)$ can be either (13.7) or (13.11), $\tau = R/\Delta t$, R is the Reynolds number, and Δt is the time step.

31.8.22 Navier-Stokes time-stepping form (20.28)

$$\tilde{a}\,(\mathbf{u},\mathbf{v};\mathbf{U}) = a\,(\mathbf{u},\mathbf{v}) + \int_\Omega (\tau\mathbf{u}\cdot\mathbf{v} + \mathbf{U}\cdot\nabla\mathbf{u}\cdot\mathbf{v})\;d\mathbf{x},$$

where $a(\cdot,\cdot)$ can be either (13.7) or (13.11), $\tau = R/\Delta t$, R is the Reynolds number, and Δt is the time step.

31.8.23 Navier-Stokes nonlinear form (20.34)

$$\hat{c}(\mathbf{u},\mathbf{w},\mathbf{v}) = c(\mathbf{u},\mathbf{w},\mathbf{v}) + c(\mathbf{w},\mathbf{u},\mathbf{v}) = \int_\Omega (\mathbf{u}\cdot\nabla\mathbf{w})\cdot\mathbf{v}\,d\mathbf{x} + \int_\Omega (\mathbf{w}\cdot\nabla\mathbf{u})\cdot\mathbf{v}\,d\mathbf{x}.$$

The directional derivative $\mathbf{u}\cdot\nabla\mathbf{w}$ is defined in Section 31.6.5.

31.8.24 Nitsche's method form (22.1)

$$a_\gamma(u,v) = \int_\Omega \nabla u\cdot\nabla v\,d\mathbf{x} + \gamma h^{-1}\oint_{\partial\Omega} uv\,dx - \oint_{\partial\Omega}\frac{\partial u}{\partial n}v\,dx - \oint_{\partial\Omega}\frac{\partial v}{\partial n}u\,dx,$$

where $\mathbf{n}$ denotes the outward-directed normal to $\partial\Omega_h$, $\gamma > 0$ is a fixed parameter and h is the mesh size.

31.8.25 BDT method form (22.16)

$$N_{1,h}(u,v) = a_h(u,v) - \oint_{\partial\Omega_h}\frac{\partial u}{\partial n}v\,ds - \oint_{\partial\Omega_h}\left(u + \delta\frac{\partial u}{\partial n}\right)\left(\frac{\partial v}{\partial n} - \gamma h^{-1}v\right)ds,$$

where $\gamma > 0$ is a fixed parameter, h is the mesh size, $\mathbf{n}$ denotes the outward-directed normal to $\partial\Omega_h$, and

$$\delta(\mathbf{x}) = \min\{s > 0\ :\ \mathbf{x} + s\mathbf{n} \in \partial\Omega\}.$$

Chapter 32

Solutions of selected exercises

32.1 Solution of Exercise 3.4

First of all, v vanishes on $\partial\Omega$ because $\epsilon < d$ where d is the distance to the boundary from $\mathbf{x}_0$. Thus all of the points where v is nonzero, namely the points $\mathbf{x}$ satisfying $|\mathbf{x}-\mathbf{x}_0| \le \epsilon$, are strictly away from the boundary. We can prove this via the triangle inequality:

$$\begin{aligned} d = \text{distance}(\mathbf{x}_0, \partial\Omega) &\le \text{distance}(\mathbf{x}, \partial\Omega) + |\mathbf{x}-\mathbf{x}_0| \\ &\le \text{distance}(\mathbf{x}, \partial\Omega) + \epsilon < \text{distance}(\mathbf{x}, \partial\Omega) + d. \end{aligned}$$

Subtracting d from both sides gives $0 < \text{distance}(\mathbf{x}, \partial\Omega)$.

The inequality $\text{distance}(\mathbf{x}_0, \partial\Omega) \le \text{distance}(\mathbf{x}, \partial\Omega) + |\mathbf{x}-\mathbf{x}_0|$ requires an explanation. We can let $\mathbf{y}$ be a closest point on $\partial\Omega$ to $\mathbf{x}$. Then the triangle inequality says that

$$|\mathbf{x}_0 - \mathbf{y}| \le |\mathbf{x}_0 - \mathbf{x}| + |\mathbf{x} - \mathbf{y}| = |\mathbf{x} - \mathbf{x}_0| + \text{distance}(\mathbf{x}, \partial\Omega).$$

But by definition, $\text{distance}(\mathbf{x}_0, \partial\Omega) \le |\mathbf{x}_0 - \mathbf{y}|$. So we conclude that

$$\text{distance}(\mathbf{x}_0, \partial\Omega) \le \text{distance}(\mathbf{x}, \partial\Omega) + |\mathbf{x}-\mathbf{x}_0|.$$

Now let us show that $v \in H^1(\Omega)$. Outside the ball of radius ϵ around $\mathbf{x}_0$, $v \equiv 0$. So we only need to assess what happens inside this ball, where $v(\mathbf{x}) = 1 - \epsilon^{-1}|\mathbf{x}-\mathbf{x}_0|$. Here v is bounded and thus square integrable. Thus we compute its gradient:

$$\nabla v(\mathbf{x}) = -\epsilon^{-1}\frac{\mathbf{x}-\mathbf{x}_0}{|\mathbf{x}-\mathbf{x}_0|}.$$

Although ∇v is not continuous at $\mathbf{x}_0$, it is bounded, and thus square integrable. Therefore $v \in H^1(\Omega)$.

32.2 Solution of Exercise 6.4

Recall from (6.3) that $g(r,\theta) = r^{2/3}\sin(\tfrac{2}{3}\theta)$. Then

$$g_{,r} = \tfrac{2}{3}r^{-1/3}\sin(\tfrac{2}{3}\theta) \qquad \text{and} \qquad g_{,rr} = -\frac{2}{9}r^{-4/3}\sin(\tfrac{2}{3}\theta).$$

Thus

$$g_{,rr} + r^{-1} g_{,r} = \left(\frac{-2}{9} + \frac{2}{3}\right) r^{-4/3} \sin(\tfrac{2}{3}\theta) = \frac{4}{9} r^{-4/3} \sin(\tfrac{2}{3}\theta).$$

On the other hand,

$$g_{,\theta\theta} = -\frac{4}{9} r^{2/3} \sin(\tfrac{2}{3}\theta) = -r^2 \big(g_{,rr} + r^{-1} g_{,r}\big).$$

Thus $\Delta g \equiv 0$.

More generally, let g be as specified in (6.8):

$$g(r,\theta) = r^{\pi/\kappa} \sin((\pi/\kappa)\theta).$$

Then

$$g_{,r} = \frac{\pi}{\kappa} r^{(\pi-\kappa)/\kappa} \sin((\pi/\kappa)\theta) \qquad \text{and} \qquad g_{,rr} = \frac{\pi(\pi-\kappa)}{\kappa^2} r^{(\pi-2\kappa)/\kappa} \sin((\pi/\kappa)\theta).$$

Thus

$$g_{,rr} + r^{-1} g_{,r} = \left(\frac{\pi}{\kappa} + \frac{\pi(\pi-\kappa)}{\kappa^2}\right) r^{(\pi-2\kappa)/\kappa} \sin((\pi/\kappa)\theta)$$

Similarly

$$g_{,\theta\theta} = -\left(\frac{\pi}{\kappa}\right)^2 r^{\pi/\kappa} \sin((\pi/\kappa)\theta).$$

Therefore

$$\Delta g = \left(\frac{\pi}{\kappa} + \frac{\pi(\pi-\kappa)}{\kappa^2} - \frac{\pi^2}{\kappa^2}\right) r^{(\pi-2\kappa)/\kappa} \sin((\pi/\kappa)\theta).$$

But

$$\frac{\pi}{\kappa} + \frac{\pi(\pi-\kappa)}{\kappa^2} - \frac{\pi^2}{\kappa^2} = \frac{\pi\kappa + \pi(\pi-\kappa) - \pi^2}{\kappa^2} = 0$$

for all κ. Thus $\Delta g \equiv 0$.

32.3 Solution of Exercise 6.7

The solution itself (figure not shown) has the symmetry as the solution in Figure 2.3 dictated by the symmetry of the domain. Thus u is the same if rotated by $\pi/2$. The code

```
solve(a == L, u, bc)
ux=grad(u)[0]
uxp=project(ux,V)
uxx=grad(uxp)[0]
uxxp=project(uxx,V)
plot(-uxxp, interactive=True)
```

was used to compute and plot $u_{,xx}$. This is depicted in Figure 32.1. We see more symmetries for the solution: $u_{,xx}$ is the same as $u_{,yy}$ rotated by $\pi/2$.

The derivatives along each boundary must vanish due to the fact that $u \equiv 0$ there. Thus we have $\Delta u = 0$ at the vertices, which is incompatible with the PDE $\Delta u = 1$ there. The effect visible in Figure 32.1 is the discontinuity of the second derivatives at the domain corners.

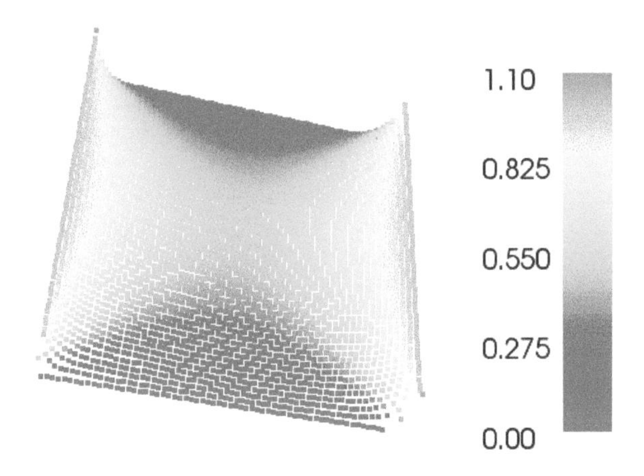

Figure 32.1: Second derivative $u_{,xx}$ for the solution to $-\Delta = 1$ on the unit square with homogeneous Dirichlet boundary conditions. Computed using a 64×64 right-triangle mesh and quartics.

32.4 Solution of Exercise 6.8

Uniqueness: Suppose there were two constants c_F^1 and c_F^2 satisfying $u - c_F^i g \in H^2(\Omega)$, $i = 1, 2$. Then

$$(c_F^1 - c_F^2)g = (u - c_F^2 g) - (u - c_F^1 g) \in H^2(\Omega),$$

which is a contradiction if $c_F^1 - c_F^2 \neq 0$ since $g \notin H^2(\Omega)$.

Linearity: Let F^1 and F^2 be two bounded linear functionals. Let $u^i \in V$ solve Poisson's problem with data F^i:

$$a(u^i, v) = F^i(v) \quad \forall v \in V.$$

Then $u^i - c_{F^i} g \in H^2(\Omega)$, $i = 1, 2$. Note that

$$a(u^1 + u^2, v) = F^1(v) + F^2(v) \quad \forall v \in V.$$

Also $u^1 + u^2 - c_{F^1} g - c_{F^2} g \in H^2(\Omega)$.

Suppose that $G = F^1 + F^2$. Let $u^G \in V$ solve Poisson's problem with data G:

$$a(u^G, v) = G(v) \quad \forall v \in V.$$

Then $u^G - c_G g \in H^2(\Omega)$ as well. By uniqueness (coercivity) of the solution of the variational problem, $u^G = u^1 + u^2$:

$$a(u^G - u^1 - u^2, v) = G(v) - F^1(v) - F^2(v) = 0 \quad \forall v \in V$$

(pick $v = u^G - u^1 - u^2$). Since $u^G = u^1 + u^2$,

$$\big(c_G - (c_{F^1} + c_{F^2})\big)g = -(u^G - c_G g) + (u^1 - c_{F^1} g) + (u^2 - c_{F^2} g) \in H^2(\Omega),$$

so we must have $c_G - (c_{F^1} + c_{F^2}) = 0$.

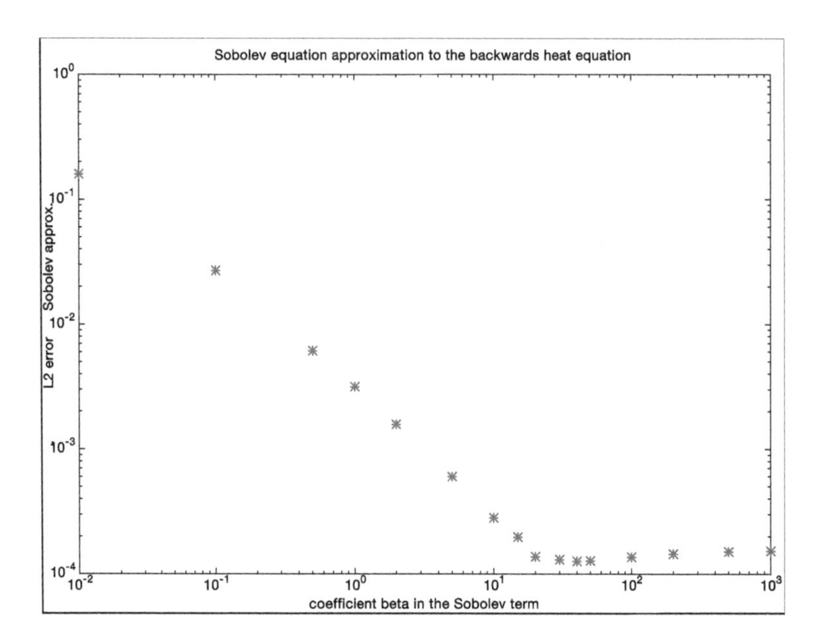

Figure 32.2: $L^2(-L, L)$ errors (32.5) in the approximation of the backwards heat equation (10.39) using the Sobolev equation approximation [124], plotted as a function of the Sobolev parameter β.

32.5 Solution of Exercise 8.9

Recall that $V = \{v \in H^1([0,1]) \,:\, v(0) = 0\}$ and that $u \in V$ satisfies

$$a(u,v) := \int_0^1 u'v' + \alpha uv' + (\beta - \alpha')uv\,dx = (f,v)_{L^2([0,1])}$$

for all $v \in V$, since $g_1 = 0$. Let us integrate by parts for the first term in the bilinear form:

$$\int_0^1 u'v' + u''v\,dx = \int_0^1 (u'v)'\,dx = u'(1)v(1),$$

since $v(0) = 0$. Thus

$$\int_0^1 u'v'\,dx = -\int_0^1 u''v\,dx + u'(1)v(1).$$

Similarly, integration by parts for the middle term in the bilinear form gives

$$\int_0^1 \alpha uv'\,dx = \int_0^1 -(\alpha u)'v\,dx + (\alpha uv)(1) = -\int_0^1 \alpha'uv + \alpha u'v\,dx + (\alpha uv)(1).$$

Therefore

$$\begin{aligned} a(u,v) &= \int_0^1 \Big(-u'' - \alpha'u - \alpha u' + (\beta - \alpha')u\Big)v\,dx + \big(u'(1) + \alpha(1)u(1)\big)v(1) \\ &= \int_0^1 \Big(-u'' - \alpha u' + (\beta - 2\alpha')u\Big)v\,dx + \big(u'(1) + \alpha(1)u(1)\big)v(1). \end{aligned} \tag{32.1}$$

Thus u satisfies the differential equation

$$-u'' - \alpha u' + (\beta - 2\alpha')u = 0$$

together with the Dirichlet condition $u(0) = 0$ and the Robin condition $u'(1)+\alpha(1)u(1) = 0$.

32.6 Solution of Exercise 9.11

The solutions of

$$-\epsilon u' + \tfrac{1}{2}u^2 = c \tag{32.2}$$

can be described uniquely by solving $u'(x) = f(u(x))$, where

$$f(u) = \epsilon^{-1}\big(\tfrac{1}{2}u^2 - c\big),$$

with some specified initial condition. For $c < 0$, $f(u) \geq -c/\epsilon$ and thus the solution u is unbounded.

By contrast, for $c \geq 0$, there are bounded solutions. The constant functions $w_\pm(x) = \pm\sqrt{2c}$ are solutions of (32.2) since $w'_\pm \equiv 0$. In this case, we can take the initial condition to be $u(x_0) = \pm\sqrt{2c}$ for any $x_0 \in \mathbb{R}$.

There are also non-constant solutions for $c > 0$. Define $v(x) = \tanh(x)$. Then $v'(x) = 1 - v(x)^2$ for all $x \in \mathbb{R}$. Now define $u(x) = a\,v(-bx)$. Then

$$u'(x) = -ab\,v'(-bx) = -ab\big(1 - v(-bx)^2\big) = -ab + (b/a)u(x)^2.$$

Therefore

$$-\epsilon u'(x) + (b\epsilon/a)u(x)^2 = \epsilon ab.$$

Thus u solves (32.2) if $(b\epsilon/a) = \frac{1}{2}$, that is

$$b = \frac{a}{2\epsilon}, \quad \text{and} \quad c = \epsilon ab = \tfrac{1}{2}a^2.$$

Therefore

$$a = \sqrt{2c} \quad \text{and} \quad b = \epsilon^{-1}\sqrt{c/2}.$$

In this case, we can take the initial condition to be $u(0) = 0$. Note that $|u(x)| < \sqrt{c/2}$ for all finite x, but the difference $\sqrt{c/2} - u(x)$ is exponentially small for $bx << 0$. In particular,

$$0 < \sqrt{c/2} - u(x) < \sqrt{2c}\,e^{2bx} = \sqrt{2c}\,e^{\sqrt{2c}\,x/\epsilon}.$$

For example, if $c = 2$, $x = -1$, and $\epsilon = 0.01$, then the error is less than $2e^{-200} \approx 1.4 \times 10^{-87}$. Thus the values of $w_+(-1)$ and $u(-1)$ are indistinguishable numerically.

When $c = 0$, the two solutions coincide: $u \equiv 0$ and $(a = b = 0)$. For $c > 0$ and $x_0 \in \mathbb{R}$ arbitrary, then $u^{x_0}(x) = u(x - x_0)$ is also a solution of (32.2) with initial condition $u^{x_0}(x_0) = 0$.

32.7 Solution of Exercise 9.13

First of all, the constant function

$$w(x) \equiv \gamma \tanh(\gamma/2\epsilon)$$

solves (9.24) with $\beta = 0$. Now we display a non-constant solution. Consider the function

$$v(x) = \gamma \tanh(-\gamma x/2\epsilon).$$

We have (see Exercise 9.12)

$$\frac{dv}{dx}(x) = -\frac{\gamma^2}{2\epsilon}\big(1 - \tanh^2(-\gamma x/\epsilon)\big) = -\frac{\gamma^2}{2\epsilon} + \frac{1}{2\epsilon}v(x)^2 \tag{32.3}$$

Thus

$$-\epsilon\frac{dv}{dx}(x) + \frac{1}{2}v(x)^2 = \frac{\gamma^2}{2}$$

for all x. In view of (9.19), v solves the first equation in (9.24), and it clearly satisfies the Dirichlet boundary condition at $x = -1$. Now examine the Neumann boundary condition at $x = 1$. Let $M = \gamma/2\epsilon$.

Using (32.3), v satisfies the Neumann condition with

$$\epsilon\beta = \frac{dv}{dx}(1) = -\gamma M\big(1 - \tanh^2(-M)\big) = -\gamma M\big(1 - (\tanh M)\big)\big(1 + (\tanh M)\big).$$

But (see Exercise 9.12)

$$0 \le 1 - \tanh M = 1 - \frac{e^M - e^{-M}}{e^M + e^{-M}} = \frac{2e^{-M}}{e^M + e^{-M}} = \frac{2e^{-2M}}{1 + e^{-2M}} \le 2e^{-2M}.$$

Therefore

$$|\epsilon\beta| = \left|\frac{dv}{dx}(1)\right| \le 4\gamma M e^{-2M}.$$

Thus $v'(1)$ is numerically indistinguishable from 0 for M large.

For $\gamma = 1$ and $\epsilon = 0.01$, we have $M = 50$ and

$$|\epsilon\beta| \le 4\gamma M e^{-2M} = 200\, e^{-100} < 10^{-41}.$$

Thus the Neumann condition at 1 is numerically the same for v and w.

The techniques in Section 5.3 can be used to indicate why the boundary value problem (9.24) is well posed. Multiply the first equation in (9.24) by v, integrate over $\Omega = [-1, 1]$, and integrate by parts to get

$$\int_{-1}^{1} u''v\, dx + \int_{-1}^{1} u'v'\, dx = \int_{-1}^{1} (u'v)'\, dx = (u'v)(1) - (u'v)(-1).$$

Thus for $v(-1) = 0$ and $u'(1) = 0$,

$$\int_{-1}^{1} -u''v\, dx = \int_{-1}^{1} u'v'\, dx.$$

Thus the natural variational form for the problem (9.24) is

$$n(u,v) = \epsilon \int_{-1}^{1} u'v'\,dx + \int_{-1}^{1} uu'v\,dx + \epsilon\beta v(1).$$

The variational formulation for (9.24) is then: mallskip find $u \in H^1(\Omega)$ such that $u(-1) = \gamma \tanh(\gamma/2\epsilon)$ and

$$n(u,v) = \epsilon\beta v(1) \quad \text{for all } v \in H^1(\Omega).$$

Note that

$$3\int_{-1}^{1} v^2 v'\,dx = \int_{-1}^{1} (v^3)'\,dx = v^3(1) - v^3(-1).$$

Thus if $v(-1) = 0$,

$$n(v,v) = \epsilon \int_{-1}^{1} (v')^2\,dx + \frac{1}{3}v(1)^3.$$

Thus we conclude that the coercivity estimate $n(v,v) \geq c\|v\|^2_{L^2(\Omega)}$ holds at least for v sufficiently small, that is when $|v(1)| \leq c$, where c is a constant depending on Sobolev's inequality on $\Omega = [-1,1]$. This provides theoretical support for using the fixed-point iteration to find $u_k \in H^1(\Omega)$ defined by

$$\epsilon \int_{-1}^{1} u_k'v'\,dx + \int_{-1}^{1} u_k u_{k-1}'v\,dx = \epsilon\beta v(1)$$

for all $v \in H^1(\Omega)$.

32.8 Solution of Exercise 10.8

Define $\Omega = [-L,L]$, $V = H_0^1(\Omega)$, and

$$a_\beta(u,v) = \int_\Omega \beta u'v' + uv\,dx, \qquad a(u,v) = \int_\Omega u'v'\,dx.$$

Then the variational formulation of the Sobolev equation is

$$a_\beta(u_t,v) - a(u,v) = 0 \quad \text{for all } v \in V.$$

Implicit Euler for this equation is

$$a_\beta(u^{n+1},v) - \tau a(u^{n+1},v) = a_\beta(u^n,v) \quad \text{for all } v \in V,$$

where τ is the time step. Notice that

$$a_\beta(w,v) - \tau a(w,v) = \int_\Omega \beta w'v' + wv - \tau w'v'\,dx = a_{\beta-\tau}(w,v).$$

Then the variational formulation of the time-stepping scheme is

$$a_{\beta-\tau}(u^{n+1},v) = a_\beta(u^n,v) \quad \text{for all } v \in V,$$

Thus a necessary condition appears to be $\tau < \beta$. An exact solution of the backwards heat equation is the Gaussian

$$u_0(x,t) := \frac{1}{(t_0-t)^{1/2}} e^{-x^2/(t_0-t)}. \tag{32.4}$$

This solution exists for $0 \le t < t_0$. The errors

$$\|u_\beta(\cdot,T) - u_0(\cdot,T)\|_{L^2(-L,L)} \tag{32.5}$$

are plotted in Figure 32.2 for $T = 0.001$. The initial data was taken to be $u_0(x) = u_0(x,0)$ with $u_0(x,t)$ as defined in (32.4) with $t_0 = 0.01$. These were computed with quartics, $L = 3$, on a grid with 10^3 points, using $\tau = 10^{-6}$ or less.

It is observed in [124] (see the error splitting in (2.9) and the bound on the term $C(t)$ in (2.11)) that the error in the Sobolev approximation increases rapidly as β is decreased beyond the optimal value. This behavior is seen in Figure 32.2. Thus one must balance "two terms against each other to obtain a best estimate" [124, page 286].

32.9 Solution of Exercise 10.11

Suppose that $\phi'(t) \le c\phi(t)$ for $t \in [0,T]$. Define $\psi(t) = e^{-ct}\phi(t)$. Then

$$\psi'(t) = -ce^{-ct}\phi(t) + e^{-ct}\phi'(t) = e^{-ct}\big(-c\phi(t) + \phi'(t)\big) \le 0$$

for $t \in [0,T]$. Then

$$\psi(t) - \psi(0) = \int_0^t \psi'(s)\,ds \le 0$$

for $t \in [0,T]$. Thus $\psi(t) \le \psi(0)$ for $t \in [0,T]$.

32.10 Solution of Exercise 10.15

Let $u(x,t) = t^{-3/2}\big((x^2/t) - \frac{1}{2}\big)e^{-x^2/t}$. Differentiating with respect to t gives

$$\begin{aligned} u_t(x,t) &= \left(-\frac{3}{2}t^{-5/2}\left(\frac{x^2}{t} - \frac{1}{2}\right) - t^{-7/2}x^2 + t^{-7/2}\left(\frac{x^2}{t} - \frac{1}{2}\right)x^2\right)e^{-x^2/t} \\ &= \left(\frac{3}{4}t^{-5/2} - 3t^{-7/2}x^2 + t^{-9/2}x^4\right)e^{-x^2/t} \end{aligned} \tag{32.6}$$

Differentiating with respect to x gives

$$u_x(x,t) = \left(2xt^{-5/2} - 2xt^{-5/2}\left(\frac{x^2}{t} - \frac{1}{2}\right)\right)e^{-x^2/t} = \big(3xt^{-5/2} - 2x^3t^{-7/2}\big)e^{-x^2/t}.$$

Differentiating again with respect to x gives

$$\begin{aligned} u_{xx}(x,t) &= \left(\big(3t^{-5/2} - 6x^2t^{-7/2}\big) - \frac{2x}{t}\big(3xt^{-5/2} - 2x^3t^{-7/2}\big)\right)e^{-x^2/t} \\ &= \big(3t^{-5/2} - 12x^2t^{-7/2} + 4x^4t^{-9/2}\big)e^{-x^2/t} = 4u_t(x,t). \end{aligned} \tag{32.7}$$

32.11 Solution of Exercise 12.2

When $\theta = 0$, (12.23) becomes

$$u^{n+1} - 2u^n + u^{n-1} + \lambda\tau^2 u^n = 0.$$

With $z = \lambda\tau^2$, this becomes

$$u^{n+1} - (2 - z)u^n + u^{n-1} = 0.$$

Substituting $\xi^n = u_n$, and dividing by ξ^{n-1}, we get the quadratic equation

$$\xi^2 - (2 - z)\xi + 1 = 0.$$

From the quadratic formula, $\xi = \xi_\pm(z)$ is given by

$$\begin{aligned}\xi_\pm(z) &= \frac{2 - z \pm \sqrt{(2-z)^2 - 4}}{2} = \frac{2 - z \pm \sqrt{-4z + z^2}}{2} \\ &= 1 - \tfrac{1}{2}z \pm \sqrt{-z + (z/2)^2} = 1 - \tfrac{1}{2}z \pm (z/2)\sqrt{-(4/z) + 1} \\ &= 1 - \tfrac{1}{2}z\big(1 \mp \sqrt{1 - 4/z}\big).\end{aligned} \tag{32.8}$$

When $0 < z < 4$, $\xi_\pm(z) = 1 - \frac{1}{2}z\big(1 \pm \iota\sqrt{(4/z) - 1}\big)$, and so

$$\begin{aligned}|\xi_\pm(z)|^2 &= (1 - \tfrac{1}{2}z)^2 + (\tfrac{1}{2}z)^2\big((4/z) - 1\big) = 1 - z + \tfrac{1}{4}z^2 + \tfrac{1}{4}z^2\big((4/z) - 1\big) \\ &= 1 - z + \tfrac{1}{4}z^2 + z - \tfrac{1}{4}z^2 = 1.\end{aligned} \tag{32.9}$$

Thus $|\xi_\pm(z)| = 1$ for all $0 < z < 4$.

When $z = 0$, there is only one root $\xi(0) = 1$, and when $z = 4$, there is only one root $\xi(4) = -1$.

When $z > 4$, $\sqrt{(4/z) - 1}$ is real, and so

$$\xi_-(z) = 1 - \tfrac{1}{2}z - \sqrt{(z/2)^2 - z} < -1 - \sqrt{(z/2)^2 - z} = -1 - \sqrt{z}\sqrt{\tfrac{1}{4}z - 1} < -1.$$

Thus $|\xi_-(z)| > 1$ for all $z > 4$.

Similarly, for $z < 0$, $\xi(z)$ is also real, and if we write $t = -z$, then $t > 0$ and

$$\xi_+(z) = 1 + \tfrac{1}{2}t + \sqrt{(t/2)^2 + t} > 1.$$

Thus $|\xi_+(z)| > 1$ for all $z < 0$.

For $z = 3$, the formula for u^n, starting with $u_{-1} = 1/2$ and $u_0 = 1$, gives

$$u = [0.5\ \ 1.0\ -1.5\ \ 0.5\ \ 1.0\ -1.5\ \ 0.5\ \ 1.0\ -1.5\ \ldots].$$

That is, $u_{3*n-1} = 1/2$, $u_{3*n} = 1$, and $u_{3*n+1} = -3/2$ for $n \geq 0$. This periodic behavior is consistent with having roots ξ that are on the unit circle in the complex plane.

For $z = 5$, the formula for u^n, starting with $u_{-1} = 1/2$ and $u_0 = 1$, gives

$$u = [0.5\ \ 1.0\ -3.5\ \ 9.5\ -25.0\ \ 65.5\ -171.5\ \ 449.0\ -1175.5\ \ 3077.5]$$

and the numbers continue to alternate in sign and grow in size. This rapid increase in size is consistent with having a root ξ with $|\xi| > 1$.

32.12 Solution of Exercise 12.4

For $\theta = \frac{1}{4}$,

$$\begin{aligned} 0 &= u^{n+1} - 2u^n + u^{n-1} + \lambda\tau^2\big(\theta u^{n+1} + (1-2\theta)u^n + \theta u^{n-1}\big) \\ &= u^{n+1} - 2u^n + u^{n-1} + \tfrac{1}{4}\lambda\tau^2\big(u^{n+1} + 2u^n + u^{n-1}\big) \\ &= u^{n+1} - 2u^n + u^{n-1} + z\big(u^{n+1} + 2u^n + u^{n-1}\big), \end{aligned}$$

where $z = \frac{1}{4}\lambda\tau^2$. Thus

$$(1+z)u^{n+1} - 2(1-z)u^n + (1+z)u^{n-1} = 0,$$

Now suppose that $u^n = \xi^n$ for some parameter ξ. Then

$$(1+z)\xi^{n+1} - 2(1-z)\xi^n + (1+z)\xi^{n-1} = 0.$$

Dividing by ξ^{n-1}, we conclude that

$$(1+z)\xi^2 - 2(1-z)\xi + (1+z) = 0,$$

From the quadratic equation, we conclude that

$$\begin{aligned} \xi(z) &= \frac{2(1-z) \pm \sqrt{4(1-z)^2 - 4(1+z)^2}}{2(1+z)} \\ &= \frac{1-z \pm \sqrt{(1-z)^2 - (1+z)^2}}{1+z} \\ &= \frac{1-z \pm 2\iota\sqrt{z}}{1+z} \end{aligned}$$

The complex modulus of $\xi(z)$ satisfies

$$|\xi(z)|^2 = \frac{(1-z)^2 + 4z}{(1+z)^2} = \frac{1+2z+z^2}{(1+z)^2} = \frac{(1+z)^2}{(1+z)^2} = 1$$

for any z. Note that

$$\xi(z) = \frac{1-z}{1+z} \pm \iota\frac{2\sqrt{z}}{1+z}.$$

Note that since $z > 0$,

$$\left(\frac{1-z}{1+z}\right)^2 = \frac{1-2z+z^2}{1+2z+z^2} \le 1,$$

so we can define t such that $\cos t = (1-z)/(1+z)$. Then

$$\sin^2 t = 1 - \cos^2 t = 1 - \frac{1-2z+z^2}{1+2z+z^2} = \frac{1+2z+z^2-(1-2z+z^2)}{1+2z+z^2} = \frac{4z}{(1+z)^2}.$$

Thus we conclude

$$\cos t = \frac{1-z}{1+z}, \quad \sin t = \frac{2\sqrt{z}}{1+z}.$$

so that

$$\xi(z) = \cos t \pm \iota \sin t = e^{\pm\iota t}.$$

When $z = 0$, $\cos t = 1$ and $\sin t = 0$. So $t = 0$. When $z \to \infty$, $\cos t \to -1$ and $\sin t \to 0$, so $t \to \pi$.

32.13 Solution of Exercise 14.3

Assume that $w \in Z_h^\perp$. By the Cauchy-Schwarz inequality (3.15),

$$(\mathcal{D}v, \mathcal{D}w)_\Pi \le \|\mathcal{D}v\|_\Pi \, \|\mathcal{D}w\|_\Pi,$$

where $\|\mathcal{D}v\|_\Pi = \sqrt{(\mathcal{D}v, \mathcal{D}v)_\Pi}$. Thus for all $0 \ne v \in Z_h^\perp$,

$$\frac{(\mathcal{D}v, \mathcal{D}w)_\Pi}{\|\mathcal{D}v\|_\Pi} \le \|\mathcal{D}w\|_\Pi.$$

Therefore

$$\|\mathcal{D}w\|_\Pi \ge \sup_{0 \ne v \in Z_h^\perp} \frac{(\mathcal{D}v, \mathcal{D}w)_\Pi}{\|\mathcal{D}v\|_\Pi}.$$

But choosing $v = w$, we have

$$\sup_{0 \ne v \in Z_h^\perp} \frac{(\mathcal{D}v, \mathcal{D}w)_\Pi}{\|\mathcal{D}v\|_\Pi} \ge \frac{(\mathcal{D}w, \mathcal{D}w)_\Pi}{\|\mathcal{D}w\|_\Pi} = \frac{\|\mathcal{D}w\|_\Pi^2}{\|\mathcal{D}w\|_\Pi} = \|\mathcal{D}w\|_\Pi.$$

Combining the inequalities, we find

$$\|\mathcal{D}w\|_\Pi \ge \sup_{0 \ne v \in Z_h^\perp} \frac{(\mathcal{D}v, \mathcal{D}w)_\Pi}{\|\mathcal{D}v\|_\Pi} \ge \|\mathcal{D}w\|_\Pi.$$

Thus

$$\|\mathcal{D}w\|_\Pi = \sup_{0 \ne v \in Z_h^\perp} \frac{(\mathcal{D}v, \mathcal{D}w)_\Pi}{\|\mathcal{D}v\|_\Pi}$$

for all $w \in Z_h^\perp$.

32.14 Solution of Exercise 16.2

The problem in Exercise 6.7, $-\Delta u = 1$ in the unit square Ω with $u = 0$ on $\partial\Omega$, was computed starting with a 2×2 mesh refinement using different degree approximations. The goal was taken to be the $L^2(\Omega)$ norm. As discussed in Exercise 6.7, the solution is not smooth at the corners, but it is in $H^2(\Omega)$. As expected, we see that cubics lead to a stronger refinement at the corners than linears, as indicated in Figure 32.3. The refinement at the corners for linears is the same as for parts of the domain away from the corners. The refinement at the corners for cubics is the finest in the domain.

Note the extreme difference in scale of the prescribed tolerances used for cubics versus linears. Thus the solution with cubics is much more accurate even thought the mesh is much coarser.

32.15 Solution of Exercise 19.4

Recall the integration by parts formula (2.10) which we rephrase as

$$\int_\Omega -w(\mathbf{x})\Delta v(\mathbf{x})\, d\mathbf{x} = \int_\Omega \nabla w(\mathbf{x}) \cdot \nabla v(\mathbf{x})\, d\mathbf{x} - \oint_{\partial\Omega} w \frac{\partial v}{\partial n}\, ds.$$

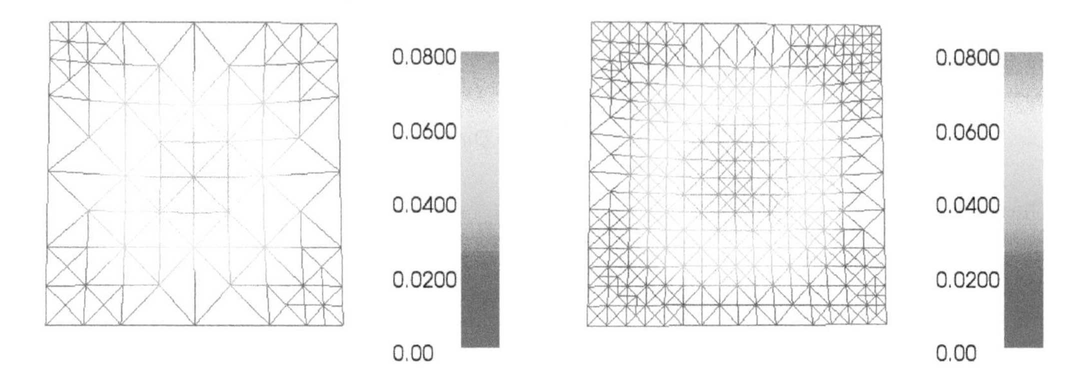

Figure 32.3: Solution of the problem in Exercise 6.7, $-\Delta u = 1$ in the unit square Ω with $u = 0$ on $\partial\Omega$, starting with a 2×2 mesh and using the $L^2(\Omega)$ norm as goal: (left) cubics with tolerance 10^{-8}, (right) linears with tolerance 0.00002.

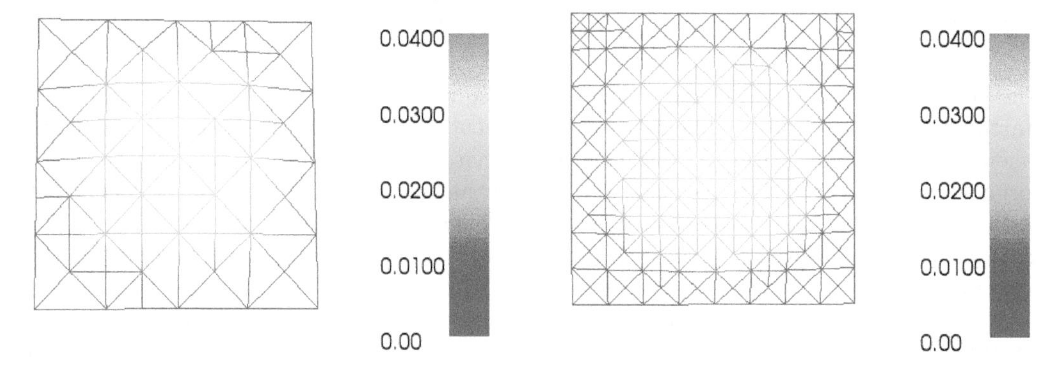

Figure 32.4: Solution of $-\Delta u = x(1-x) + y(1-y)$ in the unit square Ω with $u = 0$ on $\partial\Omega$, starting with a 2×2 mesh and using the $L^2(\Omega)$ norm as goal: (left) cubics with tolerance 10^{-9}, (right) linears with tolerance 10^{-5}.

Choosing $w = -\Delta u$, we find

$$\int_\Omega \Delta u \, \Delta v \, d\mathbf{x} = -\int_\Omega \nabla(\Delta u) \cdot \nabla v \, d\mathbf{x} + \oint_{\partial\Omega} \Delta u \frac{\partial v}{\partial n} \, ds. \tag{32.10}$$

Rewriting (2.10), we find

$$-\int_\Omega \nabla w(\mathbf{x}) \cdot \nabla v(\mathbf{x}) \, d\mathbf{x} = \int_\Omega v(\mathbf{x}) \Delta w(\mathbf{x}) \, d\mathbf{x} - \oint_{\partial\Omega} v \frac{\partial w}{\partial n} \, ds.$$

Applying this with $w = \Delta u$, we have

$$-\int_\Omega \nabla(\Delta u)(\mathbf{x}) \cdot \nabla v(\mathbf{x}) \, d\mathbf{x} = \int_\Omega v(\mathbf{x}) \Delta^2 w(\mathbf{x}) \, d\mathbf{x} - \oint_{\partial\Omega} v \frac{\partial \Delta u}{\partial n} \, ds. \tag{32.11}$$

Combining (32.10) and (32.11), we get

$$\int_\Omega \Delta u \, \Delta v \, d\mathbf{x} = \int_\Omega v(\mathbf{x}) \Delta^2 w(\mathbf{x}) \, d\mathbf{x} - \oint_{\partial\Omega} v \frac{\partial \Delta u}{\partial n} \, ds. + \oint_{\partial\Omega} \Delta u \frac{\partial v}{\partial n} \, ds.$$

32.16 Solution of Exercise 20.1

Let M be a $d \times d$ matrix and V any vector of dimension d. Then MV is the vector given by

$$(MV)_i = \sum_{j=1}^{d} M_{ij} V_j, \quad i = 1, \ldots, d.$$

Define the bilinear form $a(V, W) = V^t W$, and then $|V| = \sqrt{a(V, V)}$ is the Euclidean norm. For i fixed, let the vector W be given by $W_j = M_{ij}$, $j = 1, \ldots, d$. For each $i = 1, \ldots, d$, the Cauchy-Schwarz inequality (3.15) implies

$$|(MV)_i|^2 = |a(W, V)|^2 \le |W|^2 \, |V|^2 = \sum_{j=1}^{d} M_{ij}^2 \sum_{k=1}^{d} V_k^2.$$

Summing this over i, we get

$$\begin{aligned} |MV|^2 = \sum_i (MV)_i^2 &\le \sum_i \left(\sum_{j=1}^{d} M_{ij}^2 \sum_{k=1}^{d} V_k^2 \right) \\ &= \left(\sum_i \sum_{j=1}^{d} M_{ij}^2 \right) \sum_{k=1}^{d} V_k^2 = \|M\|_F^2 \, |V|^2. \end{aligned}$$

Taking square roots, we find $|MV| \le \|M\|_F \, |V|$ for any matrix M and vector V. We can apply Cauchy-Schwarz again to yield

$$|(MV) \cdot W| \le |MV| \, |W| \le \|M\|_F \, |V| \, |W| \quad \text{for all } V, W \in \mathbb{R}^d. \tag{32.12}$$

Now we apply this with $M = \nabla \mathbf{v}(\mathbf{x})$, $V = \mathbf{u}(\mathbf{x})$, and $W = \mathbf{w}(\mathbf{x})$. First observe that the vector $\mathbf{u}(\mathbf{x}) \cdot \nabla \mathbf{v}(\mathbf{x})$ can be written equivalently as a directional derivative and as a matrix–vector product:

$$\big(\mathbf{u}(\mathbf{x}) \cdot \nabla \mathbf{v}(\mathbf{x})\big)_i = \sum_{j=1}^{d} u_j(\mathbf{x}) v_{i,j}(\mathbf{x}) = \big((\nabla \mathbf{v}(\mathbf{x}))\mathbf{u}(\mathbf{x})\big)_i \quad \text{for all } i = 1, \ldots, d.$$

Thus $\mathbf{u}(\mathbf{x}) \cdot \nabla \mathbf{v}(\mathbf{x}) = (\nabla \mathbf{v}(\mathbf{x}))\mathbf{u}(\mathbf{x})$. Applying (32.12), we find

$$\left|(\mathbf{u}(\mathbf{x}) \cdot \nabla \mathbf{v}(\mathbf{x})) \cdot \mathbf{w}(\mathbf{x})\right| = \left|((\nabla \mathbf{v}(\mathbf{x}))\mathbf{u}(\mathbf{x})) \cdot \mathbf{w}(\mathbf{x})\right| \leq \|\nabla \mathbf{v}(\mathbf{x})\|_F |\mathbf{u}(\mathbf{x})|\, |\mathbf{w}(\mathbf{x})|$$

Integrating this over Ω gives

$$\begin{aligned}
\left|\int_\Omega (\mathbf{u}(\mathbf{x}) \cdot \nabla \mathbf{v}(\mathbf{x})) \cdot \mathbf{w}(\mathbf{x})\, d\mathbf{x}\right| &\leq \int_\Omega \left|(\mathbf{u}(\mathbf{x}) \cdot \nabla \mathbf{v}(\mathbf{x})) \cdot \mathbf{w}(\mathbf{x})\right| d\mathbf{x} \\
&\leq \int_\Omega \|\nabla \mathbf{v}(x)\|_F |\mathbf{u}(\mathbf{x})|\, |\mathbf{w}(x)|\, d\mathbf{x} \qquad (32.13) \\
&\leq \|\mathbf{u}\|_{L^\infty(\Omega)} \int_\Omega \|\nabla \mathbf{v}(x)\|_F |\mathbf{w}(x)|\, d\mathbf{x},
\end{aligned}$$

32.17 Solution of Exercise 20.4

Define $x = 1 + (ct/k)$ and write

$$\left(1 + \frac{ct}{k}\right)^k = x^k = e^{k \log x} = e^{k \log(1+(ct/k))}.$$

Now consider the function $\phi(y) = \log(1 + y)$. Then $\phi(0) = 0$ and

$$\phi'(x) = (1 + x)^{-1} \leq 1 \quad \text{for all } x \geq 0.$$

Integrating, we find

$$\log(1 + y) = \phi(y) = \int_0^y \phi'(x)\, dx = \int_0^y (1 + x)^{-1}\, dx \leq y \quad \text{for all } y \geq 0.$$

Thus

$$k \log(1 + (ct/k)) \leq k(ct/k) = ct.$$

Therefore

$$\left(1 + \frac{ct}{k}\right)^k = e^{k \log(1+(ct/k))} \leq e^{ct}. \qquad (32.14)$$

Now we examine the limit $\lim_{k\to\infty} a_k$ for $a_k = \left(1 + \frac{ct}{k}\right)^k$. From (32.14), we know that the sequence of values a_k is bounded, and they are positive. Then

$$\log(a_k) = k \log(1 + (ct/k)) = \frac{ct}{y_k} \log(1 + y_k) = ct\psi(y_k),$$

where $y_k = ct/k$ and $\psi(y) = y^{-1} \log(1 + y)$. Then

$$\lim_{k\to\infty} \log(a_k) = ct \lim_{y\to 0} \psi(y).$$

Using L'Hôpital's Rule, we write

$$\psi(y) = \frac{\log(1 + y)}{y} \qquad \text{and so} \qquad \lim_{y\to 0} \psi(y) = \lim_{y\to 0} \frac{1}{1 + y} = 1.$$

Thus

$$\lim_{k\to\infty} \log(a_k) = ct \qquad \text{and so} \qquad \lim_{k\to\infty} a_k = e^{ct}.$$

32.18 Solution of Exercise 27.6

Following the hint, we evaluate

$$(x^2 + y^2)\frac{\partial^2}{\partial x^2} \log |(x, y)|.$$

Note that $\nabla \mathbf{x} = |\mathbf{x}|^{-1}\mathbf{x}$, so $\nabla \log |\mathbf{x}| = |\mathbf{x}|^{-2}\mathbf{x}$. This means that $(\log |\mathbf{x}|)_x = x/(x^2 + y^2)$. Differentiating with respect to x, we get

$$(\log |\mathbf{x}|)_{xx} = \frac{(x^2 + y^2) - x(2x)}{(x^2 + y^2)^2} = \frac{-x^2 + y^2}{(x^2 + y^2)^2}$$

Thus

$$(x^2 + y^2)\frac{\partial^2}{\partial x^2} \log |(x, y)| = \frac{-x^2 + y^2}{x^2 + y^2} = \sin^2\theta - \cos^2\theta$$

in polar coordinates.

Bibliography

[1] Amit Acharya, Gui-Qiang G Chen, Siran Li, Marshall Slemrod, and Dehua Wang. Fluids, elasticity, geometry, and the existence of wrinkled solutions. *Archive for Rational Mechanics and Analysis*, 226(3):1009–1060, 2017.

[2] Cédric Adam, T. J. R. Hughes, Salim Bouabdallah, Malek Zarroug, and Habibou Maitournam. Selective and reduced numerical integrations for NURBS-based isogeometric analysis. *Computer Methods in Applied Mechanics and Engineering*, 284:732–761, 2015.

[3] Robert A. Adams and John J. F. Fournier. *Sobolev Spaces*, volume 140. Academic Press, 2003.

[4] Shmuel Agmon. *Lectures on Elliptic Boundary Value Problems. Prepared for Publication by B. Frank Jones, with the Assistance of George W. Batten.* AMS Chelsea Publishing, 1965.

[5] Shmuel Agmon, Avron Douglis, and Louis Nirenberg. Estimates near the boundary for solutions of elliptic partial differential equations satisfying general boundary conditions II. *Communications on Pure and Applied Mathematics*, 17(1):35–92, 1964.

[6] Mark Ainsworth. Dispersive and dissipative behaviour of high order discontinuous galerkin finite element methods. *Journal of Computational Physics*, 198(1):106–130, 2004.

[7] Mark Ainsworth and J. Tinsley Oden. A posteriori error estimation in finite element analysis. *Computer Methods in Applied Mechanics and Engineering*, 142(1):1–88, 1997.

[8] Alderson Alderson and K. L. Alderson. Auxetic materials. *Proceedings of the Institution of Mechanical Engineers, Part G: Journal of Aerospace Engineering*, 221(4):565–575, 2007.

[9] Thomas Apel, Sergei Grosman, Peter K. Jimack, and Arnd Meyer. A new methodology for anisotropic mesh refinement based upon error gradients. *Applied Numerical Mathematics*, 50(3):329–341, 2004.

[10] Todd Arbogast, Don Estep, B. Sheehan, and Simon Tavener. A posteriori error estimates for mixed finite element and finite volume methods for problems coupled through a boundary with nonmatching grids. *IMA Journal of Numerical Analysis*, 34(4):1625–1653, 2013.

[11] Denise Aregba-Driollet and Roberto Natalini. Discrete kinetic schemes for multidimensional systems of conservation laws. *SIAM Journal on Numerical Analysis*, 37(6):1973–2004, 2000.

[12] Gianni Arioli and Filippo Gazzola. A new mathematical explanation of what triggered the catastrophic torsional mode of the Tacoma Narrows Bridge. *Applied Mathematical Modelling*, 39(2):901–912, 2015.

[13] D. N. Arnold, M. Vogelius, and L. R. Scott. Regular inversion of the divergence operator with Dirichlet boundary conditions on a polygon. *Ann. Scuola Norm. Sup. Pisa Cl. Sci.-Serie IV*, XV:169–192, 1988.

[14] Douglas Arnold and Anders Logg. Periodic table of the finite elements. *SIAM News, November*, 2014.

[15] Douglas N. Arnold. Mixed finite element methods for elliptic problems. *Computer Methods in Applied Mechanics and Engineering*, 82(1-3):281–300, 1990.

[16] Douglas N. Arnold and Marie E. Rognes. Stability of Lagrange elements for the mixed Laplacian. *Calcolo*, 46(4):245–260, 2009.

[17] Gunnar Aronsson, Lawrence C. Evans, and Y. Wu. Fast/slow diffusion and growing sandpiles. *Journal of Differential Equations*, 131(2):304–335, 1996.

[18] Sheldon Axler, Paul Bourdon, and Ramey Wade. *Harmonic Function Theory*, volume 137. Springer Science & Business Media, 2013.

[19] Pascal Azerad, Jean-Luc Guermond, and Bojan Popov. Well-balanced second-order approximation of the shallow water equation with continuous finite elements. *SIAM Journal on Numerical Analysis*, 55(6):3203–3224, 2017.

[20] Ivo Babuška and Uday Banerjee. Stable generalized finite element method (SGFEM). *Computer Methods in Applied Mechanics and Engineering*, 201:91–111, 2012.

[21] Ivo Babuška and Juhani Pitkäranta. The plate paradox for hard and soft simple support. *SIAM Journal on Mathematical Analysis*, 21(3):551–576, 1990.

[22] Ivo Babuška and Werner C. Rheinboldt. A-posteriori error estimates for the finite element method. *International Journal for Numerical Methods in Engineering*, 12(10):1597–1615, 1978.

[23] Ivo Babuška and Manil Suri. Locking effects in the finite element approximation of elasticity problems. *Numerische Mathematik*, 62(1):439–463, 1992.

[24] B. Bagheri, A. Ilin, and L. R. Scott. Parallel 3-D MOSFET simulation. In *Proceedings of the* 27th *Annual Hawaii International Conference on System Sciences*, volume 1, pages 46–54, 1994.

[25] Babak Bagheri and L. R. Scott. About Analysa. Research Report UC/CS TR-2004-09, Dept. Comp. Sci., Univ. Chicago, 2004.

[26] Nathan Baker, Michael Holst, and Feng Wang. Adaptive multilevel finite element solution of the Poisson–Boltzmann equation II. Refinement at solvent-accessible surfaces in biomolecular systems. *Journal of Computational Chemistry*, 21(15):1343–1352, 2000.

[27] Nikolai Sergeevich Bakhvalov. On the convergence of a relaxation method with natural constraints on the elliptic operator. *USSR Computational Mathematics and Mathematical Physics*, 6(5):101–135, 1966.

[28] Wolfgang Bangerth and Rolf Rannacher. *Adaptive Finite Element Methods for Differential Equations.* Birkhäuser, 2013.

[29] R. E. Bank and T. Dupont. Analysis of a two-level scheme for solving finite element equations. Research Report CNA-159, Center for Numerical Analysis, Univ. Texas–Austin, 1980.

[30] Randolph E. Bank and Todd Dupont. An optimal order process for solving finite element equations. *Mathematics of Computation*, 36(153):35–51, 1981.

[31] Randolph E. Bank, editor. *Computational Aspects of VLSI Design with an Emphasis on Seminconductor Device Simulation.* Providence, Rhode Island: American Mathematical Society, 1990.

[32] J. R. Barber. Linear elasto-statics. In Jose Merodio and Giuseppe Saccomandi, editors, *Continuum Mechanics–Volume I*, page 344. Encyclopedia of Life Support Systems (EOLSS), Oxford, UK, 2008.

[33] Roland Becker and Rolf Rannacher. An optimal control approach to a posteriori error estimation in finite element methods. *Acta Numerica 2001*, 10:1–102, 2001.

[34] Martine Ben Amar and Eugenia Corvera Poiré. Pushing a non-Newtonian fluid in a Hele–Shaw cell: From fingers to needles. *Physics of fluids*, 11(7):1757–1767, 1999.

[35] Edward A. Bender. *An Introduction to Mathematical Modeling.* Courier Corporation, 2012.

[36] A. Berger, R. Scott, and G. Strang. Approximate boundary conditions in the finite element method. *Symposia Mathematica*, 10:295–313, 1972.

[37] Stefan Bergman and Menahem Schiffer. *Kernel functions and elliptic differential equations in mathematical physics.* Academic Press, 1953.

[38] J.-M. Bernard. Steady transport equation in the case where the normal component of the velocity does not vanish on the boundary. *SIAM Journal on Mathematical Analysis*, 44(2):993–1018, 2012.

[39] Jean-Marie Bernard. Solutions in H^1 of the steady transport equation in a bounded polygon with a full non-homogeneous velocity. *Journal de Mathématiques Pures et Appliquées*, 107(6):697–736, 2017.

[40] H. Berryman, J. Saltz, W. Gropp, and R. Mirchandaney. Krylov methods preconditioned with incompletely factored matrices on the CM-2. *Journal of Parallel and Distributed Computing*, 8:186–190, 1990.

[41] Graeme Austin Bird. Molecular gas dynamics. *NASA STI/Recon Technical Report A*, 76, 1976.

[42] D. Boffi. Three-dimensional finite element methods for the Stokes problem. *SIAM J. Num. Anal.*, 34:664 – 670, 1997.

[43] Richard Bois, Michel Fortin, and André Fortin. A fully optimal anisotropic mesh adaptation method based on a hierarchical error estimator. *Computer Methods in Applied Mechanics and Engineering*, 209:12–27, 2012.

[44] J. L. Bona, W. G. Pritchard, and L. R. Scott. An evaluation of a model equation for water waves. *Philos. Trans. Roy. Soc. London Ser. A 302*, pages 457–510, 1981.

[45] J. L. Bona, W. G. Pritchard, and L. R. Scott. A comparison of solutions of two model equations for long waves. In *Fluid Dynamics in Astrophysics and Geophysics, N. R. Lebovitz, ed.,*, volume 20, pages 235–267. Providence, Rhode Island: American Mathematical Society, 1983.

[46] J. L. Bona, W. G. Pritchard, and L. R. Scott. Numerical schemes for a model for nonlinear dispersive waves. *J. Comp Phys.*, 60:167–186, 1985.

[47] Y. Bourgault, M. Picasso, F. Alauzet, and A. Loseille. On the use of anisotropic a posteriori error estimators for the adaptative solution of 3D inviscid compressible flows. *International journal for numerical methods in fluids*, 59(1):47–74, 2009.

[48] Yves Bourgault and Marco Picasso. Anisotropic error estimates and space adaptivity for a semidiscrete finite element approximation of the transient transport equation. *SIAM Journal on Scientific Computing*, 35(2):A1192–A1211, 2013.

[49] Antonio Bove and Tatsuo Nishitani. Necessary conditions for local solvability for a class of differential systems. *Communications in Partial Differential Equations*, 27:1301 – 1336, 2002.

[50] James H. Bramble, Todd Dupont, and Vidar Thomée. Projection methods for Dirichlet's problem in approximating polygonal domains with boundary-value corrections. *Mathematics of Computation*, 26(120):869–879, 1972.

[51] Achi Brandt. Multi-level adaptive solutions to boundary-value problems. *Mathematics of Computation*, 31(138):333–390, 1977.

[52] Dominic Breit, Lars Diening, and Sebastian Schwarzacher. Finite element approximation of the p()-laplacian. *SIAM Journal on Numerical Analysis*, 53(1):551–572, 2015.

[53] Yann Brenier, Camillo De Lellis, and László Székelyhidi. Weak-strong uniqueness for measure-valued solutions. *Communications in mathematical physics*, 305(2):351, 2011.

[54] Susanne Brenner. Multigrid methods for the computation of singular solutions and stress intensity factors I: Corner singularities. *Mathematics of Computation*, 68(226):559–583, 1999.

[55] Susanne Brenner, Thirupathi Gudi, Michael Neilan, and Li-yeng Sung. C^0 penalty methods for the fully nonlinear Monge–Ampère equation. *Mathematics of Computation*, 80(276):1979–1995, 2011.

[56] Susanne C. Brenner. A nonconforming multigrid method for the stationary Stokes equations. *Mathematics of Computation*, pages 411–437, 1990.

[57] Susanne C. Brenner and L. Ridgway Scott. *The Mathematical Theory of Finite Element Methods*. Springer–Verlag, third edition, 2008.

[58] Jan Březina, Elisabetta Chiodaroli, and Ondřej Kreml. On contact discontinuities in multi-dimensional isentropic Euler equations. *arXiv preprint arXiv:1707.00473*, 2017.

[59] C. Brezinski and M. Gross-Cholesky. La vie et les travaux d'André Cholesky. *Bulletin de la Société des Amis de la Bibliothèque de l'Éc. Polytechnique*, 39:7–32, 2005.

[60] Franco Brezzi, Jim Douglas, and L. Donatella Marini. Two families of mixed finite elements for second order elliptic problems. *Numerische Mathematik*, 47(2):217–235, 1985.

[61] Peter N. Brown. A theoretical comparison of the Arnoldi and GMRES algorithms. *SIAM Journal on Scientific and Statistical Computing*, 12(1):58–78, 1991.

[62] Peter R. Brune, Matthew G. Knepley, and L. Ridgway Scott. Unstructured geometric multigrid in two and three dimensions on complex and graded meshes. *SIAM J. Sci. Computing*, 35(1):A173–A191, 2013.

[63] Antoni Buades, Bartomeu Coll, and Jean-Michel Morel. Image enhancement by non-local reverse heat equation. *Preprint CMLA*, 22:2006, 2006.

[64] Erik Burman and Peter Hansbo. A unified stabilized method for Stokes' and Darcy's equations. *Journal of Computational and Applied Mathematics*, 198(1):35–51, 2007.

[65] Erik Burman, Peter Hansbo, and Mats G. Larson. A cut finite element method with boundary value correction. *Mathematics of Computation*, 2017.

[66] Erik Burman and Alexander Linke. Stabilized finite element schemes for incompressible flow using Scott–Vogelius elements. *Applied Numerical Mathematics*, 58(11):1704–1719, 2008.

[67] J. Burns, A. Balogh, D. S. Gilliam, and V. I. Shubov. Numerical stationary solutions for a viscous Burgers' equation. *Journal of Mathematical Systems Estimation and Control*, 8:253–256, 1998.

[68] L. Caffarelli, E. Fabes, S. Mortola, and S. Salsa. Boundary behavior of nonnegative solutions of elliptic operators in divergence form. *Indiana University Mathematics Journal*, 30(4):621–640, 1981.

[69] Luis A Caffarelli, Ireneo Peral, and W On. On $W^{1,p}$ estimates for elliptic equations in divergence form. *Communications on pure and applied mathematics*, 51(1):1–21, 1998.

[70] Zhiqiang Cai and Shun Zhang. Recovery-based error estimator for interface problems: Conforming linear elements. *SIAM Journal on Numerical Analysis*, 47(3):2132–2156, 2009.

[71] Stephen L. Campbell, Ilse C.F. Ipsen, C. Tim Kelley, and Carl D. Meyer. Gmres and the minimal polynomial. *BIT Numerical Mathematics*, 36(4):664–675, 1996.

[72] Eric Cancès and L. Ridgway Scott. van der Waals interactions between two hydrogen atoms: The Slater-Kirkwood method revisited. *SIAM Journal on Mathematical Analysis*, 50(1):381–410, 2018.

[73] Claudio Canuto, M. Yousuff Hussaini, Alfio Quarteroni, and Thomas A. Zhang, Jr. *Spectral methods: Evolution to Complex Geometries and Applications to Fluid Dynamics.* Springer, 2007.

[74] Eduardo Casas, Andreas Günther, and Mariano Mateos. A paradox in the approximation of Dirichlet control problems in curved domains. *SIAM Journal on Control and Optimization*, 49(5):1998–2007, 2011.

[75] Michael A. Case, Vincent J. Ervin, Alexander Linke, and Leo G. Rebholz. A connection between Scott-Vogelius and grad-div stabilized Taylor-Hood FE approximations of the Navier-Stokes equations. *SIAM Journal on Numerical Analysis*, 49(4):1461–1481, 2011.

[76] Guy Chavent, Anis Younes, and Philippe Ackerer. On the finite volume reformulation of the mixed finite element method for elliptic and parabolic PDE on triangles. *Computer methods in applied mechanics and engineering*, 192(5):655–682, 2003.

[77] Gregory A. Chechkin, Dag Lukkassen, and Annette Meidell. On the Sapondzhyan–Babuška paradox. *Applicable Analysis*, 87(12):1443–1460, 2008.

[78] Gui-Qiang Chen and James Glimm. Kolmogorovs theory of turbulence and inviscid limit of the Navier–Stokes equations in $\mathbb{R}^3$. *Communications in Mathematical Physics*, 310(1):267–283, 2012.

[79] Gui-Qiang Chen, Marshall Slemrod, and Dehua Wang. Fluids, geometry, and the onset of Navier–Stokes turbulence in three space dimensions. *Physica D: Nonlinear Phenomena*, 2017.

[80] Huangxin Chen, Xuejun Xu, and Weiying Zheng. Local multilevel methods for second order elliptic problems with highly discontinuous coefficients. *J. Camp. Math*, 30:223–248, 2012.

[81] Long Chen, Michael J. Holst, and Jinchao Xu. The finite element approximation of the nonlinear Poisson–Boltzmann equation. *SIAM Journal on Numerical Analysis*, 45(6):2298–2320, 2007.

[82] Long Chen, Junping Wang, and Xiu Ye. A posteriori error estimates for weak Galerkin finite element methods for second order elliptic problems. *Journal of Scientific Computing*, 59(2):496–511, 2014.

[83] Sheng Chen, Jie Shen, and Li-Lian Wang. Generalized Jacobi functions and their applications to fractional differential equations. *Mathematics of Computation*, 85(300):1603–1638, 2016.

[84] Zhiming Chen and Shibin Dai. On the efficiency of adaptive finite element methods for elliptic problems with discontinuous coefficients. *SIAM Journal on Scientific Computing*, 24(2):443–462, 2002.

[85] R. C. Y. Chin and G. W. Hedstrom. A dispersion analysis for difference schemes: tables of generalized Airy functions. *Mathematics of Computation*, 32(144):1163–1170, 1978.

[86] Elisabetta Chiodaroli. A counterexample to well-posedness of entropy solutions to the compressible Euler system. *Journal of Hyperbolic Differential Equations*, 11(03):493–519, 2014.

[87] Elisabetta Chiodaroli, Camillo De Lellis, and Ondřej Kreml. Global ill-posedness of the isentropic system of gas dynamics. *Communications on Pure and Applied Mathematics*, 68(7):1157–1190, 2015.

[88] Elisabetta Chiodaroli and Laurent Gosse. A numerical glimpse at some non-standard solutions to compressible Euler equations. In Laurent Gosse and Roberto Natalini, editors, *Innovative Algorithms and Analysis*, pages 111–140. Springer, 2017.

[89] Elisabetta Chiodaroli and Ondrej Kreml. On the energy dissipation rate of solutions to the compressible isentropic Euler system. *Archive for Rational Mechanics and Analysis*, 214(3):1019–1049, 2014.

[90] Elisabetta Chiodaroli and Ondřej Kreml. An overview of some recent results on the Euler system of isentropic gas dynamics. *Bulletin of the Brazilian Mathematical Society, New Series*, 47(1):241–253, 2016.

[91] Elisabetta Chiodaroli and Ondřej Kreml. Non-uniqueness of admissible weak solutions to the Riemann problem for isentropic Euler equations. *Nonlinearity*, 31(4):1441, 2018.

[92] C. S. Chong, A. Senthil Kumar, and H. P. Lee. Automatic mesh-healing technique for model repair and finite element model generation. *Finite Elements in Analysis and Design*, 43(15):1109–1119, 2007.

[93] Alexandre Joel Chorin. A numerical method for solving incompressible viscous flow problems. *Journal of Computational Physics*, 2(1):12–26, 1967.

[94] Snorre Harald Christiansen and Kaibo Hu. Generalized finite element systems for smooth differential forms and Stokes problem. *arXiv preprint arXiv:1605.08657*, 2016.

[95] Doïna Cioranescu, Vivette Girault, and Kumbakonam Ramamani Rajagopal. *Mechanics and Mathematics of Fluids of the Differential Type*. Springer, 2016.

[96] Ray W. Clough. Original formulation of the finite element method. *Finite Elements in Analysis and Design*, 7(2):89–101, 1990.

[97] Bernardo Cockburn, Guido Kanschat, and Dominik Schötzau. A note on discontinuous Galerkin divergence-free solutions of the Navier–Stokes equations. *Journal of Scientific Computing*, 31(1):61–73, 2007.

[98] Ivan Cormeau. Bruce Irons: A non-conforming engineering scientist to be remembered and rediscovered. *International Journal for Numerical Methods in Engineering*, 22(1):1–10, 1986.

[99] Martin Costabel and Monique Dauge. Singularities of electromagnetic fields in polyhedral domains. *Archive for Rational Mechanics and Analysis*, 151(3):221–276, 2000.

[100] Martin Costabel, Monique Dauge, and Christoph Schwab. Exponential convergence of hp-FEM for Maxwell equations with weighted regularization in polygonal domains. *Mathematical Models and Methods in Applied Sciences*, 15(04):575–622, 2005.

[101] Richard Courant. Variational methods for the solution of problems of equilibrium and vibrations. *Bull. Amer. Math. Soc.*, 49(1):1–23, 1943.

[102] Richard Courant, Kurt Friedrichs, and Hans Lewy. Über die partiellen Differenzengleichungen der mathematischen Physik. *Mathematische annalen*, 100(1):32–74, 1928.

[103] Michael G. Crandall, Hitoshi Ishii, and Pierre-Louis Lions. Users guide to viscosity solutions of second order partial differential equations. *Bulletin of the American mathematical society*, 27(1):1–67, 1992.

[104] Michael G. Crandall and Pierre-Louis Lions. Viscosity solutions of Hamilton–Jacobi equations. *Transactions of the American Mathematical Society*, 277(1):1–42, 1983.

[105] F.A. Cruz, R.J. Poole, A.M. Afonso, F.T. Pinho, P.J. Oliveira, and M.A. Alves. A new viscoelastic benchmark flow: Stationary bifurcation in a cross-slot. *Journal of Non-Newtonian Fluid Mechanics*, 214:57 – 68, 2014.

[106] Franco Dassi, Simona Perotto, and Luca Formaggia. A priori anisotropic mesh adaptation on implicitly defined surfaces. *SIAM Journal on Scientific Computing*, 37(6):A2758–A2782, 2015.

[107] Franco Dassi, Hang Si, Simona Perotto, and Timo Streckenbach. Anisotropic finite element mesh adaptation via higher dimensional embedding. *Procedia Engineering*, 124:265–277, 2015.

[108] Victor DeCaria, William Layton, and Michael McLaughlin. A conservative, second order, unconditionally stable artificial compression method. *Computer Methods in Applied Mechanics and Engineering*, 325:733–747, 2017.

[109] Luca Dedè, Stefano Micheletti, and Simona Perotto. Anisotropic error control for environmental applications. *Applied Numerical Mathematics*, 58(9):1320–1339, 2008.

[110] Alan Demlow and Natalia Kopteva. Maximum-norm a posteriori error estimates for singularly perturbed elliptic reaction-diffusion problems. *Numerische Mathematik*, 133:707742, 2016.

[111] Ibrahima Dione, Cristian Tibirna, and José Urquiza. Stokes equations with penalised slip boundary conditions. *International Journal of Computational Fluid Dynamics*, 27(6-7):283–296, 2013.

[112] Manfred Dobrowolski, Steffen Gräf, and Christoph Pflaum. On a posteriori error estimators in the finite element method on anisotropic meshes. *Electronic Transactions on Numerical Analysis*, 8:36–45, 1999.

[113] M. H. Doolittle. Method employed in the solution of normal equations and the adjustment of a triangulation. *U.S. Coast and Geodetic Survey Report*, pages 115–120, 1878.

[114] J. Douglas, Jr. and U. Hornung. *Flow in Porous Media: Proceedings of the Oberwolfach Conference, June 21-27, 1992.* Birkhauser, 1993.

[115] James J. Duderstadt and William R. Martin. *Transport Theory.* Wiley, 1979.

[116] T. Dupont, Johnny Guzmán, and L. R. Scott. Obtaining full-order Galerkin accuracy when the boundary is polygonally approximated. *TBA*, 2018.

[117] Todd Dupont. L^2-estimates for Galerkin methods for second order hyperbolic equations. *SIAM Journal on Numerical Analysis*, 10(5):880–889, 1973.

[118] Weinan E, Bjorn Engquist, Xiantao Li, Weiqing Ren, and Eric Vanden-Eijnden. Heterogeneous multiscale methods: a review. *Commun. Comput. Phys*, 2(3):367–450, 2007.

[119] S. C. Eisenstat. Efficient implementation of a class of preconditioned conjugate gradient methods. *SIAM J. Scientific and Stat. Comput.*, 2:1–4, 1981.

[120] Charles L. Epstein and Michael O'Neil. Smoothed corners and scattered waves. *arXiv preprint arXiv:1506.08449*, 2015.

[121] John A. Evans and Thomas J. R. Hughes. Isogeometric divergence-conforming B-splines for the steady Navier–Stokes equations. *Mathematical Models and Methods in Applied Sciences*, 23(08):1421–1478, 2013.

[122] L. C. Evans, M. Feldman, and R. F. Gariepy. Fast/slow diffusion and collapsing sandpiles. *Journal of Differential Equations*, 137(1):166–209, 1997.

[123] Lawrence C. Evans. *Partial Differential Equations.* Providence, Rhode Island: American Mathematical Society, 1998.

[124] Richard E. Ewing. The approximation of certain parabolic equations backward in time by Sobolev equations. *SIAM Journal on Mathematical Analysis*, 6(2):283–294, 1975.

[125] Richard E. Ewing, Thomas F. Russell, and Mary Fanett Wheeler. Convergence analysis of an approximation of miscible displacement in porous media by mixed finite elements and a modified method of characteristics. *Computer Methods in Applied Mechanics and Engineering*, 47(1-2):73–92, 1984.

[126] Robert Eymard, Thierry Gallouët, and Raphaèle Herbin. Finite volume methods. In *Handbook of Numerical Analysis*, volume 7, pages 713–1018. Elsevier, 2000.

[127] Richard S. Falk. Approximation of the biharmonic equation by a mixed finite element method. *SIAM Journal on Numerical Analysis*, 15(3):556–567, 1978.

[128] Richard S. Falk and Michael Neilan. Stokes complexes and the construction of stable finite elements with pointwise mass conservation. *SIAM Journal on Numerical Analysis*, 51(2):1308–1326, 2013.

[129] Richard S. Falk and John E. Osborn. Error estimates for mixed methods. *RAIRO–Analyse numérique*, 14(3):249–277, 1980.

[130] Richard William Farebrother. A memoir of the life of M. H. Doolittle. *Bulletin of the Institute of Mathematics and Its Application*, 23(6/7):102, 1987.

[131] Patrick E. Farrell, David A. Ham, Simon W. Funke, and Marie E. Rognes. Automated derivation of the adjoint of high-level transient finite element programs. *SIAM Journal on Scientific Computing*, 35(4):C369–C393, 2013.

[132] Ulrik S. Fjordholm, Roger Käppeli, Siddhartha Mishra, and Eitan Tadmor. Construction of approximate entropy measure-valued solutions for hyperbolic systems of conservation laws. *Foundations of Computational Mathematics*, 17(3):763–827, 2017.

[133] David Chin-Lung Fong and Michael A. Saunders. CG versus MINRES: An empirical comparison. *Sultan Qaboos University Journal for Science*, 17(1):44–62, 2012.

[134] Luca Formaggia, Stefano Micheletti, and Simona Perotto. Anisotropic mesh adaptation in computational fluid dynamics: application to the advection–diffusion–reaction and the stokes problems. *Applied Numerical Mathematics*, 51(4):511–533, 2004.

[135] Jean Baptiste Joseph Fourier. *Théorie analytique de la chaleur.* Firmin Didot, Paris, 1822.

[136] B. Fraeijs de Veubeke. *Matrix methods of structural analysis.* [AGARDograph. Published for and on behalf of Advisory Group for Aeronautical Research and Development, North Atlantic Treaty Organization, by Pergamon Press; [distributed in the Western Hemisphere by Macmillan, New York], Oxford, New York,, 1964. Papers submitted to the Structures and Materials Panel of AGARD.

[137] Dietmar Gallistl. Rayleigh–Ritz approximation of the inf-sup constant for the divergence. *Mathematics of Computation*, 2018.

[138] Martin J. Gander and Gerhard Wanner. From Euler, Ritz, and Galerkin to modern computing. *SIAM Review*, 54(4):627–666, 2012.

[139] David Gilbarg and Neil S. Trudinger. *Elliptic Partial Differential Equations of Second Order.* Springer, second edition, 2001.

[140] V. Girault and L. Ridgway Scott. Analysis of a two-dimensional grade-two fluid model with a tangential boundary condition. *J. Math. Pures Appl.*, 78:981–1011, 1999.

[141] V. Girault and L. Ridgway Scott. Wellposedness of some Oldroyd models that lack explicit dissipation. Research Report UC/CS TR-2017-04, Dept. Comp. Sci., Univ. Chicago, 2017.

[142] Vivette Girault, Ricardo Nochetto, and L. Ridgway Scott. Maximum-norm stability of the finite element Stokes projection. *J. Math. Pures Appl.*, 84(3):279–330, 2005.

[143] Vivette Girault and Pierre-Arnaud Raviart. *Finite element approximation of the Navier–Stokes equations.* Lecture Notes in Mathematics, volume 749. Springer Verlag, Berlin, 1979.

[144] Roland Glowinski and Olivier Pironneau. Numerical methods for the first biharmonic equation and for the two-dimensional Stokes problem. *SIAM Review*, 21(2):167–212, 1979.

[145] Lars Grasedyck, Lu Wang, and Jinchao Xu. A nearly optimal multigrid method for general unstructured grids. *Numerische Mathematik*, 134(3):637–666, 2016.

[146] Anne Greenbaum. *Iterative Methods for Solving Linear Systems*, volume 17. Philadelphia: Society for Industrial and Applied Mathematics, 1997.

[147] Anne Greenbaum, Vlastimil Pták, and Zdenvěk Strakoš. Any nonincreasing convergence curve is possible for GMRES. *SIAM Journal on Matrix Analysis and Applications*, 17(3):465–469, 1996.

[148] Anne Greenbaum and Lloyd N. Trefethen. GMRES/CR and Arnoldi/Lanczos as matrix approximation problems. *SIAM Journal on Scientific Computing*, 15(2):359–368, 1994.

[149] Jean-Luc Guermond and Murtazo Nazarov. A maximum-principle preserving C0 finite element method for scalar conservation equations. *Computer Methods in Applied Mechanics and Engineering*, 272:198–213, 2014.

[150] Jean-Luc Guermond, Murtazo Nazarov, Bojan Popov, and Yong Yang. A second-order maximum principle preserving Lagrange finite element technique for nonlinear scalar conservation equations. *SIAM Journal on Numerical Analysis*, 52(4):2163–2182, 2014.

[151] Jean-Luc Guermond and Bojan Popov. Error estimates of a first-order Lagrange finite element technique for nonlinear scalar conservation equations. *SIAM Journal on Numerical Analysis*, 54(1):57–85, 2016.

[152] Jean-Luc Guermond and Bojan Popov. Invariant domains and first-order continuous finite element approximation for hyperbolic systems. *SIAM Journal on Numerical Analysis*, 54(4):2466–2489, 2016.

[153] Jean-Luc Guermond and Bojan Popov. Invariant domains and second-order continuous finite element approximation for scalar conservation equations. *SIAM Journal on Numerical Analysis*, 55(6):3120–3146, 2017.

[154] Max D. Gunzburger. *Finite Element Methods for Viscous Incompressible Flows*. Academic Press, 1989.

[155] I. A. Gustafson. Modified incomplete Cholesky (MIC) methods. In *Preconditioning Methods: Analysis and Applications*, pages 265–294. Gordon and Breach Science Publishers, 1983.

[156] Johnny Guzmán and Michael Neilan. Conforming and divergence-free Stokes elements in three dimensions. *IMA Journal of Numerical Analysis*, 34(4):1489–1508, 2014.

[157] Johnny Guzmán and Michael Neilan. Conforming and divergence-free Stokes elements on general triangular meshes. *Mathematics of Computation*, 83(285):15–36, 2014.

[158] Johnny Guzmán, Manuel A Sánchez, and Marcus Sarkis. Higher-order finite element methods for elliptic problems with interfaces. *ESAIM: Mathematical Modelling and Numerical Analysis*, 50(5):1561–1583, 2016.

[159] Johnny Guzmán and L. Ridgway Scott. Cubic Lagrange elements satisfying exact incompressibility. *SMAI JCM*, submitted, 2017.

[160] Johnny Guzmán and L. Ridgway Scott. The Scott-Vogelius finite elements revisited. *Mathematics of Computation*, to appear, 2018.

[161] Piotr Gwiazda, Agnieszka Świerczewska-Gwiazda, and Emil Wiedemann. Weak-strong uniqueness for measure-valued solutions of some compressible fluid models. *Nonlinearity*, 28(11):3873, 2015.

[162] Richard Haberman. *Mathematical Models: Mechanical Vibrations, Population Dynamics, and Traffic Flow: an introduction to applied mathematics*. Prentice–Hall, Englewood Cliffs, N.J., 1977.

[163] Antti Hannukainen, Mika Juntunen, and Rolf Stenberg. Computations with finite element methods for the Brinkman problem. *Computational Geosciences*, 15(1):155–166, Jan 2011.

[164] Stephen W. Hawking and Michael Jackson. *A brief history of time*. Bantam New York, NY, 2008.

[165] Gerald W. Hedstrom. Models of difference schemes for $u_t + u_x = 0$ by partial differential equations. *Mathematics of Computation*, 29(132):969–977, 1975.

[166] Tobias Hell and Alexander Ostermann. Compatibility conditions for Dirichlet and Neumann problems of Poisson's equation on a rectangle. *Journal of Mathematical Analysis and Applications*, 420(2):1005–1023, 2014.

[167] Thomas Hillen and Kevin J. Painter. A users guide to PDE models for chemotaxis. *Journal of Mathematical Biology*, 58(1-2):183, 2009.

[168] Steve Hofmann and Svitlana Mayboroda. Hardy and BMO spaces associated to divergence form elliptic operators. *Mathematische Annalen*, 344(1):37–116, 2009.

[169] Michael Holst, Nathan Baker, and Feng Wang. Adaptive multilevel finite element solution of the Poisson–Boltzmann equation I. Algorithms and examples. *Journal of computational chemistry*, 21(15):1319–1342, 2000.

[170] Lars Hörmander. *Linear Partial Differential Operators*. Springer–Verlag, 1969.

[171] A. Ilin, B. Bagheri, L. R. Scott, J. M. Briggs, and J. A. McCammon. Parallelization of Poisson–Boltzmann and Brownian Dynamics calculation. In *Parallel Computing in Computational Chemistry*, Washington D.C., to appear in 1995. ACS Books.

[172] Volker John, Alexander Linke, Christian Merdon, Michael Neilan, and Leo G. Rebholz. On the divergence constraint in mixed finite element methods for incompressible flows. *SIAM Review*, pages 469–544, 2016.

[173] Mika Juntunen and Rolf Stenberg. Nitsche's method for general boundary conditions. *Mathematics of Computation*, 78(267):1353–1374, 2009.

[174] Mark Kac. Can one hear the shape of a drum? *The American Mathematical Monthly*, 73(4):1–23, 1966.

[175] C. T. Kelley. *Iterative Methods for Optimization*, volume 18. Philadelphia: Society for Industrial and Applied Mathematics, 1999.

[176] R. C. Kirby, M. Knepley, A. Logg, and L. R. Scott. Optimizing the evaluation of finite element matrices. *SIAM J. Sci. Computing*, 27:741–758, 2005.

[177] R. C. Kirby, A. Logg, L. R. Scott, and A. R. Terrel. Topological optimization of the evaluation of finite element matrices. *SIAM J. Sci. Computing*, 28:224–240, 2006.

[178] R. C. Kirby and L. R. Scott. Geometric optimization of the evaluation of finite element matrices. *SIAM J. Sci. Computing*, 29:827–841, 2007.

[179] Robert C. Kirby and Anders Logg. Efficient compilation of a class of variational forms. *ACM Transactions on Mathematical Software (TOMS)*, 33(3):17, 2007.

[180] Tzanio V. Kolev, Jinchao Xu, and Yunrong Zhu. Multilevel preconditioners for reaction-diffusion problems with discontinuous coefficients. *arXiv preprint arXiv:1411.7092*, 2014.

[181] Natalia Kopteva. Maximum-norm a posteriori error estimates for singularly perturbed reaction-diffusion problems on anisotropic meshes. *SIAM Journal on Numerical Analysis*, 53(6):2519–2544, 2015.

[182] Gunilla Kreiss and Heinz-Otto Kreiss. Convergence to steady state of solutions of Burgers' equation. *Applied Numerical Mathematics*, 2(3-5):161–179, 1986.

[183] Wolfgang Krendl, Katharina Rafetseder, and Walter Zulehner. A decomposition result for biharmonic problems and the Hellan–Herrmann–Johnson method. *Electronic Transactions on Numerical Analysis*, 45:257–282, 2016.

[184] Arjan Kuijper. p-laplacian driven image processing. In *Image Processing, 2007. ICIP 2007. IEEE International Conference on*, volume 5, pages V–257. IEEE, 2007.

[185] Gerd Kunert. An a posteriori residual error estimator for the finite element method on anisotropic tetrahedral meshes. *Numerische Mathematik*, 86(3):471–490, 2000.

[186] Gerd Kunert. Robust a posteriori error estimation for a singularly perturbed reaction–diffusion equation on anisotropic tetrahedral meshes. *Advances in Computational Mathematics*, 15(1-4):237–259, 2001.

[187] Gerd Kunert and Serge Nicaise. Zienkiewicz–Zhu error estimators on anisotropic tetrahedral and triangular finite element meshes. *ESAIM: Mathematical Modelling and Numerical Analysis*, 37(6):1013–1043, 2003.

[188] Gerd Kunert and Rüdiger Verfürth. Edge residuals dominate a posteriori error estimates for linear finite element methods on anisotropic triangular and tetrahedral meshes. *Numerische Mathematik*, 86(2):283–303, 2000.

[189] Dochan Kwak and Cetin C. Kiris. Artificial compressibility method. In *Computation of Viscous Incompressible Flows*, pages 41–77. Springer, 2011.

[190] L. D. Landau and E. M. Lifshitz. *Fluid Mechanics*. Oxford: Pergammon Press, second edition, 1987.

[191] Hans Petter Langtangen and Anders Logg. *Solving PDEs in Python: The FEniCS Tutorial I*. Springer, 2016.

[192] Peter Lax and Burton Wendroff. Systems of conservation laws. *Communications on Pure and Applied mathematics*, 13(2):217–237, 1960.

[193] Peter D. Lax. Weak solutions of nonlinear hyperbolic equations and their numerical computation. *Communications on Pure and Applied Mathematics*, 7(1):159–193, 1954.

[194] Peter D. Lax and Burton Wendroff. Difference schemes for hyperbolic equations with high order of accuracy. *Communications on pure and applied mathematics*, 17(3):381–398, 1964.

[195] Young-Ju Lee, Jinbiao Wu, and Jinru Chen. Robust multigrid method for the planar linear elasticity problems. *Numerische Mathematik*, 113(3):473–496, 2009.

[196] Lew Lefton, Dongming Wei, and Yu Liu. Optimal numerical flux of power-law fluids in some partially full pipes. *International Journal of Computational Fluid Dynamics*, 28(6-10):351–362, 2014.

[197] C. C. Lin and Lee A. Segel. *Mathematics applied to deterministic problems in the natural sciences.* Philadelphia: Society for Industrial and Applied Mathematics, 1988.

[198] Alexander Linke. Collision in a cross-shaped domain – a steady 2d NavierStokes example demonstrating the importance of mass conservation in CFD. *Computer Methods in Applied Mechanics and Engineering*, 198(4144):3278 – 3286, 2009.

[199] Alexander Linke, Gunar Matthies, and Lutz Tobiska. Non-nested multi-grid solvers for mixed divergence-free Scott–Vogelius discretizations. *Computing*, 83(2-3):87–107, 2008.

[200] Alexander Linke, Leo G. Rebholz, and Nicholas E. Wilson. On the convergence rate of grad-div stabilized Taylor–Hood to Scott–Vogelius solutions for incompressible flow problems. *Journal of Mathematical Analysis and Applications*, 381(2):612–626, 2011.

[201] Jacques Louis Lions and B. V. Singbal. *Lectures on Elliptic Partial Differential Equations.* Number 10. Tata Institute of Fundamental Research Mumbai, 1957.

[202] T.-P. Liu and Joel A. Smoller. On the vacuum state for the isentropic gas dynamics equations. *Advances in Applied Mathematics*, 1:345–359, 1980.

[203] W. B. Liu and John W. Barrett. A remark on the regularity of the solutions of the p-Laplacian and its application to their finite element approximation. *Journal of Mathematical Analysis and Applications*, 178(2):470–487, 1993.

[204] Robert Kenneth Livesley. *Matrix Methods of Structural Analysis.* Oxford: Pergamon Press, 1964.

[205] A. Logg, K.A. Mardal, and G. Wells. *Automated Solution of Differential Equations by the Finite Element Method: The FEniCS Book.* Springer, 2012.

[206] Anders Logg and Garth N. Wells. Dolfin: Automated finite element computing. *ACM Transactions on Mathematical Software (TOMS)*, 37(2):20, 2010.

[207] Lynn H. Loomis. A short proof of the completeness of the Laguerre functions. *Bulletin of the American Mathematical Society*, 50(6):386–387, 1944.

[208] Menglin Lou, Huaifeng Wang, Xi Chen, and Yongmei Zhai. Structure–soil–structure interaction: literature review. *Soil Dynamics and Earthquake Engineering*, 31(12):1724–1731, 2011.

[209] D. S. Malkus and E. T. Olsen. Linear crossed triangles for incompressible media. *North-Holland Mathematics Studies*, 94:235–248, 1984.

[210] David S. Malkus and Thomas J. R. Hughes. Mixed finite element methods–reduced and selective integration techniques: a unification of concepts. *Computer Methods in Applied Mechanics and Engineering*, 15(1):63–81, 1978.

[211] Renier Gustav Marchand. *The method of manufactured solutions for the verification of computational electromagnetic codes*. PhD thesis, Stellenbosch University, 2013.

[212] Kent Andre Mardal, Xue-Cheng Tai, and Ragnar Winther. A robust finite element method for Darcy–Stokes flow. *SIAM Journal on Numerical Analysis*, 40(5):1605–1631, 2002.

[213] Kent-Andre Mardal and Ragnar Winther. Preconditioning discretizations of systems of partial differential equations. *Numerical Linear Algebra with Applications*, 18(1):1–40, 2011.

[214] Simon Markfelder and Christian Klingenberg. The Riemann problem for the multidimensional isentropic system of gas dynamics is ill-posed if it contains a shock. *Archive for Rational Mechanics and Analysis*, 227(3):967–994, 2018.

[215] Vladimir Maz'ya, Serguei Nazarov, and Boris A Plamenevskij, editors. *Asymptotic Theory of Elliptic Boundary Value Problems in Singularly Perturbed Domains*. Springer, 2000.

[216] Vladimir Gilelevich Maz'ya. *Sobolev Spaces*. New York: Springer–Verlag, 1985.

[217] Vladimir Gilelevich Maz'ya and Sergei Aleksandrovich Nazarov. About the Sapondzhyn–Babuška paradox in the plate theory. *Dokl. Akad. Nauk. Arm. Rep*, 78:127–130, 1984.

[218] Vladimir Gilelevich Maz'ya and Sergei Aleksandrovich Nazarov. Paradoxes of limit passage in solutions of boundary value problems involving the approximation of smooth domains by polygonal domains. *Izvestiya: Mathematics*, 29(3):511–533, 1987.

[219] N. G. Meyers. An L^p-estimate for the gradient of solutions of second order elliptic divergence equations. *Annali della Scuola Normale Superiore di Pisa. Ser. III.*, XVII:189–206, 1963.

[220] S Micheletti and S Perotto. Anisotropic recovery-based a posteriori error estimators for advection-diffusion-reaction problems. In Andrea Cangiani, Ruslan L. Davidchack, Emmanuil Georgoulis, Alexander N. Gorban, Jeremy Levesley, and Michael V. Tretyakov, editors, *Numerical Mathematics and Advanced Applications 2011*, pages 43–51. Springer, 2013.

[221] Stefano Micheletti and Simona Perotto. Reliability and efficiency of an anisotropic Zienkiewicz–Zhu error estimator. *Computer methods in applied mechanics and engineering*, 195(9):799–835, 2006.

[222] John W. Miles. *The Potential Theory of Unsteady Supersonic Flow.* Cambridge University Press, 1959.

[223] Hannah Morgan and L. Ridgway Scott. Towards a unified finite element method for the Stokes equations. *SIAM Journal on Scientific Computing*, 40(1):A130–A141, 2018.

[224] J. Morgan and L. R. Scott. A nodal basis for C^1 piecewise polynomials of degree $n \geq 5$. *Math. Comp.*, 29:736–740, 1975.

[225] John Morgan and L. R. Scott. The dimension of the space of C^1 piecewise–polynomials. Research Report UH/MD 78, Dept. Math., Univ. Houston, 1990.

[226] Mikael Mortensen, Hans Petter Langtangen, and Garth N. Wells. A FEniCS-based programming framework for modeling turbulent flow by the Reynolds-averaged NavierStokes equations. *Advances in Water Resources*, 34(9):1082 – 1101, 2011. New Computational Methods and Software Tools.

[227] P. Pandurang Nayak. *Automated Modeling of Physical Systems.* Springer, 1995.

[228] Sergei Aleksandrovich Nazarov and Maksim Viktorovich Olyushin. Approximation of smooth contours by polygonal ones. Paradoxes in problems for the Lamé system. *Izvestiya: Mathematics*, 61(3):619, 1997.

[229] Christopher C. Paige and Michael A. Saunders. Solution of sparse indefinite systems of linear equations. *SIAM Journal on Numerical Analysis*, 12(4):617–629, 1975.

[230] Linus Pauling and E. Bright Wilson. *Introduction to Quantum Mechanics with Applications to Chemistry.* Dover, 1985.

[231] Benoît Perthame. *Transport Equations in Biology.* Springer Science & Business Media, 2006.

[232] Martin Petzoldt. *Regularity and error estimators for elliptic problems with discontinuous coefficients.* PhD thesis, Freie Universität Berlin, Germany, 2001.

[233] Martin Petzoldt. A posteriori error estimators for elliptic equations with discontinuous coefficients. *Advances in Computational Mathematics*, 16(1):47–75, 2002.

[234] Marco Picasso. An anisotropic error indicator based on Zienkiewicz–Zhu error estimator: Application to elliptic and parabolic problems. *SIAM Journal on Scientific Computing*, 24(4):1328–1355, 2003.

[235] Marco Picasso. Adaptive finite elements with large aspect ratio based on an anisotropic error estimator involving first order derivatives. *Computer Methods in Applied Mechanics and Engineering*, 196(1):14–23, 2006.

[236] J. Pitkäranta and L. R. Scott. Error estimates for the combined spatial and angular approximations of the transport equation for slab geometry. *SIAM J. Num. Anal.*, 20:922–950, 1983.

[237] M. J. D. Powell. Piecewise quadratic surface fitting for contour plotting. In *Software for Numerical Mathematics*, pages 253–271. Academic Press, 1974.

[238] Jinshui Qin. *On the convergence of some low order mixed finite elements for incompressible fluids.* PhD thesis, Penn State, 1994.

[239] Jinshui Qin and Shangyou Zhang. Stability and approximability of the $\mathcal{P}1$–$\mathcal{P}0$ element for Stokes equations. *International Journal for Numerical Methods in Fluids*, 54(5):497–515, 2007.

[240] Katharina Rafetseder and Walter Zulehner. A decomposition result for Kirchhoff plate bending problems and a new discretization approach. *arXiv preprint arXiv:1703.07962*, 2017.

[241] Ekkehard Ramm, E. Rank, R. Rannacher, K. Schweizerhof, E. Stein, W. Wendland, G. Wittum, Peter Wriggers, and Walter Wunderlich. *Error-controlled Adaptive Finite Elements in Solid Mechanics.* John Wiley & Sons, 2003.

[242] R. Rannacher and L. R. Scott. Some optimal error estimates for piecewise linear finite element approximations. *Math. Comp.*, 38:437–445, 1982.

[243] Rolf Rannacher. Finite-element approximation of simply supported plates and the Babuška paradox. *Zeitschrift für Angewandte Mathematik und Mechanik*, 59(3):T73–T76, 1979.

[244] Luis G. Reyna and Michael J. Ward. On the exponentially slow motion of a viscous shock. *Communications on Pure and Applied Mathematics*, 48(2):79–120, 1995.

[245] G. Rieder. On the plate paradox of Sapondzhyan and Babuška. *Mechanics Research Communications*, 1(1):51–53, 1974.

[246] Nancy Rodriguez. *Applied Partial Differential Equations in Crime Modeling and Biological Aggregation.* PhD thesis, University of California, Los Angeles, 2011.

[247] Marie E. Rognes. Automated testing of saddle point stability conditions. In A. Logg, K.A. Mardal, and G. Wells, editors, *Automated Solution of Differential Equations by the Finite Element Method: The FEniCS Book*, pages 657–671. Springer, 2012.

[248] Marie E. Rognes, Robert C. Kirby, and Anders Logg. Efficient assembly of H(div) and H(curl) conforming finite elements. *SIAM Journal on Scientific Computing*, 31(6):4130–4151, 2009.

[249] Marie E. Rognes and Anders Logg. Automated goal-oriented error control I: Stationary variational problems. *SIAM Journal on Scientific Computing*, 35(3):C173–C193, 2013.

[250] Walter Rudin. *Functional analysis.* New York: McGraw–Hill, second edition, 1991.

[251] Youcef Saad and Martin H. Schultz. GMRES: A generalized minimal residual algorithm for solving nonsymmetric linear systems. *SIAM Journal on Scientific and Statistical Computing*, 7(3):856–869, 1986.

[252] Laure Saint-Raymond. A microscopic point of view on singularities in fluid models. In *Shocks, Singularities and Oscillations in Nonlinear Optics and Fluid Mechanics*, pages 205–259. Springer, 2017.

[253] Stephan Schmidt. A two stage CVT/eikonal convection mesh deformation approach for large nodal deformations. *arXiv preprint arXiv:1411.7663*, 2014.

[254] Dominik Schötzau, Christoph Schwab, and Rolf Stenberg. Mixed hp-FEM on anisotropic meshes II: Hanging nodes and tensor products of boundary layer meshes. *Numerische Mathematik*, 83(4):667–697, 1999.

[255] L. R. Scott. Elliptic preconditioners using fast summation techniques. In *Domain Decomposition Methods in Science and Engineering (Proceedings of the Seventh International Conference on Domain Decomposition, October 27-30, 1993, The Pennsylvania State University), D. E. Keyes & J. Xu, eds.*, volume Contemproary Mathematics 180, pages 311–323. Providence, Rhode Island: American Mathematical Society, 1995.

[256] L. R. Scott, A. Ilin, R. Metcalfe, and B. Bagheri. Fast algorithms for solving high-order finite element equations for incompressible flow. In *Proceedings of the International Conference on Spectral and High Order Methods*, pages 221–232, Houston, TX, 1995. University of Houston.

[257] L. R. Scott and M. Vogelius. Conforming finite element methods for incompressible and nearly incompressible continua. In *Large Scale Computations in Fluid Mechanics, B. E. Engquist, et al., eds.*, volume 22 (Part 2), pages 221–244. Providence: AMS, 1985.

[258] L. R. Scott and M. Vogelius. Norm estimates for a maximal right inverse of the divergence operator in spaces of piecewise polynomials. *M^2AN (formerly R.A.I.R.O. Analyse Numérique)*, 19:111–143, 1985.

[259] L. Ridgway Scott. *Numerical Analysis*. Princeton Univ. Press, 2011.

[260] R. Scott. A survey of displacement methods for the plate bending problem. In *Formulations and Computational Algorithms in Finite Element Analysis, K.-J. Bathe, J. T. Oden, and W. Wunderlich, eds.*, pages 855–876. Cambridge: M. I. T. Press, 1977.

[261] Ridgway Scott. Interpolated boundary conditions in the finite element method. *SIAM J. Numer. Anal.*, 12:404–427, 1975.

[262] Jie Shen and Li-Lian Wang. Some recent advances on spectral methods for unbounded domains. *Communications in Computational Physics*, 5(2-4):195–241, 2009.

[263] Ralph Edwin Showalter and T. Wo Ting. Pseudoparabolic partial differential equations. *SIAM Journal on Mathematical Analysis*, 1(1):1–26, 1970.

[264] Chi-Wang Shu. Discontinuous Galerkin methods: General approach and stability. In *Numerical Solutions of Partial Differential Equations*, pages 149–201. Birkhäuser, 2008.

[265] Kunibert G. Siebert. An a posteriori error estimator for anisotropic refinement. *Numerische Mathematik*, 73(3):373–398, 1996.

[266] Gary A. Sod. A survey of several finite difference methods for systems of nonlinear hyperbolic conservation laws. *Journal of Computational Physics*, 27(1):1 – 31, 1978.

[267] Pavel Šolín, Jakub Červený, and Ivo Doležel. Arbitrary-level hanging nodes and automatic adaptivity in the hp-FEM. *Mathematics and Computers in Simulation*, 77(1):117–132, 2008.

[268] Rob Stevenson. An optimal adaptive finite element method. *SIAM Journal on Numerical Analysis*, 42(5):2188–2217, 2005.

[269] G. W. Stewart. *Matrix Algorithms, Volume I: Basic Decompositions.* Philadelphia: Society for Industrial and Applied Mathematics, 1998.

[270] G. Strang. *Linear Algebra.* Cambridge–Wellesly Press, 1991.

[271] Guido Sweers. A survey on boundary conditions for the biharmonic. *Complex Variables and Elliptic Equations*, 54(2):79–93, 2009.

[272] V. Szebehely, D. Saari, J. Waldvogel, and U. Kirchgraber. Eduard L. Stiefel (1909–1978). *Celestial Mechanics and Dynamical Astronomy*, 21:2–4, Jan. 1980. 10.1007/BF01230237.

[273] Luc Tartar. *An Introduction to Sobolev Spaces and Interpolation Spaces.* Springer, Berlin, Heidelberg, 2007.

[274] Clifford Henry Taubes. *Modeling Differential Equations in Biology.* Cambridge University Press, second edition, 2008.

[275] V. Thomee. *Galerkin Finite Element Methods for Parabolic Problems.* Springer Verlag, 1997.

[276] Ioannis Toulopoulos and Thomas Wick. Numerical methods for power-law diffusion problems. *SIAM Journal on Scientific Computing*, 39(3):A681–A710, 2017.

[277] Chrysoula Tsogka and Armand Wirgin. Simulation of seismic response in an idealized city. *Soil Dynamics and Earthquake Engineering*, 23(5):391–402, 2003.

[278] K. K. Tung. *Topics in Mathematical Modeling.* Princeton University Press, Princeton, N.J., 2007.

[279] Subith S. Vasu, David F. Davidson, and Ronald K. Hanson. Jet fuel ignition delay times: Shock tube experiments over wide conditions and surrogate model predictions. *Combustion and Flame*, 152(1):125 – 143, 2008.

[280] R Verfürth. Finite element approximation of steady Navier–Stokes equations with mixed boundary conditions. *RAIRO–Modélisation mathématique et analyse numérique*, 19(3):461–475, 1985.

[281] Rüdiger Verfürth. *A posteriori Error Estimation Techniques for Finite Element Methods.* Oxford University Press, 2013.

[282] Martin Vohralík. Guaranteed and fully robust a posteriori error estimates for conforming discretizations of diffusion problems with discontinuous coefficients. *Journal of Scientific Computing*, 46(3):397–438, 2011.

[283] M. N. Vu, S. Geniaut, P. Massin, and J. J. Marigo. Numerical investigation on corner singularities in cracked plates using the G-theta method with an adapted θ field. *Theoretical and Applied Fracture Mechanics*, 77:59 – 68, 2015.

[284] Stephen Whitaker. Flow in porous media I: A theoretical derivation of Darcy's law. *Transport in porous media*, 1(1):3–25, 1986.

[285] Xiaoping Xie, Jinchao Xu, and Guangri Xue. Uniformly-stable finite element methods for Darcy–Stokes–Brinkman models. *Journal of Computational Mathematics*, pages 437–455, 2008.

[286] J. Yan and C.W. Shu. A local discontinuous Galerkin method for KdV type equations. *SIAM Journal on Numerical Analysis*, pages 769–791, 2003.

[287] Qinghui Zhang, Ivo Babuška, and Uday Banerjee. Robustness in stable generalized finite element methods (SGFEM) applied to Poisson problems with crack singularities. *Computer Methods in Applied Mechanics and Engineering*, 311:476–502, 2016.

[288] S. Zhang and L. R. Scott. Finite element interpolation of non–smooth functions satisfying boundary conditions. *Math. Comp.*, 54:483–493, 1990.

[289] Shangyou Zhang. Divergence-free finite elements on tetrahedral grids for $k \geq 6$. *Mathematics of Computation*, 80(274):669–695, 2011.

[290] Shangyou Zhang. Quadratic divergence-free finite elements on Powell–Sabin tetrahedral grids. *Calcolo*, 48(3):211–244, 2011.

[291] Shangyou Zhang and L. R. Scott. Higher dimensional non-nested multigrid methods. *Math. Comp.*, 58:457–466, 1992.

[292] O. C. Zienkiewicz. *The Finite Element Method.* McGraw–Hill, London; New York, third edition, 1977. First ed. (1967) published under title: The finite element method in structural and continuum mechanics; 2d ed. (1971) published under title: The finite element method in engineering science.

Index

Lightning Source UK Ltd.
Milton Keynes UK
UKHW05n0431270918
329327UK00004BC/8/P